Recent Titles in This Series

M000238708

136 **Masayoshi Miyanishi,** Algebraic geometry, 1994
135 **Masaru Takeuchi,** Modern spherical functions, 1994
134 **V. V. Prasolov,** Problems and theorems in linear algebra, 1994
133 **P. I. Naumkin and I. A. Shishmarev,** Nonlinear nonlocal equations in the theory of waves, 1994
132 **Hajime Urakawa,** Calculus of variations and harmonic maps, 1993
131 **V. V. Sharko,** Functions on manifolds: Algebraic and topological aspects, 1993
130 **V. V. Vershinin,** Cobordisms and spectral sequences, 1993
129 **Mitsuo Morimoto,** An introduction to Sato's hyperfunctions, 1993
128 **V. P. Orevkov,** Complexity of proofs and their transformations in axiomatic theories, 1993
127 **F. L. Zak,** Tangents and secants of algebraic varieties, 1993
126 **M. L. Agranovskiĭ,** Invariant function spaces on homogeneous manifolds of Lie groups and applications, 1993
125 **Masayoshi Nagata,** Theory of commutative fields, 1993
124 **Masahisa Adachi,** Embeddings and immersions, 1993
123 **M. A. Akivis and B. A. Rosenfeld,** Élie Cartan (1869–1951), 1993
122 **Zhang Guan-Hou,** Theory of entire and meromorphic functions: Deficient and asymptotic values and singular directions, 1993
121 **I. B. Fesenko and S. V. Vostokov,** Local fields and their extensions: A constructive approach, 1993
120 **Takeyuki Hida and Masuyuki Hitsuda,** Gaussian processes, 1993
119 **M. V. Karasev and V. P. Maslov,** Nonlinear Poisson brackets. Geometry and quantization, 1993
118 **Kenkichi Iwasawa,** Algebraic functions, 1993
117 **Boris Zilber,** Uncountably categorical theories, 1993
116 **G. M. Fel′dman,** Arithmetic of probability distributions, and characterization problems on abelian groups, 1993
115 **Nikolai V. Ivanov,** Subgroups of Teichmüller modular groups, 1992
114 **Seizô Itô,** Diffusion equations, 1992
113 **Michail Zhitomirskiĭ,** Typical singularities of differential 1-forms and Pfaffian equations, 1992
112 **S. A. Lomov,** Introduction to the general theory of singular perturbations, 1992
111 **Simon Gindikin,** Tube domains and the Cauchy problem, 1992
110 **B. V. Shabat,** Introduction to complex analysis Part II. Functions of several variables, 1992
109 **Isao Miyadera,** Nonlinear semigroups, 1992
108 **Takeo Yokonuma,** Tensor spaces and exterior algebra, 1992
107 **B. M. Makarov, M. G. Goluzina, A. A. Lodkin, and A. N. Podkorytov,** Selected problems in real analysis, 1992
106 **G.-C. Wen,** Conformal mappings and boundary value problems, 1992
105 **D. R. Yafaev,** Mathematical scattering theory: General theory, 1992
104 **R. L. Dobrushin, R. Kotecký, and S. Shlosman,** Wulff construction: A global shape from local interaction, 1992
103 **A. K. Tsikh,** Multidimensional residues and their applications, 1992
102 **A. M. Il′in,** Matching of asymptotic expansions of solutions of boundary value problems, 1992
101 **Zhang Zhi-fen, Ding Tong-ren, Huang Wen-zao, and Dong Zhen-xi,** Qualitative theory of differential equations, 1992
100 **V. L. Popov,** Groups, generators, syzygies, and orbits in invariant theory, 1992
99 **Norio Shimakura,** Partial differential operators of elliptic type, 1992
98 **V. A. Vassiliev,** Complements of discriminants of smooth maps: Topology and applications, 1992 (revised edition, 1994)
97 **Itiro Tamura,** Topology of foliations: An introduction, 1992
96 **A. I. Markushevich,** Introduction to the classical theory of Abelian functions, 1992

(*Continued in the back of this publication*)

Algebraic Geometry

TRANSLATIONS OF
MATHEMATICAL
MONOGRAPHS

VOLUME 136

Masayoshi Miyanishi

Algebraic Geometry

Translated by
Masayoshi Miyanishi

American Mathematical Society
Providence, Rhode Island

代数幾何学

DAISŪ KIKAGAKU
(Algebraic Geometry)

by Masayoshi Miyanishi

Originally published in Japanese by Shokabo Publishing Co., Ltd., Tokyo in 1990.

Translated from the Japanese by Masayoshi Miyanishi

1991 *Mathematics Subject Classification.* Primary 14–01;
Secondary 13–01, 14A10, 14A15, 14J99.

ABSTRACT. This book covers algebraic geometry from the beginnings to an introduction of algebraic surfaces, viz., to the gate from which the classification of algebraic surfaces starts. The book has three parts. The first part provides the necessary basic results from commutative algebras and the theory of sheaves and its cohomologies. The second part is on schemes and algebraic varieties. The third part is on algebraic curves and surfaces, placing emphasis on the use of linear systems and the associated rational mappings.

Library of Congress Cataloging-in-Publication Data

Miyanishi, Masayoshi, 1940–
[Daisū kikagaku. English]
Algebraic geometry/Masayoshi Miyanishi; translated by Masayoshi Miyanishi.
p. cm. — (Translations of mathematical monographs, ISSN 0065-9282; v. 136)
Includes bibliographical references and index.
ISBN 0-8218-4615-9 (acid-free)
1. Geometry, Algebraic. I. Title. II. Series.
QA564.M5713 1994 94-2018
516.3′5—dc20 CIP

⊗ The paper used in this book is acid-free and falls within the guidelines
established to ensure permanence and durability.
Information on Copying and Reprinting can be found in the back of this volume.
This volume was typeset using $\mathcal{A}_{\mathcal{M}}\mathcal{S}$-TEX,
the American Mathematical Society's TEX macro system.

10 9 8 7 6 5 4 3 2 02 01 00 99 98

Contents

Preface to the English Edition

The interesting theory, where one first experiences the beauty in learning algebraic geometry, is perhaps the theory of algebraic curves and surfaces. The theory of algebraic surfaces is particularly important when one further studies higher-dimensional algebraic varieties.

In order to approach this theory through modern algebraic methods, one is required to have a basic knowledge of local rings, sheaves, cohomologies, projective varieties, linear systems of divisors, etc. This basic knowledge may include all results given in introductory textbooks devoted to these subjects, and it takes some time to get familiar with them.

This book grew out from the author's attempts to find a shortcut and thus, lead students effectively to an understanding of algebraic surfaces. This book, originally written in Japanese, is designed so that readers with only knowledge of algebra at an undergraduate level can start learning algebraic geometry by themselves. The description is, therefore, self-contained as much as possible.

The book consists of three parts. The first part gives background in commutative algebras, sheaf theory, and related cohomology theory. The second part introduces schemes and algebraic varieties, where one can learn the basic language of algebraic geometry. The last part is devoted to guiding the readers to the gate from which the classification of algebraic surfaces starts. It is most desirable that readers continue to further their learning through other books on algebraic surfaces.

While preparing the English translation, the author is indebted to Drs. Koji Yokogawa and Hiroyuki Ito for technical assistance in typesetting the manuscript using LaTeX.

M. Miyanishi
June 1993

Preface

Students often say they get interested in algebraic geometry and start learning it by themselves, only to find that there are too many prerequisites; they get lost in preliminary results. The knowledge of algebra and geometry that is taught in college is not sufficient for reading through most of the serious textbooks in algebraic geometry. One needs knowledge of ring theory, field theory, local rings, and transcendental field extensions, even sheaf theory and cohomologies with coefficients in sheaves, which are certainly beyond the level of college mathematics. But if one waits to begin the study of algebraic geometry until after absorbing all the necessary knowledge, then one may have lost interest.

So it is most desirable if such basic results appear in a textbook in algebraic geometry when they are needed. In writing this book, the author tried to prove or recall results when needed.

This book, meant for senior undergraduate students and for graduate students, will guide students from the beginnings of algebraic geometry to an introduction of algebraic surfaces, viz., to the gate from which the classification of algebraic surfaces starts. The readers are advised to read higher textbooks or research papers after completing this book.

In order to keep the book to a reasonable size, some results were not included, and even the included results are not stated in full generality.

The book consists of three parts. The first part provides the necessary basic results. The second part is on schemes and algebraic varieties. The third part is on algebraic surfaces. When we refer to results stated in the same part, we refer to them in a form such as Theorem 3.1, and when we refer to results in different parts, we include the part as in Theorem II.3.1.

At the end of each chapter; some results are given as problems; brief solutions are given at the end of the book.

The author was encouraged to write this book by Professor S. Murakami of Osaka University and given frequent and warm encouragement from Mr. S. Hosoki of Shokabo Publ. Co. The author would like to express his sincere gratitude to both of them.

M. Miyanishi
June 1990

Part I

Preliminaries

CHAPTER 1

Theorem of Lüroth

Let k be a field. If an extension field L of k is generated by finitely many elements $x_1, \dots, x_n$ over k, it is called a *finitely generated extension* of k and is denoted by $L = k(x_1, \dots, x_n)$. For variables $X_1, \dots, X_n$, $k[X_1, \dots, X_n]$ denotes a polynomial ring in n variables over k and $k(X_1, \dots, X_n)$ denotes its quotient field. We call $k(X_1, \dots, X_n)$ a *purely transcendental extension in n variables* over k or an *n-dimensional rational function field*, and call its elements *rational functions*.

DEFINITION 1.1. Let L/k be a field extension. An element ξ of L is called *transcendental* over k or *algebraically independent* over k if ξ is not algebraic over k. For elements $\xi_1, \dots, \xi_r$ of L, we say that $\xi_1, \dots, \xi_r$ are *transcendental* or *algebraically independent* over k if ξ_i is transcendental over $k(\xi_1, \dots, \xi_{i-1})$ for each i, $1 \le i \le r$.

The following result shows that the definition of $\xi_1, \dots, \xi_r$ being transcendental over k does not depend on the ordering of $\xi_1, \dots, \xi_r$.

LEMMA 1.2. *For elements $\xi_1, \dots, \xi_r$ of L, the following conditions are equivalent*:
(1) *$\xi_1, \dots, \xi_r$ are transcendental over k.*
(2) *For any permutation σ of $\{1, \dots, r\}$ and for each i, $1 \le i \le r$, $\xi_{\sigma(i)}$ is transcendental over $k(\xi_{\sigma(1)}, \dots, \xi_{\sigma(i-1)})$.*

PROOF. It suffices to show that (1) implies (2). Since any permutation is expressed as a product of transpositions $(i-1, i)$, we have only to show the following:

For each j, $1 \le j \le i$, if ξ_j is transcendental over $k(\xi_1, \dots, \xi_{j-1})$, then ξ_{i-1} is transcendental over $k(\xi_1, \dots, \xi_{i-2}, \xi_i)$.

Suppose ξ_{i-1} is algebraic over $k(\xi_1, \dots, \xi_{i-2}, \xi_i)$. Then there exists an algebraic relation

$$(*) \qquad \begin{gathered} a_0(\xi_{i-1})^N + a_1(\xi_{i-1})^{N-1} + \cdots + a_N = 0, \\ a_j \in k[\xi_1, \dots, \xi_{i-2}, \xi_i], \quad a_0 a_N \ne 0, \quad \gcd(a_0, \dots, a_N) = 1, \end{gathered}$$

where $a_j \notin k[\xi_1, \dots, \xi_{i-2}]$ for some j. Let N_j be the ξ_i-degree of a_j, and write

$$a_j = a_{j0}\xi_i^{N_j} + (\text{terms of lower degree in } \xi_i), \qquad a_{j0}, \dots \in k[\xi_1, \dots, \xi_{i-2}].$$

Let $M = \max\{N_j ; 0 \le j \le N\}$. Then we can write the relation $(*)$ as

$$(**) \qquad \left(\sum_{N_j = M} a_{j0}(\xi_{i-1})^{N-j} \right) \xi_i^M + (\text{terms of lower degree in } \xi_i) = 0.$$

Since ξ_{i-1} is transcendental over $k(\xi_1, \dots, \xi_{i-2})$, we have

$$\sum_{N_j=M} a_{j0}(\xi_{i-1})^{N-j} \neq 0.$$

Hence, the relation $(**)$ shows that ξ_i is algebraic over $k(\xi_1, \dots, \xi_{i-1})$. This contradicts the assumption (1). □

LEMMA 1.3. *Let $L = k(x_1, \dots, x_n)$ be a finitely generated extension of k, and let $\xi_1, \dots, \xi_r$ be elements of L. Then the following assertions hold:*

(1) *If $\xi_1, \dots, \xi_r$ are transcendental over k, then $r \leq n$.*
(If no subsets of L strictly containing $\{\xi_1, \dots, \xi_r\}$ are purely transcendental over k, then $\{\xi_1, \dots, \xi_r\}$ is called a maximal system of transcendental elements *and r is called its* length.)

(2) *The length r of a maximal system of transcendental elements is a constant independent of the choice.*

(3) *One can choose a maximal system of transcendental elements $\{\eta_1, \dots, \eta_r\}$ as a subset of $\{x_1, \dots, x_n\}$.*

PROOF. As a subset of $\{x_1, \dots, x_n\}$, we choose a system $\{\eta_1, \dots, \eta_s\}$ consisting of elements transcendental over k by the following process applied to $x_1, \dots, x_n$ one by one. If x_1 is transcendental over k, we pick it up. If x_1 is algebraic over k, we throw it away. Similarly, if x_i is transcendental over $k(x_1, \dots, x_{i-1})$, we pick it up. Otherwise, we throw it away. Applying this process from x_1 to x_n, we denote the elements that we picked up by $\eta_1, \dots, \eta_s$. Then $s \leq n$, and $L/k(\eta_1, \dots, \eta_s)$ is an algebraic extension.

Suppose now $\xi_1, \dots, \xi_r$ are transcendental over k. Since ξ_1 is algebraic over $k(\eta_1, \dots, \eta_s)$, we have

$$(*) \qquad a_0(\xi_1)^N + a_1(\xi_1)^{N-1} + \dots + a_N = 0, \qquad a_j \in k[\eta_1, \dots, \eta_s],\ a_0 a_N \neq 0.$$

Since ξ_1 is transcendental over k, $a_j \notin k$ for some j. After relabelling $\{\eta_1, \dots, \eta_s\}$ if necessary, we may (and shall) assume that

$$\begin{aligned} &a_j = a_{j0}\eta_1^{N_j} + (\text{terms of lower degree in } \eta_1), \\ &a_{j0}, \dots \in k[\eta_2, \dots, \eta_s], \\ &a_{j_0} \neq 0 \text{ if } a_j \neq 0; \qquad N_j = 0 \text{ if } a_j = 0. \end{aligned}$$

Set $M = \max\{N_j; 0 \leq j \leq N\}$, and rewrite $(*)$ as

$$\left(\sum_{N_j=M} a_{j0}(\xi_1)^{N-j}\right)\eta_1^M + (\text{terms of lower degree in } \eta_1) = 0.$$

Then the coefficient of $\eta_1^M \neq 0$. Hence, η_1 is algebraic over $k(\xi_1, \eta_2, \dots, \eta_s)$. So ξ_2 is algebraic over $k(\xi_1, \eta_2, \dots, \eta_s)$. Since ξ_2 is transcendental over $k(\xi_1)$, the above argument enables us to replace ξ_2 by one of $\eta_2, \dots, \eta_s$, say η_2. One may thus assume that η_2 is algebraic over $k(\xi_1, \xi_2, \eta_3, \dots, \eta_s)$. If L is algebraic over $k(\xi_1, \dots, \xi_i, \eta_{i+1}, \dots, \eta_s)$ $(i < r)$, then one can repeat the above argument to ξ_{i+1} because ξ_{i+1} is transcendental over $k(\xi_1, \dots, \xi_i)$ and replace ξ_{i+1} by one of $\eta_{i+1}, \dots, \eta_s$. Hence, by induction, we have $r \leq s \leq n$.

Suppose $\{\xi_1, \ldots, \xi_r\}$ is a maximal system of transcendental elements. Then L is algebraic over $k(\xi_1, \ldots, \xi_r)$. If one exchanges the roles of $\{\xi_1, \ldots, \xi_r\}$ and $\{\eta_1, \ldots, \eta_s\}$ in the above argument, one knons $s \leq r$. □

DEFINITION 1.4. Let $L = k(x_1, \ldots, x_n)$ be a finitely generated extension of k. A maximal system of transcendental elements $\{\xi_1, \ldots, \xi_r\}$ such as in Lemma 1.3 is called a *transcendence basis* of L over k, and its length r is called the *transcendence degree* of L/k. We write $r = \operatorname{tr.deg}_k L$. If $r = 0$, then L/k is a finite algebraic extension.

The following is a significant result which we often refer to in this book. The proof is taken from Nagata [7].

LEMMA 1.5. *Let L/k be a finitely generated extension, and let M be a subfield containing k. Then M/k is a finitely generated extension and* $\operatorname{tr.deg}_k M \leq \operatorname{tr.deg}_k L$.

PROOF.

CASE (1) M/k IS AN ALGEBRAIC EXTENSION. Let $\{\xi_1, \ldots, \xi_r\}$ be a transcendence basis of L/k. Since $M(\xi_1, \ldots, \xi_{i-1})/k(\xi_1, \ldots, \xi_{i-1})$ is an algebraic extension, ξ_i is transcendental over $M(\xi_1, \ldots, \xi_{i-1})$. Hence, $\xi_1, \ldots, \xi_r$ are transcendental over M. Let $\{m_1, \ldots, m_t\}$ be a set of elements of M which are linearly independent over k. We shall show that $m_1, \ldots, m_t$ are linearly independent over $k(\xi_1, \ldots, \xi_r)$ as well. Suppose

$$f_1 m_1 + \cdots + f_t m_t = 0, \qquad f_j \in k(\xi_1, \ldots, \xi_r).$$

Replacing $f_1, \ldots, f_t$ by $gf_1, \ldots, gf_t$, ($g \in k[\xi_1, \ldots, \xi_r]$), we may assume that $f_1, \ldots, f_t \in k[\xi_1, \ldots, \xi_r]$. Writing

$$f_j = \sum_a a_\alpha^{(j)} \xi^\alpha, \qquad \xi^\alpha = \xi_1^{\alpha_1} \cdots \xi_r^{\alpha_r}, \ \alpha = (\alpha_1, \ldots, \alpha_r), a_\alpha^{(j)} \in k,$$

we have $\sum_\alpha \sum_{j=1}^t a_\alpha^{(j)} m_j \xi^\alpha = 0$. Since $\sum_{j=1}^t a_\alpha^{(j)} m_j \in M$ and $\xi_1, \ldots, \xi_r$ are transcendental over M, we have $\sum_{j=1}^t a_\alpha^{(j)} m_j = 0$ for each α. Hence, $a_\alpha^{(j)} = 0$ for each α and each j. This entails $f_j = 0$ for each j. So we have

$$t \leq [L : k(\xi_1, \ldots, \xi_r)] < +\infty.$$

The extension M/k is, therefore, a finite algebraic extension.

CASE (2) M/k IS NOT NECESSARILY AN ALGEBRAIC EXTENSION. Choose a transcendence basis $\{\xi_1, \ldots, \xi_r\}$ of L/k in such a way that $\{\xi_1, \ldots, \xi_a\}$ is a maximal system of transcendental elements of M/k. Then $L/k(\xi_1, \ldots, \xi_a)$ is a finitely generated extension, and $M/k(\xi_1, \ldots, \xi_a)$ is an algebraic extension. Case (1) implies $[M : k(\xi_1, \ldots, \xi_a)] < +\infty$. Hence, M/k is a finitely generated extension. Since $\{\xi_1, \ldots, \xi_a\}$ is a transcendence basis of M/k, we have $\operatorname{tr.deg}_k M \leq \operatorname{tr.deg}_k L$. □

DEFINITION 1.6. Let L/k be a finitely generated extension. We say that L/k is a *separable extension* if there exists a transcendence basis $\{\xi_1, \ldots, \xi_r\}$ of L/k such that $L/k(\xi_1, \ldots, \xi_r)$ is a separable algebraic extension. We then say that $\{\xi_1, \ldots, \xi_r\}$ is a *separating transcendence basis*.

If the field k has characteristic zero, a finitely generated extension L/k is always a separable extension. This is, however, not the case if the characteristic p of k is nonzero. As an example, let $p = 2$, and $L = k(x, y)$, where $x^2 + y^2 = a$ with $a \in k$,

$a^{1/2} \notin k$. Then L/k is not separable. In fact, $(x+y)\otimes 1 - 1 \otimes a^{1/2}$ is a nilpotent element in $L \otimes_k k(a^{1/2})$, and hence, L/k is not separable by the next result.

LEMMA 1.7. *Let L/k be a separable extension. Then we have the following assertions*:

(1) *We can express $L = k(\xi_1, \ldots, \xi_r, \eta)$ with $F(\xi_1, \ldots, \xi_r, \eta) = 0$, where $r = \operatorname{tr.deg}_k L$ and $F(X_1, \ldots, X_r, Y)$ is an irreducible polynomial over k.*

(2) *Suppose k has characteristic $p \neq 0$. Define a subfield $k^{p^{-s}}$ of an algebraic closure $\bar{k}$ of k by*

$$k^{p^{-s}} = \{a^{p^{-s}}; a \in k\} \qquad (s \geq 0).$$

Then there are no nilpotent elements in $L \otimes_k k^{p^{-s}}$ for each s, $s \geq 0$.

PROOF. (1) Let $\{\xi_1, \ldots, \xi_r\}$ be a separating transcendence basis of L/k. Then $L/k(\xi_1, \ldots, \xi_r)$ is a simple extension since it is a separable algebraic extension. Hence, we may write $L = k(\xi_1, \ldots, \xi_r, \eta)$, where η is a root of a separable polynomial over $k(\xi_1, \ldots, \xi_r)$,

$$G(\xi, Y) = a_0 Y^N + a_1 Y^{N-1} + \cdots + a_N = 0, \qquad a_i \in k(\xi_1, \ldots, \xi_r).$$

(2) Set $k' = k^{p^{-s}}$. Since $\xi_1, \ldots, \xi_r$ are transcendental over k', $k' \otimes_k k(\xi_1, \ldots, \xi_r)$ is a field, which we denote by $k'(\xi_1, \ldots, \xi_r)$. Then $k'(\xi_1, \ldots, \xi_r)/k(\xi_1, \ldots, \xi_r)$ is a purely inseparable extension. Since

$$L \otimes_k k' = L \otimes_{k(\xi_1, \ldots, \xi_r)} k'(\xi_1, \ldots, \xi_r),$$

we can consider $L/k(\xi_1, \ldots, \xi_r)$ and $k'(\xi_1, \ldots, \xi_r)/k(\xi_1, \ldots, \xi_r)$ instead of L/k and k'/k, respectively, and we have only to show that if L/k is a separable algebraic extension and k'/k is a purely inseparable extension, $L \otimes_k k'$ has no nilpotent elements. If we write $L = k[X]/(f(X))$, then $L \otimes_k k' = k'[X]/(f(X))$, where $f(X)$ is a separable, irreducible polynomial over k. Hence, $\gcd(f(X), f'(X)) = 1$. This holds also over k'. Hence, $L \otimes_k k'$ is a field. So $L \otimes_k k'$ has no nilpotent elements. □

Let L/k be a finitely generated extension. If condition (2) of Lemma 1.7 holds; namely, if

$(*)$ $L \otimes_k k^{p^{-s}}$ has no nilpotent elements for each $s \geq 0$, then L/k is a separable extension. For a proof, see Nagata [7]. Let $\bar{k}$ be an algebraic closure of k. We say that L/k is a *regular extension* if $L \otimes_k \bar{k}$ is an integral domain. Since $\bar{k}$ is a flat k-module (see Problem I.1.9), the functor $\otimes_k \bar{k}$ is injective. This implies that an intermediate field extension M/k of a regular extension L/k is a regular extension as well. If k is algebraically closed, then every finitely generated extension L/k is a regular extension. By the above criterion $(*)$ of separability, any regular extension is a separable extension.

LEMMA 1.8. *Let L/k be a finitely generated extension. Then the following conditions are equivalent*:

(1) *L/k is a regular extension.*

(2) *L/k is a separable extension, and k is algebraically closed in L.*

PROOF. (1) *implies* (2). We shall show that k is algebraically closed in L. Suppose an element a of L not in k is algebraic over k. Let $f(X)$ be a minimal polynomial of a over k. Then $\deg f(X) > 0$. Write

$$f(X) = g(X^{p^e}), \qquad g'(X) \not\equiv 0,$$
$$g(X) = \prod_{i=1}^{m}(X - \alpha_i), \qquad \alpha_i \in \bar{k}.$$

Then $k(a) \otimes_k \bar{k}$ is a subring of $L \otimes_k \bar{k}$, and

$$k(a) \otimes_k \bar{k} \cong \bar{k}[X]/(f(X)) \cong \bar{k}[X]/\left(\prod_{i=1}^{m}(X^{p^e} - \alpha_i)\right) \cong \prod_{i=1}^{m}\bar{k}[X]/(X^{p^e} - \alpha_i).$$

Hence, $k(a) \otimes_k \bar{k}$ is not an integral domain, and this contradicts the hypothesis that $L \otimes_k \bar{k}$ is an integral domain.

(2) *implies* (1). It suffices to show that $L \otimes_k k'$ is an integral domain for a finite normal extension k'/k. Set $k'' = \{a \in k';\ a \text{ is purely inseparable over } k\}$. Then k'' is a subfield of k', and k'/k'' is a Galois extension. Since L/k is a separable extension, $L \otimes_k k''$ is a field and $L \otimes_k k''/k''$ is a separable extension. We shall see that k'' is algebraically closed in $L \otimes_k k''$. Suppose $a'' = \sum_\lambda b_\lambda \otimes a_\lambda$ ($b_\lambda \in L$, $a_\lambda \in k''$) is algebraic over k''. Since $a_\lambda^{p^s} \in k$ (for each λ) for some integer $s > 0$, $a''^{p^s} = \sum_\lambda b_\lambda^{p^s} a_\lambda^{p^s} \otimes 1$ is an element of L and algebraic over k. Hence, $a''^{p^s} \in k$ by the hypothesis. If $a'' \notin k''$, then $L \otimes_k k''$ would not be separable over k''. Hence, $a'' \in k''$.

It suffices, therefore, to show that

If k'/k is a Galois extension, then $L \otimes_k k'$ is a field.

Let $\mathfrak{m}$ be a maximal ideal of $L \otimes_k k'$. The residue field $L \otimes_k k'/\mathfrak{m}$ then contains L and k' as subfields and is generated by L and k'. We write $L \otimes_k k'/\mathfrak{m}$ as $L(k')$ and call it a composite field of L and k'. We claim that $L(k')/L$ is a Galois extension and $[L(k') : L] = [k' : k]$. In fact, write $k' = k(a)$, and let $a_1 = a, a_2, \ldots, a_r$ be all conjugates of a over k. Then $L(k') = L(a)$ and $L(k')/L$ is a Galois extension because $a_1, \ldots, a_r \in L(k')$. Let $f(X) = \prod_{i=1}^{r}(X - a_i)$, and let $f_1(X)$ be a minimal polynomial of a over L. Then $f_1(X) | f(X)$. Since we can write $f_1(X) = \prod_{j=1}^{s}(X - a_{i_j})$, the coefficients of $f_1(X)$ are polynomials in $a_{i_1}, \ldots, a_{i_s}$. Hence, they are the elements of $L \cap k'$. Since $L \cap k' = k$ by the hypothesis, we have $f_1(X) \in k[X]$. This implies $f_1(X) = f(X)$. So $[L(k') : L] = [k' : k]$, and the claim is verified. Since the natural surjection $\pi\colon L \otimes_k k' \to L(k')$ is an L-homomorphism and $[L \otimes_k k' : L] = [k' : k]$, the homomorphism π is an isomorphism. $L \otimes_k k'$ is, therefore, a field. □

If one replaces the field extension L/K by a k-algebra A in the foregoing, what kind of results can one expect? We shall consider this problem. In the following, a ring signifies a commutative ring with identity element 1.

DEFINITION 1.9. Let S be an integral domain and let R be a subring. If an element x of S is a root of a monic polynomial $f(X) = X^n + a_1X^{n-1} + \cdots + a_n$ with coefficients in R (i.e., $f(x) = 0$), we say that x is *integral* over R. If every element of S is integral over R, we say that S is *integral* over R, or S is an *integral extension* of R.

LEMMA 1.10. *Let S be an integral domain, and let R be a subring. Then the following assertions hold*:

(1) *The following three conditions on an element x of S are equivalent*:

(i) *x is integral over R.*

(ii) *$R[x]$ is a finitely generated R-module.*

(iii) *There exists an R-subalgebra R' of S containing x which is a finitely generated R-module.*

(2) *If elements x, y of S are integral over R, then $x \pm y$ and xy are integral over R. Hence, $\widetilde{R} = \{x \in S;\ x \text{ is integral over } R\}$ is an R-subalgebra of S.*

(3) *If S is integral over R, then the following two conditions are equivalent*:

(i) *R is a field.*

(ii) *S is a field.*

(4) *For integral domains $T \supset S \supset R$, if S is integral over R and T is integral over S then so is T over R.*

PROOF. (1) (i) *implies* (ii). Suppose $f(x) = x^n + a_1x^{n-1} + \cdots + a_n = 0$ $(a_i \in R)$. Then $R[x] = R \cdot 1 + Rx + \cdots + Rx^{n-1}$.

(ii) *implies* (iii). Take $R[x]$ as R'.

(iii) *implies* (i). Write $R' = \sum_{i=1}^t Rm_i$. Then we can write $xm_i = \sum_{j=1}^t a_{ij}m_j$ $(a_{ij} \in R)$. The matrix representation of this relation is $A\,{}^t(m_1, \dots, m_t) = 0$, where $A = (x\delta_{ij} - a_{ij})$. Let $\widetilde{A}$ be the cofactor matrix of A, and let $d = \det A$. Then ${}^t\widetilde{A}A = dE_t$, where E_t is the identity matrix. Hence, $dm_j = 0$ for each j. On the other hand, since one can express $1 = \sum_{i=1}^t b_i m_i$ $(b_i \in R)$, $d = \sum_{i=1}^t b_i d m_i = 0$. The expansion of d yields a monic relation of x,

$$d = x^t - \mathrm{Tr}(a_{ij})x^{t-1} + \cdots + \det(-(a_{ij})).$$

Hence, x is integral over R.

(2) Since both $R[x]$ and $R[y]$ are finitely generated R-modules, $R[x, y]$ is also a finitely generated R-module. We then know by (iii) of (1) that $x \pm y$ and xy are integral over R.

(3) (i) *implies* (ii). It suffices to show that any nonzero element x of S has an inverse x^{-1}. Since x is integral over R, we have

$$x^n + a_1x^{n-1} + \cdots + a_n = 0, \qquad a_i \in R.$$

We may assume here that $a_n \neq 0$. Then

$$1 = -a_n^{-1}(x^{n-1} + a_1x^{n-2} + \cdots + a_{n-1})x \quad \text{with } a_n^{-1} \in R;$$

whence, $x^{-1} = -a_n^{-1}(x^{n-1} + a_1x^{n-2} + \cdots + a_{n-1}) \in S$.

(ii) *implies* (i). Let y be a nonzero element of R. Then $y^{-1} \in S$ and y^{-1} is integral over R. Hence,

$$(y^{-1})^m + b_1(y^{-1})^{m-1} + \cdots + b_m = 0, \qquad b_j \in R.$$

We then have $1 = -y(b_1 + \cdots + b_my^{m-1})$; whence, $y^{-1} = -(b_1 + \cdots + b_my^{m-1}) \in R$. This shows that R is a field.

(4) Let z be an element of T. Since z is integral over S, we have $z^n + c_1z^{n-1} + \cdots + c_n = 0$ $(c_i \in S)$. Hence, $R[c_1, \dots, c_n, z]$ is a finitely generated $R[c_1, \dots, c_n]$-module. Meanwhile, $R[c_1, \dots, c_n]$ is a finitely generated R-module because $c_1, \dots, c_n$

are integral over R. By (iii) of (1) above, we can conclude that z is integral over R. □

DEFINITION 1.11. The subring $\widetilde{R}$ of S defined in (2) of Lemma 1.10 is called the *integral closure* of R in S. If $\widetilde{R} = R$, we say that R is *integrally closed* in S. When S is the quotient field $Q(R)$ of R, $\widetilde{R}$ is called the *normalization* of R. If R is integraly closed in $Q(R)$, we call R an *integrally closed integral domain.*

We shall next recall basic results on noetherian rings.

LEMMA 1.12. *The following four conditions on a ring are equivalent:*

(i) *For an arbitrary ascending chain of ideals* $I_0 \subseteq I_1 \subseteq \cdots \subseteq I_i \subseteq \cdots$, *there exists* $N > 0$ *such that* $I_N = I_{N+1} = \cdots$. (*When this condition is satisfied, we say that R satisfies the* ascending chain condition.)

(ii) *Introduce in the set* $\{I; I$ *is a proper ideal of* $R\}$ *an order* $I \leq J$ *by inclusion* $I \subseteq J$. *Then an arbitrary subset* $\mathfrak{S}$ *has a maximal element.* (*When this condition is satisfied, we say that R satisfies the* maximal condition.)

(iii) *An arbitrary ideal of R is a finitely generated ideal.*

(iv) *An R-submodule of a finitely generated R-module is a finitely generated R-module.*

PROOF. (i) *implies* (ii). We have only to prove that $\mathfrak{S}$ is an inductively ordered set. Then we can apply Zorn's lemma to $\mathfrak{S}$. Meanwhile, if $\{I_\lambda\}_{\lambda\in\Lambda}$ is a totally ordered subset of $\mathfrak{S}$, the ascending chain condition obviously implies that it has the greatest element.

(ii) *implies* (i). Let $I_0 \subseteq I_1 \subseteq \cdots \subseteq I_i \subseteq \cdots$ be an ascending chain of ideals. Then the set $\mathfrak{S} = \{I_i; i \geq 0\}$ has a maximal element I_N which must be the greatest element.

(i) *implies* (iii). Let I be an ideal of R. If $I \neq (0)$, then take $a_0 \in I - (0)$ and set $I_0 = (a_0)$. If $I \neq I_0$, take $a_1 \in I - I_0$ and set $I_1 = (a_0, a_1)$. Repeating this process, we can find an ascending chain of ideals $I_0 \subsetneqq I_1 \subsetneqq I_2 \subsetneqq \cdots$, but this process must terminate if R satisfies the ascending chain condition. Hence, $I = (a_0, a_1, \ldots, a_N)$.

(iii) *implies* (i). Let $I_0 \subseteq I_1 \subseteq \cdots \subseteq I_i \subseteq \cdots$ be an ascending chain of ideals. Let $I = \bigcup_{i\geq 0} I_i$. Then I is an ideal of R. By the condition (iii), I is written as $I = (a_0, a_1, \ldots, a_n)$. Then there exists $N > 0$ such that $a_i \in I_N$ for each i. Then $I_N = I_{N+1} = \cdots$.

(iii) *implies* (iv). Let M be a finitely generated R-module, and let N be an R-submodule. We write $M = Rz_1 + \cdots + Rz_m$. Consider the case $m = 1$. Let $I = \{a \in R; az_1 \in N\}$. Then I is an ideal of R. So by (iii), we can write $I = (a_1, \ldots, a_n)$. For any $v \in N$, write $v = az_1$. Then $a \in I$ and $a = \alpha_1 a_1 + \cdots + \alpha_n a_n$. Hence, $v = \alpha_1(a_1 z_1) + \cdots + \alpha_n(a_n z_1)$. So $N \subseteq \sum_{i=1}^n R(a_i z_1)$. Besides, $a_i z_1 \in N$ for each i, and hence, $\sum_{i=1}^n R(a_i z_1) \subseteq N$ obviously. So $N = \sum_{i=1}^n R(a_i z_1)$ and N is a finitely generated R-module. If $m > 1$, we shall proceed by induction on m. Set $M_1 = Rz_2 + \cdots + Rz_m$ and $N_1 = N \cap M_1$. By the induction hypothesis, N_1 is a finitely generated R-module. So write $N_1 = \sum_{i=1}^r Rh_i$. Set $I = \{a \in R; (az_1 + M_1) \cap N \neq \emptyset\}$. Then I is an ideal of R. If we write $I = (a_1, \ldots, a_s)$ by the condition (iii), there exist elements $g_1, \ldots, g_s$ of N such that $g_j - a_j z_1 \in M_1$ for each j. Take an arbitrary element z of N and write $z = \alpha_1 z_1 + \cdots + \alpha_m z_m$. Then $\alpha_1 \in I$. So if we write $\alpha_1 = \beta_1 a_1 + \cdots + \beta_s a_s$, $z - \sum_{j=1}^s \beta_j g_j \in M_1 \cap N = N_1$. Hence, $z \in \sum_{j=1}^s Rg_j + \sum_{i=1}^r Rh_i$. Therefore, we have $N = \sum_{j=1}^s Rg_j + \sum_{i=1}^r Rh_i$.

(iv) *implies* (iii). R is a finitely generated R-module, and any ideal I of R is an R-submodule. Hence, the condition (iv) implies apparently the condition (iii). □

By definition, a ring R is a *noetherian* ring if R satisfies the above four conditions. If an R-algebra S is generated (as an R-algebra) by finitely many elements $f_1, \dots, f_n$, we write $S = R[f_1, \dots, f_n]$ and call S a finitely generated R-algebra. S is then the image of an R-homomorphism from a polynomial ring $R[x_1, \dots, x_n]$ over R to S defined by $x_i \mapsto f_i$ for each i.

LEMMA 1.13. *Let R be a noetherian ring. Then the following assertions hold:*
(1) *The residue ring R/I is a noetherian ring.*
(2) *Let S be a multiplicatively closed subset of R. Then the quotient ring R_S (denoted also by $S^{-1}R$) is a noetherian ring.*

PROOF. (1) The assertion follows from the fact that the correspondence of ideals $\{J;$ an ideal of $R,\ J \supset I\} \to \{\bar{J};$ an ideal of $R/I\}$ given by $J \mapsto J/I$ is a one-to-one correspondence which preserves the inclusion relation.
(2) The correspondence of ideals $\{J;$ an ideal of $R,\ J \cap S = \emptyset\} \to \{J';$ a proper ideal of $R_S\}$ given by $J \mapsto JR_S$ is a surjective mapping which preserves the inclusion relation. The assertion follows from this fact. □

LEMMA 1.14. *A polynomial ring $R[x_1, \dots, x_n]$ over a noetherian ring R is also noetherian. Hence, a finitely generated R-algebra is noetherian.*

PROOF. By induction on n, it suffices to prove the assertion in the case $n = 1$. Let I be a proper ideal of $R[x]$, and let

$$\mathfrak{a} = \{c \in R;\ \text{for some } f(x) \in I,\ f(x) = cx^n + (\text{terms of lower degree})\}.$$

Then $\mathfrak{a}$ is an ideal of R. Write $\mathfrak{a} = \sum_{i=1}^{r} a_i R$, and let $f_i = a_i x^{n_i} +$ (terms of lower degree) be an element of I corresponding to a_i. Set $m = \max\{n_i;\ 1 \le i \le r\}$. Replacing f_i by $f_i x^{m-n_i}$, we may assume $n_1 = \cdots = n_r = m$. Let $M = R \cdot 1 + Rx + \cdots + Rx^{m-1}$ and $N = I \cap M$. Then M is a finitely generated R-module, and we can write $N = \sum_{j=1}^{t} Rg_j$. We shall then show that $I = \sum_{i=1}^{r} R[x]f_i + \sum_{j=1}^{t} R[x]g_j$. For $g \in I$, $g = cx^n +$ (terms of lower degree), where $c \in \mathfrak{a}$. Write $c = \alpha_1 a_1 + \cdots + \alpha_r a_r$. If $n \ge m$, $\deg(g - \sum_{i=1}^{r} \alpha_i f_i x^{n-m}) < n$ and $g - \sum_{i=1}^{r} \alpha_i f_i x^{n-m} \in I$. Continuing this argument, we find $h_1, \dots, h_r \in R[x]$ such that $\deg(g - \sum_{i=1}^{r} h_i f_i) < m$. Then $g - \sum_{i=1}^{r} h_i f_i \in I \cap M = N$. So, $g \in \sum_{i=1}^{r} R[x]f_i + \sum_{j=1}^{t} R[x]g_j$. Then we know $I = \sum_{i=1}^{r} R[x]f_i + \sum_{j=1}^{t} R[x]g_j$. □

The following is an analogue of Lemma 1.3 in ring theory.

THEOREM 1.15 (Noether's Normalization Theorem). *Let k be a field, let R be a finitely generated k-algebra domain*[1] *and let L be the quotient field of R. Then there exists a transcendence basis $\{x_1, \dots, x_n\}$ such that $x_1, \dots, x_n \in R$ and R is integral over a polynomial ring $k[x_1, \dots, x_n]$, where $n = \operatorname{tr.deg}_k L$.*

PROOF. Since R is a finitely generated k-algebra domain, we can express R as the residue ring $R = k[Y_1, \dots, Y_m]/\mathfrak{P}$ of a polynomial ring, where $m \ge n$ and $\mathfrak{P}$ is a prime ideal. Consider first the case $m = n$. Let $y_i = Y_i \pmod{\mathfrak{P}}$. Then $R = k[y_1, \dots, y_n]$ and $L = k(y_1, \dots, y_n)$. Since we can find a transcendence basis of L/k as a subset

[1] A k-algebra domain means a k-algebra which is an integral domain.

of $\{y_1, \dots, y_n\}$ and since $n = \operatorname{tr.deg}_k L$, we know that $y_1, \dots, y_n$ are algebraically independent over k. If $\mathfrak{P} \neq (0)$, then any nonzero element $F(Y_1, \dots, Y_n)$ of $\mathfrak{P}$ would give a nontrivial algebraic relation $F(y_1, \dots, y_n) = 0$. This implies $\mathfrak{P} = (0)$. Namely, R is a polynomial ring over k. Consider next the case $m > n$. Since $\mathfrak{P} \neq (0)$, there exists a nontrivial algebraic relation $f(y_1, \dots, y_m) = 0$. Set $z_i = y_i - y_1^{r_i}$ $(2 \le i \le m)$, where we choose r_i's in such a way that $0 \ll r_2 \ll r_3 \ll \cdots \ll r_m$. Then we have

$$\begin{aligned} f(y_1, \dots, y_m) &= f(y_1, z_2 + y_1^{r_2}, \dots, z_m + y_1^{r_m}) \\ &= b y_1^N + \begin{pmatrix} \text{terms of lower degree in } y_1 \\ \text{with coefficients in } k[z_2, \dots, z_m] \end{pmatrix} = 0, \end{aligned}$$

where $b \in k^* = k - (0)$. Hence, y_1 is integral over $k[z_2, \dots, z_m]$. Since $y_i = z_i + y_1^{r_i}$, y_i is integral over $k[z_2, \dots, z_m]$ as well for $2 \le i \le m$. Namely, R is integral over $k[z_2, \dots, z_m]$. Consider next $k[z_2, \dots, z_m]$ instead of R. Then by induction on $m - n$, we know that there exists a transcendence basis $x_1, \dots, x_n$ as required in the assertion. □

In order to state results which are derived from Theorem 1.15, we need the following definition and some preparations.

DEFINITION 1.16. Let R be a ring. A *prime ideal sequence of length n* is an ascending chain of prime ideals of R

$$\mathfrak{p}_0 \subsetneqq \mathfrak{p}_1 \subsetneqq \cdots \subsetneqq \mathfrak{p}_n .$$

The supremum of the length of a prime ideal sequence is called the *Krull dimension* of R and denoted by $\text{K-}\dim R$ (which could be ∞). When R is a finitely generated algebra domain over a field k, the transcendence degree of the quotient field $Q(R)/k$ is called the *dimension* of R and is denoted by $\dim R$. Whenever we know $\text{K-}\dim R = \dim R$, we represent it by $\dim R$.

We shall summarize basic results on maximal ideals in the following:

LEMMA 1.17. *Let R be a ring. We then have the following assertions:*

(1) *Given a proper ideal I of R, there exists a maximal ideal containing I.*

(2) *For a proper ideal $\mathfrak{m}$, $\mathfrak{m}$ is a maximal ideal if and only if $R/\mathfrak{m}$ is a field. A maximal ideal is, therefore, a prime ideal. The ring R has a unique maximal ideal $\mathfrak{m}$ if and only if all elements of $R - \mathfrak{m}$ are invertible elements. (If R has a unique maximal ideal $\mathfrak{m}$, R is called a* local ring *and is expressed by a pair $(R, \mathfrak{m})$.)*

(3) *If $\mathfrak{p}$ is a prime ideal, then $R - \mathfrak{p}$ is a multiplicatively closed set, and the quotient ring $R_{\mathfrak{p}}$ of R with respect to $R - \mathfrak{p}$ is a local ring with maximal ideal $\mathfrak{p}R_{\mathfrak{p}}$.*

PROOF. (1) Given an ideal I, let $\mathfrak{S} = \{J; I \subseteq J \subsetneqq R\}$ be the set of proper ideals containing I. Introduce an order $\ge$ by the inclusion relation: $J_2 \ge J_1$ if and only if $J_2 \supseteq J_1$. Then with this order, $\mathfrak{S}$ is an inductively ordered set. So by Zorn's lemma, there exists a maximal element $\mathfrak{m}$ in $\mathfrak{S}$, and $\mathfrak{m}$ is a maximal ideal of R containing I.

(2) $\mathfrak{m}$ is a maximal ideal if and only if (0) is the unique proper ideal of $R/\mathfrak{m}$. This is equivalent to saying that $R/\mathfrak{m}$ is a field. It then follows that $R/\mathfrak{m}$ is an integral domain. Hence, $\mathfrak{m}$ is a prime ideal. If $\mathfrak{m}$ is a unique maximal ideal, then we have $xR = R$ for each $x \in R - \mathfrak{m}$; whence, x is invertible. The converse follows immediately from the next observation:

If there exists a maximal ideal $\mathfrak{m}'$ other than $\mathfrak{m}$, any element of $\mathfrak{m}' - \mathfrak{m}$ is not invertible.

(3) follows from (2). □

LEMMA 1.18. *Let S be an integral domain, and let R be a subring. Assume that S is integral over R. Then we have:*

(1) (Lying-over Theorem). *For an arbitrary prime ideal $\mathfrak{p}$ of R there exists a prime ideal $\mathfrak{P}$ of S such that $\mathfrak{P} \cap R = \mathfrak{p}$. If $\mathfrak{P}'$ is a prime ideal of S with $\mathfrak{P} \subseteq \mathfrak{P}'$ and $\mathfrak{P}' \cap R = \mathfrak{p}$, then $\mathfrak{P} = \mathfrak{P}'$.*

(2) (Going-up Theorem). *For any prime ideal sequence*

$$\mathfrak{p}_0 \subsetneqq \mathfrak{p}_1 \subsetneqq \cdots \subsetneqq \mathfrak{p}_n$$

of R there exists a prime ideal sequence

$$\mathfrak{P}_0 \subsetneqq \mathfrak{P}_1 \subsetneqq \cdots \subsetneqq \mathfrak{P}_n$$

of S such that $\mathfrak{P}_i \cap R = \mathfrak{p}_i$ $(0 \le i \le n)$.

(3) *We have the equality* $\text{K-}\dim S = \text{K-}\dim R$.

PROOF. (1) Let $T = R - \mathfrak{p}$. Then T is a multiplicatively closed subset of R and S. Suppose $\mathfrak{P}$ is a prime ideal of S_T such that $\mathfrak{P} \cap R_\mathfrak{p} = \mathfrak{p}R_\mathfrak{p}$. Then we have $(\mathfrak{P} \cap S) \cap R = \mathfrak{P} \cap R_\mathfrak{p} \cap R = \mathfrak{p}R_\mathfrak{p} \cap R = \mathfrak{p}$, and $\mathfrak{P} \cap S$ is a prime ideal of S as required. So by replacing R and S by $R_\mathfrak{p}$ and S_T, respectively, we may (and shall) assume that R is a local ring with maximal ideal $\mathfrak{p}$. Let $\mathfrak{m}$ be an arbitrary maximal ideal of S, and let $\mathfrak{q} = \mathfrak{m} \cap R$. Then $R/\mathfrak{q}$ is a subring of $S/\mathfrak{m}$ and $S/\mathfrak{m}$ is integral over $R/\mathfrak{q}$. So $R/\mathfrak{q}$ is a field by Lemma 1.10 (3). Namely, $\mathfrak{q}$ is a maximal ideal. Hence, $\mathfrak{q} = \mathfrak{p}$. Then we take $\mathfrak{m}$ as a prime ideal $\mathfrak{P}$ which we require. Next suppose $\mathfrak{P} \cap R = \mathfrak{P}' \cap R$. Replacing as above R and S by $R_\mathfrak{p}$ and S_T, respectively, we may assume that $(R, \mathfrak{p})$ is a local ring. Since $S/\mathfrak{P}$ is an integral extension of a field $R/\mathfrak{p}$, $\mathfrak{P}$ is a maximal ideal of S. So $\mathfrak{P} = \mathfrak{P}'$ provided $\mathfrak{P} \subseteq \mathfrak{P}'$.

(2) By induction on n, we have only to treat the case $n = 1$. By (1) above, there exists a prime ideal $\mathfrak{P}_0$ of S such that $\mathfrak{P}_0 \cap R = \mathfrak{p}_0$. By replacing S and R by S_T and $R_{\mathfrak{p}_1}$ respectively, we may assume that $(R, \mathfrak{p}_1)$ is a local ring, where $T = R - \mathfrak{p}_1$. Here $\mathfrak{P}_0$ is not a maximal ideal of S because $S/\mathfrak{P}_0$ is an integral extension of $R/\mathfrak{p}_0$ and $R/\mathfrak{p}_0$ is not a field. As $\mathfrak{P}_1$, take a maximal ideal of S containing $\mathfrak{P}_0$. The argument in (1) above then shows that $\mathfrak{P}_1 \cap R = \mathfrak{p}_1$.

(3) Given a prime ideal sequence $\mathfrak{P}_0 \subsetneqq \mathfrak{P}_1 \subsetneqq \cdots \subsetneqq \mathfrak{P}_n$ of S, the sequence $\mathfrak{p}_0 \subsetneqq \mathfrak{p}_1 \subsetneqq \cdots \subsetneqq \mathfrak{p}_n$ with $\mathfrak{p}_i = \mathfrak{P}_i \cap R$ is a prime ideal sequence of R. Hence, $\text{K-}\dim R \le \text{K-}\dim S$. The converse inequality follows from (2) above. □

After these preparations, we shall prove the next result.

THEOREM 1.19. *With the same assumptions as in Theorem* 1.15, *we have* $\text{K-}\dim R = \dim R$.

PROOF. We shall prove the assertion by induction on n. If $n = 0$, then R is a field and the equality holds obviously. Assume that the equality holds provided $\dim R \le n - 1$. Consider first the case where R is a polynomial ring $k[x_1, \ldots, x_n]$. Let $(0) = \mathfrak{p}_0 \subsetneqq \mathfrak{p}_1 \subsetneqq \cdots \subsetneqq \mathfrak{p}_r$ be a prime ideal sequence of R. Then $\overline{R} = R/\mathfrak{p}_1$ is a finitely generated k-algebra domain, and $Q(\overline{R}) = k(\bar{x}_1, \ldots, \bar{x}_n)$, where $\bar{x}_i = x_i \pmod{\mathfrak{p}_1}$. Since a nonzero element in $\mathfrak{p}_1$ provides a nontrivial algebraic relation among $\bar{x}_1, \ldots, \bar{x}_n$, we have $\operatorname{tr.deg}_k Q(\overline{R}) < n$. By the induction hypothesis, $r -$

$1 \leq n-1$. Hence, $r \leq n$. This implies $\mathrm{K}\text{-}\dim R \leq \dim R$. Besides, we have a prime ideal sequence $(0) \subsetneqq (x_1) \subsetneqq (x_1, x_2) \subsetneqq \cdots \subsetneqq (x_1, \ldots, x_n)$ of R; whence, $\mathrm{K}\text{-}\dim R \geq n$. Therefore, $\mathrm{K}\text{-}\dim R = \dim R = n$. If R is not necessarily a polynomial ring, R contains a polynomial ring $k[x_1, \ldots, x_n]$ and R is an integral extension of $k[x_1, \ldots, x_n]$. By Lemma 1.18 (3), we know that $\mathrm{K}\text{-}\dim R = \mathrm{K}\text{-}\dim k[x_1, \ldots, x_n] = n$. □

We shall next recall a decomposition of an ideal into an intersection of primary ideals in a noetherian ring.

DEFINITION 1.20. A proper ideal $\mathfrak{q}$ of a ring R is a *primary ideal* if it satisfies the condition

$$ab \in \mathfrak{q},\ a \notin \mathfrak{q} \quad \text{implies} \quad b^n \in \mathfrak{q} \text{ for some } n > 0.$$

Taking the contrapositive, it is equivalent to saying that

$$ab \in \mathfrak{q},\ b^n \notin \mathfrak{q} \quad \text{for every } n > 0 \quad \text{implies} \quad a \in \mathfrak{q}.$$

An ideal I of R is a *reducible ideal* if $I = J_1 \cap J_2$ with two proper ideals $J_1, J_2 (\supsetneqq I)$. An ideal which is not reducible is called an *irreducible ideal.*

LEMMA 1.21. (1) *If $\mathfrak{q}$ is a primary ideal the radical ideal $\sqrt{\mathfrak{q}} = \{a \in R;\ a^n \in \mathfrak{q}$ for some $n > 0\}$ is a prime ideal. (We say that $\sqrt{\mathfrak{q}}$ is the prime ideal* associated to $\mathfrak{q}$ *and $\mathfrak{q}$ belongs to $\sqrt{\mathfrak{q}}$.)*

(2) *Let $\mathfrak{q}$ be an ideal of R. If $\mathfrak{q} \supset \mathfrak{m}^n$ (for some $n > 0$) with a maximal ideal $\mathfrak{m}$, then $\mathfrak{q}$ is a primary ideal.*

(3) *Let $\mathfrak{q}_i$ $(1 \leq i \leq r)$ be primary ideals belonging to one and the same prime ideal $\mathfrak{p}$. Then $\mathfrak{q}_1 \cap \cdots \cap \mathfrak{q}_r$ is a primary ideal belonging to $\mathfrak{p}$.*

PROOF. (1) If $ab \in \sqrt{\mathfrak{q}}$ and $b \notin \sqrt{\mathfrak{q}}$, then $(ab)^r \in \mathfrak{q}$ and $(b^r)^n \notin \mathfrak{q}$ (for every $n > 0$). So $a^r \in \mathfrak{q}$, i.e., $a \in \sqrt{\mathfrak{q}}$.

(2) Obviously, $\sqrt{\mathfrak{q}} = \mathfrak{m}$. Suppose $ab \in \mathfrak{q}$ and $b \notin \sqrt{\mathfrak{q}}$. Since $bR + \mathfrak{m}^n = R$, we have $bx + y = 1$ for $x \in R$ and $y \in \mathfrak{m}^n$. Then $a = abx + ay \in \mathfrak{q}$.

(3) If $ab \in \mathfrak{q}_1 \cap \cdots \cap \mathfrak{q}_r$ and $b \notin \mathfrak{p}$, then $a \in \mathfrak{q}_i$ (for each i). Hence, $a \in \mathfrak{q}_1 \cap \cdots \cap \mathfrak{q}_r$. In general, we have $\sqrt{I_1 \cap \cdots \cap I_r} = \sqrt{I_1} \cap \cdots \cap \sqrt{I_r}$; whence, $\sqrt{\mathfrak{q}_1 \cap \cdots \cap \mathfrak{q}_r} = \mathfrak{p}$. □

LEMMA 1.22. *Let R be a noetherian ring. Then we have:*

(1) *An arbitrary proper ideal I of R is written as the intersection $I = J_1 \cap \cdots \cap J_r$ of finitely many irreducible ideals $J_1, \ldots, J_n$.*

(2) *An irreducible ideal I is a primary ideal.*

PROOF. (1) We proceed by *reductio absurdum.* Let $\mathfrak{S}$ be the set of proper ideals of R which cannot be written as the intersection of finitely many irreducible ideals. Suppose $\mathfrak{S}$ is not the empty set. Introduce an order in $\mathfrak{S}$ by the inclusion; that is, $I_1 \leq I_2$ if $I_1 \subseteq I_2$. Since R is a noetherian ring, $\mathfrak{S}$ has a maximal element by Lemma 1.12. Let J be a maximal element of $\mathfrak{S}$. Then J is a reducible ideal. Hence, $J = J_1 \cap J_2$ for ideals J_1, J_2 $(J \subsetneqq J_i \subsetneqq R,\ i = 1, 2)$. Since $J_i \notin \mathfrak{S}$, we may write $J_i = J_{i1} \cap \cdots \cap J_{ir_i}$ as the intersection of irreducible ideals. Then $J = \bigcap_{i=1,2} \bigcap_{j=1}^{r_i} J_{ij}$ which is the intersection of irreducible ideals. This contradicts the choice of J.

(2) Suppose $ab \in I$ and $b^n \notin I$ (for each $n > 0$). Let $J_n = \{x \in R;\ b^n x \in I\}$ (which we denote also by $(I : b^n)$). Then J_n is a proper ideal of R and $J_1 \subseteq J_2 \subseteq \cdots \subset J_n \subseteq \cdots$. Since R is a noetherian ring, $J_m = J_{m+1} = \cdots$ for some $m > 0$. Let $I_1 = I + aR$ and $I_2 = I + b^m R$. Then $I \subseteq I_1 \cap I_2$. We shall show that $I_1 \cap I_2 \subseteq I$. Write an

element x of $I_1 \cap I_2$ as $x = \alpha + ay = \beta + b^m z$ with $\alpha, \beta \in I$ and $y, z \in R$. Then $b^{m+1}z = b(\alpha - \beta) + aby \in I$; whence, $z \in J_{m+1} = J_m$. So $b^m z \in I$ and $x \in I$, accordingly. This implies $I = I_1 \cap I_2$. Since I is an irreducible ideal by hypothesis and since $I_2 \neq I$, we have $I = I_1$. Hence, $a \in I$. □

As a corollary of Lemma 1.22, we have the next result.

THEOREM 1.23. (1) *An arbitrary ideal I of a noetherian ring R has a primary ideal decomposition $I = \mathfrak{q}_1 \cap \cdots \cap \mathfrak{q}_n$ satisfying the following two conditions*:

(i) $\sqrt{\mathfrak{q}_i} \neq \sqrt{\mathfrak{q}_j}$ *if* $i \neq j$.

(ii) $I \subsetneqq \mathfrak{q}_1 \cap \cdots \cap \check{\mathfrak{q}}_i \cap \cdots \cap \mathfrak{q}_m$ *for each i, where $\check{\mathfrak{q}}_i$ means that $\mathfrak{q}_i$ is omitted.*

(*We call such a decomposition the* shortest expression by primary ideals.)

(2) *Let $I = \mathfrak{q}_1 \cap \cdots \cap \mathfrak{q}_n$ be the shortest expression of I by primary ideals. Then the set of ideals $\{\sqrt{\mathfrak{q}_i}; 1 \leq i \leq n\}$ coincides with the set $\{\mathfrak{p}$; $\mathfrak{p}$ is a prime ideal of R, $\mathfrak{p} = (I : a)$ for some $a \in R\}$. This set is, therefore, determined uniquely by the ideal I. (Here $(I : a) = \{x \in R;\ ax \in I\}$ by definition, and we call it an* ideal quotient *of I by (a). We call $\sqrt{\mathfrak{q}_i}$ a* prime divisor *of I.)*

(3) *Let $\{\mathfrak{p}_1, \ldots, \mathfrak{p}_r\}$ exhaust all minimal prime divisors of I. Then $\sqrt{I} = \mathfrak{p}_1 \cap \cdots \cap \mathfrak{p}_r$ and $\sqrt{I} \subsetneqq \mathfrak{p}_1 \cap \cdots \cap \check{\mathfrak{p}}_i \cap \cdots \cap \mathfrak{p}_r$ for each i.*

(*This decomposition is called the* prime divisor decomposition *of $\sqrt{I}$.)*

PROOF. (1) By Lemma 1.22, there exists a primary ideal decomposition $I = \mathfrak{q}_1 \cap \cdots \cap \mathfrak{q}_n$. If $\mathfrak{q}_1 \cap \cdots \cap \check{\mathfrak{q}}_i \cap \cdots \cap \mathfrak{q}_n = I$, we consider a decomposition of I with $\mathfrak{q}_i$, omitted. Hence, we may assume that no $\mathfrak{q}_i$ of $I = \mathfrak{q}_1 \cap \cdots \cap \mathfrak{q}_n$ is redundant. For any prime ideal $\mathfrak{p}$ in $\{\sqrt{\mathfrak{q}_i};\ 1 \leq i \leq n\}$, the intersection of all $\mathfrak{q}_i$'s with $\sqrt{\mathfrak{q}_i} = \mathfrak{p}$ is a primary ideal by virtue of Lemma 1.21. So we may assume that the condition (i) is satisfied as well.

(2) Suppose $(I : a)$ equals to a prime ideal $\mathfrak{p}$. Then $(I : a) = \bigcap_{i=1}^n (\mathfrak{q}_i : a)$, $(\mathfrak{q}_i : a) \subseteq \mathfrak{p}$ (for some i). Since $\mathfrak{p} \subseteq (\mathfrak{q}_i : a)$ also, we have $\mathfrak{p} = (\mathfrak{q}_i : a)$. Note here that if $\mathfrak{q}$ is a primary ideal and $(\mathfrak{q} : a) \neq R$, then $\sqrt{(\mathfrak{q} : a)} = \sqrt{\mathfrak{q}}$. (In fact, $\sqrt{\mathfrak{q}} \subseteq \sqrt{(\mathfrak{q} : a)}$ because $\mathfrak{q} \subseteq (\mathfrak{q} : a)$. For $x \in \sqrt{(\mathfrak{q} : a)}$, $ax^N \in \mathfrak{q}$ for some $N > 0$, and $x^{NM} \in \mathfrak{q}$ for some $M > 0$ because $a \notin \mathfrak{q}$. Hence, $x \in \sqrt{\mathfrak{q}}$.) Thereby we know that $\mathfrak{p} = \sqrt{\mathfrak{q}_i}$. Conversely, suppose $\mathfrak{p} = \sqrt{\mathfrak{q}_i}$. We shall show that $\mathfrak{p} = (I : a)$ for some $a \in R$. Take an element $a \in \mathfrak{q}_1 \cap \cdots \cap \check{\mathfrak{q}}_i \cap \cdots \cap \mathfrak{q}_n - I$. Then $(I : a) = (\mathfrak{q}_i : a)$. Moreover, since $((I : a) : b) = (I : ab)$ and $(\mathfrak{q}_i : a)$ is a primary ideal belonging to $\mathfrak{p}$, we have only to show that $\mathfrak{p} = (\mathfrak{q} : a)$ for some $a \in R$ provided $\mathfrak{q}$ is a primary ideal belonging to $\mathfrak{p}$. Let $\mathfrak{S} = \{J; J = (\mathfrak{q} : a),\ \mathfrak{q} \subseteq J \subseteq \mathfrak{p}\}$ and define in $\mathfrak{S}$ an order by $J_1 \leq J_2$ if $J_1 \subseteq J_2$. Here $\mathfrak{S} \neq \emptyset$ because $c \notin \mathfrak{p}$ entails $(\mathfrak{q} : c) = \mathfrak{q} \in \mathfrak{S}$. Moreover, since R is a noetherian ring, $\mathfrak{S}$ has a maximal element. We shall show that if $(\mathfrak{q} : a)$ is a maximal element, then $\mathfrak{p} = (\mathfrak{q} : a)$. Suppose $(\mathfrak{q} : a) \subsetneqq \mathfrak{p}$. Then since $\mathfrak{p} = \sqrt{(\mathfrak{q} : a)}$, there exists an element b of $\mathfrak{p} - (\mathfrak{q} : a)$ such that $b \notin \mathfrak{q} : a)$ and $b^2 \in (\mathfrak{q} : a)$. Then $(\mathfrak{q} : a) \subsetneqq (\mathfrak{q} : ab) \subseteq \mathfrak{p}$. This contradicts the maximality of $(\mathfrak{q} : a)$. Hence, $\mathfrak{p} = (\mathfrak{q} : a)$.

(3) Let $I = \mathfrak{q}_1 \cap \cdots \cap \mathfrak{q}_n$ be the shortest expression by primary ideals. Then $\sqrt{I} = \sqrt{\mathfrak{q}_1} \cap \cdots \cap \sqrt{\mathfrak{q}_n}$. If $\{\mathfrak{p}_1, \ldots, \mathfrak{p}_n\}$ is the set of minimal prime divisors of I, we have apparently $\sqrt{I} = \mathfrak{p}_i \cap \cdots \cap \mathfrak{p}_r$. If $\mathfrak{p}_1 \cap \cdots \cap \check{\mathfrak{p}}_i \cap \cdots \cap \mathfrak{p}_r = \sqrt{I}$, then $\mathfrak{p}_i \supseteq \prod_{j \neq i} \mathfrak{p}_j$, and hence, $\mathfrak{p}_i \supseteq p_j$ for some $j \neq i$, which is a contradiction. □

A nonminimal prime divisor of I is called an *embedded prime divisor* of I. We shall explain in the Part II what the prime divisor decomposition of $\sqrt{I}$ means geometrically.

THEOREM 1.24. (1) *Let I be a proper ideal of R. Then $\sqrt{I} = \bigcap \mathfrak{p}$, where $\mathfrak{p}$ ranges over all prime ideals containing I.*

(2) (The Nullstellensatz of Hilbert). *Let R be a finitely generated algebra over a field k, and let I be a proper ideal of R. Then $\sqrt{I} = \bigcap \mathfrak{m}$, where $\mathfrak{m}$ ranges over all maximal ideals containing I.*

PROOF. (1) Apparently, $\sqrt{I} \subseteq \bigcap_{\mathfrak{p} \supseteq I} \mathfrak{p}$. Suppose $x \in \bigcap \mathfrak{p}$ and $x \notin \sqrt{I}$. Then $S = \{x^i; i \geq 0\}$ is a multiplicatively closed subset of R with $S \cap I = \emptyset$, where $x^0 = 1$. Since $IR_S \neq R_S$ in the quotient ring R_S, there exists a maximal ideal $\mathfrak{M}$ of R_S containing IR_S. Let $\mathfrak{p}' = \{a \in R;\ a/1 \in \mathfrak{M}\}$. Then $\mathfrak{p}'$ is a prime ideal of R such that $\mathfrak{p}' \supseteq I$ and $\mathfrak{p}' \cap S = \emptyset$. However, this is a contradiction because $x \in \bigcap \mathfrak{p} \subseteq \mathfrak{p}'$ and $x \in S$. Hence $\bigcap_{\mathfrak{p} \supseteq I} \mathfrak{p} = \sqrt{I}$.

(2) It suffices to show that if x is an element of R with $x \notin \sqrt{I}$, then there exists a maximal ideal $\mathfrak{m}$ of R such that $I \subseteq \mathfrak{m}$ and $x \notin \mathfrak{m}$. For such an element x, let $S = \{x^i;\ i \geq 0\}$ as in (1) above. Then S is a multiplicatively closed subset of R, and R_S is a finitely generated algebra over k. Since $I \cap S = \emptyset$, we have $IR_S \neq R_S$. Let $\mathfrak{M}$ be a maximal ideal of R_S containing IR_S and let $\mathfrak{m} = \{a \in R;\ a/1 \in \mathfrak{M}\}$. Then $I \subseteq \mathfrak{m}$ and $x \notin \mathfrak{m}$. We shall show that $\mathfrak{m}$ is a maximal ideal of R. Let $\overline{R} = R/\mathfrak{m}$. Then $\overline{R}$ is a finitely generated algebra domain over k and the residue class y of x is a nonzero element of $\overline{R}$. We shall show that $\dim \overline{R}[1/y] = 0$. Suppose $\dim \overline{R}[1/y] > 0$. Then there exists a prime ideal $\overline{\mathfrak{P}}$ of $\overline{R}$ with $y \notin \overline{\mathfrak{P}}$. Let $\mathfrak{P} = \{a \in R;\ a(\operatorname{mod} \mathfrak{m}) \in \overline{\mathfrak{P}}\}$. Then $\mathfrak{P}$ is a prime ideal of R such that $x \notin \mathfrak{P}$ and $\mathfrak{m} \subsetneqq \mathfrak{P}$. Hence, $\mathfrak{M} = \mathfrak{m}R_S \subsetneqq \mathfrak{P}R_S \neq R_S$ which contradicts the maximality of $\mathfrak{M}$. So $\dim \overline{R}[1/y] = 0$, and $\overline{R}[1/y]$ is a field. Then we conclude by Lemma 1.25 below that $\overline{R}$ is a field. Accordingly, $\mathfrak{m}$ is a maximal ideal of R. □

LEMMA 1.25. *Let R be a finitely generated algebra domain over a field k, and let y be a nonzero element of R. If $R[1/y]$ is a field, then so is R.*

PROOF. Let $n = \dim R$. We have only to show that $n = 0$. Suppose $n > 0$. By Noether's normalization theorem, R is an integral extension of $A = k[x_1, \ldots, x_n]$. Since y is integral over A, we have

$$y^m + a_1 y^{m-1} + \cdots + a_m = 0, \qquad a_i \in A,\ a_m \neq 0.$$

Since $R[1/y]$ is a field by hypothesis, $y \in \mathfrak{P}$ for any prime ideal $\mathfrak{P}(\neq (0))$ of R. Recall that for any prime ideal $\mathfrak{p}(\neq (0))$ of A there exists a prime ideal $\mathfrak{P}$ of R with $\mathfrak{P} \cap A = \mathfrak{p}$. Since $y \in \mathfrak{P}$, we have $a_m \in \mathfrak{p}$. Note also that since A is a unique factorization domain (UFD), any irreducible element f of A is a prime element. Namely, the principal ideal (f) is a prime ideal of A. So by the foregoing argument, $a_m \in (f)$. Hence, f is a prime factor of a_m. Therefore, A has only finitely many irreducible elements. This is a contradiction. (Prove that A has infinitely many, mutually prime, irreducible polynomials.) Hence, $n = 0$. □

In the subsequent paragraphs, we shall describe the relationships betwen normal rings and discrete valuation rings.

DEFINITION 1.26. (1) A noetherian integral domain R is called a *normal ring* if it is integrally closed.

(2) Let $\mathcal{O}$ be a subring of a field L. $\mathcal{O}$ is called a *valuation ring* of L if $\mathcal{O}$ satisfies the following two conditions:

(i) $\mathcal{O} \neq L$,

(ii) for each $x \in L$, either $x \in \mathcal{O}$ or $x^{-1} \in \mathcal{O}$.

A valuation ring $\mathcal{O}$ is called a *discrete valuation ring* (abbreviated as DVR) if it is noetherian.

LEMMA 1.27. *Let L be a field, and let $\mathcal{O}$ be a valuation ring of L.*

(1) *Set $\mathfrak{m} = \{x \in \mathcal{O}: x = 0$ or $x^{-1} \notin \mathcal{O}\}$. Then $(\mathcal{O}, \mathfrak{m})$ is a local ring.*

(2) *L is the quotient field of $\mathcal{O}$, and $\mathcal{O}$ is an integrally closed, integral domain.*

(3) *$\mathcal{O}$ is a discrete valuation ring if and only if $\mathfrak{m}$ is principal, i.e., $\mathfrak{m} = t\mathcal{O}$, and $\bigcap_{n\geq 0} \mathfrak{m}^n = (0)$.*

(4) *For a discrete valuation ring $\mathcal{O}$, define a mapping $v: L \to \mathbb{Z} \cup (\infty)$ by $v(0) = \infty$ and $v(x) = n$ if and only if $xt^{-n} \in \mathcal{O} - \mathfrak{m}$ for $x \in L^* := L - (0)$. Then v satisfies the following properties:*

  (i) *$v(x) = \infty$ if and only if $x = 0$.*

  (ii) *$v(xy) = v(x) + v(y)$.*

  (iii) *$v(x+y) \geq \min(v(x), v(y))$.*

In terms of the mapping v, one can write $\mathcal{O} = \{x \in L; v(x) \geq 0\}$ and $\mathfrak{m} = \{x \in L: v(x) > 0\}$. ($v$ is called the discrete valuation *associated with $\mathcal{O}$.)*

PROOF. (1) We shall show that $x, y \in \mathfrak{m}$ implies $x + y \in \mathfrak{m}$. We may assume $x \neq 0$, $y \neq 0$, and $x + y \neq 0$. We have $y/x \in \mathcal{O}$ or $x/y \in \mathcal{O}$. If $y/x \in \mathcal{O}$, then $(x+y)/x \in \mathcal{O}$. Furthermore, if $x + y \notin \mathfrak{m}$, then $(x+y)^{-1} \in \mathcal{O}$, and hence, $x^{-1} \in \mathcal{O}$. This contradicts the choice of x. Hence, $x + y \in \mathfrak{m}$. One can treat the case $x/y \in \mathcal{O}$ in a similar fashion. For $a \in \mathcal{O}$ and $x \in \mathfrak{m}$, $(ax)^{-1} \in \mathcal{O}$ implies $a \cdot (ax)^{-1} = x^{-1} \in \mathcal{O}$, which is a contradiction. Hence, $ax \in \mathfrak{m}$. The above observations imply that $\mathfrak{m}$ is an ideal of $\mathcal{O}$. Furthermore, since $a^{-1} \in \mathcal{O}$ for each $a \in \mathcal{O} - \mathfrak{m}$, $(\mathcal{O}, \mathfrak{m})$ is a local ring by Lemma 1.17.

(2) For $x \in L^*$, either $x \in \mathcal{O}$ or $x^{-1} \in \mathcal{O}$. Hence $L = Q(\mathcal{O})$. Suppose an element x of L is integral over $\mathcal{O}$ and x satisfies a monic relation $x^n + a_1x^{n-1} + \cdots + a_n = 0$, $a_i \in \mathcal{O}$. If $x \notin \mathcal{O}$, then $x^{-1} \in \mathfrak{m}$. So $1 = -(a_1x^{-1} + \cdots + a_nx^{-n}) \in \mathfrak{m}$, and this is a contradiction. Hence, $x \in \mathcal{O}$. We note here that $\mathfrak{m} \neq (0)$. In fact, if $\mathfrak{m} = (0)$, then $\mathcal{O} = L$ and $\mathcal{O}$ is not a valuation ring.

(3) "Only if" part. Since $\mathcal{O}$ is a noetherian ring, we can express $\mathfrak{m} = (x_1, \ldots, x_n)$. Since $x_ix_j^{-1} \in \mathcal{O}$ or $x_jx_i^{-1} \in \mathcal{O}$, we may assume, after a change of indices, that $x_jx_i^{-1} \in \mathcal{O}$ whenever $i < j$. Then $\mathfrak{m} = x_1\mathcal{O}$, so we have only to put $t = x_1$. Let $J = \bigcap_{n>0} \mathfrak{m}^n$. Since $\mathfrak{m}^n = t^n\mathcal{O}$, we have $a \in J$ if and only if $t^n | a$ for each $n > 0$. Thence, $J = \mathfrak{m}J$. Then $J = (0)$ by Nakayama's lemma (see Lemma 1.28 below).

"If" part. Suppose $\mathfrak{m} = t\mathcal{O}$ and $\bigcap_{n>0} \mathfrak{m}^n = (0)$. Then for each $x \in \mathcal{O} - (0)$ we can uniquely determine an integer $n \geq 0$ such that $t^n | x$ and $t^{n+1} \nmid x$. Set $v(x) = n$. For each $x \in L - \mathcal{O}$, we set $v(x) = -v(x^{-1})$ as $x^{-1} \in \mathcal{O}$. Setting $v(0) = \infty$, we can readily ascertain that the mapping $v: L \to \mathbf{Z} \cup (\infty)$ satisfies three properties of the assertion (4) above. Given a nonzero, proper ideal I of $\mathcal{O}$, set $r = \min\{v(x); x \in I\}$. Since $I \neq (0)$, r is determined as a positive integer. For each $x \in I$, $x \in t^r\mathcal{O}$ because $v(xt^{-r}) \geq 0$. Take an element x_0 of I with $v(x_0) = r$. Since $v(t^rx_0^{-1}) = 0$, $t^rx_0^{-1}$ is an invertible element of $\mathcal{O}$. Hence, $t^r \in I$. So $I = t^r\mathcal{O}$. Since every ideal of $\mathcal{O}$ is principal (hence finitely generated), $\mathcal{O}$ is a noetherian ring.

(4) This part is easily verified. □

The following result is frequently referred to as *Nakayama's lemma*.

LEMMA 1.28. *Let R be a noetherian ring and let J be the Jacobson radical (= the intersection of all maximal ideals of R). Let M be a finitely generated R-module. If M satisfies the condition $M = JM$, then $M = (0)$.*

PROOF. Write $M = Rm_1 + \cdots + Rm_s$. Since $M = JM$, one can write $m_i = \sum_{j=1}^{s} a_{ij}m_j$ $(a_{ij} \in J)$, or equivalently $(\delta_{ij} - a_{ij})^t(m_1, \ldots, m_s) = (0)$ if it is represented by the matrices. Let $d = \det(\delta_{ij} - a_{ij})$. Then $dm_i = 0$ for each i. Here, developing d, we can write $d = 1 + a$ $(a \in J)$. Hence, d is an invertible element of R. (If $dR \neq R$, there exists a maximal ideal $\mathfrak{m}$ of R containing dR. Hence, $d \in \mathfrak{m}$ and $1 \in \mathfrak{m}$ because $a \in J \subset \mathfrak{m}$. This is a contradiction.) Hence, $m_i = 0$ for each i. Namely, we have $M = (0)$. □

LEMMA 1.29. *Let $(R, \mathfrak{m})$ be a normal local ring with* K-dim $R = 1$. *Then R is a discrete valuation ring of $Q(R)$.*

PROOF. It suffices to show that for an element yx^{-1} of $Q(R)$ $(x, y \in R - (0))$, either $yx^{-1} \in R$ or $xy^{-1} \in R$. If $x \notin \mathfrak{m}$, then $yx^{-1} \in R$. Similarly, $xy^{-1} \in R$ if $y \notin \mathfrak{m}$. Hence, we have only to consider the case $x, y \in \mathfrak{m}$. We shall show that the hypothesis $yx^{-1} \notin R$ and $xy^{-1} \notin R$ leads to a contradiction. Let $I = \{a \in R;\ a(xy^{-1}) \in R\}$. Then I is a proper ideal of R and $I \neq (0)$ because $x \in I$. Consider the prime divisor decomposition $\sqrt{I} = \mathfrak{p}_1 \cap \cdots \cap \mathfrak{p}_s$. Then $\mathfrak{p}_i \subseteq \mathfrak{m}$(for each i). Since K-dim $R = 1$, we have $\mathfrak{p}_i = \mathfrak{m}$ for each i. Hence $\sqrt{I} = \mathfrak{m}$. So $I \supseteq \mathfrak{m}^n$ for some $n > 0$. Let n be the smallest positive integer such that $I \supseteq \mathfrak{m}^n$. Then $\mathfrak{m}^n \cdot (yx^{-1}) \subseteq R$ by the choice of n. More precisely, we have $\mathfrak{m}^n \cdot (yx^{-1}) \subseteq \mathfrak{m}$. In fact, if we assume $\mathfrak{m}^n \cdot (yx^{-1}) \not\subseteq \mathfrak{m}$, then there is some $w \in \mathfrak{m}^n$ with $w(yx^{-1}) = u \in R - \mathfrak{m}$, and accordingly $xy^{-1} = wu^{-1} \in R$ which contradicts the hypothesis. Now fix an element $u \in \mathfrak{m}^{m-1}$, and let $b = u(yx^{-1})$. Then $b\mathfrak{m} \subseteq \mathfrak{m}$. If we write $\mathfrak{m} = Rz_1 + \cdots + Rz_r$, then $bz_i = \sum_{j=1}^{r} c_{ij}z_j$ $(c_{ij} \in R)$ for each i. Let $d = \det(b\delta_{ij} - c_{ij})$. Then $dz_j = 0$ for each j. Since R is an integral domain and $\mathfrak{m} \neq (0)$, we have $d = 0$. Expanding d, we know that b is integral over R. Meanwhile, since R is integrally closed, we have $b \in R$. Hence, $\mathfrak{m}^{n-1} \cdot (yx^{-1}) \subseteq R$. This contradicts the choice of n. □

In order to discuss further relationships between normal rings and discrete valuation rings, we need more definitions and preparations.

DEFINITION 1.30. Let $\mathfrak{p}$ be a prime ideal of a ring R. The *height* of $\mathfrak{p}$ (denoted by ht $\mathfrak{p}$) is the supremum of the length h of a prime ideal sequence $\mathfrak{p}_0 \subsetneqq \mathfrak{p}_1 \subsetneqq \cdots \subsetneqq \mathfrak{p}_h = \mathfrak{p}$ which terminates at $\mathfrak{p}$. By virtue of the one-to-one correspondence $\mathfrak{Q} \mapsto \mathfrak{q} = \{x \in R;\ x/1 \in \mathfrak{Q}\}$, $\mathfrak{q} \mapsto \mathfrak{q}R_{\mathfrak{p}}$ between prime ideals of $R_{\mathfrak{p}}$ and prime ideals of R contained in $\mathfrak{p}$, we have ht $\mathfrak{p}$ = K-dim $R_{\mathfrak{p}}$. When R is a noetherian ring and I is an ideal of R, we define the *height* of I by ht $I = \inf_{\mathfrak{p}}$ ht $\mathfrak{p}$, where $\mathfrak{p}$ ranges over all prime divisors of I.

The following results will be used in a proof of Lemma 1.32.

LEMMA 1.31 (Lemma of Artin-Rees). *Let R be a noetherian ring, and let $\mathfrak{a}$ be its ideal. Then we have the following:*

(1) *Let I, J be ideals of R. Then there exists an integer $r \geq 0$ such that $\mathfrak{a}^m I \cap J = \mathfrak{a}^{m-r}(\mathfrak{a}^r I \cap J)$ for each $m \geq r$.*

(2) *Let $L = \bigcap_{n>0} \mathfrak{a}^n$. Then $\mathfrak{a}L = L$.*

Proof. (1) Write $\mathfrak{a} = (a_1, \dots, a_n)$. Given n variables $x_1, \dots, x_n$, we denote the polynomial ring $R[x_1, \dots, x_n]$ by A. For an integer $m > 0$, define

$$S_m = \left\{ f(x_1, \dots, x_n) \in A; \begin{array}{l} f \text{ is a homogeneous polynomial of degree } m \text{ and} \\ f(a_1, \dots, a_n) \in \mathfrak{a}^m I \cap J \end{array} \right\}$$

and $S = \bigcup_{m>0} S_m$. Let $\tilde{\mathfrak{a}}$ be the ideal of A generated by elements of S. Then $\tilde{\mathfrak{a}}$ is a homogeneous ideal (cf. Problem II.3.1). Namely, $f \in \tilde{\mathfrak{a}}$ implies that any homogeneous part f_m of f is an element of $\tilde{\mathfrak{a}}$. Since A is a noetherian ring, $\tilde{\mathfrak{a}}$ is generated by finitely many elements $f_1, \dots, f_t$ which we may assume to be homogeneous. Let $d_i = \deg f_i$, and let $r = \max\{d_i; 1 \le i \le t\}$. Take m so that $m \ge r$. If $a \in \mathfrak{a}^m I \cap J$ there exists an element $f(x_1, \dots, x_n)$ of S_m such that $a = f(a_1, \dots, a_n)$. Since $f \in \tilde{\mathfrak{a}}$, $f = f_1 g_1 + \dots + f_t g_t$, where g_i is a homogeneous polynomial of degree $m - d_i$. Hence, we have

$$\begin{aligned} a = f(a_1, \dots, a_n) &= \sum_{i=1}^{t} f_i(a_1, \dots, a_n) g_i(a_1, \dots, a_n) \\ &\in \sum_{i=1}^{t} \mathfrak{a}^{m-d_i}(\mathfrak{a}^{d_i} I \cap J) \subseteq \mathfrak{a}^{m-r}(\mathfrak{a}^r I \cap J). \end{aligned}$$

So $\mathfrak{a}^m I \cap J \subseteq \mathfrak{a}^{m-r}(\mathfrak{a}^r I \cap J)$. The other inclusion is apparent.

(2) Set $I = R$ and $J = L$ in (1) above. Then $\mathfrak{a}^m \cap L = \mathfrak{a}^{m-r}(\mathfrak{a}^r \cap L)$ if $m \ge r$. Hence, $L = \mathfrak{a}^{m-r} L$. Now take $r + 1$ as m. □

Lemma 1.32. (1) *Let R be a noetherian domain, let a be a nonzero element of R with $aR \ne R$, and let $\mathfrak{p}$ be a prime divisor of aR. Let $\mathfrak{p}^{-1} = \{\xi \in Q(R); \xi\mathfrak{p} \subseteq R\}$. Then $\mathfrak{p}^{-1}$ is an R-module and $R \subsetneqq \mathfrak{p}^{-1}$.*

(2) *Let $(R, \mathfrak{m})$ be a noetherian local domain such that $\mathfrak{m} \ne (0)$ and $\mathfrak{m} \cdot \mathfrak{m}^{-1} = R$. Then R is a discrete valuation ring.*

Proof. (1) By Theorem 1.23, we can write $\mathfrak{p} = (aR : b)$ for some $b \in R$. Then $ba^{-1} \in \mathfrak{p}^{-1}$. If $ba^{-1} \in R$, then $b = ac$ for some $c \in R$, and $\mathfrak{p} \in R$ which is a contradiction. So $ba^{-1} \notin R$. Hence, $R \subsetneqq \mathfrak{p}^{-1}$.

(2) Let $J = \bigcap_{n>0} \mathfrak{m}^n$. By Lemma 1.31, we have $\mathfrak{m}J = J$. By Nakayama's lemma (Lemma 1.28), we know $J = (0)$. Hence, $\mathfrak{m} \ne \mathfrak{m}^2$. Let t be an element of $\mathfrak{m} - \mathfrak{m}^2$. Then $t\mathfrak{m}^{-1} \subseteq \mathfrak{m} \cdot \mathfrak{m}^{-1} = R$. If $t\mathfrak{m}^{-1} \ne R$, then $t\mathfrak{m}^{-1} \subseteq \mathfrak{m}$, and hence, $tR = t\mathfrak{m}^{-1} \cdot \mathfrak{m} \subseteq \mathfrak{m}^2$, which contradicts the choice of t. So, $t\mathfrak{m}^{-1} = R$. Therefore, $tR = t\mathfrak{m}^{-1} \cdot \mathfrak{m} = \mathfrak{m}$. We shall show that R is a valuation ring. Let $\xi \in Q(R)$, and write $\xi = yx^{-1}$ with $x, y \in R$. Write $x = t^r u$, $y = t^s v$ ($r, s \ge 0$; u, v are invertible elements of R). If $s \ge r$, then $\xi = t^{s-r}(u^{-1}v) \in R$. If $s < r$, $\xi^{-1} = t^{r-s}(uv^{-1}) \in R$. Hence, R is a valuation ring. Now R is a DVR by virtue of Lemma 1.27. □

The following result shows that there exists a significant relationship between normal rings and discrete valuation rings.

Theorem 1.33. *Let R be a normal ring. Then we have the following:*

(1) *For a nonzero principal ideal $aR (\ne R)$, any prime divisor has height 1.*

(2) *If $\mathfrak{p}$ is a prime ideal of height 1, then $R_\mathfrak{p}$ is a discrete valuation ring of $Q(R)$.*

(3) *If $\mathfrak{p}$ ranges over all prime ideals of height 1, then $R = \bigcap_\mathfrak{p} R_\mathfrak{p}$ as subrings of $Q(R)$.*

(4) *If* K-dim $R = 1$, *then any valuation ring* $\mathcal{O}$ *of* $Q(R)$ *containing* R *can be written as* $\mathcal{O} = R_\mathfrak{p}$, *where* $\mathfrak{p}$ *is a prime ideal of height* 1. *In particular,* $\mathcal{O}$ *is a DVR.*

PROOF. (1) if $\mathfrak{p}$ is a prime divisor of aR, then $\mathfrak{p}R_\mathfrak{p}$ is a prime divisor of $aR_\mathfrak{p}$. (Indeed, $(aR : b)R_\mathfrak{p} = (aR_\mathfrak{p} : b)$.) Hence, replacing R by $R_\mathfrak{p}$, we may assume that $(R, \mathfrak{p})$ is a local ring. Here we have $R \subsetneqq \mathfrak{p}^{-1}$ by Lemma 1.32 (1). If $\mathfrak{p} \cdot \mathfrak{p}^{-1} = R$ holds the assertion (2) of the same lemma implies that R is a DVR. Hence, $\mathrm{ht}\,\mathfrak{p} = 1$. Suppose $\mathfrak{p} \cdot \mathfrak{p}^{-1} \neq R$. Then $\mathfrak{p} \cdot \mathfrak{p}^{-1} \subseteq \mathfrak{p}$ since $\mathfrak{p} \cdot \mathfrak{p}^{-1} \subsetneqq R$. Thence, we know that every element $\xi \in \mathfrak{p}^{-1}$ is integral over R (cf. the proof of Lemma 1.29). Since R is a normal ring, we have $\xi \in R$. Hence, $\mathfrak{p}^{-1} = R$ which is a contradiction.

(2) $R_\mathfrak{p}$ is a DVR by Lemma 1.29.

(3) Let $D = \bigcap_\mathfrak{p} R_\mathfrak{p}$. Then $R \subseteq D$ apparently. We shall show the inclusion $D \subseteq R$. Let $\xi \in D$ and write $\xi = yx^{-1}$ $(x, y \in R)$. For every prime ideal $\mathfrak{p}$ of height 1 we have $yx^{-1} \in R_\mathfrak{p}$. So $y \in xR_\mathfrak{p} \cap R$. If x is an invertible element then $\xi \in R$. So we may assume $xR \neq R$. Let $xR = \mathfrak{q}_1 \cap \cdots \cap \mathfrak{q}_n$ be the shortest expression by primary ideals of xR, and let $\mathfrak{p}_i = \sqrt{\mathfrak{q}_i}$. Then $\mathfrak{p}_i$ has height 1 by (1) above. Hence, $\mathfrak{p}_i \not\subseteq \mathfrak{p}_j$ and $\mathfrak{q}_i \not\subseteq \mathfrak{q}_j$ whenever $i \neq j$. So for $\mathfrak{q} = \mathfrak{q}_i$ and $\mathfrak{p} = \mathfrak{p}_i$, we have $xR_\mathfrak{p} = \mathfrak{q}R_\mathfrak{p}$ and $\mathfrak{q}R_\mathfrak{p} \cap R = \mathfrak{q}$. Hence, $y \in \bigcap_{i=1}^n (xR_{\mathfrak{p}_i} \cap R) = \bigcap_{i=1}^n \mathfrak{q}_i = xR$, and $\xi \in R$. Consequently, we know $D = R$.

(4) Let $\mathfrak{m}$ be the maximal ideal of $\mathcal{O}$, and let $\mathfrak{p} = \mathfrak{m} \cap R$. Since $R \subseteq \mathcal{O}$, we have $\mathfrak{p} \neq (0)$. In fact, if $\mathfrak{p} = (0)$, then $R - (0) \subseteq \mathcal{O} - \mathfrak{m}$, and hence, $Q(R) \subseteq \mathcal{O}$. This is a contradiction. Since K-dim $R = 1$, we have $\mathrm{ht}\,\mathfrak{p} = 1$. Hence, $R_\mathfrak{p}$ is a DVR of $Q(R)$, $R_\mathfrak{p} \subseteq \mathcal{O}$, and $\mathfrak{m} \cap R_\mathfrak{p} = \mathfrak{p}R_\mathfrak{p}$. (We then say that $\mathcal{O}$ *dominates* $R_\mathfrak{p}$ and express it as $\mathcal{O} \geq R_\mathfrak{p}$.) If both $\mathcal{O}$ and $R_\mathfrak{p}$ are valuation rings, then $\mathcal{O} = R_\mathfrak{p}$. In fact, if $\xi \in \mathcal{O} - R_\mathfrak{p}$, then $\xi^{-1} \in \mathfrak{p}R_\mathfrak{p} \subseteq \mathfrak{m}$ which is absurd. □

The next result is also indispensable in the study of algebraic varieties.

THEOREM 1.34. *Let* A *be a finitely generated algebra domain over a field* k, *let* $L = Q(A)$, *let* M/L *be a finite algebraic field extension, and let* B *be the integral closure of* A *in* M. *Then* B *is a finitely generated* A*-module. Consequently,* B *is a finitely generated* k*-algebra domain.*

PROOF. The proof is given only in the case where the characteristic of k is zero. With $r = \dim A$, A is an integral extension of a polynomial ring $k[x_1, \ldots, x_r]$ in r variables. Moreover, M is a finite algebraic extension of $k(x_1, \ldots, x_r)$, and B is the integral closure of $k[x_1, \ldots, x_r]$ in M. So, considering $k[x_1, \ldots, x_r]$ instead of A if necessary, we may assume that A is a normal ring (cf. Problem I.1.3). Furthermore, let $\widetilde{M}$ be the smallest Galois extension of L containing M, and let $\widetilde{B}$ be the integral closure of A in $\widetilde{M}$. Then B is a subring of $\widetilde{B}$. If $\widetilde{B}$ is a finitely generated A-module, then so is B because A is a noetherian ring. We may therefore assume that M/L is a Galois extension. Since M is a simple extension of L, we may assume that $M = L(\theta)$ and θ is integral over A. Then $\theta \in B$. Let $n = [M : L]$ and $\mathrm{Gal}(M/L) = \{\sigma_1, \ldots, \sigma_n\}$. Express an arbitrary element b of B as $b = \sum_{i=0}^{n-1} \alpha_i \theta^i$ $(\alpha_i \in L)$. Then $\sigma_j(b) = \sum_{i=0}^{n-1} \alpha_i (\sigma_j(\theta))^i$. Taking the matrix representation, we have ${}^t(\sigma_1(b), \ldots, \sigma_n(b)) = E \cdot {}^t(\alpha_0, \ldots, \alpha_{n-1})$, where $E = (\sigma_i(\theta)^{j-1})_{1 \leq i,j \leq n}$. Let $d = \det E$. Then $d = \prod_{i<j}(\sigma_j(\theta) - \sigma_i(\theta)) \neq 0$ and $\sigma_i(d) = \pm d$ for each i. Hence, $d^2 \in L$. On the other hand, $\sigma_i(\theta)$ is integral over A because θ is integral over A and $\sigma_i(\theta)$ is conjugate to θ. Namely, $\sigma_i(\theta) \in B$ for each i. So $d^2 \in L \cap B$. Since A is a normal ring, we have $d^2 \in A$. Let E' be the cofactor matrix of E. Then

${}^t(\alpha_0, \dots, \alpha_{n-1}) = d^{-1} \cdot {}^tE' \cdot {}^t(\sigma_1(b), \dots, \sigma_n(b))$. Hence, $\alpha_{i-1} = \sum_j (d_{ij}/d)\sigma_j(b)$ $(d_{ij} \in B)$. Let $c = d^2$, and let $c_i = \sum_j d d_{ij}\sigma_j(b)$. Then $c_i \in B$ because $d_{ij} \in B$. Moreover, $c_i \in L \cap B = A$ because $c_i = c\alpha_{i-1}$. Hence, $b = \sum_{i=0}^{n-1} \alpha_i \theta^i \in \sum_{i=0}^{n-1} A \cdot (\theta^i/c)$. Since B is a submodule of a finitely generated A-module $\sum_{i=0}^{n-1} A \cdot (\theta^i/c)$, B is therefore a finitely generated A-module. □

We shall now state and prove Lüroth's theorem, which is the title of this chapter, and its analogues in the theory of algebras. The formulation of Lüroth's theorem is taken from Nagata [7]. We shall begin with a necessary general result.

LEMMA 1.35. *Let k be a field, let x be an element algebraically independent over k, and let $y = f(x)/g(x)$ be an element of $k(x)$ not in k, where f, g are mutually prime elements of $k[x]$. Consider a polynomial ring $k(y)[X]$ over the field $k(y)$, where X is a variable. Then an element $g(X)y - f(X)$ is an irreducible element of $k(y)[X]$. Hence, a field extension $k(x)/k(y)$ has degree equal to* $\max(\deg f, \deg g)$.

PROOF. Since X and y are algebraically independent over k, we can consider a polynomial ring $k[X, y]$ in two variables. The polynomial $g(X)y - f(X)$ is irreducible as an element of $k(X)[y]$ because it is linear in y, and it is a primitive polynomial of $k[X, y]$ because $\gcd(f(X), g(X)) = 1$. Hence, $g(X)y - f(X)$ is an irreducible element of $k[X, y]$. (This follows from the arguments used to show that a polynomial ring $R[y]$ in one variable over a unique factorization domain R is also a unique factorization domain.) If $g(X)y - f(X)$ is reducible as an element of $k(y)[X]$, we can find elements $F(y, X)$, $G(y, X)$ of $k[y, X]$ $(\deg_X F > 0, \deg_X G > 0)$ and an element $\rho(y)$ of $k[y]$ such that $\rho(y)(g(X)y - f(X)) = F(y, X)G(y, X)$. Since $g(X)y - f(X)$ is an irreducible element of $k[y, X]$, either $F|\rho(y)$ or $G|\rho(y)$. But this is absurd. □

THEOREM 1.36 (Lüroth's theorem). *Let k be an infinite field and let $k(x_1, \dots, x_r)$ be a purely transcendental extension of k in r variables. If an intermediate field L of $k(x_1, \dots, x_r)/k$ has $\operatorname{tr.deg}_k L = 1$, then L/k is a purely transcendental extension. Namely, there exists a transcendental element t of L over k such that $L = k(t)$.*

PROOF. First of all, consider the case $r = 1$. Let $x = x_1$. Since x is algebraic over L by the hypothesis, we write the minimal polynomial of x over L as

$$h(X) = X^n + c_1X^{n-1} + \cdots + c_n, \qquad c_i \in L.$$

Since $c_i \in h(x)$, multiplying an element of $k[x]$ to both sides, we may write

$$h'(X, x) = d_0(x)X^n + d_1(x)X^{n-1} + \cdots + d_n(x),$$
$$d_i(x) \in k[x], \qquad \gcd(d_0, \dots, d_n) = 1.$$

Since x is algebraically independent over k, $c_i \notin k$ for some i. Let $c = c_i$, and write $c = f(x)/g(x)$ with f, $g \in k[x]$ and $\gcd(f, g) = 1$. Then $g|d_0$ and $f|d_i$. By Lemma 1.35, $f(X) - cg(X)$ is an irreducible polynomial in X over $k(c)$, and $m := \max(\deg f, \deg g) = [k(x) : k(c)]$. On the other hand, since $k(c) \subseteq L \subseteq k(x)$, we have

$$f(X) - cg(X) = h(X)q(X) \quad \text{with } q(X) \in L[X].$$

There exists, therefore, $\varphi(x) \in k[x]$ and $q'(X, x) \in k[x, X]$ such that

$$(*) \qquad \varphi(x)(f(X)g(x) - f(x)g(X)) = h'(X, x)q'(X, x).$$

Since the coefficients $d_0(x), \dots, d_n(x)$ of $h'(X, x)$ have no common factors, we know that $\varphi(x)|q'(X,x)$. Hence, we may assume $\varphi(x)=1$. In the polynomial equation $(*)$ in x and X, $\deg_x(\text{left side}) = m$ and $\deg_x(\text{right side}) \geq \max(\deg_x d_i; 0 \leq i \leq n) \geq m$. Hence, $\deg_x(\text{right side}) = m$, and consequently $q'(X,x) \in k[X]$. If $q'(X) \notin k$, there is a root α of $q'(X) = 0$ in an algebraic closure $\overline{k}$ of k. Then the equation $(*)$ yields $f(\alpha)g(x) - f(x)g(\alpha) = 0$, where either $f(\alpha) \neq 0$ or $g(\alpha) \neq 0$ because $\gcd(f,g) = 1$. (In fact, if $f(\alpha) = g(\alpha) = 0$, then $\gcd(f,g) \neq 1$ in $\overline{k}[x]$. By the Euclidean algorithm, we have $\gcd(f,g) \in k[x]$ which is a contradiction.) If $g(\alpha) \neq 0$, then $f(x)/g(x) = f(\alpha)/g(\alpha) \in \overline{k}$. Hence, c is algebraic over k, and this is absurd. If $f(\alpha) \neq 0$, the same argument implies $c^{-1} \in \overline{k}$, and this is a contradiction. So $q'(X) \in k$. Then $f(X) - cg(X) = (d_0(x)/g(x))h(X)$. By noting $d_0/g \in k[x]$ and comparing the coefficients of both sides of this equation, we know that $d_0/g \in k(c)$ and $h(X) \in k(c)[X]$. This implies that $[k(x) : k(c)] = [k(x) : L]$. Since $k(c) \subseteq L$, we conclude that $k(c) = L$. So L is a purely transcendental extension of k.

Consider next the case $r > 1$. Since $\text{tr.deg}_k L = 1$, we may assume that one of $x_1, \ldots, x_r$, say x_1, is algebraically independent over L. Then $L(x_1)$ is an intermediate field of a purely transcendental extension $k(x_1)(x_2, \ldots, x_r)$ of $k(x_1)$, and $\text{tr.deg}_{k(x_1)} L(x_1) = 1$. Hence, by induction on r, we may assume that $L(x_1) = k(x_1)(t) = k(t)(x_1)$. Then we conclude $L \cong k(t)$ (k-isomorphism) by the following lemma. □

LEMMA 1.37. *Let k be an infinite field, and let L_1, L_2 be finitely generated field extensions over k. If $L_1(x) = L_2(x)$ with an element x algebraically independent over L_1 and L_2, then L_1 is k-isomorphic to L_2.*

For a proof, we refer to Nagata [**7**, Lemma 3.12.3].

Lüroth's theorem holds ture without the assumption that k is an infinite field. The following problem is called a *problem of Lüroth type*.

Let k be a field, and let L be an intermediate field of a purely transcendental extension $k(x_1, \ldots, x_r)/k$. Is L a purely transcendental extension of k?

If k is an algebraically closed field of characteristic zero and $\text{tr.deg}_k L = 2$, then L/k is a purely transcendental extension (A theorem of Zariski). There is, however, a counterexample if the characteristic of k is positive and $\text{tr.deg}_k L = 2$. In case $\text{tr.deg}_k L \geq 3$, the problem is negatively answered even when the characteristic of k is zero.

The next problem is called a *problem of Zariski type*.

Let k be a field, and let L_1, L_2 be finitely generated extensions of k. If $L_1(x_1, \ldots, x_n)$ is k-isomorphic to $L_2(x_1, \ldots, x_n)$ for variables $x_1, \ldots, x_n$, is L_1 k-isomorphic to L_2?

Concerning this last problem, both positive and negative results are known. By virtue of Lüroth's theorem, $L_1 \cong L_2$ (k-isomorphism) provided L_1/k is a purely transcendental extension and $\text{tr.deg}_k L_1 = 1$. One of the counterexamples is obtained in the case where k is an algebraically closed field of characteristic zero, L_1/k is a purely transcendental extension, $\text{tr.deg}_k L_2 = 3$, and $n = 3$.

An analogue of Theorem 1.36 in the theory of algebras is the following:

THEOREM 1.38. *Let k be an algebraically closed field, and let $k[x_1, \ldots, x_r]$ be a polynomial ring in r variables. Let A be a k-subalgebra of $k[x_1, \ldots, x_r]$ such that A is integrally closed and* $\text{tr.deg}_k Q(A) = 1$. *Then A is a polynomial ring in one variable over k.*

We have to prepare two auxiliary results to prove this theorem.

LEMMA 1.39. *Let k be an algebraically closed field, and let A be a k-subalgebra of a polynomial ring $k[x_1, \dots, x_r]$ with* $\operatorname{tr.deg}_k Q(A) = 1$. *Then A is a finitely generated k-algebra.*

PROOF. First of all, consider the case $r = 1$. Write $x = x_1$. Let f be an element of $A - k$. Then x is integral over $k[f]$. Hence $k[x]$ is a finitely generated $k[f]$-module (Lemma 1.10). Since $k[f] \subseteq A \subseteq k[x]$, A is a finitely generated $k[f]$-module as well. Hence, A is a finitely generated k-algebra.

Next consider the case $r > 1$. We shall show by induction on r that there exists a surjective k-algebra homomorphism $\varphi : k[x_1, \dots, x_r] \to k[x]$ such that its restriction φ_A on A yields an isomorphism of A and $\varphi(A)$. If this is done, we can identity A with a k-subalgebra $\varphi(A)$ of $k[x]$, and we are reduced to the first case.

If $A \subset k[x_1, \dots, x_{r-1}]$, then A is a finitely generated k-algebra by the induction hypothesis. Suppose $A \not\subset k[x_1, \dots, x_{r-1}]$. Let $\mathfrak{M} = (x_1, \dots, x_r)$ be the maximal ideal of $k[x_1, \dots, x_r]$, and let $\mathfrak{m} = A \cap \mathfrak{M}$. Since $k \subseteq A/\mathfrak{m} \subseteq k[x_1, \dots, x_r]/\mathfrak{M} = k$, $\mathfrak{m}$ is a maximal ideal of A. Consider a prime ideal $(x_1^n - x_r)$ $(n = 1, 2, \dots)$. Then $\mathfrak{p} := (x_1^n - x_r) \cap A \subsetneqq \mathfrak{m}$ for some $n > 0$. In fact, if we choose $f \in A - k$ so that $f \notin k[x_1, \dots, x_{r-1}]$, then we can identify $f \pmod{\mathfrak{p}}$ with $f(x_1, \dots, x_{r-1}, x_1^n)$. So we have only to choose n so that $f(x_1, \dots, x_{r-1}, x_1^n) \notin k$. We shall then show that $\mathfrak{p} = (0)$. Suppose $\mathfrak{p} \neq (0)$. Choose elements y, z of A so that $y \in \mathfrak{m} - \mathfrak{p}$ and $z \in \mathfrak{p} - (0)$. Then y and z are algebraically dependent over k because $\operatorname{tr.deg}_k Q(A) = 1$. Hence, there exists an irreducible polynomial $f(Y, Z)$ in $k[Y, Z]$ such that $f(y, z) = 0$. Write $f(y, z) = y^s + a_1 y^{s-1} + \cdots + a_s + z g(y, z) = 0$ $(a_i \in k)$. Since k is an algebraically closed field, $y^s + a_1 y^{s-1} + \cdots + a_s = \prod_{i=1}^s (y - \alpha_i)$ $(\alpha_i \in k)$. Since $z \in \mathfrak{p}$, we have $\prod_{i=1}^s (y - \alpha_i) \in \mathfrak{p}$. Accordingly, $y - \alpha_i \in \mathfrak{p}$ for some i. Since $y \notin \mathfrak{p}$, we know $\alpha_i \neq 0$. Meanwhile, $y(0, \dots, 0) = 0$ if we put $x_1 = \cdots = x_r = 0$. Similarly, $w(0, \dots, 0) = 0$ for every element w of $\mathfrak{p}$. However, this is a contradiction. So $\mathfrak{p} = (0)$. Now define a homomorphism $\psi \colon k[x_1, \dots, x_r] \to k[x_1, \dots, x_{r-1}]$ by $\psi(x_i) = x_i (1 \le i \le r - 1)$ and $\psi(x_r) = x_1^n$. Then the restriction ψ_A of ψ onto A is injective. Since we may then identify A with a k-subalgebra of $k[x_1, \dots, x_{r-1}]$, the induction hypothesis guarantees the existence of a surjective homomorphism $\varphi \colon k[x_1, \dots, x_r] \to k[x]$ as required. □

Take A as stated in Theorem 1.38. Then A is a finitely generated k-algebra of dimension 1 and a normal ring. By Theorem 1.36, $Q(A)$ is a purely transcendental extension $k(t)$ over k. We shall prove the following:

LEMMA 1.40. *Let k be an algebraically closed field. Then the following assertions hold:*

(1) *Let $k(t)$ be a purely transcendental extension of dimension* 1 *over k. Then there is a one-to-one correspondence between the set of valuation rings of $k(t)$ containing k and the set $k \cup (\infty)$.*

(2) *A finitely generated, normal domain A over k with* $\dim A = 1$ *and $Q(A) = k(t)$ is written as a quotient ring $k[x, f(x)^{-1}]$ $(f(x) \in k[x])$ of a polynomial ring $k[x]$.*

PROOF. (1) By (4) of Theorem 1.33, a valuation ring of $k(t)$ is a DVR. Let $\mathscr{O}$ be a DVR of $k(t)$ containing k, and let $\mathfrak{m}$ be its maximal ideal. Suppose $t \in \mathscr{O}$. Noting that $k[t] \subseteq \mathscr{O}$, let $\mathfrak{p} = \mathfrak{m} \cap k[t]$. Then $\mathfrak{p}$ is a maximal ideal of $k[t]$. In fact, $\mathfrak{p} = (0)$ otherwise; whence, $k(t) \subseteq \mathscr{O}$. This is a contradiction. Then $k[t]/\mathfrak{p}$ is a finitely generated k-algebra domain and a field. By Theorem 1.15 and (3) of Lemma 1.10, $k[t]/\mathfrak{p}$ is a finite algebraic extension of k. Since k is an algebraically closed field, $k[t]/\mathfrak{p} = k$. Hence, $\mathfrak{p} = (t - \alpha)$ with $\alpha \in k$. By (4) of Theorem 1.33, we have

$\mathcal{O} = k[t]_{(t-\alpha)}$. Suppose $t \notin \mathcal{O}$. Then $t^{-1} \in \mathfrak{m}, k[t^{-1}] \subseteq \mathcal{O}$ and $\mathfrak{p} := \mathfrak{m} \cap k[t^{-1}] = (t^{-1})$. In this case, $\mathcal{O}$ corresponds to $t^{-1} = 0$ (considered as $t = \infty$) and $\mathcal{O} = k[t^{-1}]_{(t^{-1})}$.

(2) Let $y_1, \ldots, y_r$ constitute a system of generators of a k-algebra A. Then $A = k[y_1, \ldots, y_r]$ and $y_i = f_i(t)/g_i(t)$, $(f_i, g_i \in k[t], \gcd(f_i, g_i) = 1 (1 \leq i \leq r))$ because $Q(A) = k(t)$. Here we shall show that there are finitely many valuation rings $(\mathcal{O}, \mathfrak{m})$ of $k(t)$ such that $g_i(t) \in \mathfrak{m}$ for some i. If $\mathcal{O}$ is written as $\mathcal{O} = k[t]_{(t-\alpha)}$ (for some $\alpha \in k$), then $g_i(t) \in \mathfrak{m}$ if and only if $g_i(\alpha) = 0$. Since there are finitely many roots of $\prod_{i=1}^{r} g_i(t) = 0$, there are finitely many valuation rings corresponding to these roots together with $\mathcal{O}_\infty := k[t^{-1}]_{(t^{-1})}$. Hence, $A \subset \mathcal{O}$ for any valuation ring $\mathcal{O}$, except for finitely many valuation rings.

We shall show that given an arbitrary element y of $A - k$, there exists a valuation ring $\mathcal{O}$ of $k(t)$ such that $y \notin \mathcal{O}$. Write $y = f(t)/g(t)$ $(f, g \in k[t], \gcd(f, g) = 1)$. Suppose $g \notin k$. Let α be an element of k with $g(\alpha) = 0$, and let $\mathcal{O}_\alpha = k[t]_{(t-\alpha)}$. If $y \in \mathcal{O}_\alpha$, then y is written as $y = a(t)/b(t)$ with $a, b \in k[t]$, $\gcd(a, b) = 1$ and $b(\alpha) \neq 0$. Moreover, $f(t)b(t) = a(t)g(t)$, where $f(\alpha)b(\alpha) \neq 0$ and $a(\alpha)g(\alpha) = 0$. This is a contradiction. Hence, $y \notin \mathcal{O}_\alpha$. Suppose $g \in k$. Then $y = g^{-1}(f(u^{-1})u^d/u^d)$, where $u = t^{-1}$, $d = \deg_t f$, and $f(u^{-1})u^d \in k[u]$. Hence, $y \notin \mathcal{O}_\infty$. Therefore, there exists a valuation ring $\mathcal{O}$ with $A \not\subset \mathcal{O}$. If $\mathcal{O} = \mathcal{O}_\alpha$ with $\alpha \in k$, then we may assume $\mathcal{O} = \mathcal{O}_\infty$ by replacing t by $(t-\alpha)^{-1}$. Let $\mathcal{O}_{\alpha_i}$ $(\alpha_i \in k;\ 1 \leq i \leq n)$ exhaust valuation rings of $k(t)$ (except for $\mathcal{O}_\infty$) such that $A \not\subset \mathcal{O}_{\alpha_i}$. We have shown that there are finitely many of such valuation rings. Let $f(t) = \prod_{i=1}^{n}(t - \alpha_i)$. By Theorem 1.33, there is a one-to-one correspondence between the set $\{\mathfrak{p};$ a prime ideal of A of height $1\}$ and the set $\{\mathcal{O};$ a valuation ring of $k(t)$ with $\mathcal{O} \supset A\}$, and we have $A = \bigcap_{\mathfrak{p}} A_{\mathfrak{p}}$. Consequently, we have

$$A = \bigcap_{\mathfrak{p}} A_{\mathfrak{p}} = \bigcap_{\mathcal{O} \supset A} \mathcal{O} = \bigcap_{\substack{\alpha \in k, \\ \alpha \neq \alpha_i}} \mathcal{O}_\alpha = k[t, f(t)^{-1}]. \qquad \square$$

PROOF OF THEOREM 1.38. It suffices to prove the following result:

> Let A be a k-subalgebra of a polynomial ring $k[x_1, \ldots, x_r]$, and let $A^* = \{$invertible element of $A\}$. Then $A^* = k^* = k - (0)$.

This follows readily from the fact $A^* \subseteq k[x_1, \ldots, x_r]^* = k^*$. Since $A = k[t, f(t)^{-1}]$, $k^* \subsetneq A^*$ provided $f(t) \notin k$. This is a contradiction. So, $f(t) \in k$ and $A = k[t]$. $\square$

I.1. Problems

1. Show that $k' \otimes_k k(\xi_1, \ldots, \xi_r)$ is a field if k'/k is a purely inseparable extension and $\xi_1, \ldots, \xi_r$ are elements transcendental over k.
2. Show that if k'/k is a purely inseparable extension and $f(x) \in k[x]$ is a separable, irreducible polynomial, then $f(x)$ is also a separable irreducible polynomial as an element of $k'[x]$. Here we say that $f(x)$ is a separable polynomial when $f(x) = 0$ has no multiple roots in an algebraic closure of k.
3. Verify that a unique factorization domain is an integrally closed, integral domain. A polynomial ring $k[x_1, \ldots, x_n]$ over a field is, in particular, an integrally closed, integral domain. Verify also that a quotient ring R_S of an integrally closed, integral domain R with respect to a multiplicatively closed subset S is an integrally closed, integral domain.

4. Let R be a noetherian domain. Show that a necessary and sufficient condition for R to be a normal ring is that $R_{\mathfrak{m}}$ is a normal ring for every maximal ideal $\mathfrak{m}$ of R. (Hint: For $\xi \in Q(R)$ which is integral over R, show that the ideal $I = \{a \in R; a\xi \in R\}$ equals to R.)
5. Show that in a polynomial ring $k[x_1, \ldots, x_n]$, a prime ideal next big to (0) is a principal ideal.
6. For an ideal $I = (x^2, xy)$ of a polynomial ring $R = k[x, y]$ in two variables, prove the following results.
(1) $I = (x) \cap (x^2, y)$ is a decomposition of I into primary ideals. Hence, (x) and (x, y) exhaust all prime divisors of I. Here (x, y) is an embedded prime divisor of I because $(x) \subsetneqq (x, y)$.
(2) $(x) = (I : x + y)$ and $(x, y) = (I : x)$.
7. Show that $A/\mathfrak{m}$ is a finite algebraic extension of k if k is a field, A is a finitely generated k-algebra, and $\mathfrak{m}$ is a maximal ideal of A. Show that if k is an algebraically closed field, then every maximal ideal of a polynomial ring $k[x_1, \ldots, x_n]$ is expressed as $(x_1 - \alpha_1, \ldots, x_n - \alpha_n)$ $(\alpha_i \in k)$. Show that there is a one-to-one correspondence between the set of maximal ideals of $k[x_1, \ldots, x_n]$ and the set $k^n = \{(\alpha_1, \ldots, \alpha_n); \alpha_i \in k\}$.
8. Let k be an algebraically closed field, let $k[x]$ be a polynomial ring in one variable, let $f(x)$ be a polynomial of degree n without multiple factors, and let $A = k[x, f(x)^{-1}]$. Show that k^* is a subgroup of A^* and A^*/k^* is a free abelian group of rank n. Here A^* is an abelian group with respect to the multiplication in A and is called the *multiplicative group* of A.
9. Verify the following assertions.
(1) Let $(A, \mathfrak{m})$ be a noetherian local ring, and let $r = \text{K-}\dim A$. Then there exist elements $u_1, \ldots, u_r$ of $\mathfrak{m}$ such that the ideal $(u_1, \ldots, u_r)$ is a primary ideal belonging to $\mathfrak{m}$. Then $\{u_1, \ldots, u_r\}$ is called a *system of parameters* of A. (Use the following *Altitude Theorem of Krull* (cf. Lemmas II.4.8 and II.4.9): Let R be a noetherian ring, and let $\mathfrak{a}$ be an ideal generated by r elements. Each minimal prime divisor $\mathfrak{p}$ of $\mathfrak{a}$ then has $\operatorname{ht}\mathfrak{p} \leq r$. For a proof of the Altitude Theorem, see Nagata **[8, p. 26]**.)
(2) Let S be a finitely generated algebra over a field k, let $\mathfrak{m}$ be a maximal ideal, and let $A = S_{\mathfrak{m}}$. Then $\text{K-}\dim A = \operatorname{tr.deg}_k Q(S)$.
(3) Let $\varphi\colon (A, \mathfrak{m}) \to (B, \mathfrak{n})$ be a homomorphism of noetherian local rings such that $\varphi^{-1}(\mathfrak{n}) \subseteq \mathfrak{m}$, which is then called a *local homomorphism*. Then we have

$$\text{K-}\dim B \leq \text{K-}\dim A + \text{K-}\dim(B/\mathfrak{m}B)$$

10. With the notations in problem 9 above, assume that B is a flat A-module. (Namely, for an injective homomorphism of A-modules $f: P \to Q$, $f \otimes_A B: P \otimes_A B \to Q \otimes_A B$ is also an injective homomorphism.) Then the equality holds in (3) of problem 9.
11. Let R be a principal ideal domain, and let M be an R-module. Show that M is a flat R-module if and only if M is a torsion-free R-module.

CHAPTER 2

Theory of Sheaves and Cohomologies

When we treat manifolds, including algebraic varieties to be discussed in the present book, we often discuss global and local properties combined together. There, central roles are played by cohomologies with coefficients in sheaves. In this chapter, we discuss cohomology theories on ringed spaces.

DEFINITION 2.1. Let I be a directed set. An *inductive system* (or *I-inductive system*) of sets indexed by I consists of sets and mappings $\mathfrak{S} = \{S_i\ (i \in I), f_{ji}: S_i \to S_j\ (i < j)\}$ satisfying the properties: $f_{ki} = f_{kj} \cdot f_{ji}$ whenever $i < j < k$, and $f_{ii} = \mathrm{id}_{S_i}$ for each $i \in I$. Let $\mathfrak{S}' = \{S'_i\ (i \in I), f'_{ji}: S'_i \to S'_j\ (i < j)\}$ be another I-inductive system of sets. A collection of mappings $\{\tau_i: S_i \to S'_i;\ i \in I\}$ is called a *morphism* of I-inductive systems if $f'_{ji} \cdot \tau_i = \tau_j \cdot f_{ji}$ whenever $i < j$. We abbreviate an I-inductive system $\mathfrak{S}$ by $(S_i)_{i\in I}$ and a morphism of I-inductive systems $\{\tau_i: S_i \to S'_i; i \in I\}$ by $(\tau_i)_{i\in I}: (S_i)_{i\in I} \to (S'_i)_{i\in I}$. Let $\mathfrak{S} = (S_i)_{i\in I}$ be an I-inductive system. Given a set S and a collection of mappings $\{\sigma_i: S_i \to S; i \in I\}$, S is called an *inductive limit* of $\mathfrak{S}$ (denoted by $S = \varinjlim_I S_i$ if the following two conditions are satisfied:

(i) $\sigma_j \cdot f_{ji} = \sigma_i$ whenever $i < j$. Namely, $(\sigma_i)_{i\in I}: (S_i)_{i\in I} \to S$ is a morphism of I-inductive systems, where S denotes an I-inductive system $S_i = S$, $f_{ji} = \mathrm{id}_S$ $(i < j)$.

(ii) If $(\tau_i)_{i\in I}: (S_i)_{i\in I} \to T$ is a morphism of I-inductive systems, then there exists uniquely a mapping of sets $\rho: S \to T$ such that $\tau_i = \rho \cdot \sigma_i$ for each $i \in I$.

In the above definition, if we replace sets by abelian groups and mappings of sets by homomorphisms of abelian groups, then we can define I-inductive systems of abelian groups and their inductive limits in the same fashion. If we consider a ring R, R-modules and homomorphisms of R-modules, we can also define I-inductive systems of R-modules and their inductive limits.

LEMMA 2.2. *Let $\mathfrak{S} = (S_i)_{i\in I}$ be an I-inductive system of sets (or rings, or R-modules, resp.) indexed by a directed set I. Then there exists an inductive limit $\varinjlim_I S_i$ which is a set (or a ring, or an R-module, resp.).*

PROOF. We consider each case separately. When $\mathfrak{S}$ is an inductive system of sets, introduce an equivalence relation on a direct sum $S' = \coprod_i S_i$ as follows: For $s_i \in S_i$, $s_j \in S_j$, $s_i \sim s_j$ if for some $k \in I, i < k, j < k$, $f_{ki}(s_i) = f_{kj}(s_j)$. Let S be the set of equivalence classes $S'/\sim$, and let $\sigma_i: S_i \to S$ be a composite of the natural embedding S_i into S' and the residue mapping ($s' \mapsto$ the equivalence class of s'). Then $\{\sigma_i: S_i \to S; i \in I\}$ is an inductive limit. Consider the case where $\mathfrak{S}$ is an inductive system of rings. Define the sum and the product of two elements $\sigma_i(x), \sigma_j(y)$ of $S (x \in S_i, y \in S_j)$ by $\sigma_i(x) + \sigma_j(y) = \sigma_k(f_{ki}(x) + f_{kj}(y))$ and

$\sigma_i(x)\sigma_j(y) = \sigma_k(f_{ki}(x)f_{kj}(y))$, where $i < k, j < k$. We can readily ascertain that this definition is independent of the choice of representatives x, y of the equivalence classes $\sigma_i(x)$, $\sigma_i(y)$ and the choice of an index k. In this way, S is a ring with respect to the above-defined sum and product. The mapping $\sigma_i\colon S_i \to S$ is then a ring homomorphism. S is an inductive limit of $\mathfrak{S}$ as rings. When $\mathfrak{S}$ is an inductive system of R-modules, we have only to define the sum and the scalar product by an element of R on S as in the case of rings: $\sigma_i(x) + \sigma_j(y) = \sigma_k(f_{ki}(x) + f_{kj}(y))$, $a\sigma_i(x) = \sigma_i(ax)(a \in R)$. □

Consider anew an I-inductive system of commutative rings $\mathfrak{A} = \{A_i\ (i \in I), \alpha_{ji}\colon A_i \to A_j\ (i < j)\}$. An I-inductive system of modules $\mathfrak{M} = \{M_i\ (i \in I), f_{ji}\colon M_i \to M_j (i < j)\}$ is, by definition, *compatible* with $\mathfrak{A}$ if M_i is an A_i-module for all i and $f_{ji}(a_i m_i) = \alpha_{ji}(a_i) f_{ji}(m_i)$ for each $a_i \in A_i$ and for each $m_i \in M_i\ (i < j)$. We say simply that $\mathfrak{M}$ is an I-inductive system of $\mathfrak{A}$-modules. Let $\mathfrak{M}' = \{M_i', f_{ji}'\}$ be another I-inductive system of $\mathfrak{A}$-modules. A homomorphism of I-inductive systems of $\mathfrak{A}$-modules $(\varphi_i)_{i\in I}\colon \mathfrak{M}' \to \mathfrak{M}$ is, by definition, a collection of A_i-module homomorphisms $\varphi_i\colon M_i' \to M_i$ (for all $i \in I$) such that $\varphi_j(a_{ji}(a_i)f_{ji}'(m_i')) = \alpha_{ji}(a_i)f_{ji}\varphi_i(m_i')$ $(a_i \in A_i, m_i' \in M_i')$ whenever $i < j$. With a homomorphism of I-inductive systems of $\mathfrak{A}$-modules $(\psi_i)_{i\in I}\colon \mathfrak{M} \to \mathfrak{M}'' = \{M_i'', f_{ji}''\}$, we say that a sequence

$$0 \to \mathfrak{M}' \xrightarrow{(\varphi_i)} \mathfrak{M} \xrightarrow{(\psi_i)} \mathfrak{M}'' \to 0$$

is an *exact sequence of I-inductive systems* of $\mathfrak{A}$-modules if

$$0 \to M_i' \xrightarrow{\varphi_i} M_i \xrightarrow{\psi_i} M_i'' \to 0$$

is an exact sequence of A_i-modules for each i.

LEMMA 2.3. *Let*

$$0 \to \mathfrak{M}' \xrightarrow{(\varphi_i)} \mathfrak{M} \xrightarrow{(\psi_i)} \mathfrak{M}'' \to 0$$

be an exact sequence of I-inductive systems of $\mathfrak{A}$-modules. Then the natural sequence of $\varinjlim_I A_i$ modules

$$0 \to \varinjlim_I M_i' \xrightarrow{\varphi} \varinjlim_I M_i \xrightarrow{\psi} \varinjlim_I M_i'' \to 0$$

is exact.

PROOF. An element z of $\varinjlim_I M_i''$ is represented by $z_i \in M_i''$ for some i and $\psi_i\colon M_i \to M_i''$ is surjective. Hence, ψ is surjective. Suppose $\psi(y) = 0$ for $y \in \varinjlim_I M_i$, where y is represented by $y_i \in M_i$ for some i. Since $f_{ji}''(\psi_i(y_i)) = 0$ for some $j > i$ and $f_{ji}''(\psi_i(y_i)) = \psi_j(f_{ji}(y_i))$, there exists $x_j \in M_j'$ such that $f_{ji}(y_i) = \varphi_j(x_j)$. Let $x \in \varinjlim_I M_i'$ be represented by x_j. Then $y = \varphi(x)$. Hence, $\operatorname{Ker}\psi = \operatorname{Im}\varphi$. Suppose $\varphi(x) = 0$ for $x \in \varinjlim_I M_i'$. Let $x_i \in M_i'$ represent x. Since $f_{ji}(\varphi_i(x_i)) = \varphi_j(f_{ji}'(x_i)) = 0$ for some $j > i$ and φ_j is injective, we have $f_{ji}'(x_i) = 0$. Thence, $x = 0$, and φ is injective. □

Let X be a topological space. We define a *presheaf* of sets on X as follows.

DEFINITION 2.4. A presheaf of sets $\mathscr{P}$ on a space X assigns a set $\mathscr{P}(U)$ to each open set U of X and a mapping of sets $\rho_{VU}\colon \mathscr{P}(U) \to \mathscr{P}(V)$, called the *restriction morphism*, to each inclusion of open sets $V \subseteq U$, subject to the conditions: For open sets $W \subseteq V \subseteq U$ it holds that $\rho_{WU} = \rho_{WV} \cdot \rho_{VU}$, and also, $\rho_{UU} = \mathrm{id}_{\mathscr{P}(U)}$ for all U. We denote ρ_{VU} also by ρ_V^U.

In the above definition, the set $\mathscr{P}(\emptyset)$ is usually not assigned for the empty set $\emptyset$. Instead of assigning sets and mappings of sets, we can consider abelian groups $\mathscr{P}(U)$ (or commutative rings, or modules, resp.) and homomorphisms $\rho_{VU}\colon \mathscr{P}(U) \to \mathscr{P}(V)$ of abelian groups (or commutative rings, or modules, resp.) to define a presheaf of abelian groups (or commutative rings, or modules, resp.). We then take $\mathscr{P}(\emptyset)$ to be (0). We call a presheaf of abelian groups simply an *abelian presheaf*.

Let $\mathscr{P}$, $\mathscr{Q}$ be presheaves of sets on X. We say that a *morphism* (or a *homomorphism*) of presheaves $u\colon \mathscr{P} \to \mathscr{Q}$ is given if a mapping of sets of $u(U)\colon \mathscr{P}(U) \to \mathscr{Q}(U)$ corresponds to each open set U and the equality $\rho_{VU} \cdot u(U) = u(V) \cdot \rho_{VU}$ holds for any inclusion of open sets $V \subseteq U$. Here we have used the same notation ρ_{VU} to denote the restriction morphisms of $\mathscr{P}$ and $\mathscr{Q}$. We can define a composite $v \cdot u\colon \mathscr{P} \to \mathscr{R}$ of morphisms of presheaves $u\colon \mathscr{P} \to \mathscr{Q}$ and $v\colon \mathscr{Q} \to \mathscr{R}$. Considering abelian presheaves or presheaves of commutative rings instead of presheaves of sets, we can define a morphism of abelian presheaves or a morphism of presheaves of commutative rings.

A presheaf $\mathscr{P}$ on X is called a *sheaf* if it satisfies the following two conditions (F_1) and (F_2) for an arbitrary open set U of X and an arbitrary open covering $\mathfrak{U} = \{U_\alpha; \alpha \in A\}$ of U:

(F_1) If for $x, y \in \mathscr{P}(U)$ $\rho_\alpha(x) = \rho_\alpha(y)$ for each $\alpha \in A$, then $x = y$, where $\rho_\alpha = \rho_{U_\alpha U}$.

(F_2) If for $\prod_\alpha x_\alpha \in \prod_\alpha \mathscr{P}(U_\alpha)$ $\rho^\alpha_{\alpha\beta}(x_\alpha) = \rho^\beta_{\alpha\beta}(x_\beta)$ for each $\alpha, \beta \in A$, then $x_\alpha = \rho_\alpha(x)$ for some $x \in \mathscr{P}(U)$, where $U_{\alpha\beta} = U_\alpha \cap U_\beta$ and $\rho^\alpha_{\alpha\beta} = \rho_{U_{\alpha\beta} U_\alpha}$.

We can summarize these two conditions by saying that the sequence

$$\text{(F)} \qquad \mathscr{P}(U) \overset{(1)}{\to} \prod_\alpha \mathscr{P}(U_\alpha) \underset{(3)}{\overset{(2)}{\rightrightarrows}} \prod_{\alpha,\beta} \mathscr{P}(U_{\alpha\beta})$$

is exact where the mappings numbered (1), (2), and (3) signify, respectively, the mappings $x \mapsto \prod_\alpha \rho_\alpha(x)$, $\prod_\alpha x_\alpha \mapsto \prod_{\alpha,\beta} \rho^\alpha_{\alpha\beta}(x_\alpha)$, and $\prod_\alpha x_\alpha \mapsto \prod_{\alpha,\beta} \rho^\alpha_{\beta\alpha}(x_\alpha)$. Note here that in the product $\prod_{\alpha,\beta} \mathscr{P}(U_{\alpha\beta})$ the components $\mathscr{P}(U_{\alpha\beta})$ and $\mathscr{P}(U_{\beta\alpha})$ are distingushed from each other.

When $\mathscr{P}$ and $\mathscr{Q}$ are sheaves, a morphism of presheaves $u\colon \mathscr{P} \to \mathscr{Q}$ is called a *morphism of sheaves*.

Let $\mathscr{P}$ be a presheaf on X and let x be a point of X. Let T_x be the set of open neighborhoods of x. Then T_x is a directed set by defining an order in T_x by $U < V$ if $V \subset U$. A collection $\{\mathscr{P}(U); U \in T_x\}$ forms an inductive system indexed by T_x. Its inductive limit $\varinjlim_{T_x} \mathscr{P}(U)$, denoted by $\mathscr{P}_x$, is called the *stalk* of $\mathscr{P}$ at x. If $\mathscr{P}$ is an abelian presheaf or a presheaf of commutative rings the stalk $\mathscr{P}_x$ has the same algebraic structure. If $u\colon \mathscr{P} \to \mathscr{Q}$ is a morphism of presheaves, then we can naturally define a mapping of stalks $u_x\colon \mathscr{P}_x \to \mathscr{Q}_x$.

When we treat presheaves or sheaves in the present book, we frequently consider the following situation. Let $\mathscr{A}$ be a presheaf (or a sheaf) of commutative rings on X. A presheaf (or a sheaf) of modules $\mathscr{M}$ on X is called a *presheaf* (or a *sheaf*) *of $\mathscr{A}$-modules* if $\mathscr{M}(U)$ is an $\mathscr{A}(U)$-module for any open set U and the restriction morphisms $\rho_{\mathscr{M},VU}$ and $\rho_{\mathscr{A},VU}$ of $\mathscr{M}$ and $\mathscr{A}$ are compatible with each other for $V \subseteq U$, i.e., $\rho_{\mathscr{M},VU}(am) = \rho_{\mathscr{A},VU}(a)\rho_{\mathscr{M},VU}(m)$ for $m \in \mathscr{M}(U)$ and $a \in \mathscr{A}(U)$. We define a homomorphism of presheaves (or sheaves) of $\mathscr{A}$-modules $f\colon \mathscr{M} \to \mathscr{N}$ as a collection of $\mathscr{A}(U)$-module homomorphisms $f(U)\colon \mathscr{M}(U) \to \mathscr{N}(U)$ for each open set U such that $f(U)$ and $f(V)$ commute with the restriction morphisms $\rho_{\mathscr{M},VU}$ and $\rho_{\mathscr{N},VU}$ of $\mathscr{M}$ and $\mathscr{N}$ whenever $V \subseteq U$. Looking at the stalks at $x \in X$, we see at once that $\mathscr{M}_x$ is an $\mathscr{A}_x$-module and $f_x\colon \mathscr{M}_x \to \mathscr{N}_x$ is a homomorphism of $\mathscr{A}_x$-modules.

A sequence of presheaves of $\mathscr{A}$-modules

$$(*) \qquad \cdots \to \mathscr{M}_{i-1} \overset{f_{i-1}}{\to} \mathscr{M}_i \overset{f_i}{\to} \mathscr{M}_{i+1} \overset{f_{i+1}}{\to} \mathscr{M}_{i+2} \to \cdots$$

is called an exact sequence if

$$(*)_U \qquad \cdots \to \mathscr{M}_{i-1}(U) \overset{f_{i-1}(U)}{\to} \mathscr{M}_i(U) \overset{f_i(U)}{\to} \mathscr{M}_{i+1}(U) \overset{f_{i+1}(U)}{\to} \cdots$$

is an exact sequence of $\mathscr{A}(U)$-modules for every open set U. The sequence of stalks

$$(*)_x \qquad \cdots \to \mathscr{M}_{i-1,x} \overset{f_{i-1,x}}{\to} \mathscr{M}_{i,x} \overset{f_{i,x}}{\to} \mathscr{M}_{i+1,x} \overset{f_{i+1,x}}{\to} \cdots$$

is then an *exact sequence* of $\mathscr{A}_x$-modules by Lemma 2.3.

For a presheaf $\mathscr{P}$ on X, we define the *sheafification* ${}^a\mathscr{P}$ of $\mathscr{P}$. For this purpose, we consider the set of stalks $\{\mathscr{P}_x; x \in X\}$ and the direct sum $\widetilde{\mathscr{P}} = \coprod_{x\in X} \mathscr{P}_x$. Define a topology on $\widetilde{\mathscr{P}}$ as follows. Consider a subset $V(U, a) = \{a_x; x \in U\}$ of $\widetilde{\mathscr{P}}$ for an open set U of X and $a \in \mathscr{P}(U)$, where a_x denotes the element of $\mathscr{P}_x$ (regarded as a point) determined by a. When U ranges over all open sets of X and a ranges over all elements of $\mathscr{P}(U)$, we can define a topology on $\widetilde{\mathscr{P}}$ with $\{V(U, a)\}$ as a fundamental system of open neighborhoods. In fact, for $v \in V(U, a) \cap V(U', a')$, there is an $x \in U \cap U'$ with $a_x = a'_x = v$. So by the definition of $\mathscr{P}_x$, there exists an open set W of X such that $x \in W \subseteq U \cap U'$ and $\rho_{WU}(a) = \rho_{WU'}(a')(= b)$. Then $V(W, b) \subseteq V(U, a) \cap V(U', a')$. Define a mapping $\pi\colon \widetilde{\mathscr{P}} \to X$ by $v \in \mathscr{P}_x \mapsto x \in X$. Then π is clearly a continuous mapping, and for each $v \in \mathscr{P}_x \subset \widetilde{\mathscr{P}}$, an open neighborhood $V(U, a)$ of v is homeomorphic to an open neighborhood U of $x = \pi(v)$. So π is locally homeomorphic. A pair of $\widetilde{\mathscr{P}}$ together with the projection π (or simply $\pi\colon \widetilde{\mathscr{P}} \to X$) is called the *sheafifying space* of $\mathscr{P}$. For an open set U of X, a continuous mapping $s\colon U \to \mathscr{P}$ is called a *section of* π (or $\mathscr{P}$) over U if $\pi|_U \cdot s = \mathrm{id}_U$. Define a presheaf $\mathscr{F}$ by $U \mapsto \mathscr{F}(U) = \{s\colon U \mapsto \widetilde{\mathscr{P}}$; a section over $U\}$, $\rho_{VU}\colon s \in \mathscr{F}(U) \mapsto s|_V \in \mathscr{F}(V)$. Then we have the following result.

LEMMA 2.5. (1) *$\mathscr{F}$ is a sheaf. If $\mathscr{P}$ is a presheaf of abelian groups, commutative rings or modules, $\mathscr{F}$ has the corresponding algebraic structure.* (*We call $\mathscr{F}$ the* sheafification *of $\mathscr{P}$ and denote it by ${}^a\mathscr{P}$.*)

(2) *Define a morphism of presheaves $u\colon \mathscr{P} \to \mathscr{F}$ by $u(U)\colon a \in \mathscr{P}(U) \mapsto s_a \in \mathscr{F}(U)$, where $s_\alpha\colon x \in U \mapsto a_x \in \widetilde{\mathscr{P}}$. Then u has the following property: If $v\colon \mathscr{P} \to \mathscr{G}$ is a morphism to a sheaf $\mathscr{G}$, then there exists a unique morphism of sheaves $\tilde{v}\colon \mathscr{F} \to \mathscr{G}$ such that $v = \tilde{v} \cdot u$.*

(3) *$({}^a\mathscr{P})_x = \mathscr{P}_x$ for each $x \in X$.*

(4) *${}^a\mathscr{F} = \mathscr{F}$ for a sheaf $\mathscr{F}$.*

PROOF. (1) It suffices to show that the foregoing two conditions (F_1), (F_2) hold for $\mathscr{F}$. Let U be an open set of X and let $\mathfrak{U} = \{U_\alpha; \alpha \in A\}$ be an open covering of U. Given $s, t \in \mathscr{F}(U)$ with $\rho_\alpha(s) = \rho_\alpha(t)$ for each $\alpha \in A$, then $s(x) = t(x)$ for each $x \in U$. Hence, $s = t$. Given $s_\alpha \in \mathscr{F}(U_\alpha)$ (for all $\alpha \in A$) with $s_\alpha|_{U_{\alpha\beta}} = s_\beta|_{U_{\alpha\beta}}$ for each $\alpha, \beta \in A$, define a mapping $s\colon U \to \widetilde{\mathscr{P}}$ by $s|_{U_\alpha} = s_\alpha$. Then s is apparently a continuous mapping and $\pi|_U \cdot s = \mathrm{id}_U$. Thereby, $\mathscr{F}$ is a sheaf. If $\mathscr{P}$ is, for example, an abelian presheaf, define the sum $s+t$ for $s, t \in \mathscr{F}(U)$ by $(s+t)(x) = s(x)+t(x)$ (the sum in $\mathscr{P}_x$). Then $\mathscr{F}$ is a sheaf of abelian groups. The same arguments apply to the other cases.

(2) For an open set U of X define a mapping $\tilde{v}(U)\colon \mathscr{F}(U) \to \mathscr{G}(U)$ as follows. An element s of $\mathscr{F}(U)$ is a section of $\widetilde{\mathscr{P}}$ over U. Since $s(x) \in \mathscr{P}_x$ for $x \in U$, there exist an open neighborhood U_x of x and $a(x) \in \mathscr{P}(U_x)$ such that $V(U_x, a(x)) = s(U_x)$. (Note that $s(U)$ is an open neighborhood of $s(x)$ in $\widetilde{\mathscr{P}}$.) Since $\{U_x; x \in U\}$ is an open covering of U, we may assume that there exist an open covering $\mathfrak{U} = \{U_\alpha; \alpha \in A\}$ and $a_\alpha \in \mathscr{P}(U_\alpha)$ for each $\alpha \in A$ such that $V(U_\alpha, a_\alpha) = s(U_\alpha)$. Then since for each $\alpha, \beta \in A$ $(a_\alpha)_x = (a_\beta)_x = s(x)$ for each $x \in U_{\alpha\beta}$, there exists an open covering $\mathfrak{V}_{\alpha\beta} = \{V_{\alpha\beta\gamma}; \gamma \in B_{\alpha\beta}\}$ of $U_{\alpha\beta}$ such that $a_\alpha|_{V_{\alpha\beta\gamma}} = a_\beta|_{V_{\alpha\beta\gamma}}$ for each $\gamma \in B_{\alpha\beta}$. Set $g_\alpha = v(U_\alpha)(a_\alpha)$. Then $g_\alpha \in \mathscr{G}(U_\alpha)$ and $g_\alpha|_{V_{\alpha\beta\gamma}} = v(a_\alpha|_{V_{\alpha\beta\gamma}}) = v(a_\beta|_{V_{\alpha\beta\gamma}}) = g_\beta|_{V_{\alpha\beta\gamma}}$ for each $\alpha, \beta \in A$. Since $\mathscr{G}$ is a sheaf, $g_\alpha|_{U_{\alpha\beta}} = g_\beta|_{U_{\alpha\beta}}$. Hence, there exists uniquely an element g of $\mathscr{G}(U)$ such that $g_\alpha = g|_{U_\alpha}$ for each $\alpha \in A$. We then define $\tilde{v}(U)(s) = g$. We can thus define a morphism of presheaves $\tilde{v}\colon \mathscr{F} \to \mathscr{G}$. The definition of u and $\tilde{v}$ implies apparently that $v = \tilde{v} \cdot u$.

(3) This part is immediate from the definition.

(4) This part can be proved in the same fashion as for (2) above. □

By virtue of (2) of Lemma 2.5, a morphism of presheaves $w\colon \mathscr{P} \to \mathscr{Q}$ determines uniquely a morphism of sheaves ${}^a w\colon {}^a\mathscr{P} \to {}^a\mathscr{Q}$ such that $u_{\mathscr{Q}} \cdot w = {}^a w \cdot u_{\mathscr{P}}$, where $u_{\mathscr{P}}\colon \mathscr{P} \to {}^a\mathscr{P}$ and $u_{\mathscr{Q}}\colon \mathscr{Q} \to {}^a\mathscr{Q}$ are the morphisms given in Lemma 2.5.

We call a sheaf of abelian groups simply an *abelian sheaf*. For a while, we shall treat abelian sheaves and homomorphisms of abelian sheaves exclusively. A sequence consisting of abelian sheaves and homomorphisms

$$(*) \qquad \cdots \to \mathscr{F}_{i-1} \xrightarrow{\varphi_{i-1}} \mathscr{F}_i \xrightarrow{\varphi_i} \mathscr{F}_{i+1} \xrightarrow{\varphi_{i+1}} \mathscr{F}_{i+2} \to \cdots$$

is called an *exact sequence of sheaves* if the sequence of stalks

$$(*)_x \qquad \cdots \to \mathscr{F}_{i-1.x} \xrightarrow{\varphi_{i-1.x}} \mathscr{F}_{i.x} \xrightarrow{\varphi_{i.x}} \mathscr{F}_{i+1.x} \xrightarrow{\varphi_{i+1.x}} \cdots$$

is an exact sequence for each $x \in X$.

We shall prove the following result.

LEMMA 2.6. (1) *Let $\varphi\colon \mathscr{F} \to \mathscr{G}$ be a homomorphism of abelian sheaves. Define presheaves $\mathscr{K}$ and $\mathscr{C}'$ by $\mathscr{K}(U) = \operatorname{Ker}\varphi(U)$ and $\mathscr{C}'(U) = \operatorname{Coker}\varphi(U)$. Then $\mathscr{K}$ is a sheaf, though $\mathscr{C}'$ is not necessarily a sheaf. With $\mathscr{C} = {}^a\mathscr{C}'$, we have the following exact sequence of abelian sheaves*

$$0 \to \mathscr{K} \to \mathscr{F} \xrightarrow{\varphi} \mathscr{G} \to \mathscr{C} \to 0.$$

(*We call $\mathscr{K}$ and $\mathscr{C}$ the* kernel *and the* cokernel *of φ, respectively, and write $\mathscr{K} = \operatorname{Ker}\varphi$ and $\mathscr{C} = \operatorname{Coker}\varphi$.*)

(2) *For an exact sequence of abelian presheaves*

$$\cdots \to \mathscr{M}_{i-1} \xrightarrow{f_{i-1}} \mathscr{M}_i \xrightarrow{f_i} \mathscr{M}_{i+1} \xrightarrow{f_{i+1}} \mathscr{M}_{i+2} \to \cdots,$$

the sequence of their sheafifications

$$\cdots \to \mathscr{F}_{i-1} \xrightarrow{\varphi_{i-1}} \mathscr{F}_i \xrightarrow{\varphi_i} \mathscr{F}_{i+1} \xrightarrow{\varphi_{i+1}} \mathscr{F}_{i+2} \to \cdots$$

is an exact sequence of sheaves, where $\mathscr{F}_i = {}^a\mathscr{M}_i$ and $\varphi_i = {}^a f_i$.

PROOF. (1) Let U be an open set of X, and let $\mathfrak{U} = \{U_\alpha; \alpha \in A\}$ be an open covering of U. Then we have the following commutative diagram:

$$\begin{array}{ccccccccccc}
 & & 0 & & 0 & & 0 & & 0 & & \\
 & & \downarrow & & \downarrow & & \downarrow & & \downarrow & & \\
0 & \longrightarrow & \mathscr{K}(U) & \longrightarrow & \mathscr{F}(U) & \xrightarrow{\varphi(U)} & \mathscr{G}(U) & \longrightarrow & \mathscr{C}'(U) & \longrightarrow & 0 \\
 & & \downarrow & & \downarrow & & \downarrow & & \downarrow & & \\
0 & \longrightarrow & \prod_\alpha \mathscr{K}(U_\alpha) & \longrightarrow & \prod_\alpha \mathscr{F}(U_\alpha) & \xrightarrow{\prod \varphi(U_\alpha)} & \prod_\alpha \mathscr{G}(U_\alpha) & \longrightarrow & \prod_\alpha \mathscr{C}'(U_\alpha) & \longrightarrow & 0 \\
 & & \downdownarrows & & \downdownarrows & & \downdownarrows & & \downdownarrows & & \\
0 & \longrightarrow & \prod_{\alpha,\beta} \mathscr{K}(U_{\alpha\beta}) & \longrightarrow & \prod_{\alpha,\beta} \mathscr{F}(U_{\alpha\beta}) & \xrightarrow{\prod \varphi(U_{\alpha\beta})} & \prod_{\alpha,\beta} \mathscr{G}(U_{\alpha\beta}) & \longrightarrow & \prod_{\alpha,\beta} \mathscr{C}'(U_{\alpha\beta}) & \longrightarrow & 0.
\end{array}$$

Here three rows are exact sequences by the definition and the middle two columns are also exact sequences by the definition of sheaf. In the sequence (F) considered in the definition of sheaf, we may replace homomorphisms (2) and (3) from $\prod_\alpha \mathscr{F}(U_\alpha)$ to $\prod_{\alpha,\beta} \mathscr{F}(U_{\alpha\beta})$ by a single homomorphism $(2)-(3)$. Then by chasing the above diagram, we know that the leftmost column is an exact sequence, though we cannot conclude that the rightmost column is an exact sequence. (As problem I.2.2 shows, there are examples for which the right column is not an exact sequence.) Let $\rho' : \mathscr{G} \to \mathscr{C}'$ be the morphism of presheaves determined naturally by the definition of $\mathscr{C}'$. Then $\rho := {}^a\rho' : \mathscr{G} \to \mathscr{C} := {}^a\mathscr{C}'$ is a morphism of sheaves. Let $\iota : \mathscr{K} \to \mathscr{F}$ be the natural morphism of presheaves. Then ι is a morphism of sheaves. Hence, we obtain a sequence of abelian sheaves

$$0 \to \mathscr{K} \xrightarrow{\iota} \mathscr{F} \xrightarrow{\varphi} \mathscr{G} \xrightarrow{\rho} \mathscr{C} \to 0.$$

For each $x \in X$, if U ranges over the set of open neighborhoods of x, the sequence of inductive limits

$$0 \to \varinjlim_{x \in U} \mathscr{K}(U) \to \varinjlim_{x \in U} \mathscr{F}(U) \to \varinjlim_{x \in U} \mathscr{G}(U) \to \varinjlim_{x \in U} \mathscr{C}'(U) \to 0$$

is an exact sequence by Lemma 2.3. If we note that $({}^a\mathscr{P})_x = \mathscr{P}_x$, we obtain an exact sequence of stalks

$$0 \to \mathscr{K}_x \xrightarrow{\iota_x} \mathscr{F}_x \xrightarrow{\varphi_x} \mathscr{G}_x \xrightarrow{\rho_x} \mathscr{C}_x \to 0.$$

The sequence $(*)$ is therefore an exact sequence.

(2) Since the inductive limit $\varinjlim_{x \in U}$ preserves the exactness of sequence, we obtain, as in the above proof, an exact sequence of stalks

$$\cdots \to \mathscr{M}_{i-1,x} \xrightarrow{f_{i-1,x}} \mathscr{M}_{i,x} \xrightarrow{f_{i,x}} \mathscr{M}_{i+1,x} \xrightarrow{f_{i+1,x}} \mathscr{M}_{i+2,x} \to \cdots.$$

Noting that $\mathscr{F}_{i,x} = ({}^a\mathscr{M}_i)_x$ and $f_{i,x} = ({}^a f_i)_x$, we know that the sequence is exact as stated. □

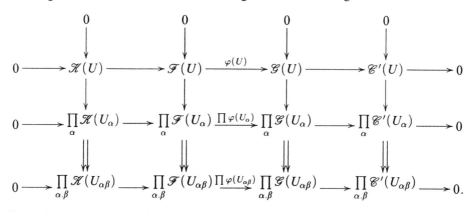

Let $f : X \to Y$ be a continuous mapping from topological spaces X to Y. We shall treat below only abelian presheaves and sheaves. Let $\mathscr{P}$ be a presheaf on X. We define a presheaf $f_*\mathscr{P}$ on Y by $f_*\mathscr{P}(V) = \mathscr{P}(f^{-1}(V))$ and the restriction morphism $\rho_{V'V}(f_*\mathscr{P}) = \rho_{f^{-1}(V')f^{-1}(V)}(\mathscr{P})$. We call $f_*\mathscr{P}$ the *direct image* of $\mathscr{P}$ by f. Let $\mathscr{Q}$ be a presheaf on Y. We define a presheaf $f^\bullet\mathscr{Q}$ on X by $f^\bullet\mathscr{Q}(U) = \varinjlim_{f(U)\subseteq V} \mathscr{Q}(V)$, where V ranges over all open sets V of Y containing $f(U)$. The restriction morphism for $f^\bullet\mathscr{Q}$ is derived naturally from the one for $\mathscr{Q}$. If $\mathscr{G}$ is a sheaf on Y, we denote the sheafification ${}^a(f^\bullet\mathscr{G})$ by $f^*\mathscr{G}$ and call it the *inverse image* of $\mathscr{G}$ by f.

LEMMA 2.7. (1) *If $\mathscr{F}$ is a sheaf on X, $f_*\mathscr{F}$ is a sheaf on Y.*

(2) *If $\mathscr{G}$ is a sheaf on Y, then $(f^*\mathscr{G})_x = \mathscr{G}_{f(x)}$ for each $x \in X$.*

(3) *If $\mathscr{F}$ is a sheaf on X and $\mathscr{G}$ is a sheaf on Y, we have* $\mathrm{Hom}_X(f^*\mathscr{G}, \mathscr{F}) \cong \mathrm{Hom}_Y(\mathscr{G}, f_*\mathscr{F})$, *where* $\mathrm{Hom}_X(\ ,\ )$ *or* $\mathrm{Hom}_Y(\ ,\ )$ *denotes the group of all homomorphisms of given sheaves.*

PROOF. (1) Let V be an open set of Y, and let $\mathfrak{V} = \{V_\lambda; \lambda \in \Lambda\}$ be an open covering of V. Then $f^{-1}(V)$ is an open set of X and $f^{-1}(\mathfrak{V}) := \{f^{-1}(V_\lambda); \lambda \in \Lambda\}$ is an open covering of $f^{-1}(V)$. $f_*\mathscr{F}$ is then a sheaf because the following sequence is exact

$$\mathscr{F}(f^{-1}(V)) \to \prod_\lambda \mathscr{F}(f^{-1}(V_\lambda)) \rightrightarrows \prod_{\lambda,\mu} \mathscr{F}(f^{-1}(V_\lambda) \cap f^{-1}(V_\mu)).$$

(2) By (3) of Lemma 2.5, $(f^*\mathscr{G})_x = (f^\bullet\mathscr{G})_x$. If U ranges over all open neighborhoods of x, we have

$$(f^\bullet\mathscr{G})_x = \varinjlim_{x\in U}(f^\bullet\mathscr{G})(U) = \varinjlim_{x\in U}\ \varinjlim_{f(U)\subseteq V} \mathscr{G}(V),$$

where it is easy to see that the last double inductive limit is equal to $\varinjlim_{f(x)\in V} \mathscr{G}(V)$, V ranging over all open neighborhoods of $f(x)$.

(3) Let $\varphi\colon f^*\mathscr{G} \to \mathscr{F}$ be a homomorphism of abelian sheaves on X. Namely, we have a homomorphism $\varphi(U)\colon f^*\mathscr{G}(U) \to \mathscr{F}(U)$ for every open set U of X such that $\varphi(U)$ and $\varphi(U')$ commute with the restriction morphisms whenever $U' \subseteq U$. By the definition of sheafification, an element s of $f^*\mathscr{G}(U)$ is determined by giving an open covering $\{U_\alpha; \alpha \in A\}$ of U and $s_\alpha \in f^\bullet\mathscr{G}(U_\alpha)$ for each $\alpha \in A$ such that $(s_\alpha)_x = (s_\beta)_x$ for each $x \in U_{\alpha\beta}; \alpha, \beta \in A$. Let $t_\alpha = \varphi(U_\alpha)(s_\alpha)$. Since $\mathscr{F}$ is a sheaf, $t_\alpha \in \mathscr{F}(U_\alpha)$ $(\alpha \in A)$ patch together to form $t \in \mathscr{F}(U)$. This t is equal to $\varphi(U)(s)$. Thence, giving an element φ of $\mathrm{Hom}_X(f^*\mathscr{G}, \mathscr{F})$ is equivalent to giving a morphism of abelian presheaves $\varphi'\colon f^\bullet\mathscr{G} \to \mathscr{F}$. Since $f^\bullet\mathscr{G}(U) = \varinjlim_{f(U)\subseteq V} \mathscr{G}(V)$ for an open set U of X, giving $\varphi'(U)\colon f^\bullet\mathscr{G}(U) \to \mathscr{F}(U)$ is equivalent to giving $\psi'(V)\colon \mathscr{G}(V) \to \mathscr{F}(U)$ for all open sets V of Y with $f(U) \subseteq V$ so that $\psi'(V) = \psi'(V')\rho_{V'V}$ whenever $f(U) \subseteq V' \subset V$. Namely, $\psi'(V)$ is a composite of $\rho_{U f^{-1}(V)}$ and $\psi(V)\colon \mathscr{G}(V) \to \mathscr{F}(f^{-1}(V))$. Therefore, giving $\varphi'\colon f^\bullet\mathscr{G} \to \mathscr{F}$ is equivalent to giving $\psi\colon \mathscr{G} \to f_*\mathscr{F}$. □

A *ringed space* is a pair $(X, \mathscr{A})$ consisting of a topological space X and a sheaf of commutative rings. If the stalk $\mathscr{A}_x$ is a local ring for each $x \in X$ we call $(X, \mathscr{A})$ a *local ringed space* and write $\mathscr{O}_X$ instead of $\mathscr{A}$. We then denote the stalk by $\mathscr{O}_{X,x}$, the maximal ideal by $\mathfrak{m}_{X,x}$ and the residue field by $k(x)$. A morphism from a ringed space $(X, \mathscr{A})$ to a ringed space $(Y, \mathscr{B})$ is a pair $\Phi = (f, \varphi)$ consisting of a continuous mapping $f\colon X \to Y$ and a homomorphism $\varphi\colon \mathscr{B} \to f_*\mathscr{A}$ of sheaves of commutative rings. We often write f for Φ. By Lemma 2.7, we may equivalently give a homomorphism $\varphi^\#\colon f^*\mathscr{B} \to \mathscr{A}$ of sheaves of commutative rings instead of φ.

A morphism of ringed spaces $(f,\varphi)\colon (X,\mathscr{O}_X)\to(Y,\mathscr{O}_Y)$ is, by definition, a *morphism of local ringed spaces* if $(\varphi^{\#})_x\colon (f^*\mathscr{O}_Y)_x=\mathscr{O}_{Y,f(x)}\to\mathscr{O}_{X,x}$ is a homomorphism of local rings, called also a *local homomorphism*, i.e., $(\varphi^{\#})_x(\mathfrak{m}_{Y,f(x)})\subseteq\mathfrak{m}_{X,x}$, for each $x\in X$. Here note that $(\varphi^{\#})_x$ is a composite of $\varphi_y\colon\mathscr{O}_{Y,y}\to(f_*\mathscr{O}_X)_y$ and the natural homomorphism $(f_*\mathscr{O}_X)_y=\varinjlim_{y\in V}\mathscr{O}_X(f^{-1}(V))\to\varinjlim_{x\in U}\mathscr{O}_X(U)=\mathscr{O}_{X,x}$, where $y=f(x)$. A composite of morphisms of ringed spaces $(f,\varphi)\colon(X,\mathscr{A})\to(Y,\mathscr{B})$ and $(g,\psi)\colon(Y,\mathscr{B})\to(Z,\mathscr{C})$ is $(g\cdot f,g_*(\varphi)\cdot\psi)$.

We shall consider various sheaves of $\mathscr{A}$-modules on a ringed space $(X,\mathscr{A})$. We call a sheaf of $\mathscr{A}$-modules simply an $\mathscr{A}$*-Module*. From two $\mathscr{A}$-Modules $\mathscr{F}$ and $\mathscr{G}$, we can define the following three $\mathscr{A}$-Modules $\mathscr{F}\oplus\mathscr{G}$, $\mathscr{F}\oplus_{\mathscr{A}}\mathscr{G}$ and $\mathscr{H}om_{\mathscr{A}}(\mathscr{F},\mathscr{G})$. First of all, we define a direct sum $\mathscr{F}\oplus\mathscr{G}$ by $(\mathscr{F}\oplus\mathscr{G})(U)=\mathscr{F}(U)\oplus\mathscr{G}(U)$. In the case of a tensor product $\mathscr{F}\otimes_{\mathscr{A}}\mathscr{G}$, define a presheaf $\mathscr{P}$ by $\mathscr{P}(U)=\mathscr{F}(U)\otimes_{\mathscr{A}(U)}\mathscr{G}(U)$ which is not necessarily a sheaf (cf. problem I.2.3). Then we define $\mathscr{F}\otimes_{\mathscr{A}}\mathscr{G}$ as ${}^a\mathscr{P}$. In order to define the third sheaf, define $\mathrm{Hom}_{\mathscr{A}}(\mathscr{F},\mathscr{G})$ as the set of all homomorphisms of $\mathscr{A}$-Modules $\varphi\colon\mathscr{F}\to\mathscr{G}$. $\mathrm{Hom}_{\mathscr{A}}(\mathscr{F},\mathscr{G})$ is an $\mathscr{A}(X)$-module if we define a sum $\varphi+\psi$ by $(\varphi+\psi)(U)=\varphi(U)+\psi(U)$ for $\varphi,\psi\in\mathrm{Hom}_{\mathscr{A}}(\mathscr{F},\mathscr{G})$ and a scaler product $\alpha\varphi$ by $(\alpha\varphi)(U)=\rho_{UX}(\alpha)\cdot\varphi(U)$ for $\alpha\in\mathscr{A}(X)$. Write $\mathscr{A}_U,\mathscr{F}_U$, and $\mathscr{G}_U$ the sheaves on U obtained by restricting $\mathscr{A},\mathscr{F}$ and $\mathscr{G}$ onto an open set U of X, respectively. For open sets $V\subseteq U$, $\varphi\in\mathrm{Hom}_{\mathscr{A}_U}(\mathscr{F}_U,\mathscr{G}_U)\mapsto\varphi_V\in\mathrm{Hom}_{\mathscr{A}_V}(\mathscr{F}_V,\mathscr{G}_V)$ is a homomorphism of modules which is compatible with the restriction morphism $\rho_{VU}\colon\mathscr{A}(U)\to\mathscr{A}(V)$. We denote this mapping by the same notation ρ_{VU}. Then $\{\mathrm{Hom}_{\mathscr{A}_U}(\mathscr{F}_U,\mathscr{G}_U),\rho_{VU}\}$ forms a presheaf of $\mathscr{A}$-modules $\mathscr{H}$ on X. Now let U be an open set of X and let $\{U_\alpha;\alpha\in A\}$ be an open covering of U. If for $\varphi,\psi\in\mathrm{Hom}_{\mathscr{A}_U}(\mathscr{F}_U,\mathscr{G}_U)$, $\varphi|_{U_\alpha}=\psi|_{U_\alpha}$ for each $\alpha\in A$, then $\varphi=\psi$ because $\mathscr{G}$ is a sheaf. Suppose $\varphi_\alpha\in\mathrm{Hom}_{\mathscr{A}_{U_\alpha}}(\mathscr{F}_{U_\alpha},\mathscr{G}_{U_\alpha})$ $(\alpha\in A)$ is given so that $\varphi_\alpha|_{U_{\alpha\beta}}=\varphi_\beta|_{U_{\alpha\beta}}$ for each $\alpha,\beta\in A$. Since $\mathscr{G}$ is a sheaf, we can construct $\varphi\in\mathrm{Hom}_{\mathscr{A}_U}(\mathscr{F}_U,\mathscr{G}_U)$ in such a way that $\varphi|_{U_\alpha}=\varphi_\alpha$ for each $\alpha\in A$. Hence, the presheaf $\mathscr{H}$ is a sheaf which we denote by $\mathscr{H}om_{\mathscr{A}}(\mathscr{F},\mathscr{G})$. In particular, if $\mathscr{G}=\mathscr{A}$, then we define $\mathscr{F}^\vee:=\mathscr{H}om_{\mathscr{A}}(\mathscr{F},\mathscr{A})$ and call it the *dual sheaf* of $\mathscr{F}$.

LEMMA 2.8. *With the above notations,* $(\mathscr{F}\otimes_{\mathscr{A}}\mathscr{G})_x\cong\mathscr{F}_x\otimes_{\mathscr{A}_x}\mathscr{G}_x$ *for each* $x\in X$.

PROOF. We have $(\mathscr{F}\otimes_{\mathscr{A}}\mathscr{G})_x=\varinjlim_{x\in U}\mathscr{P}(U)=\varinjlim_{x\in U}\mathscr{F}(U)\otimes_{\mathscr{A}(U)}\mathscr{G}(U)=\mathscr{F}_x\otimes_{\mathscr{A}_x}\mathscr{G}_x$, where we use a general fact in the last equality that the inductive limit commutes with the tensor product. □

Let $\Phi=(f,\varphi)\colon(X,\mathscr{A})\to(Y,\mathscr{B})$ be a morphism of ringed spaces. The direct image $f_*\mathscr{F}$ of an $\mathscr{A}$-Module $\mathscr{F}$ is an $f_*\mathscr{A}$-Module. We regard $f_*\mathscr{F}$ as a $\mathscr{B}$-Module via a homomorphism of sheaves of rings $\varphi\colon\mathscr{B}\to f_*\mathscr{A}$ and denote it by $\Phi_*\mathscr{F}$. We call it the *direct image* of $\mathscr{F}$ by Φ. If $\mathscr{G}$ is a $\mathscr{B}$-Module, then $f^*\mathscr{G}$ is an $f^*\mathscr{B}$-Module. Let $\Phi^*\mathscr{G}=\mathscr{A}\otimes_{f^*\mathscr{B}}f^*\mathscr{G}$ in view of a homomorphism of sheaves of rings $\varphi^{\#}\colon f^*\mathscr{B}\to\mathscr{A}$. Then $\Phi^*\mathscr{G}$ is an $\mathscr{A}$-Module. We call this the *inverse image* of $\mathscr{G}$ by Φ. There is the following adjoint relation between the functors of taking the direct image and the inverse image $\mathscr{F}\mapsto\Phi_*\mathscr{F}$ and $\mathscr{G}\mapsto\Phi^*\mathscr{G}$.

LEMMA 2.9. *With the above notations,* $\mathrm{Hom}_{\mathscr{A}}(\Phi^*\mathscr{G},\mathscr{F})\cong\mathrm{Hom}_{\mathscr{B}}(\mathscr{G},\Phi_*\mathscr{F})$.

PROOF. Giving $\sigma\in\mathrm{Hom}_{\mathscr{A}}(\Phi^*\mathscr{G},\mathscr{F})$ is equivalent to giving an $\mathscr{A}(U)$-homomorphism $\sigma(U)\colon\Phi^*\mathscr{G}(U)\to\mathscr{F}(U)$ for each open set U which is compatible with the restriction morphisms. $\sigma(U)$ is given as follows. Namely, $\sigma(U)$ is represented by a collection of homomorphisms of $\mathscr{A}(U_\alpha)$-modules $\sigma_\alpha\colon\mathscr{A}(U_\alpha)\otimes_{f^*\mathscr{B}(U_\alpha)}f^*\mathscr{G}(U_\alpha)\to$

$\mathscr{F}(U_\alpha)$ $(\alpha \in A)$ such that $\sigma_\alpha|_{U_{\alpha\beta.\lambda}} = \sigma_\beta|_{U_{\alpha\beta.\lambda}}$ for each $\alpha, \beta \in A$ and each $\lambda \in A_{\alpha\beta}$), where $\{U_\alpha; \alpha \in A\}$ is an open covering of U and $\{U_{\alpha\beta.\lambda}; \lambda \in A_{\alpha\beta}\}$ is an open covering of $U_{\alpha\beta}$ for each $\alpha, \beta \in A$. Furthermore, giving a homomorphism of $\mathscr{A}(U_\alpha)$-modules σ_σ is equivalent to giving a homomorphism of $f^*\mathscr{B}(U_\alpha)$-modules $\sigma'_\alpha\colon f^*\mathscr{G}(U_\alpha) \to \mathscr{F}(U_\alpha)$, where we regard the $\mathscr{A}(U_\alpha)$-module $\mathscr{F}(U_\alpha)$ as an $f^*\mathscr{B}(U_\alpha)$-module via a ring homomorphism $f^*\mathscr{B}(U_\alpha) \to \mathscr{A}(U_\alpha)$. By the above hypothesis, $\sigma'_\alpha|_{U_{\alpha\beta.\lambda}} = \sigma'_\beta|_{U_{\alpha\beta.\lambda}}$ for each $\lambda \in A_{\alpha\beta}$. Since $\mathscr{F}$ is a sheaf, $\sigma'_{\alpha|_{U_{\alpha\beta}}} = \sigma'_\beta|_{U_{\alpha\beta}}$ for each $\alpha, \beta \in A$. Hence, $\{\sigma'_\alpha; \alpha \in A\}$ determines a homomorphism of $f^*\mathscr{B}(U)$-modules $\sigma'(U)\colon f^*\mathscr{G}(U) \to \mathscr{F}(U)$. Conversely, given a homomorphism of $f^*\mathscr{B}(U)$-modules $\sigma'(U)\colon f^*\mathscr{G}(U) \to \mathscr{F}(U)$ for every open set U which is compatible with the restriction morphisms, we can determine a homomorphism of $\mathscr{A}(U)$-modules $\sigma(U)\colon \Phi^*\mathscr{G}(U) \to \mathscr{F}(U)$. In sum, $\mathrm{Hom}_{\mathscr{A}}(\Phi^*\mathscr{G}, \mathscr{F}) \cong \mathrm{Hom}_{f^*\mathscr{B}}(f^*\mathscr{G}, \mathscr{F})$. An element $\sigma' \in \mathrm{Hom}_{f^*\mathscr{B}}(f^*\mathscr{G}, \mathscr{F})$ gives, by Lemma 2.7, a homomorphism of abelian sheaves $\tau\colon \mathscr{G} \to f_*\mathscr{F}$, which we can show easily to be a homomorphism of $\mathscr{B}$-Modules. Conversely, given $\tau \in \mathrm{Hom}_{\mathscr{B}}(\mathscr{G}, \Phi_*\mathscr{F})$ we can determine $\sigma' \in \mathrm{Hom}_{f^*\mathscr{B}}(f^*\mathscr{G}, \mathscr{F})$. □

We shall consider various conditions on $\mathscr{A}$-Modules, where $(X, \mathscr{A})$ is a ringed space. For an $\mathscr{A}$-Module $\mathscr{F}$, a homomorphism $u\colon \mathscr{A} \to \mathscr{F}$ determines an element $s \in \mathscr{F}(X)$ as $s = u(X)(1)$, and vice versa. Let I be any index set and let $\mathscr{A}^{(I)}$ denote a direct sum $\bigoplus_{i \in I} \mathscr{A} e_i$. Namely, we define $(\bigoplus_{i \in I} \mathscr{A} e_i)(U) = \bigoplus_{i \in I} \mathscr{A}(U) e_i|_U$, where $e_i|_U = \rho_{UX}(e_i)$. We call $\{e_i; i \in I\}$ a *free basis* of $\mathscr{A}^{(I)}$. Giving a homomorphism of $\mathscr{A}$-modules $u\colon \mathscr{A}^{(I)} \to \mathscr{F}$ is equivalent to giving a collection of elements $\{s_i; i \in I\}$ of $\mathscr{F}(X)$ such that $u(X)(e_i) = s_i$. If I is a finite set of n elements, we denote $\mathscr{A}^{(I)}$ by $\mathscr{A}^n$. Concerning the u above, u is surjective, i.e., $\mathrm{Coker}\, u = (0)$, if and only if $\mathscr{F}_x = \sum_{i \in I} \mathscr{A}_x (s_i)_x$ for each $x \in X$.

DEFINITION 2.10. Let $\mathscr{F}$ be an $\mathscr{A}$-Module.

(1) $\mathscr{F}$ is *quasicoherent* if, for each $x \in X$, there exist an open neighborhood U of x and an exact sequence of $\mathscr{A}_U$-Modules

$$(\mathscr{A}_U)^{(J)} \to (\mathscr{A}_U)^{(I)} \to \mathscr{F}_U \to 0,$$

where $\mathscr{A}|_U$ and $\mathscr{F}|_U$ are the restrictions of $\mathscr{A}$ and $\mathscr{F}$ onto U. (We also write $\mathscr{A}_U$ and $\mathscr{F}_U$). Here I and J are not necessarily finite sets.

(2) $\mathscr{F}$ is *finitely generated* if, for each $x \in X$, there exist an open neighborhood U of x and elements s_i $(1 \le i \le n)$ of $\mathscr{F}(U)$ such that $\mathscr{F}_y = \sum_{i=1}^n \mathscr{A}_y (s_i)_y$ for each $y \in U$. Here the integer n may differ depending on the point x. We can define $\mathscr{F}$ to be finitely generated equivalently by saying that there exists a surjective homomorphism

$$(\mathscr{A}_U)^n \to \mathscr{F}_U \to 0.$$

(3) $\mathscr{F}$ is *coherent* if the following two conditions (i), (ii) are satisfied:
  - (i) $\mathscr{F}$ is finitely generated.
  - (ii) For every open set U of X, every positive integer n and an arbitrary homomorphism of $\mathscr{A}_U$-Modules $\varphi\colon (\mathscr{A}_U)^n \to \mathscr{F}_U$, $\mathrm{Ker}\,\varphi$ is a finitely generated $\mathscr{A}_U$-Module.

(4) $\mathscr{F}$ is *locally free* if, for each $x \in X$, there exist an open neighborhood U of x and a positive integer n such that $\mathscr{F}_U \cong (\mathscr{A}_U)^n$.

An *ideal sheaf* of $\mathscr{A}$ is a subsheaf $\mathscr{I}$ of $\mathscr{A}$-modules of $\mathscr{A}$, i.e., the inclusion $\mathscr{I} \hookrightarrow \mathscr{A}$ is a homomorphism of $\mathscr{A}$-Modules. Then $\mathscr{I}(U)$ is an ideal of $\mathscr{A}(U)$ for every open set U of X.

LEMMA 2.11. (1) *$\mathscr{A}$ is a finitely generated, quasicoherent $\mathscr{A}$-Module.*

(2) *If $\mathscr{F}$ and $\mathscr{G}$ are finitely generated $\mathscr{A}$-Modules, both a direct sum $\mathscr{F} \oplus \mathscr{G}$ and a tensor product $\mathscr{F} \otimes_{\mathscr{A}} \mathscr{G}$ are finitely generated. If $\mathscr{H}$ is a sub-$\mathscr{A}$-Module of a finitely generated $\mathscr{A}$-Module $\mathscr{F}$, then $\mathscr{F}/\mathscr{H}$ is finitely generated.*

(3) *If $\mathscr{F}$ is finitely generated, then* $\operatorname{Supp}\mathscr{F} := \{x \in X; \mathscr{F}_x \neq (0)\}$ *is a closed subset of X.*

PROOF. (1) It is apparent from the definition that $\mathscr{A}$ is a finitely generated, quasicoherent $\mathscr{A}$-Module.

(2) For each $x \in X$, there exist an open neighborhood U of x, elements s_i $(1 \leq i \leq n)$ of $\mathscr{F}(U)$ and t_j $(1 \leq j \leq m)$ of $\mathscr{G}(U)$ such that $\mathscr{F}_y = \sum_{i=1}^{n} \mathscr{A}_y(s_i)_y$ and $\mathscr{G}_y = \sum_{j=1}^{m} \mathscr{A}_y(t_j)_y$ for each $y \in U$. Then

$$(\mathscr{F} \oplus \mathscr{G})_y = \sum_{i=1}^{n} \mathscr{A}_y(s_i)_y \oplus \sum_{j=1}^{m} \mathscr{A}_y(t_j)_y$$

and

$$(\mathscr{F} \otimes_{\mathscr{A}} \mathscr{G})_y = \sum_{i=1}^{n} \sum_{j=1}^{m} \mathscr{A}_y((s_i)_y \otimes (t_j)_y)$$

for each $y \in U$. Hence, both $\mathscr{F} \oplus \mathscr{G}$ and $\mathscr{F} \otimes_{\mathscr{A}} \mathscr{G}$ are finitely generated.

(3) For $x \notin \operatorname{Supp}\mathscr{F}$, there exist an open neighborhood U of x and elements s_i $(1 \leq i \leq n)$ of $\mathscr{F}(U)$ such that $\mathscr{F}_y = \sum_{i=1}^{n} \mathscr{A}_y(s_i)_y$ for each $y \in U$. Since $\mathscr{F}_x = 0$ by the hypothesis, replacing U by a smaller one if necessary, we may assume that $(s_i)_y = 0$ (for each $y \in U, 1 \leq i \leq n$). Then $\mathscr{F}_y = 0$ for each $y \in U$ and $U \subseteq X - \operatorname{Supp}\mathscr{F}$. Namely, $X - \operatorname{Supp}\mathscr{F}$ is an open set. □

From now on we shall mainly treat quasicoherent and coherent Modules on a ringed space and, for this purpose, state basic properties of coherent Modules.

THEOREM 2.12. *Let $(X, \mathscr{A})$ be a ringed space, and let*

$$0 \to \mathscr{F} \xrightarrow{f} \mathscr{G} \xrightarrow{g} \mathscr{H} \to 0$$

be an exact sequence of $\mathscr{A}$-modules. If two of $\mathscr{F}$, $\mathscr{G}$, and $\mathscr{H}$ are coherent the third is coherent as well.

PROOF.

CASE 1. $\mathscr{G}$ AND $\mathscr{H}$ ARE COHERENT. Since $\mathscr{G}$ is finitely generated, there exist an open neighborhood U of x and a surjective morphism $u\colon (\mathscr{A}_U)^p \to \mathscr{G}_U$ for each $x \in X$. Since $\mathscr{H}$ is coherent, $\operatorname{Ker}(g \cdot u)$ is a finitely generated $\mathscr{A}_U$-Module. Hence, by replacing U by a smaller open neighborhood of x if necessary, we obtain a commutative diagram

$$\begin{array}{ccccccccc}
 & & (\mathscr{A}_U)^q & \xrightarrow{v} & (\mathscr{A}_U)^p & \xrightarrow{g\cdot u} & \mathscr{H}_U & \longrightarrow & 0 \\
 & & \downarrow{\scriptstyle w} & & \downarrow{\scriptstyle u} & & \| & & \\
0 & \longrightarrow & \mathscr{F}_U & \xrightarrow{f} & \mathscr{G}_U & \xrightarrow{g} & \mathscr{H}_U & \longrightarrow & 0
\end{array}$$

such that each row is an exact sequence. Here the morphism $w\colon (\mathscr{A}_U)^q \to \mathscr{F}_U$ induced by u is a surjective morphism. (Verify this by considering stalks.) Hence, $\mathscr{F}$ is finitely generated. Meanwhile, since $\mathscr{F}$ is a sub-$\mathscr{A}$-Module of $\mathscr{G}$, the second condition of coherency for $\mathscr{F}$ follows from that for $\mathscr{G}$.

CASE 2. $\mathscr{F}$ AND $\mathscr{G}$ ARE COHERENT. Since $\mathscr{G}$ is finitely generated, $\mathscr{H}$ is also finitely generated by Lemma 2.11. We shall show that for any homomorphism $u\colon (\mathscr{A}_U)^n \to \mathscr{H}_U$, $\operatorname{Ker} u$ is a finitely generated $\mathscr{A}_U$-Module. In order to show that $\operatorname{Ker} u$ is finitely generated, we may consider a small open neighborhood of each point of U. Hence, we may assume that u decomposes as

$$(\mathscr{A}_U)^n \xrightarrow{v} \mathscr{G}_U \xrightarrow{g} \mathscr{H}_U.$$

Since $\mathscr{F}$ is finitely generated, we may further assume that there exists a surjective homomorphism $e\colon (\mathscr{A}_U)^m \to \mathscr{F}_U$. Now consider the following commutative diagram

$$\begin{array}{ccccccccc}
 & & 0 & & & & & & \\
 & & \uparrow & & & & & & \\
0 & \longrightarrow & \mathscr{F}_U & \xrightarrow{f} & \mathscr{G}_U & \xrightarrow{g} & \mathscr{H}_U & \longrightarrow & 0 \\
 & & \uparrow{\scriptstyle e} & & \uparrow{\scriptstyle t} & \nwarrow{\scriptstyle v} & \uparrow{\scriptstyle u} & & \\
0 & \longrightarrow & (\mathscr{A}_U)^m & \underset{r}{\overset{h}{\rightleftarrows}} & (\mathscr{A}_U)^{m+n} & \underset{s}{\overset{k}{\rightleftarrows}} & (\mathscr{A}_U)^n & \longrightarrow & 0 \\
 & & & & \uparrow{\scriptstyle w} & & \uparrow{\scriptstyle kw} & & \\
 & & & & (\mathscr{A}_U)^p & = & (\mathscr{A}_U)^p & &
\end{array}$$

where h, k, r, s are homomorphisms associated with the direct sum decomposition $(\mathscr{A}_U)^{m+n} = (\mathscr{A}_U)^m \oplus (\mathscr{A}_U)^n$. Namely, we have $r \cdot h = 1$, $k \cdot s = 1$, $k \cdot h = 0$, $r \cdot s = 0$, and $h \cdot r + s \cdot k = 1$. Let $t = f \cdot e \cdot r + v \cdot k$. Since $\mathscr{G}$ is coherent, there exists a surjective homomorphism $w\colon (\mathscr{A}_U)^p \to \operatorname{Ker} t$ with U replaced by a smaller one if necessary. Then it is easy to show by the diagram chasing that the right column $(\mathscr{A}_U)^p \xrightarrow{kw} (\mathscr{A}_U)^n \xrightarrow{u} \mathscr{H}_U$ is an exact sequence.

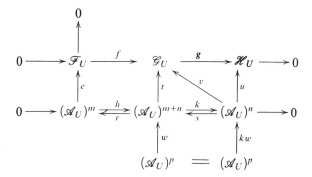

CASE 3. $\mathscr{F}$ AND $\mathscr{H}$ ARE COHERENT. First of all, we shall show that $\mathscr{G}$ is finitely generated. Since $\mathscr{F}$ and $\mathscr{H}$ are finitely generated, for each $x \in X$ there exist surjective homomorphisms $e\colon (\mathscr{A}_U)^m \to \mathscr{F}_U$ and $u\colon (\mathscr{A}_U)^n \to \mathscr{H}_U$ on a suitable open neighborhood U of x. We may assume that u decomposes as $(\mathscr{A}_U)^n \xrightarrow{v} \mathscr{G}_U \xrightarrow{g} \mathscr{H}_U$. Employing the commutative diagram in the case (2), we let $t = f \cdot e \cdot r + v \cdot k$. Then $t\colon (\mathscr{A}_U)^{m+n} \to \mathscr{G}_U$ is a surjective homomorphism. Hence, $\mathscr{G}$ is finitely generated. Next we shall verify the second condition of coherency for $\mathscr{G}$. Let U be anew an arbitrary open set, and let $u\colon (\mathscr{A}_U)^n \to \mathscr{G}_U$ be an arbitrary homomorphism. In order to show that $\operatorname{Ker} u$ is finitely generated, fix a point x of U. Since $\operatorname{Ker} g \cdot u$ is finitely generated with $g \cdot u\colon (\mathscr{A}_U)^n \to \mathscr{H}_U$, replacing U by a smaller open neighborhood of x if necessary, we may assume that there exists a surjective homomorphism $v\colon (\mathscr{A}_U)^m \to \operatorname{Ker} g \cdot u$. Then there exists a homomorphism of $\mathscr{A}_U$-Modules $w\colon (\mathscr{A}_U)^m \to \mathscr{F}_U$ such that $f \cdot w = u \cdot v$. Since $\mathscr{F}$ is coherent, replacing U by a smaller open neighborhood of x if necessary, we may assume that there exists a surjective homomorphism $p\colon (\mathscr{A}_U)^l \to \operatorname{Ker} w$. Thereby we obtain the following

commutative diagram.

$$\begin{array}{ccccccccc}
0 & \longrightarrow & \mathscr{F}_U & \xrightarrow{f} & \mathscr{G}_U & \xrightarrow{g} & \mathscr{H}_U & \longrightarrow & 0 \\
 & & \uparrow{\scriptstyle w} & & \uparrow{\scriptstyle u} & & \| & & \\
 & & (\mathscr{A}_U)^m & \xrightarrow{v} & (\mathscr{A}_U)^n & \xrightarrow{g\cdot u} & \mathscr{H}_U & & \\
 & & \uparrow{\scriptstyle p} & & \uparrow{\scriptstyle v\cdot p} & & & & \\
 & & (\mathscr{A}_U)^l & \xrightarrow{\mathrm{id}} & (\mathscr{A}_U)^l & & & &
\end{array}$$

It is then easy to show by chasing this diagram that the middle column $(\mathscr{A}_U)^l \overset{v\cdot p}{\to} (\mathscr{A}_U)^n \overset{u}{\to} \mathscr{G}_U$ is an exact sequence.

□

THEOREM 2.13. *For a ringed space* $(X, \mathscr{A})$ *we have:*

(1) *For a homomorphism* $u: \mathscr{F} \to \mathscr{G}$ *of coherent* $\mathscr{A}$*-Modules,* $\operatorname{Ker} u$, $\operatorname{Coker} u$, *and* $\operatorname{Im} u$ *are coherent* $\mathscr{A}$*-Modules.*[1]

(2) *For coherent* $\mathscr{A}$*-Modules* $\mathscr{F}$ *and* $\mathscr{G}$, $\mathscr{F} \otimes_{\mathscr{A}} \mathscr{G}$ *and* $\mathscr{H}om_{\mathscr{A}}(\mathscr{F}, \mathscr{G})$ *are coherent* $\mathscr{A}$*-Modules.*

(3) *For* $\mathscr{A}$*-Modules* $\mathscr{F}$ *and* $\mathscr{G}$, *we have* $\mathscr{H}om_{\mathscr{A}}(\mathscr{F}, \mathscr{G})_x \cong \operatorname{Hom}_{\mathscr{A}_x}(\mathscr{F}_x, \mathscr{G}_x)$ *(for each* $x \in X$*) provided* $\mathscr{F}$ *is coherent.*

PROOF. (1) Since $\mathscr{F}$ is finitely generated, so is the quotient Module $\operatorname{Im} u$. Furthermore, since $\operatorname{Im} u$ is a sub-$\mathscr{A}$-Module of $\mathscr{G}$, the second condition of coherency holds for $\operatorname{Im} u$. Hence, $\operatorname{Im} u$ is coherent. Since $\operatorname{Ker} u$ and $\operatorname{Coker} u$ appear in the next exact sequences

$$0 \to \operatorname{Ker} u \to \mathscr{F} \to \operatorname{Im} u \to 0,$$

$$0 \to \operatorname{Im} u \to \mathscr{G} \to \operatorname{Coker} u \to 0,$$

$\operatorname{Ker} u$ and $\operatorname{Coker} u$ are coherent in view of Theorem 2.12.

(2) By Lemma 2.11, $\mathscr{F} \otimes_{\mathscr{A}} \mathscr{G}$ is finitely generated. Since $\mathscr{F}$ is coherent, for each $x \in X$ we find an open neighborhood U of x and an exact sequence

$$(*) \qquad (\mathscr{A}_U)^m \overset{v}{\to} (\mathscr{A}_U)^n \overset{u}{\to} \mathscr{F}_U \to 0.$$

Taking tensor products of $\mathscr{G}_U$ with the terms of the exact sequence $(*)$, we obtain the next exact sequence

$$(**) \qquad (\mathscr{G}_U)^m \overset{v'}{\to} (\mathscr{G}_U)^n \overset{u'}{\to} \mathscr{F}_U \otimes_{\mathscr{A}_U} \mathscr{G}_U \to 0.$$

We remark here the following simple fact. Namely, if $\mathscr{F}$ is an $\mathscr{A}$-Module and $\{U_\lambda; \lambda \in \Lambda\}$ is an open covering of X, then $\mathscr{F}$ is coherent if and only if $\mathscr{F}_{U_\lambda}$ is a coherent $\mathscr{A}_{U_\lambda}$-Module for every $\lambda \in \Lambda$. By the result (1) above, the exact sequence $(**)$ shows that $(\mathscr{F} \otimes_{\mathscr{A}} \mathscr{G})_U = \mathscr{F}_U \otimes_{\mathscr{A}_U} \mathscr{G}_U$ is a coherent $\mathscr{A}_U$-Module. So $\mathscr{F} \otimes_{\mathscr{A}} \mathscr{G}$ is a coherent $\mathscr{A}$-Module by the above remark.

[1] With a natural injective homomorphism $i: \operatorname{Ker} u \to \mathscr{F}$, we define $\operatorname{Im} u$ as $\operatorname{Coker} i$.

The exact sequence $(*)$ also gives rise to an exact sequence

$$0 \to \mathscr{H}om_{\mathscr{A}}(\mathscr{F}, \mathscr{G})_U \xrightarrow{u^*} (\mathscr{G}_U)^n \xrightarrow{v^*} (\mathscr{G}_U)^m,$$

where $\mathscr{H}om_{\mathscr{A}}(\mathscr{F}, \mathscr{G})_U \cong \mathscr{H}om_{\mathscr{A}_U}(\mathscr{F}_U, \mathscr{G}_U)$ and $\mathscr{H}om_{\mathscr{A}_U}((\mathscr{A}_U)^n, \mathscr{G}_U) \cong (\mathscr{G}_U)^n$. By the result (1) above, $\mathscr{H}om_{\mathscr{A}}(\mathscr{F}, \mathscr{G})_U$ is a coherent $\mathscr{A}_U$-Module. Hence, $\mathscr{H}om_{\mathscr{A}}(\mathscr{F}, \mathscr{G})$ is coherent.

(3) The exact sequence $(*)$ in (2) gives rise to an exact sequence of stalks

$$(\mathscr{A}_x)^m \xrightarrow{v_x} (\mathscr{A}_x)^n \xrightarrow{u_x} \mathscr{F}_x \to 0.$$

This implies that the two rows are exact sequences in the following commutative diagram

$$\begin{array}{ccccccc}
0 \longrightarrow & \mathrm{Hom}_{\mathscr{A}_x}(\mathscr{F}_x, \mathscr{G}_x) & \xrightarrow{u_x^*} & \mathrm{Hom}_{\mathscr{A}_x}((\mathscr{A}_x)^n, \mathscr{G}_x) & \xrightarrow{v_x^*} & \mathrm{Hom}_{\mathscr{A}_x}((\mathscr{A}_x)^m, \mathscr{G}_x) \\
& \uparrow & & \uparrow \cong & & \uparrow \cong \\
0 \longrightarrow & \mathscr{H}om_{\mathscr{A}_U}(\mathscr{F}_U, \mathscr{G}_U)_x & \longrightarrow & \mathscr{H}om_{\mathscr{A}_U}((\mathscr{A}_u)^n, \mathscr{G}_U)_x & \longrightarrow & \mathscr{H}om_{\mathscr{A}_U}((\mathscr{A}_U)^m, \mathscr{G}_U)_x.
\end{array}$$

Thus, we obtain $\mathscr{H}om_{\mathscr{A}}(\mathscr{F}, \mathscr{G})_x \cong \mathrm{Hom}_{\mathscr{A}_x}(\mathscr{F}_x, \mathscr{G}_x)$. □

Now we shall discuss cohomologies of $\mathscr{A}$-Modules on a ringed space $(X, \mathscr{A})$. Let R be a commutative ring. An R-module I is called an *injective R-module* if it satisfies the condition: Given an injective homomorphism of R-modules $f: M \to N$ and an arbitrary R-homomorphism $g: M \to I$, there exists an R-homomorphism $h: N \to I$ such that $g = h \cdot f$. As a dual notion, we have a notion of *projective R-module*. Namely, an R-module P is a projective R-module if P satisfies the condition: Given a surjective homomorphism of R-modules $f: N \to M$ and an arbitrary R-homomorphism $g: P \to M$, there exists an R-homomorphism $h: P \to N$ such that $g = f \cdot h$. *An arbitrary R-module M is isomorphic to an R-submodule of an injective R-module* (cf. [1]). Similarly, M is isomorphic to an R-quotient module of a projective R-module.

These notions of R-modules can be generalized to the corresponding notions of $\mathscr{A}$-Modules. An $\mathscr{A}$-Module $\mathscr{I}$ is called an *injective $\mathscr{A}$-Module* if, for an arbitrary injective homomorphism of $\mathscr{A}$-Modules $\varphi: \mathscr{F} \to \mathscr{G}$ and an arbitrary homomorphism $\psi: \mathscr{F} \to \mathscr{I}$, there exists an $\mathscr{A}$-homomorphism $\theta: \mathscr{G} \to \mathscr{I}$ such that $\psi = \theta \cdot \varphi$. As a dual notion, we can define a *projective $\mathscr{A}$-Module*.

LEMMA 2.14. *Any $\mathscr{A}$-module $\mathscr{F}$ is embedded into an injective $\mathscr{A}$-Module as a sub-$\mathscr{A}$-Module.*

PROOF. Any stalk $\mathscr{F}_x$ of $\mathscr{F}$ can be embedded into an injective $\mathscr{A}_x$-module I_x as we remarked above. For an open set U of X, let $\mathscr{I}(U) = \prod_{x \in U} I_x$, which is an $\mathscr{A}(U)$-module by the rule: $a\xi = (a_x \xi_x)_{x \in U}$ for $a \in \mathscr{A}(U)$ and $\xi = (\xi_x)_{x \in U} \in \mathscr{I}(U)$. So $\{\mathscr{I}(U); U \subseteq X\}$ is a presheaf $\mathscr{I}$ of $\mathscr{A}$-modules. It is easy to show that $\mathscr{I}$ is, in fact, an $\mathscr{A}$-Module. We shall show that $\mathscr{I}$ is injective, that is to say, $u^*: \mathrm{Hom}_{\mathscr{A}}(\mathscr{H}, \mathscr{I}) \to \mathrm{Hom}_{\mathscr{A}}(\mathscr{G}, \mathscr{I})$, $\varphi \mapsto \varphi \cdot u$, is surjective for any injective homomorphism of $\mathscr{A}$-Modules $u: \mathscr{G} \to \mathscr{H}$. Note here that $\mathrm{Hom}_{\mathscr{A}}(\mathscr{G}, \mathscr{I}) \cong \prod_{x \in X} \mathrm{Hom}_{\mathscr{A}_x}(\mathscr{G}_x, \mathscr{I}_x)$, $\mathscr{I}_x = I_x$ for each $x \in X$. This can be shown as follows. Let X_d be the underlying set of X with the discrete topology, and let $f: X_d \to X$ be the identity mapping as sets. Then f is continuous. Let $\mathscr{A}'$ be a sheaf of commutative rings on X_d defined by $U \mapsto \mathscr{A}'(U) = \prod_{x \in U} \mathscr{A}_x$. Then $(X_d, \mathscr{A}')$ is a ringed space and f is naturally a morphism of ringed spaces. The associated homomorphism of sheaves of rings $\mathscr{A} \to f_*\mathscr{A}'$ is given by $a \in \mathscr{A}(U) \mapsto (a_x)_{x\in U} \in \mathscr{A}'(U)$. If $\mathscr{I}'$ is an $\mathscr{A}'$-Module on X_d defined by $\mathscr{I}'(U) = \prod_{x\in U} I_x$, then $\mathscr{I} = f_*\mathscr{I}'$. By Lemma 2.9, we have

$$\mathrm{Hom}_{\mathscr{A}}(\mathscr{G},\mathscr{I}) \cong \mathrm{Hom}_{\mathscr{A}'}(f^*\mathscr{G},\mathscr{I}') \cong \prod_{x\in X} \mathrm{Hom}_{\mathscr{A}_x}(\mathscr{G}_x,\mathscr{I}_x),$$

where we note that $f^*\mathscr{G}(U) = \prod_{x\in U}\mathscr{G}_x$. Similarly, $\mathrm{Hom}_{\mathscr{A}}(\mathscr{H},\mathscr{I}) \cong \prod_{x\in X}\mathrm{Hom}_{\mathscr{A}_x}(\mathscr{H}_x,\mathscr{I}_x)$. Since $u_x\colon \mathscr{G}_x \to \mathscr{H}_x$ is an injective homomorphism of $\mathscr{A}_x$-modules, $u_x^*\colon \mathrm{Hom}_{\mathscr{A}_x}(\mathscr{H}_x,\mathscr{I}_x) \to \mathrm{Hom}_{\mathscr{A}_x}(\mathscr{G}_x,\mathscr{I}_x)$ is surjective. So $u^* = \prod_{x\in X} u_x^*\colon \mathrm{Hom}_{\mathscr{A}}(\mathscr{H},\mathscr{I}) \to \mathrm{Hom}_{\mathscr{A}}(\mathscr{G},\mathscr{I})$ is surjective as well. Hence, $\mathscr{I}$ is an injective $\mathscr{A}$-Module. Meanwhile, define $\mathscr{F}(U) \to \prod_{x\in U}\mathscr{F}_x$ by $s \mapsto (s_x)_{x\in U}$ and $\prod_{x\in U}\mathscr{F}_x \to \prod_{x\in U} I_x$ as the product of embeddings $\mathscr{F}_x \hookrightarrow I_x$. Then the composite of these homomorphisms $\mathscr{F}(U) \to \mathscr{I}(U)$ is an injective homomorphism. So $\mathscr{F}$ is embedded into an injective $\mathscr{A}$-Module $\mathscr{I}$. □

Let $\mathscr{F}$ be an $\mathscr{A}$-Module. An *injective resolution* of $\mathscr{F}$ is an exact sequence

$$0 \to \mathscr{F} \xrightarrow{\eta} \mathscr{I}^0 \xrightarrow{\Delta^0} \mathscr{I}^1 \xrightarrow{\Delta^1} \mathscr{I}^2 \to \cdots \xrightarrow{\Delta^{n-1}} \mathscr{I}^n \xrightarrow{\Delta^n} \cdots$$

such that $\mathscr{I}^j$ $(j \geq 0)$ is an injective $\mathscr{A}$-Module. Given a homomorphism of $\mathscr{A}$-Modules $\alpha\colon \mathscr{F} \to \mathscr{F}'$ and an injective resolution of $\mathscr{F}'$

$$0 \to \mathscr{F}' \xrightarrow{\eta'} \mathscr{I}'^0 \xrightarrow{\Delta'^0} \mathscr{I}'^1 \xrightarrow{\Delta'^1} \mathscr{I}'^2 \to \cdots \xrightarrow{\Delta'^{n-1}} \mathscr{I}'^n \xrightarrow{\Delta'^n} \cdots,$$

there exists a homomorphism of $\mathscr{A}$-Modules $\alpha^n\colon \mathscr{I}^n \to \mathscr{I}'^n$ $(n \geq 0)$ such that $\eta' \cdot \alpha = \alpha^0 \cdot \eta$ and $\Delta'^n \cdot \alpha^n = \alpha^{n+1} \cdot \Delta^n$ $(n \geq 0)$. In fact, since $\mathscr{I}'^0$ is injective, we find α^0 with $\eta' \cdot \alpha = \alpha^0 \cdot \eta$. Suppose α^i $(0 \leq i \leq n)$ is constructed. Look at $\Delta'^n \cdot \alpha^n$. Since $\Delta'^n \cdot \alpha^n \cdot \Delta^{n-1} = \Delta'^n \cdot \Delta'^{n-1} \cdot \alpha^{n-1} = 0$, we have a decomposition $\Delta'^n \cdot \alpha^n\colon \mathscr{I}^n \to \mathrm{Im}\,\Delta^n \to \mathscr{I}'^{n+1}$. Since $\mathrm{Im}\,\Delta^n$ is a subsheaf of $\mathscr{I}^{n+1}$ and $\mathscr{I}'^{n+1}$ is injective, we find $\alpha^{n+1}\colon \mathscr{I}^{n+1} \to \mathscr{I}'^{n+1}$ with $\Delta'^n \cdot \alpha^n = \alpha^{n+1} \cdot \Delta^n$. We call $\{\alpha^n\}_{n\geq 0}$ an *extension* of α. Let $\{\alpha'^n\}_{n\geq 0}$ be another extension of α. Then there are $\mathscr{A}$-homomorphisms $\{\beta^n\colon \mathscr{I}^{n+1} \to \mathscr{I}'^n\}_{n\geq 0}$ such that $\alpha^0 - \alpha'^0 = \beta^0 \cdot \Delta^0$ and $\alpha^n - \alpha'^n = \Delta'^{n-1} \cdot \beta^{n-1} + \beta^n \cdot \Delta^n$ $(n \geq 1)$. In fact, since $(\alpha^0 - \alpha'^0) \cdot \eta = \eta' \cdot (\alpha - \alpha) = 0$, there is a decomposition $\alpha^0 - \alpha'^0\colon \mathscr{I}^0 \to \mathrm{Im}\,\Delta^0 \to \mathscr{I}'^0$. Hence, there exists a homomorphism $\beta^0\colon \mathscr{I}^1 \to \mathscr{I}'^0$ such that $\alpha^0 - \alpha'^0 = \beta^0 \cdot \Delta^0$. Suppose β^i $(0 \leq i < n)$ is constructed. Then we have

$$\begin{aligned}(\alpha^n - \alpha'^n - \Delta'^{n-1} \cdot \beta^{n-1}) \cdot \Delta^{n-1} &= \Delta'^{n-1} \cdot (\alpha^{n-1} - \alpha'^{n-1} - \beta^{n-1} \cdot \Delta^{n-1}) \\ &= \Delta'^{n-1} \cdot (\Delta'^{n-2} \cdot \beta^{n-2}) = 0.\end{aligned}$$

Hence there exists a homomorphism $\beta^n\colon \mathscr{I}^{n+1} \to \mathscr{I}'^n$ such that $\alpha^n - \alpha'^n - \Delta'^{n-1} \cdot \beta^{n-1} = \beta^n \cdot \Delta^n$. We then say that the extensions $\{\alpha^n\}_{n\geq 0}$ and $\{\alpha'^n\}_{n\geq 0}$ are *homotopic* via $\{\beta^n\colon \mathscr{I}^{n+1} \to \mathscr{I}'^n\}_{n\geq 0}$.

Given an $\mathscr{A}$-Module $\mathscr{F}$, there is an embedding $\eta\colon \mathscr{F} \to \mathscr{I}^0$ of $\mathscr{F}$ into an injective $\mathscr{A}$-Module $\mathscr{I}^0$ by Lemma 2.14. Considering $\mathrm{Coker}\,\eta$ for $\mathscr{F}$, we see there is an embedding $\mathrm{Coker}\,\eta \to \mathscr{I}^1$ into an injective $\mathscr{A}$-Module $\mathscr{I}^1$. By composing this embedding with the natural surjection $\mathscr{I}^0 \to \mathrm{Coker}\,\eta$, we have a homomorphism $\Delta^0\colon \mathscr{I}^0 \to \mathscr{I}^1$. Next consider $\mathrm{Coker}\,\Delta^0$. Repeating this argument, we obtain an injective resolution of $\mathscr{F}$.

We can find injective resolutions in more restricted situations

LEMMA 2.15. *Let*

$$0 \to \mathscr{F}_1 \xrightarrow{\alpha} \mathscr{F}_2 \xrightarrow{\beta} \mathscr{F}_3 \to 0$$

be an exact sequence of $\mathscr{A}$-Modules. Then there exists an injective resolution of $\mathscr{F}_i$ $(i = 1, 2, 3)$

$$0 \to \mathscr{F}_i \xrightarrow{\eta_i} \mathscr{I}_i^0 \xrightarrow{\Delta_i^0} \mathscr{I}_i^1 \xrightarrow{\Delta_i^1} \cdots \xrightarrow{\Delta_i^{n-1}} \mathscr{I}_i^n \xrightarrow{\Delta_i^n} \cdots$$

such that the following diagram is commutative:

$$\begin{array}{ccccccccccccc}
 & & 0 & & 0 & & 0 & & & & 0 & & \\
 & & \downarrow & & \downarrow & & \downarrow & & & & \downarrow & & \\
0 & \to & \mathscr{F}_1 & \xrightarrow{\eta_1} & \mathscr{I}_1^0 & \xrightarrow{\Delta_1^0} & \mathscr{I}_1^1 & \to & \cdots & \to & \mathscr{I}_1^n & \xrightarrow{\Delta_1^n} & \cdots \\
 & & \downarrow \alpha & & \downarrow \alpha^0 & & \downarrow \alpha^1 & & & & \downarrow \alpha^n & & \\
0 & \to & \mathscr{F}_2 & \xrightarrow{\eta_2} & \mathscr{I}_2^0 & \xrightarrow{\Delta_2^0} & \mathscr{I}_2^1 & \to & \cdots & \to & \mathscr{I}_2^n & \xrightarrow{\Delta_2^n} & \cdots \\
 & & \downarrow \beta & & \downarrow \beta^0 & & \downarrow \beta^1 & & & & \downarrow \beta^n & & \\
0 & \to & \mathscr{F}_3 & \xrightarrow{\eta_3} & \mathscr{I}_3^0 & \xrightarrow{\Delta_3^0} & \mathscr{I}_3^1 & \to & \cdots & \to & \mathscr{I}_3^n & \xrightarrow{\Delta_3^n} & \cdots \\
 & & \downarrow & & \downarrow & & \downarrow & & & & \downarrow & & \\
 & & 0 & & 0 & & 0 & & & & 0 & &
\end{array}$$

where each column is an exact sequence and accordingly, $\mathscr{I}_2^n \cong \mathscr{I}_1^n \oplus \mathscr{I}_3^n$ for all $n \geq 0$.

PROOF. Let $\eta_1 : \mathscr{F}_1 \to \mathscr{I}_1^0$ be an embedding into an injective $\mathscr{A}$-Module. Consider a homomorphism $(\alpha, -\eta_1) : \mathscr{F}_1 \to \mathscr{F}_2 \oplus \mathscr{I}_1^0$. Let $\mathscr{G} = \operatorname{Coker}(\alpha, -\eta_1)$. Considering an embedding $\mathscr{G} \hookrightarrow \mathscr{I}$ into an injective $\mathscr{A}$-Module and composing this embedding with the natural homomorphism $\mathscr{I}_1^0 \to \mathscr{F}_2 \oplus \mathscr{I}_1^0 \to \mathscr{G}$ (or $\mathscr{F}_2 \to \mathscr{F}_2 \oplus \mathscr{I}_1^0 \to \mathscr{G}$, resp.), we have a homomorphism $\alpha'^0 : \mathscr{I}_1^0 \to \mathscr{G}$ (or $\eta_2' : \mathscr{F}_2 \to \mathscr{I}$, resp.), where $\mathscr{I}_1^0 \to \mathscr{F}_2 \oplus \mathscr{I}_1^0$ (or $\mathscr{F}_2 \to \mathscr{F}_2 \oplus \mathscr{I}_1^0$, resp.) is given by $a \mapsto (0, a)$ (or $b \mapsto (b, 0)$, resp.). Both α'^0 and η_2' are injective. Let $\mathscr{J} = \operatorname{Coker} \alpha'^0$ and let $\beta'^0 : \mathscr{I} \to \mathscr{J}$ be the natural surjection. Since $\mathscr{I}_1^0$ is injective we have a homomorphism $\gamma : \mathscr{I} \to \mathscr{I}_1^0$ such that $\gamma \cdot \alpha'^0 = 1$ (= the identity morphism of $\mathscr{I}_1^0$). Hence, there is a decomposition $\mathscr{I} = \alpha'^0(\mathscr{I}_1^0) \oplus \operatorname{Ker} \gamma$, where $\operatorname{Ker} \gamma \cong \mathscr{J}$. $\operatorname{Ker} \gamma$ is apparently an injective $\mathscr{A}$-Module. Here there is a homomorphism $\eta_3' : \mathscr{F}_3 \to \mathscr{J}$ such that $\beta'^0 \cdot \eta_2' = \eta_3' \cdot \beta$, though η_3' is not necessarily injective. So we take an embedding $\nu : \mathscr{F}_3 \hookrightarrow \mathscr{K}$ into an injective $\mathscr{A}$-Module and put $\mathscr{I}_3^0 = \mathscr{J} \oplus \mathscr{K}$, $\eta_3 = (\eta_3', \nu) : \mathscr{F}_3 \to \mathscr{I}_3^0$, $\mathscr{I}_2^0 = \mathscr{I} \oplus \mathscr{K}$, $\eta_2 = (\eta_2', \nu \cdot \beta) : \mathscr{F}_2 \to \mathscr{I}_2^0$, and $\alpha^0 = (\alpha'^0, 0) : \mathscr{I}_1^0 \to \mathscr{I}_2^0$. Then we have the following commutative diagram.

$$\begin{array}{ccccccccc}
 & & 0 & & 0 & & 0 & & \\
 & & \downarrow & & \downarrow & & \downarrow & & \\
0 & \longrightarrow & \mathscr{F}_1 & \xrightarrow{\alpha} & \mathscr{F}_2 & \xrightarrow{\beta} & \mathscr{F}_3 & \longrightarrow & 0 \\
 & & \downarrow \eta_1^0 & & \downarrow \eta_2^0 & & \downarrow \eta_3^0 & & \\
0 & \longrightarrow & \mathscr{I}_1^0 & \xrightarrow{\alpha^0} & \mathscr{I}_2^0 & \xrightarrow{\beta^0} & \mathscr{I}_3^0 & \longrightarrow & 0
\end{array}$$

Let $\mathscr{G}_j = \operatorname{Coker} \eta_j^0$ $(j = 1, 2, 3)$. Then the above diagram yields an exact sequence

$$0 \to \mathscr{G}_1 \xrightarrow{\alpha'} \mathscr{G}_2 \xrightarrow{\beta'} \mathscr{G}_3 \to 0.$$

Repeating the foregoing argument, we can embed this exact sequence into an exact sequence of injective $\mathscr{A}$-Modules

$$0 \to \mathscr{I}_1^1 \xrightarrow{\alpha^1} \mathscr{I}_2^1 \xrightarrow{\beta^1} \mathscr{I}_3^1 \to 0.$$

Again repeating this argument, we obtain an exact sequence of injective resolutions as required in the statement. The nth exact sequence of this injective resolution

$$0 \to \mathscr{I}_1^n \xrightarrow{\alpha^n} \mathscr{I}_2^n \xrightarrow{\beta^n} \mathscr{I}_3^n \to 0$$

splits. Namely, we have $\mathscr{I}_2^n \cong \mathscr{I}_1^n \oplus \mathscr{I}_3^n$. □

For a sheaf $\mathscr{F}$ on X and an open set U, we often write $\Gamma(U, \mathscr{F})$ instead of $\mathscr{F}(U)$ and call it the *set of sections* of $\mathscr{F}$ over U.

For an exact sequence of $\mathscr{A}$-Modules

$$0 \to \mathscr{F} \xrightarrow{f} \mathscr{G} \xrightarrow{g} \mathscr{H} \to 0,$$

the sequence of $\Gamma(U, \mathscr{A})$-modules

$$0 \to \Gamma(U, \mathscr{F}) \xrightarrow{f(U)} \Gamma(U, \mathscr{G}) \xrightarrow{g(U)} \Gamma(U, \mathscr{H})$$

is exact. (In fact, $\mathscr{F}$ is isomorphic to $\operatorname{Ker} g$.) Taking an injective resolution of an $\mathscr{A}$-Module $\mathscr{F}$

$$0 \to \mathscr{F} \xrightarrow{\eta} \mathscr{I}^0 \xrightarrow{\Delta^0} \mathscr{I}^1 \xrightarrow{\Delta^1} \mathscr{I}^2 \to \cdots \xrightarrow{\Delta^{n-1}} \mathscr{I}^n \xrightarrow{\Delta^n} \cdots$$

and applying the functor $\Gamma(U, \cdot)$, we obtain a sequence

$$0 \to \Gamma(U, \mathscr{F}) \xrightarrow{\varepsilon} \Gamma(U, \mathscr{I}^0) \xrightarrow{\delta^0} \Gamma(U, \mathscr{I}^1) \xrightarrow{\delta^1} \cdots$$
$$\xrightarrow{\delta^{n-1}} \Gamma(U, \mathscr{I}^n) \xrightarrow{\delta^n} \cdots,$$

where $\varepsilon = \eta(U)$ and $\delta^i = \Delta^i(U)$ $(i \geq 0)$. Here $\delta^i \cdot \delta^{i-1} = 0$ $(i \geq 1)$. Thereby we obtain a complex

$$(*) \qquad 0 \to \Gamma(U, \mathscr{I}^0) \xrightarrow{\delta^0} \Gamma(U, \mathscr{I}^1) \xrightarrow{\delta^1} \cdots \xrightarrow{\delta^{n-1}} \Gamma(U, \mathscr{I}^n) \xrightarrow{\delta^n} \cdots.$$

Since $\delta^i \cdot \delta^{i-1} = 0$ we have $\operatorname{Im} \delta^{i-1} \subseteq \operatorname{Ker} \delta^i$ $(i \geq 0)$, where we put $\delta^{-1} = 0$. We denote the $\Gamma(U, \mathscr{A})$-module $\operatorname{Ker} \delta^i / \operatorname{Im} \delta^{i-1}$ by $H^i(U, \mathscr{F})$. $H^i(U, \mathscr{F})$ is independent of the choice of an injective resolution of $\mathscr{F}$ by the reason we explain below. Take another injective resolution of $\mathscr{F}$,

$$0 \to \mathscr{F} \xrightarrow{\eta'} \mathscr{I}'^0 \xrightarrow{\Delta'^0} \mathscr{I}'^1 \xrightarrow{\Delta'^1} \cdots \xrightarrow{\Delta'^{n-1}} \mathscr{I}'^n \xrightarrow{\Delta'^n} \cdots.$$

As we have seen earlier, there exist $\mathscr{A}$-homomorphisms $\alpha^n : \mathscr{I}^n \to \mathscr{I}'^n$ and $\beta^n : \mathscr{I}'^n \to \mathscr{I}^n$ $(n \geq 0)$ such that $\eta' = \alpha^0 \eta$, $\eta = \beta^0 \eta'$, $\Delta'^n \cdot \alpha^n = \alpha^{n+1} \cdot \Delta^n$, and $\Delta^n \cdot \beta^n = \beta^{n+1} \cdot \Delta'^n$. Furthermore, there exist $\mathscr{A}$-homomorphisms $\rho^n : \mathscr{I}^{n+1} \to \mathscr{I}^n$ and $\sigma^n : \mathscr{I}'^{n+1} \to \mathscr{I}'^n$ $(n \geq 0)$ such that $1 - \beta^0 \cdot \alpha^0 = \rho^0 \cdot \Delta^0$, $1 - \alpha^0 \cdot \beta^0 = \sigma^0 \cdot \Delta'^0$, $1 - \beta^n \cdot \alpha^n = \Delta^{n-1} \cdot \rho^{n-1} + \rho^n \cdot \Delta^n$, and $1 - \alpha^n \cdot \beta^n = \Delta'^{n-1} \cdot \sigma^{n-1} + \sigma^n \cdot \Delta'^n$ $(n \geq 1)$. Let

$\varepsilon' = \eta'(U)$, $\delta'^i = \Delta'^i(U)$, $a^n = \alpha^n(U)$, $b^n = \beta^n(U)$, $r^n = \rho^n(U)$, and $s^n = \sigma^n(U)$. Then between the complex $(*)$ and a complex

$$(**) \qquad 0 \to \Gamma(U,\mathscr{I}'^0) \xrightarrow{\delta'^0} \Gamma(U,\mathscr{I}'^1) \xrightarrow{\delta'^1} \cdots \xrightarrow{\delta'^{n-1}} \Gamma(U,\mathscr{I}'^n) \xrightarrow{\delta'^n} \cdots$$

there are the following relations:

$$(***) \qquad \begin{cases} \varepsilon' = a^0 \cdot \varepsilon, \varepsilon = b^0 \cdot \varepsilon', \\ \delta'^n \cdot a^n = a^{n+1} \cdot \delta^n, \delta^n \cdot b^n = b^{n+1} \cdot \delta'^n \qquad (n \geq 0), \\ 1 - b^0 \cdot a^0 = r^0 \cdot \delta^0, 1 - a^0 \cdot b^0 = s^0 \cdot \delta'^0, \\ 1 - b^n \cdot a^n = \delta^{n-1} \cdot r^{n-1} + r^n \cdot \delta^n, \\ 1 - a^n \cdot b^n = \delta'^{n-1} \cdot s^{n-1} + s^n \cdot \delta'^n \qquad (n \geq 1). \end{cases}$$

First of all, since $\operatorname{Ker}\delta^0 = \operatorname{Im}\varepsilon$ and $\operatorname{Ker}\delta'^0 = \operatorname{Im}\varepsilon'$, one gets $\operatorname{Ker}\delta^0 \cong \operatorname{Ker}\delta'^0$ via homomorphisms a^0 and b^0, from which it follows that $H^0(U,\mathscr{F})$ is independent of the choice of an injective resolution of $\mathscr{F}$. The homomorphisms a^n and b^n induce homomorphisms $\operatorname{Ker}\delta^n/\operatorname{Im}\delta^{n-1} \to \operatorname{Ker}\delta'^n/\operatorname{Im}\delta'^{n-1}$ and $\operatorname{Ker}\delta'^n/\operatorname{Im}\delta'^{n-1} \to \operatorname{Ker}\delta^n/\operatorname{Im}\delta^{n-1}$ respectively, and it is easily shown by the relations $(**)$ that they are the converses of each other. Hence, $H^n(U,\mathscr{F})$ $(n \geq 1)$ is independent of the choice of an injective resolution of $\mathscr{F}$. We call $H^n(U,\mathscr{F})$ the nth *cohomology* of $\mathscr{F}$ over U. Below, we mainly treat the case $U = X$.

Let $f: \mathscr{F} \to \mathscr{G}$ be a homomorphism of $\mathscr{A}$-Modules. Take injective resolutions of $\mathscr{F}$ and $\mathscr{G}$,

$$0 \to \mathscr{F} \xrightarrow{\eta} \mathscr{I}^0 \xrightarrow{\Delta^0} \mathscr{I}^1 \xrightarrow{\Delta^1} \cdots \xrightarrow{\Delta^{n-1}} \mathscr{I}^n \xrightarrow{\Delta^n} \cdots,$$

$$0 \to \mathscr{G} \xrightarrow{\varepsilon} \mathscr{J}^0 \xrightarrow{\gamma^0} \mathscr{J}^1 \xrightarrow{\gamma^1} \cdots \xrightarrow{\gamma^{n-1}} \mathscr{J}^n \xrightarrow{\gamma^n} \cdots.$$

Then there exists an extension $\{f^n: \mathscr{I}^n \to \mathscr{J}^n\}_{n \geq 0}$ of f such that $\gamma^n \cdot f^n = f^{n+1} \cdot \Delta^n$. This extension induces a homomorphism of $\Gamma(U,\mathscr{A})$-modules $H^n(U,f): H^n(U,\mathscr{F}) \to H^n(U,\mathscr{G})$. As we have observed earlier, two extensions $\{f^n\}_{n \geq 0}$ and $\{f'^n\}_{n \geq 0}$ of f are homotopic to each other. Thereby, we can readily show that $H^n(U,f)$ is independent of the choice of extensions of f. If $f: \mathscr{F} \to \mathscr{G}$ and $g: \mathscr{G} \to \mathscr{H}$ are homomorphisms of $\mathscr{A}$-Modules, then we have $H^n(U,g \cdot f) = H^n(U,g) \cdot H^n(U,f)$.

Next we shall consider a morphism of ringed spaces $\Phi = (f,\varphi): (X,\mathscr{A}) \to (Y,\mathscr{B})$. To simplify the notations, we let f represent the pair (f,φ). For an exact sequence of $\mathscr{A}$-Modules

$$0 \to \mathscr{F} \xrightarrow{\alpha} \mathscr{G} \xrightarrow{\beta} \mathscr{H} \to 0,$$

the sequence of $\mathscr{B}$-Modules consisting of direct images by f,

$$0 \to f_*\mathscr{F} \xrightarrow{f_*\alpha} f_*\mathscr{G} \xrightarrow{f_*\beta} f_*\mathscr{H}$$

is an exact sequence. (The functor f_* is, therefore, a left-exact functor.) This is the case because

$$0 \to \Gamma(f^{-1}(V),\mathscr{F}) \xrightarrow{\alpha(f^{-1}(V))} \Gamma(f^{-1}(V),\mathscr{G}) \xrightarrow{\beta(f^{-1}(V))} \Gamma(f^{-1}(V),\mathscr{H})$$

is an exact sequence for an open set V of Y.

Take again an injective resolution of $\mathscr{F}$,

$$0 \to \mathscr{F} \xrightarrow{\eta} \mathscr{I}^0 \xrightarrow{\Delta^0} \mathscr{I}^1 \xrightarrow{\Delta^1} \cdots \xrightarrow{\Delta^{n-1}} \mathscr{I}^n \xrightarrow{\Delta^n} \cdots$$

and consider a complex of $\mathscr{B}$-Modules

$$0 \to f_*\mathscr{I}^0 \xrightarrow{f_*\Delta^0} f_*\mathscr{I}^1 \xrightarrow{f_*\Delta^1} \cdots \xrightarrow{f_*\Delta^{n-1}} f_*\mathscr{I}^n \xrightarrow{f_*\Delta^n} \cdots .$$

A $\mathscr{B}$-Module $\operatorname{Ker} f_*\Delta^n / \operatorname{Im} f_*\Delta^{n-1}$ $(n \geq 0)$ is independent of the choice of an injective resolution of $\mathscr{F}$ up to isomorphisms. This can be shown by the same argument as for $H^n(U, \mathscr{F})$. We denote the $\mathscr{B}$-Module $\operatorname{Ker} f_*\Delta^n / \operatorname{Im} f_*\Delta^{n-1}$ by $R^n f_*\mathscr{F}$ and call it the nth *higher direct image* of $\mathscr{F}$ by f. We have $R^0 f_*\mathscr{F} \cong f_*\mathscr{F}$. For a homomorphism $\alpha \colon \mathscr{F} \to \mathscr{G}$ of $\mathscr{A}$-Modules, we can define a homomorphism $R^n f_*(\alpha) \colon R^n f_*\mathscr{F} \to R^n f_*\mathscr{G}$. As in the previous case, we have $R^n f_*(\beta \cdot \alpha) = R^n f_*(\beta) \cdot R^n f_*(\alpha)$.

THEOREM 2.16. *Let $(X, \mathscr{A})$ be a ringed space, and let*

$$0 \to \mathscr{F}_1 \xrightarrow{\alpha} \mathscr{F}_2 \xrightarrow{\beta} \mathscr{F}_3 \to 0$$

be an exact sequence of $\mathscr{A}$-Modules. Then we have:

(1) *For each $n \geq 0$ there is a homomorphism of $\Gamma(U, \mathscr{A})$-modules $\delta^n \colon H^n(U, \mathscr{F}_3) \to H^{n+1}(U, \mathscr{F}_1)$ such that the following sequence is an exact sequence*:

$$\begin{aligned}0 \to H^0(U, \mathscr{F}_1) &\xrightarrow{\alpha^0} H^0(U, \mathscr{F}_2) \xrightarrow{\beta^0} H^0(U, \mathscr{F}_3) \xrightarrow{\delta^0} H^1(U, \mathscr{F}_1)\\ &\xrightarrow{\alpha^1} H^1(U, \mathscr{F}_2) \xrightarrow{\beta^1} H^1(U, \mathscr{F}_3) \xrightarrow{\delta^1} \cdots \to H^n(U, \mathscr{F}_1)\\ &\xrightarrow{\alpha^n} H^n(U, \mathscr{F}_2) \xrightarrow{\beta^n} H^n(U, \mathscr{F}_3) \xrightarrow{\delta^n} H^{n+1}(U, \mathscr{F}_1) \to \cdots ,\end{aligned}$$

where U is an open set of X, $\alpha^n = H^n(U, \alpha)$, and $\beta^n = H^n(U, \beta)$.

(2) *Let $f \colon (X, \mathscr{A}) \to (Y, \mathscr{B})$ be a morphism of ringed spaces. Then there is a homomorphism of $\mathscr{B}$-Modules $\delta^n \colon R^n f_*\mathscr{F}_3 \to R^{n+1} f_*\mathscr{F}_1$ such that the following sequence of $\mathscr{B}$-Modules is an exact sequence*:

$$\begin{aligned}0 \to R^0 f_*\mathscr{F}_1 &\xrightarrow{\alpha^0} R^0 f_*\mathscr{F}_2 \xrightarrow{\beta^0} R^0 f_*\mathscr{F}_3 \xrightarrow{\delta^0} R^1 f_*\mathscr{F}_1\\ &\xrightarrow{\alpha^1} R^1 f_*\mathscr{F}_2 \xrightarrow{\beta^1} R^1 f_*\mathscr{F}_3 \xrightarrow{\delta^1} \cdots \to R^n f_*\mathscr{F}_1\\ &\xrightarrow{\alpha^n} R^n f_*\mathscr{F}_2 \xrightarrow{\beta^n} R^n f_*\mathscr{F}_3 \xrightarrow{\delta^n} R^{n+1} f_*\mathscr{F}_1 \to \cdots ,\end{aligned}$$

where we denote $R^n f_*(\alpha)$, $R^n f_*(\beta)$ by α^n, β^n respectively by abuse of notation.

PROOF. (1) We use the injective resolution of an exact sequence which we constructed in Lemma 2.15. Let $L^i = \Gamma(U, \mathscr{I}_1^i)$, $M^i = \Gamma(U, \mathscr{I}_2^i)$, and $N^i = \Gamma(U, \mathscr{I}_3^i)$. Moreover, in order to avoid complexity of notation, we write α^i, β^i for $\Gamma(U, \alpha^i)$, $\Gamma(U, \beta^i)$, respectively, and d^i for $\Gamma(U, \Delta_j^i)$ $(i \geq 0, 1 \leq j \leq 3)$ indistinctively. The following sequence is a complex

$$L^\bullet \colon 0 \to L^0 \xrightarrow{d^0} L^1 \xrightarrow{d^1} \cdots \xrightarrow{d^{n-1}} L^n \xrightarrow{d^n} \cdots .$$

Similarly, we have complexes $M^\bullet$ and $N^\bullet$, and $\alpha^\bullet = \{\alpha^n \colon L^n \to M^n\}_{n \geq 0}$ and

$\beta^\bullet = \{\beta^n : M^n \to N^n\}_{n\geq 0}$ are homomorphisms of complexes of R $(= \Gamma(U, \mathscr{A}))$-modules. Namely, we have $d^n \cdot \alpha^n = \alpha^{n+1} \cdot d^n$ and $d^n \cdot \beta^n = \beta^{n+1} \cdot d^n$ for each $n \geq 0$. Furthermore,

$$0 \to L^n \overset{\alpha^n}{\to} M^n \overset{\beta^n}{\to} N^n \to 0 \quad (n \geq 0)$$

is an exact sequence. In fact, this follows from the splitting $\mathscr{I}_2^n \cong \mathscr{I}_1^n \oplus \mathscr{I}_3^n$. In sum, we have an exact sequence of complexes

$$0 \to L^\bullet \overset{\alpha^\bullet}{\to} M^\bullet \overset{\beta^\bullet}{\to} N^\bullet \to 0.$$

Let $H^n(L^\bullet) = \operatorname{Ker} d^n / \operatorname{Im} d^{n-1}$, where $d^{-1} = 0$. Likewise, we define $H^n(M^\bullet)$ and $H^n(N^\bullet)$. Suppose $z \in N^n$ with $d^n(z) = 0$. Then $\beta^n(y) = z$ for $y \in M^n$. Since $\beta^{n+1} \cdot d^n(y) = d^n \cdot \beta^n(y) = d^n z = 0$, $d^n(y) = \alpha^{n+1}(x)$ for some $x \in L^{n+1}$. Since $\alpha^{n+2} \cdot d^{n+1}(x) = d^{n+1} \cdot \alpha^{n+1}(x) = d^{n+1} \cdot d^n(y) = 0$ and α^{n+2} is injective, we have $x \in \operatorname{Ker} d^{n+1}$. Then the residue class $[x]$ of x in $H^{n+1}(L^\bullet)$ is independent of the choice of y and determined only by z. Furthermore, $[x]$ is independent of the choice of a representant z in the residue class $[z]$. If we define a mapping $\delta^n : H^n(N^\bullet) \to H^{n+1}(L^\bullet)$ by $\delta^n([z]) = [x]$, then δ^n is a homomorphism of R-modules. It is an elementary diagram chase to ascertain that the following sequence of R-modules and R-homomorphisms is an exact sequence

$$0 \to H^0(L^\bullet) \overset{\alpha^0}{\to} H^0(M^\bullet) \overset{\beta^0}{\to} H^0(N^\bullet) \overset{\delta^0}{\to} H^1(L^\bullet) \to \cdots$$

$$\to H^n(L^\bullet) \overset{\alpha^n}{\to} H^n(M^\bullet) \overset{\beta^n}{\to} H^n(N^\bullet) \overset{\delta^n}{\to} H^{n+1}(L^\bullet) \to \cdots$$

The details are left to readers. This exact sequence is nothing but the cohomology exact sequence stated in (1) above.

(2) A similar argument to the one above can be applied to prove that the sequence of $\mathscr{B}$-Modules consisting of higher direct images is an exact sequence. A crucial point is that since $\mathscr{I}_j^n$ is an injective Module we have a splitting $\mathscr{I}_2^n \cong \mathscr{I}_1^n \oplus \mathscr{I}_3^n$. □

If $\mathscr{I}$ is an injective $\mathscr{A}$-Module, then

$$0 \to \mathscr{I} \overset{\text{id}}{\to} \mathscr{I} \to 0 \to \cdots$$

is an injective resolution of $\mathscr{I}$. Hence, $H^n(U, \mathscr{I}) = (0)$ for each $n > 0$. Here we shall review again the cohomology groups from a bit more general viewpoint. Let $(X, \mathscr{A})$ be a ringed space, and let U be an open set of X. A family of functors $\{K^n(U, \cdot)\}_{n\geq 0}$ which assign a $\Gamma(U, \mathscr{A})$-module $K^n(U, \mathscr{F})$ to an $\mathscr{A}$-Module $\mathscr{F}$ is called a *cohomology functor* or a *cohomology theory* if $\{K^n(U, \cdot)\}_{n\geq 0}$ satisfy the following three conditions:

(1) To a homomorphism of $\mathscr{A}$-Modules $f : \mathscr{F} \to \mathscr{G}$ there corresponds a $\Gamma(U, \mathscr{A})$-homomorphism $K^n(U, f) : K^n(U, \mathscr{F}) \to K^n(U, \mathscr{G})$, and $K^n(U, g \cdot f) = K^n(U, g) \cdot K^n(U, f)$ and $K^n(U, \mathrm{id}_{\mathscr{F}}) = \mathrm{id}_{K^n(U, \mathscr{F})}$.

(2) $K^0(U, \mathscr{F}) = \mathscr{F}(U)$ and $K^n(U, \mathscr{I}) = (0)$ (all $n > 0$) for every injective $\mathscr{A}$-Module $\mathscr{I}$.

(3) For an exact sequence of $\mathscr{A}$-Modules

$$0 \to \mathscr{F}_1 \xrightarrow{\alpha} \mathscr{F}_2 \xrightarrow{\beta} \mathscr{F}_3 \to 0,$$

there is a homomorphism of $\Gamma(U, \mathscr{A})$-modules $\partial^n \colon K^n(U, \mathscr{F}_3) \to K^{n+1}(U, \mathscr{F}_1)$ for each $n \geq 0$ which makes the following sequence exact

$$\begin{aligned} 0 \to K^0(U, \mathscr{F}_1) &\xrightarrow{\alpha^0} K^0(U, \mathscr{F}_2) \xrightarrow{\beta^0} K^0(U, \mathscr{F}_3) \xrightarrow{\partial^0} K^1(U, \mathscr{F}_1) \\ &\xrightarrow{\alpha^1} K^1(U, \mathscr{F}_2) \xrightarrow{\beta^1} \cdots \to K^n(U, \mathscr{F}_1) \xrightarrow{\alpha^n} K^n(U, \mathscr{F}_2) \\ &\xrightarrow{\beta^n} K^n(U. \mathscr{F}_3) \xrightarrow{\partial^n} K^{n+1}(U, \mathscr{F}_1) \to \cdots, \end{aligned}$$

where $\alpha^n = K^n(U, \alpha)$ and $\beta^n = K^n(U, \beta)$.

Under these circumstances, we have the following result.

LEMMA 2.17. *Let $\{K^n(U, \cdot)\}_{n \geq 0}$ be a cohomology functor on a ringed space $(X, \mathscr{A})$. Then the functor coincides with the cohomology functor $\{H^n(U, \cdot)\}_{n \geq 0}$ defined in Theorem* 2.16.

PROOF. Let $\mathscr{F}$ be an $\mathscr{A}$-Module and let

$$0 \to \mathscr{F} \xrightarrow{\eta} \mathscr{I}^0 \xrightarrow{\Delta^0} \mathscr{I}^1 \xrightarrow{\Delta^1} \cdots \xrightarrow{\Delta^{n-1}} \mathscr{I}^n \xrightarrow{\Delta^n} \mathscr{I}^{n+1} \to \cdots$$

be an injective resolution of $\mathscr{F}$. Setting $\mathscr{K}^n = \operatorname{Im} \Delta^n$, we have exact sequences

$$0 \to \mathscr{F} \xrightarrow{\eta} \mathscr{I}^0 \to \mathscr{K}^0 \to 0,$$

$$0 \to \mathscr{K}^{n-1} \to \mathscr{I}^n \to \mathscr{K}^n \to 0 \quad (n \geq 1).$$

Noting that $H^i(U, \mathscr{I}^n) = K^i(U, \mathscr{I}^n) = (0)$ (for each $i > 0$ and each $n \geq 0$), we employ the condition (3) to obtain the isomorphisms

$$H^1(U, \mathscr{F}) \cong \operatorname{Coker}(\mathscr{I}^0(U) \to \mathscr{K}^0(U)) \cong K^1(U, \mathscr{F}),$$

$$H^{n+1}(U, \mathscr{F}) \cong H^n(U, \mathscr{K}^0) \cong H^{n-1}(U, \mathscr{K}^1) \cong \cdots \cong H^1(U, \mathscr{K}^{n-1}),$$

$$K^{n+1}(U, \mathscr{F}) \cong K^n(U, \mathscr{K}^0) \cong K^{n-1}(U, \mathscr{K}^1) \cong \cdots \cong K^1(U, \mathscr{K}^{n-1}) \quad (\text{for every } n \geq 1).$$

Hence, we have an isomorphism $\varphi^n(\mathscr{F}) \colon H^n(U, \mathscr{F}) \xrightarrow{\sim} K^n(U, \mathscr{F})$. By the construction of an isomorphism $\varphi^1(\mathscr{F})$, we can easily verify $\varphi^n(\mathscr{G}) \cdot H^n(U, f) = K^n(U, f) \cdot \varphi^n(\mathscr{F})$ (for every $n \geq 0$) for a homomorphism of $\mathscr{A}$-Modules $f \colon \mathscr{F} \to \mathscr{G}$. □

Since the cohomology groups $H^n(U, \mathscr{F})$ are defined in terms of an injective resolution of $\mathscr{F}$, it is not easy to compute $H^n(U, \mathscr{F})$ for specific examples by pursuing the definitions. For this reason, we define Čech cohomologies and make supplementary use of them in concrete computations. In the subsequent arguments, we consider the case $U = X$; the case $U \subset X$ can be treated in the same fashion. Let $\mathfrak{U} = \{U_i\}_{i \in I}$ be an open covering of X. For $s = (i_0, \dots, i_n) \in I^{n+1}$, we set $U_s = U_{i_0} \cap U_{i_1} \cap \cdots \cap U_{i_n}$. An element $\alpha = (\alpha(s))_{s \in I^{n+1}}$ of $\prod_{s \in I^{n+1}} \mathscr{F}(U_s)$ is called a *Čech n-cochain* with coefficients in $\mathscr{F}$ if it satisfies the following two conditions:

(i) For $s = (i_0, i_1, \dots, i_n)$, $\alpha(s) = 0$ provided $U_s = \emptyset$ or $i_j = i_k$ for some $j, k; j \neq k$.

(ii) Excluding the case (i) above, we set $\sigma(s) = (i_{\sigma(0)}, i_{\sigma(1)}, \dots, i_{\sigma(n)})$ for any permutation σ of $\{0, 1, \dots, n\}$. Then $\alpha(\sigma(s)) = \operatorname{sgn}(\sigma) \cdot \alpha(s)$.

The set of all Čech n-cochains with coefficients in $\mathscr{F}$ forms a $\Gamma(X, \mathscr{A})$-module $C^n(\mathfrak{U}, \mathscr{F})$. For an $\mathscr{A}$-homomorphism $f: \mathscr{F} \to \mathscr{G}$, we define a $\Gamma(X, \mathscr{A})$-homomorphism $f^n: C^n(\mathfrak{U}, \mathscr{F}) \to C^n(\mathfrak{U}, \mathscr{G})$ by

$$(f^n \alpha)(s) = f(U_s)(\alpha(s)).$$

We also define a $\Gamma(X, \mathscr{A})$-homomorphism $d^n: C^n(\mathfrak{U}, \mathscr{F}) \to C^{n+1}(\mathfrak{U}, \mathscr{F})$ by

$$(d^n \alpha)(t) = \sum_{j=0}^{n+1} (-1)^j \alpha(t_j)|_{U_t}$$

for $\alpha \in C^n(\mathfrak{U}, \mathscr{F})$ and $t = (i_0, \cdots, i_{n+1})$, where t_j denotes $(i_0, \cdots, \check{i}_j, \cdots, i_{n+1})$ which is obtained from t by removing i_j. It is a straightforward computation to show that $d^{n+1} \cdot d^n = 0$ for each $n \geq 0$. Hence, we have a complex with boundary operators $\{d^n\}_{n \geq 0}$,

$$C^0(\mathfrak{U}, \mathscr{F}) \xrightarrow{d^0} C^1(\mathfrak{U}, \mathscr{F}) \xrightarrow{d^1} \cdots \xrightarrow{d^{n-1}} C^n(\mathfrak{U}, \mathscr{F})$$
$$\xrightarrow{d^n} C^{n+1}(\mathfrak{U}, \mathscr{F}) \to \cdots$$

which we denote by $C^\bullet(\mathfrak{U}, \mathscr{F})$. The cohomology group of this complex is $H^n(\mathfrak{U}, \mathscr{F})$. Namely, $H^n(\mathfrak{U}, \mathscr{F}) = \operatorname{Ker} d^n / \operatorname{Im} d^{n-1}$. We denote $\operatorname{Ker} d^n$, $\operatorname{Im} d^{n-1}$ by $Z^n(\mathfrak{U}, \mathscr{F})$, $B^n(\mathfrak{U}, \mathscr{F})$, respectively, and call elements of respective groups *Čech n-cocycles* and *Čech n-coboundaries*. In particular, $H^0(\mathfrak{U}, \mathscr{F}) = \Gamma(X, \mathscr{F})$. (Verify this.) An $\mathscr{A}$-homomorphism $f: \mathscr{F} \to \mathscr{G}$ induces a homomorphism of Čech complexes

$$f^\bullet = \{f^n\}_{n \geq 0}: C^\bullet(\mathfrak{U}, \mathscr{F}) \to C^\bullet(\mathfrak{U}, \mathscr{G})$$

and accordingly a $\Gamma(X, \mathscr{A})$-homomorphism $f^n: H^n(\mathfrak{U}, \mathscr{F}) \to H^n(\mathfrak{U}, \mathscr{G})$ $(n \geq 0)$.

Let $\mathfrak{V} = \{V_\lambda\}_{\lambda \in \Lambda}$ be another open covering of X. We say that $\mathfrak{V}$ is a *refinement* of $\mathfrak{U}$ (notation: $\mathfrak{U} < \mathfrak{V}$) if there is a mapping $\varphi: \Lambda \to I$ such that $V_\lambda \subset U_{\varphi(\lambda)}$ (for each $\lambda \in \Lambda$). Utilizing this mapping φ, we define a homomorphism of complexes

$$\varphi^\bullet = \{\varphi^n\}_{n \geq 0}: C^\bullet(\mathfrak{U}, \mathscr{F}) \to C^\bullet(\mathfrak{V}, \mathscr{F})$$

in the following fashion: For $\alpha \in C^n(\mathfrak{U}, \mathscr{F})$ and $t = (\lambda_0, \cdots, \lambda_n)$, $(\varphi^n \alpha)(t) = \alpha(\varphi(t))|_{V_t}$, where $\varphi(t) = (\varphi(\lambda_0), \ldots, \varphi(\lambda_n))$ and $V_t = V_{\lambda_0} \cap \cdots \cap V_{\lambda_n} (\subseteq U_{\varphi(t)})$. If $\psi: \Lambda \to I$ is another mapping with $V_\lambda \subseteq U_{\psi(\lambda)}$ for each $\lambda \in \Lambda$, then $\psi^\bullet = \{\psi^n\}_{n \geq 0}$ is homotopic to $\varphi^\bullet$. In fact, if we define $\rho^n: C^{n+1}(\mathfrak{U}, \mathscr{F}) \to C^n(\mathfrak{V}, \mathscr{F})$ by

$$(\rho^n \alpha)(t) = \sum_{j=0}^{n} (-1)^j \alpha(\varphi(\lambda_0), \cdots, \varphi(\lambda_j), \psi(\lambda_j), \cdots, \psi(\lambda_n))|_{V_t}$$
$$t = (\lambda_0, \ldots, \lambda_n)$$

and $\rho^{-1} = 0$, then we have a relation

$$\varphi^n - \psi^n = d^{n-1} \cdot \rho^{n-1} + \rho^n \cdot d^n \qquad (n \geq 0).$$

(Verify this.) Hence, two homomorphisms $H^n(\mathfrak{U}, \mathscr{F}) \to H^n(\mathfrak{V}, \mathscr{F})$ induced by φ^n and ψ^n coincide with each other. We denote this homomorphism by $\sigma_{\mathfrak{V}\mathfrak{U}}$. For refinements of open coverings $\mathfrak{U} < \mathfrak{V} < \mathfrak{W}$, we have $\sigma_{\mathfrak{W}\mathfrak{V}} \cdot \sigma_{\mathfrak{V}\mathfrak{U}} = \sigma_{\mathfrak{W}\mathfrak{U}}$. So we can define an inductive limit of $\{H^n(\mathfrak{U}, \mathscr{F}), \sigma_{\mathfrak{V}\mathfrak{U}}\}$ and write $\check{H}^n(X, \mathscr{F}) = \varinjlim_{\mathfrak{U}} H^n(\mathfrak{U}, \mathscr{F})$

(for each $n \geq 0$). We call this group the *nth Čech cohomology*. Here we have $\check{H}^0(X, \mathscr{F}) = H^0(\mathfrak{U}, \mathscr{F}) = \Gamma(X, \mathscr{F})$.

We have thus defined the ordinary cohomology group $H^n(X, \mathscr{F})$ and the Čech cohomology group $\check{H}^n(X, \mathscr{F})$. So it is now our task to examine conditions under which these two cohomologies coincide with each other.

Let $\mathfrak{U}$ be an open covering of X. We define a presheaf $\mathscr{C}^n(\mathfrak{U}, \mathscr{F})$ by assigning $C^n(V \cap \mathfrak{U}, \mathscr{F}|_V)$ to an open set V of X, where $V \cap \mathfrak{U}$ is an open covering $\{V \cap U_i\}_{i \in I}$ of V and $C^n(V \cap \mathfrak{U}, \mathscr{F}|_V)$ is a $\Gamma(V, \mathscr{A})$-module consisting of all Čech n-cochains with coefficients in $\mathscr{F}|_V$. It is easy to verify that $\mathscr{C}^n(\mathfrak{U}, \mathscr{F})$ is an $\mathscr{A}$-Module. The boundary operators

$$d^n(V) \colon C^n(V \cap \mathfrak{U}, \mathscr{F}|_V) \to C^{n+1}(V \cap \mathfrak{U}, \mathscr{F}|_V)$$

give rise to a homomorphism of $\mathscr{A}$-Modules $d^n \colon \mathscr{C}^n(\mathfrak{U}, \mathscr{F}) \to \mathscr{C}^{n+1}(\mathfrak{U}, \mathscr{F})$. Hence, we obtain a complex $\mathscr{C}^\bullet(\mathfrak{U}, \mathscr{F})$ of $\mathscr{A}$-Modules

$$0 \to \mathscr{C}^0(\mathfrak{U}, \mathscr{F}) \xrightarrow{d^0} \mathscr{C}^1(\mathfrak{U}, \mathscr{F}) \xrightarrow{d^1} \cdots \xrightarrow{d^{n-1}} \mathscr{C}^n(\mathfrak{U}, \mathscr{F}) \xrightarrow{d^n} \cdots .$$

Here if we define a homomorphism of $\mathscr{A}$-Modules $j \colon \mathscr{F} \to \mathscr{C}^0(\mathfrak{U}, \mathscr{F})$ by $\alpha \in \mathscr{F}(V) \mapsto (\alpha|_{V \cap U_i})_{i \in I} \in C^0(V \cap \mathfrak{U}, \mathscr{F}|_V)$, we have the following result.

Lemma 2.18. (1) *Complementing the complex $\mathscr{C}^\bullet(\mathfrak{U}, \mathscr{F})$, we obtain an exact sequence, which we call the* Čech resolution *of $\mathscr{F}$*

$$(*) \qquad \begin{aligned} 0 \to \mathscr{F} \xrightarrow{j} \mathscr{C}^0(\mathfrak{U}, \mathscr{F}) \xrightarrow{d^0} \mathscr{C}^1(\mathfrak{U}, \mathscr{F}) \xrightarrow{d^1} \cdots \\ \xrightarrow{d^{n-1}} \mathscr{C}^n(\mathfrak{U}, \mathscr{F}) \xrightarrow{d^n} \mathscr{C}^{n+1}(\mathfrak{U}, \mathscr{F}) \to \cdots . \end{aligned}$$

The complex $C^\bullet(\mathfrak{U}, \mathscr{F})$ is obtained from $\mathscr{C}^\bullet(\mathfrak{U}, \mathscr{F})$ by applying the functor $\Gamma(X, \cdot)$ to each term and homomorphism of $\mathscr{C}^\bullet(\mathfrak{U}, \mathscr{F})$.

(2) *For an injective resolution of $\mathscr{F}$*

$$0 \to \mathscr{F} \xrightarrow{\eta} \mathscr{I}^0 \xrightarrow{\Delta^0} \mathscr{I}^1 \xrightarrow{\Delta^1} \cdots \xrightarrow{\Delta^{n-1}} \mathscr{I}^n \xrightarrow{\Delta^n} \cdots ,$$

there exists a homomorphism $\theta^n \colon \mathscr{C}^n(\mathfrak{U}, \mathscr{F}) \to \mathscr{I}^n$ $(n \geq 0)$ such that $\theta^0 \cdot j = \eta$ and $\theta^{n+1} \cdot d^n = \Delta^n \cdot \theta^n$ for each $n \geq 0$. Hence, there exists a $\Gamma(X, \mathscr{A})$-homomorphism of cohomology modules $\theta^n_{\mathfrak{U}} \colon H^n(\mathfrak{U}, \mathscr{F}) \to H^n(X, \mathscr{F})$ for all $n \geq 0$.

Proof. (1) For $x \in X$ and $n > 0$, an element $\overline{\alpha}$ of $\mathscr{C}^n(\mathfrak{U}, \mathscr{F})_x$ is represented by an element α of $\mathscr{C}^n(\mathfrak{U}, \mathscr{F})(U)$, where U is an open neighborhood of x. We may choose U so that $U \subset U_0$ for some $0 \in I$. Then $U \cap U_{\tilde{s}} = U \cap U_s$ for $s = (i_0, \ldots, i_{n-1})$ and $\tilde{s} = (0, i_0, \ldots, i_{n-1})$. Define an element β of $\mathscr{C}^{n-1}(\mathfrak{U}, \mathscr{F})(U)$ by $\beta(s) = \alpha(\tilde{s})$. Then we have

$$(d\beta)(t) = \sum_{k=0}^{n} (-1)^k \beta(t_k) = \sum_{k=0}^{n} (-1)^k \alpha(\tilde{t}_k),$$

where $t = (i_0, \ldots, i_n)$, $t_k = (i_0, \ldots, \check{i}_k, \ldots, i_n)$, $\tilde{t} = (0, i_0, \ldots, i_n)$, and $\tilde{t}_k = (0, i_0, \ldots, \check{i}_k, \ldots, i_n)$. Suppose $d^n(\overline{\alpha}) = 0$. We may assume $d^n(\alpha) = 0$ by replacing U by a smaller one if necessary. Then

$$(d\alpha)(\tilde{t}) = \alpha(t) - \sum_{k=0}^{n}(-1)^k \alpha(\tilde{t}_k) = 0.$$

Hence, $\alpha = d^{n-1}\beta$. Thereby, $\operatorname{Ker} d^n = \operatorname{Im} d^{n-1}$ for each $n > 0$. By a similar argument, we can show that $\operatorname{Ker} d^0 \cong \mathscr{F}$. The last half of the assertion (1) can be readily verified by the definition.

(2) Extending the identity morphism $\mathrm{id}_{\mathscr{F}} : \mathscr{F} \xrightarrow{\sim} \mathscr{F}$, we obtain a homomorphism $\theta^n : \mathscr{C}^n(\mathfrak{U}, \mathscr{F}) \to \mathscr{I}^n$ $(n \geq 0)$. Two extensions $\mathscr{C}^n(\mathfrak{U}, \mathscr{F}) \to \mathscr{I}^n$ of $\mathrm{id}_{\mathscr{F}}$ are homotopic to each other. This can be shown by mimicking the argument which we applied to two injective resolutions of $\mathscr{F}$. □

The homomorphism $\theta^n_{\mathfrak{U}} : H^n(\mathfrak{U}, \mathscr{F}) \to H^n(X, \mathscr{F})$ which we defined in Lemma 2.18 satisfies $\theta^n_{\mathfrak{V}} \cdot \sigma_{\mathfrak{V}\mathfrak{U}} = \theta^n_{\mathfrak{U}}$ for a refinement of open coverings $\mathfrak{U} < \mathfrak{V}$. So we define a homomorphism of $\Gamma(X, \mathscr{A})$-modules $\check{\theta}^n : \check{H}^n(X, \mathscr{F}) \to H^n(X, \mathscr{F})$ by $\check{\theta}^n = \varinjlim_{\mathfrak{U}} \theta^n_{\mathfrak{U}}$.

A sheaf $\mathscr{S}$ on X is called a *scattered sheaf* (or a *flasque sheaf*) if the restriction morphism $\rho_{UX} : \Gamma(X, \mathscr{S}) \to \Gamma(U, \mathscr{S})$ is surjective for any open set U of X.

LEMMA 2.19. (1) *An injective $\mathscr{A}$-Module is a scattered sheaf.*

(2) *For an exact sequence of $\mathscr{A}$-Modules*

$$0 \to \mathscr{F}_1 \xrightarrow{\alpha} \mathscr{F}_2 \xrightarrow{\beta} \mathscr{F}_3 \to 0$$

with a scattered sheaf $\mathscr{F}_1$, the sequence

$$0 \to \Gamma(U, \mathscr{F}_1) \xrightarrow{\alpha(U)} \Gamma(U, \mathscr{F}_2) \xrightarrow{\beta(U)} \Gamma(U, \mathscr{F}_3) \to 0$$

is exact for any open set U.

(3) *Let*

$$0 \to \mathscr{F}_1 \xrightarrow{\alpha} \mathscr{F}_2 \xrightarrow{\beta} \mathscr{F}_3 \to 0$$

be an exact sequence of $\mathscr{A}$-Modules. If $\mathscr{F}_1$ and $\mathscr{F}_2$ are scattered sheaves, then so is $\mathscr{F}_3$.

PROOF. (1) Let $\widetilde{\mathscr{A}}$ be the sheafifying space of $\mathscr{A}$ and let $\pi : \widetilde{\mathscr{A}} \to X$ be the natural surjective morphism. For an open set U of X and $F = X - U$, define a presheaf of $\mathscr{A}$-modules $\mathscr{A}_{[F]}$ as follows: For an open set V, $\mathscr{A}_{[F]}(V) = \{s : F \cap V \to \pi^{-1}(F \cap V); s$ is a continuous mapping and a section of $\pi\}$, where $F \cap V$ and $\pi^{-1}(F \cap V)$ are endowed with the induced topologies of X and $\widetilde{\mathscr{A}}$, respectively. It is easy to show that $\mathscr{A}_{[F]}$ is an $\mathscr{A}$-Module and $(\mathscr{A}_{[F]})_x = 0$ for each $x \in U$. Furthermore, a homomorphism of $\mathscr{A}$-Modules $p : \mathscr{A} \to \mathscr{A}_{[F]}$ given by $p(V) : s \in \mathscr{A}(V) \mapsto s|_{F \cap V} \in \mathscr{A}_{[F]}(V)$ is surjective. (Show that the homomorphism of stalks $p_x : \mathscr{A}_x \to (\mathscr{A}_{[F]})_x$ is surjective.) Denote by $\mathscr{A}_{[U]}$ the kernel of p. By the definition, $\mathscr{A}_{[U]}(V) = \{s \in \mathscr{A}(V); s|_{F \cap V} = 0\}$ and $(\mathscr{A}_{[U]})_x = 0$ (for each $x \in F$). We obtain, therefore, an exact sequence of $\mathscr{A}$-Modules

$$0 \to \mathscr{A}_{[U]} \to \mathscr{A} \xrightarrow{p} \mathscr{A}_{[F]} \to 0.$$

For an $\mathscr{A}$-Module $\mathscr{F}$, we have $\mathrm{Hom}_{\mathscr{A}}(\mathscr{A}_{[U]}, \mathscr{F}) \cong \Gamma(U, \mathscr{F})$. In fact, since $\mathscr{A}_{[U]}(U) = \mathscr{A}(U)$, the mapping θ which assigns $\varphi(U)(1_{\mathscr{A}(U)}) \in \Gamma(U, \mathscr{F})$ to $\varphi \in \mathrm{Hom}_{\mathscr{A}}(\mathscr{A}_{[U]}, \mathscr{F})$ is an isomorphism, where $1_{\mathscr{A}(U)}$ is the identity element of the ring $\mathscr{A}(U)$. In fact, it is easy to show that θ is injective. In order to show that θ is surjective, we define $\varphi \in \mathrm{Hom}_{\mathscr{A}}(\mathscr{A}_{[U]}, \mathscr{F})$ for $f \in \Gamma(U, \mathscr{F})$ in the following way: $\varphi(V)(s) = s\rho_{V\cap U, U}(f)(s \in \mathscr{A}_{[U]}(V))$ for an open set V of X. If $V \cap F = \emptyset$, then $V \cap U = V$ and $s\rho_{V\cap U, U}(f) \in \mathscr{F}(V)$. If $V \cap F \neq \emptyset$, then $s|_{F\cap V} = 0$ and $\mathrm{Supp}(s) := \{x \in V; s_x \neq 0\} \subset V \cap U$. Hence, $s\rho_{V\cap U, U}(f)$ is regarded as an element of $\mathscr{F}(V)$. Anyway, $\varphi(V)(s)$ is well defined as an element of $\mathscr{F}(V)$. Apparently, $\theta(\varphi) = f$. So θ is an isomorphism. Now let $\mathscr{I}$ be an injective $\mathscr{A}$-Module. Then we have an exact sequence

$$\begin{array}{ccccccccc}
0 \longrightarrow & \mathrm{Hom}_{\mathscr{A}}(\mathscr{A}_{[F]}, \mathscr{I}) & \longrightarrow & \mathrm{Hom}_{\mathscr{A}}(\mathscr{A}, \mathscr{I}) & \longrightarrow & \mathrm{Hom}_{\mathscr{A}}(\mathscr{A}_{[U]}, \mathscr{I}) & \longrightarrow 0 \\
 & & & \downarrow \cong & & \downarrow \cong & \\
 & & & \Gamma(X, \mathscr{I}) & \xrightarrow{\rho_{UX}} & \Gamma(U, \mathscr{I}) & .
\end{array}$$

This implies that $\mathscr{I}$ is a scattered sheaf.

(2) Considering $\mathscr{F}_i|_U$ instead of $\mathscr{F}_i$, we may assume that $U = X$. Since $\Gamma(X, \cdot)$ is left-exact, it suffices to show that $\beta(X)\colon \mathscr{F}_2(X) \to \mathscr{F}_3(X)$ is surjective. Fix an element $u \in \mathscr{F}_3(X)$. Let $\mathfrak{S}$ be the set of all pairs (V, t) of an open set V of X and an element $t \in \mathscr{F}_2(V)$ with $\beta(V)(t) = \rho_{VX}(u)$. Introduce an order in $\mathfrak{S}$ by setting $(V_1, t_1) \geq (V_2, t_2)$ if and only if $V_1 \supseteq V_2$ and $t_2 = t_1|_{V_2}$. Then $\mathfrak{S}$ is an inductively ordered set. So by Zorn's lemma, $\mathfrak{S}$ has a maximal element, say (U, t). If $U = X$, then $\beta(X)(t) = u$. Suppose $U \neq X$. For $x \in X - U$, there exist an open neighborhood V of x and an element $t' \in \mathscr{F}_2(V)$ with $\beta(V)(t') = \rho_{VX}(u)$. Here $t'|_{V\cap U} - t|_{V\cap U} = \alpha(V \cap U)(s)$ with $s \in \mathscr{F}_1(V \cap U)$. Since $\mathscr{F}_1$ is a scattered sheaf, $s = s_0|_{V\cap U}$ for some $s_0 \in \mathscr{F}_1(X)$. Now define $\tilde{t} \in \mathscr{F}_2(V \cup U)$ by $\tilde{t}|_U = t$ and $\tilde{t}|_V = t' - \alpha(V)(s_0|_V)$. Since $(V \cup U, \tilde{t}) > (U, t)$, this contradicts the maximality of an element (U, t). Therefore, $\beta(X)$ is surjective.

(3) This part is straightforward. We omit the proof. □

COROLLARY 2.20. *Let $\mathscr{F}$ be a scattered $\mathscr{A}$-Module. Then for any open covering $\mathfrak{U}$ of X, $H^n(\mathfrak{U}, \mathscr{F}) = (0)$ for each $n > 0$. Hence, $\check{H}^n(X, \mathscr{F}) = (0)$ for each $n > 0$.*

PROOF. Sheaves $\mathscr{C}^n(\mathfrak{U}, \mathscr{F})$ which appear in the Čech resolution of $\mathscr{F}$ are scattered sheaves (cf. problem I.2.4). The result as stated above follow from Lemmas 2.18 and 2.19. □

Consider an $\mathscr{A}$-Module $\mathscr{F}$ and its injective resolution

$$0 \to \mathscr{F} \xrightarrow{\eta} \mathscr{I}^0 \xrightarrow{\Delta^0} \mathscr{I}^1 \xrightarrow{\Delta^1} \cdots \xrightarrow{\Delta^{n-1}} \mathscr{I}^n \xrightarrow{\Delta^n} \cdots .$$

Let $\mathfrak{U}$ be an open covering of X. The Čech resolutions of $\mathscr{F}$ and $\mathscr{I}^j$ for each $j \geq 0$

with respect to $\mathfrak{U}$ give rise to the following commutative diagram

$$
\begin{array}{ccccccccccc}
 & & 0 & & 0 & & & & 0 & & \\
 & & \downarrow & & \downarrow & & & & \downarrow & & \\
0 & \longrightarrow & \mathscr{F} & \xrightarrow{\eta} & \mathscr{I}^0 & \xrightarrow{\Delta^0} & \cdots & \xrightarrow{\Delta^{n-1}} & \mathscr{I}^n & \xrightarrow{\Delta^n} & \cdots \\
 & & \downarrow{\scriptstyle j} & & \downarrow{\scriptstyle j} & & & & \downarrow{\scriptstyle j} & & \\
0 & \longrightarrow & \mathscr{C}^0(\mathfrak{U},\mathscr{F}) & \xrightarrow{\eta} & \mathscr{C}^0(\mathfrak{U},\mathscr{I}^0) & \xrightarrow{\Delta^0} & \cdots & \xrightarrow{\Delta^{n-1}} & \mathscr{C}^0(\mathfrak{U},\mathscr{I}^n) & \xrightarrow{\Delta^n} & \cdots \\
 & & \downarrow{\scriptstyle d^0} & & \downarrow{\scriptstyle d^0} & & & & \downarrow{\scriptstyle d^0} & & \\
0 & \longrightarrow & \mathscr{C}^1(\mathfrak{U},\mathscr{F}) & \xrightarrow{\eta} & \mathscr{C}^1(\mathfrak{U},\mathscr{I}^0) & \xrightarrow{\Delta^0} & \cdots & \xrightarrow{\Delta^{n-1}} & \mathscr{C}^1(\mathfrak{U},\mathscr{I}^n) & \xrightarrow{\Delta^n} & \cdots \\
 & & \downarrow{\scriptstyle d^1} & & \downarrow{\scriptstyle d^1} & & & & \downarrow{\scriptstyle d^1} & & \\
 & & \vdots & & \vdots & & & & \vdots & & \\
 & & \downarrow{\scriptstyle d^{m-1}} & & \downarrow{\scriptstyle d^{m-1}} & & & & \downarrow{\scriptstyle d^{m-1}} & & \\
0 & \longrightarrow & \mathscr{C}^m(\mathfrak{U},\mathscr{F}) & \xrightarrow{\eta} & \mathscr{C}^m(\mathfrak{U},\mathscr{I}^0) & \xrightarrow{\Delta^0} & \cdots & \xrightarrow{\Delta^{n-1}} & \mathscr{C}^m(\mathfrak{U},\mathscr{I}^n) & \xrightarrow{\Delta^n} & \cdots \\
 & & \downarrow{\scriptstyle d^m} & & \downarrow{\scriptstyle d^m} & & & & \downarrow{\scriptstyle d^m} & & \\
 & & \vdots & & \vdots & & & & \vdots & &
\end{array}
$$

where all rows and columns are exact sequences. Applying the functor $\Gamma(X,\cdot)$ to this commutative diagram, we obtain the following commutative diagram

$$
\begin{array}{ccccccccccc}
 & & 0 & & 0 & & & & 0 & & \\
 & & \downarrow & & \downarrow & & & & \downarrow & & \\
0 & \longrightarrow & \Gamma(X,\mathscr{F}) & \xrightarrow{\varepsilon} & \Gamma(X,\mathscr{I}^0) & \xrightarrow{\delta^0} & \cdots & \xrightarrow{\delta^{n-1}} & \Gamma(X,\mathscr{I}^n) & \xrightarrow{\delta^n} & \cdots \\
 & & \downarrow{\scriptstyle j} & & \downarrow{\scriptstyle j} & & & & \downarrow{\scriptstyle j} & & \\
0 & \longrightarrow & C^0(\mathfrak{U},\mathscr{F}) & \xrightarrow{\varepsilon} & C^0(\mathfrak{U},\mathscr{I}^0) & \xrightarrow{\delta^0} & \cdots & \xrightarrow{\delta^{n-1}} & C^0(\mathfrak{U},\mathscr{I}^n) & \xrightarrow{\delta^n} & \cdots \\
 & & \downarrow{\scriptstyle \mathbf{d}^0} & & \downarrow{\scriptstyle \mathbf{d}^0} & & & & \downarrow{\scriptstyle \mathbf{d}^0} & & \\
0 & \longrightarrow & C^1(\mathfrak{U},\mathscr{F}) & \xrightarrow{\varepsilon} & C^1(\mathfrak{U},\mathscr{I}^0) & \xrightarrow{\delta^0} & \cdots & \xrightarrow{\delta^{n-1}} & C^1(\mathfrak{U},\mathscr{I}^n) & \xrightarrow{\delta^n} & \cdots \\
 & & \downarrow{\scriptstyle d^1} & & \downarrow{\scriptstyle d^1} & & & & \downarrow{\scriptstyle d^1} & & \\
 & & \vdots & & \vdots & & & & \vdots & & \\
 & & \downarrow{\scriptstyle d^{m-1}} & & \downarrow{\scriptstyle d^{m-1}} & & & & \downarrow{\scriptstyle d^{m-1}} & & \\
0 & \longrightarrow & C^m(\mathfrak{U},\mathscr{F}) & \xrightarrow{\varepsilon} & C^m(\mathfrak{U},\mathscr{I}^0) & \xrightarrow{\delta^0} & \cdots & \xrightarrow{\delta^{n-1}} & C^m(\mathfrak{U},\mathscr{I}^n) & \xrightarrow{\delta^n} & \cdots \\
 & & \downarrow{\scriptstyle d^m} & & \downarrow{\scriptstyle d^m} & & & & \downarrow{\scriptstyle d^m} & & \\
 & & \vdots & & \vdots & & & & \vdots & &
\end{array}
$$

where all columns except the leftmost column are exact sequences by Corollary 2.20.

Furthermore, the diagram with the top row and the leftmost column replaced by the zero row and zero column is regarded as a double complex with two boundary operators. To be precise, a collection of R-modules and R-homomorphisms $C = \{C^{m,n}, d^m\colon C^{m,n} \to C^{m+1,n}, \delta^n\colon C^{m,n} \to C^{m,n+1};\ m \geq 0, n \geq 0\}$ is called a *double complex* if $d^{m+1} \cdot d^m = \delta^{n+1} \cdot \delta^n = \delta^n \cdot d^m + d^m \cdot \delta^n = 0$. In order to regard the above diagram with the first row and the first column replaced by the zero row and the zero column as a double complex, we have only to take $\{C^{m,n} = C^m(\mathfrak{U}, \mathscr{I}^n),\ d^m\colon C^{m,n} \to C^{m+1,n}, (-1)^m\delta^m\colon C^{m,n} \to C^{m,n+1};\ m \geq 0, n \geq 0\}$. Given a double complex $C = \{C^{m,n}, d^m, \delta^n\}$, we can produce subcomplexes as follows:

(1) For each $n \geq 0$, $C_I^{\bullet n} = \{C^{p,n}, d\colon C^{p,n} \to C^{p+1,n}\}_{p\geq 0}$. We denote the cohomology group of this complex by $H_I^{m,n}$.

(2) For each $m \geq 0$, $C_{II}^{m\bullet} = \{C^{m,p}, \delta\colon C^{m,p} \to C^{m,p+1}\}_{p\geq 0}$. We denote the cohomology group by $H_{II}^{m,n}$.

(3) $C^\bullet = \{C^p, \Delta\colon C^p \to C^{p+1}\}_{p\geq 0}$, where $C^p = \sum_{m+n=p} C^{m,n}$ and $\Delta = d + \delta$. We denote the cohomology group by $H^p(C^\bullet)$.

(4) $K^\bullet = \{K^p, d\colon K^p \to K^{p+1}\}_{p\geq 0}$, where $K^p = \operatorname{Ker}(\delta\colon C^{p,0} \to C^{p,1})$. We denote the cohomology group by $H^p(K^\bullet)$.

(5) $L^\bullet = \{L^p, \delta\colon L^p \to L^{p+1}\}_{p\geq 0}$, where $L^p = \operatorname{Ker}(d\colon C^{0,p} \to C^{1,p})$. We denote the cohomology group by $H^p(L^\bullet)$.

Lemma 2.21. *Suppose $H_I^{m,n} = (0)$ for every pair (m, n) with $m > 0$ and $n \geq 0$. Then the injective homomorphism of complexes $L^\bullet \to C^\bullet$ induced naturally by the double complex C gives rise to an isomorphism $H^p(L^\bullet) \xrightarrow{\sim} H^p(C^\bullet)$ for each $p \geq 0$.*

Proof. Note that $\delta = \Delta$ on the complex $L^\bullet$. Let $N^\bullet = C^\bullet/L^\bullet$. Then we have an exact sequence of complexes $0 \to L^\bullet \to C^\bullet \to N^\bullet \to 0$ which yields the following exact sequence (the proof being the same as in Theorem 2.16):

$$\begin{array}{cccccccccc} 0 & \to & H^0(L^\bullet) & \to & H^0(C^\bullet) & \to & H^0(N^\bullet) & \to & H^1(L^\bullet) & \to & H^1(C^\bullet) \\ & \to & H^1(N^\bullet) & \to & \cdots & \to & H^p(L^\bullet) & \to & H^p(C^\bullet) & \to & H^p(N^\bullet) \\ & \to & H^{p+1}(L^\bullet) & \to & \cdots & & & & & & \end{array}$$

If $H^p(N^\bullet) = (0)$ for each $p \geq 0$, we have an isomorphism $H^p(L^\bullet) \xrightarrow{\sim} H^p(C^\bullet)$ for each $p \geq 0$ by the above exact sequence.

Define here a subcomplex $N_h^\bullet$ $(h \geq 0)$ of $N^\bullet$ by $N_h^\bullet = \{N_h^p, \Delta\colon N_h^p \to N_h^{p+1}\}_{p\geq 0}$, where $N_h^p = \sum_{n\geq h} N^{p-n,n}$ with $N^{p-n,n}=$ the image of $C^{p-n,n}$ and Δ is the boundary operator induced by $d + \delta$. Apparently, $N_0^\bullet = N^\bullet$ and $N_h^p = (0)$ $(p < h)$. Furthermore, $N_{h+1}^\bullet$ is a subcomplex of $N_h^\bullet$, and $N_h^\bullet/N_{h+1}^\bullet$ is a complex as exhibited by

$$\begin{array}{ccccccccccc} 0 & \longrightarrow \cdots \longrightarrow & 0 & \longrightarrow & N^{0,h} & \xrightarrow{d} & N^{1,h} & \xrightarrow{d} \cdots \longrightarrow & N^{n-h,h} & \longrightarrow \cdots \\ & & & & \Vert & & \Vert & & \Vert & \\ & & & & C^{0,h}/\operatorname{Ker} d & & C^{1,h} & & C^{n-h,h} & \end{array}$$

Hence, $H^p(N_h^\bullet/N_{h+1}^\bullet) = (0)$ for each $p < h$, $H^h(N_h^\bullet/N_{h+1}^\bullet) = (0)$, and $H^n(N_h^\bullet/N_{h+1}^\bullet) = H_I^{n-h,h} = (0)$ for each $n > h$ by the hypothesis. Applying these results to the cohomology exact sequence which is given by an exact sequence of complexes

$$0 \to N_{h+1}^\bullet \to N_h^\bullet \to N_h^\bullet/N_{h+1}^\bullet \to 0,$$

we obtain $H^n(N_h^\bullet) \cong H^n(N_{h+1}^\bullet)$ for each $n \geq 0$, each $h \geq 0$. □

Summarizing the above results, we obtain the following result.

THEOREM 2.22. *Let $\mathscr{F}$ be an $\mathscr{A}$-Module over a ringed space $(X, \mathscr{A})$, and let $\mathfrak{U} = \{U_i\}_{i\in I}$ be an open covering of X. Then we have:*

(1) *Suppose the cohomology group $H^n(U_s, \mathscr{F})$ defined by an injective resolution of $\mathscr{F}$ vanishes for each $n > 0$ and for each $s = (i_0, \dots, i_m) \in I^{m+1}$, where $m \geq 0$, too, is arbitrary. Then $H^n(\mathfrak{U}, \mathscr{F}) \cong H^n(X, \mathscr{F})$ for each $n \geq 0$.*

(2) *Assume that for each open covering $\mathfrak{V}$ of X there exists an open covering $\mathfrak{W}$ which is a refinement of $\mathfrak{V}$ and which satisfies the condition above in (1). Then $\check{H}^n(X, \mathscr{F}) \cong H^n(X, \mathscr{F})$ for each $n \geq 0$.*

PROOF. (1) Look at the double complex $C = \{C^m(\mathfrak{U}, \mathscr{I}^n), d^m, \delta^n\}$ which we gave right after Corollary 2.20. Since $\mathscr{I}^n$ is a scattered sheaf, $H_I^{m,n} = (0)$ (for each $m > 0$ and each $n \geq 0$). The hypothesis on $\mathfrak{U}$ and $\mathscr{F}$ also implies $H_{II}^{m,n} = (0)$ (for each $m \geq 0$ and each $n > 0$). Thence, $H^p(L^\bullet) \cong H^p(K^\bullet)$ (for each $p \geq 0$) by Lemma 2.21. Since $H^p(L^\bullet) = H^p(X, \mathscr{F})$ and $H^p(K^\bullet) = H^p(\mathfrak{U}, \mathscr{F})$, we obtain an isomorphism as stated in (1).

(2) This part is clear by the definition of $\check{H}^m(X, \mathscr{F})$. □

In order to compare two cohomologies $\{\check{H}^n(X, \cdot)\}_{n\geq 0}$ and $\{H^n(X, \cdot)\}_{n\geq 0}$ we can employ Lemma 2.17 in several cases. By Lemma 2.19 and Corollary 2.20, $\check{H}^n(X, \mathscr{I}) = (0)$ $(n > 0)$ for an injective $\mathscr{A}$-Module $\mathscr{I}$. Hence, it suffices to check whether or not an exact sequence of $\mathscr{A}$-Modules

$$0 \to \mathscr{F}_1 \xrightarrow{\alpha} \mathscr{F}_2 \xrightarrow{\beta} \mathscr{F}_3 \to 0$$

gives rise to an exact sequence of Čech cohomology groups:

$$\begin{aligned}
0 \to \check{H}^0(X, \mathscr{F}_1) &\xrightarrow{\alpha^0} \check{H}^0(X, \mathscr{F}_2) \xrightarrow{\beta^0} \check{H}^0(X, \mathscr{F}_3) \\
&\xrightarrow{\partial^0} \check{H}^1(X, \mathscr{F}_1) \xrightarrow{\alpha^1} \check{H}^1(X, \mathscr{F}_2) \xrightarrow{\beta^1} \check{H}^1(X, \mathscr{F}_3) \to \cdots \\
&\xrightarrow{\partial^{n-1}} \check{H}^n(X, \mathscr{F}_1) \xrightarrow{\alpha^n} \check{H}^n(X, \mathscr{F}_2) \xrightarrow{\beta^n} \check{H}^n(X, \mathscr{F}_3) \\
&\xrightarrow{\partial^n} \check{H}^{n+1}(X, \mathscr{F}_1) \to \cdots .
\end{aligned}$$

This holds if X is a paracompact topological space. (Recall that X is *paracompact* by definition if X is a Hausdorff topological space and each open covering $\mathfrak{U}$ of X has an open covering $\mathfrak{V}$ which is a refinement of $\mathfrak{U}$ and is locally finite. We say that an open covering $\mathfrak{V}$ is *locally finite* if, for each $x \in X$, there is an open neighborhood W of x which meets only finitely many open sets belonging to the covering $\mathfrak{V}$.) The following result is proved in [1] though we do not make use of it in the present book.

THEOREM 2.23. *If X is paracompact, we have $\check{H}^n(X, \mathscr{F}) \cong H^n(X, \mathscr{F})$ (all $n \geq 0$) for an arbitrary $\mathscr{A}$-Module $\mathscr{F}$.*

In order to ultilize cohomology theories effectively, we often use the spectral sequences which we now explain.

DEFINITION 2.24. Let R be a commutative ring. A collection of R-modules and R-homomorphisms $E = \{E_r^{p,q}, d_r^{p,q}, Z_\infty(E_2^{p,q}), B_\infty(E_2^{p,q}), E^n; p, q, n, r \in \mathbf{Z}, r \geq 2\}$ is called a *spectral sequence* if it satisfies the following conditions (1)–(5).

(1) $E_r^{p,q}$ and E^n are R-modules.

(2) $d_r^{p,q}\colon E_r^{p,q} \to E_r^{p+r,q-r+1}$ is an R-homomorphism, and

$$d_r^{p+r,q-r+1} \cdot d_r^{p,q} = 0.$$

(3) Let $Z_{r+1}(E_r^{p,q}) = \mathrm{Ker}(d_r^{p,q})$ and $B_{r+1}(E_r^{p,q}) = \mathrm{Im}(d_r^{p-r,q+r-1})$. Then (by (2)) an R-module inclusion $B_{r+1}(E_r^{p,q}) \subset Z_{r+1}(E_r^{p,q})$ obtains, and there is an isomorphism

$$\alpha_r^{p,q}\colon Z_{r+1}(E_r^{p,q})/B_{r+1}(E_r^{p,q}) \xrightarrow{\sim} E_{r+1}^{p,q}.$$

By induction on $s = k - r$, we define the R-submodules $Z_k(E_r^{p,q})$ and $B_k(E_r^{p,q})$ $(k \geq r+1)$ of $E_r^{p,q}$ as follows. When $s = 1$, they are already defined. Suppose they are defined up to $s - 1$. By means of the isomorphism $\alpha_r^{p,q}$, we can identify $E_{r+1}^{p,q}$ with an R-submodule of $E_r^{p,q}/B_{r+1}(E_r^{p,q})$. With the natural surjective homomorphism $\pi\colon E_r^{p,q} \to E_r^{p,q}/B_{r+1}(E_r^{p,q})$, we define $Z_k(E_r^{p,q}) := \pi^{-1}(Z_k(E_{r+1}^{p,q}))$ and $B_k(E_r^{p,q}) := \pi^{-1}(B_k(E_{r+1}^{p,q}))$. We set $B_r(E_r^{p,q}) = (0)$ and $Z_r(E_r^{p,q}) = E_r^{p,q}$. Then we have the following inclusion relations:

$$(0) = B_r(E_r^{p,q}) \subset B_{r+1}(E_r^{p,q}) \subset \cdots \subset B_k(E_r^{p,q}) \subset \cdots \subset Z_k(E_r^{p,q})$$
$$\subset \cdots \subset Z_{r+1}(E_r^{p,q}) \subset Z_r(E_r^{p,q}) = E_r^{p,q}.$$

Note here that $E_k^{p,q} \cong Z_k(E_r^{p,q})/B_k(E_r^{p,q})$ $(k \geq r)$.

(4) There exist R-submodules $B_\infty(E_2^{p,q})$ and $Z_\infty(E_2^{p,q})$ of $E_2^{p,q}$ such that

$$B_k(E_2^{p,q}) \subset B_\infty(E_2^{p,q}) \subset Z_\infty(E_2^{p,q}) \subset Z_k(E_2^{p,q}) \qquad (k \geq 2).$$

(5) E^n has a descending chain of R-submodules (called a *filtration*)

$$E^n \supset \cdots \supset F^p(E^n) \supset F^{p+1}(E^n) \supset \cdots$$

such that $\mathrm{gr}_p(E^n) \cong E_\infty^{p,q} := Z_\infty(E_2^{p,q})/B_\infty(E_2^{p,q})$ $(n = p+q)$, where $\mathrm{gr}_p(E^n) := F^p(E^n)/F^{p+1}(E^n)$.

We call $\{E^n\}_{n\in\mathbf{Z}}$ the *abutement* of E. We simply write the spectral sequence E as $E = \{E_r^{p,q}, E^n\}$.

A spectral sequence $E = \{E_r^{p,q}, E^n\}$ is called *biregular* if the following two conditions are satisfied:

(i) $Z_\infty(E_2^{p,q}) = Z_k(E_2^{p,q})$ and $B_\infty(E_2^{p,q}) = B_k(E_2^{p,q})$ for some $k \geq 3$.

(ii) For each n there exist integers $l(n)$ and $m(n)$ $(l(n) \geq m(n))$ such that $F^{l(n)}(E^n) = (0)$ and $F^{m(n)}(E^n) = E^n$.

In what follows, in order to simplify the situation, we only consider spectral sequences which are biregular and *lie in the first quadrant*. Namely, we consider a biregular spectral sequence $E = \{E_r^{p,q}, E^n\}$ such that $E_2^{p,q} = (0)$ whenever $p < 0$ or $q < 0$.

LEMMA 2.25. *Suppose a spectral sequence $E = \{E_r^{p,q}, E^n\}$ lies in the first quadrant. Then we have*:

(1) *If $r > p$, then $B_k(E_r^{p,q}) = (0)$ for each $k > r$. If $r > q+1$, then $E_r^{p,q} = Z_k(E_r^{p,q})$ for each $k > r$.*

(2) *If $p \leq 0$, then $F^p(E^n) = F^{p-1}(E^n) = \cdots$.*
If $p > n$, then $F^p(E^n) = F^{p+1}(E^n) = \cdots$.

PROOF. (1) The hypothesis that $E_2^{p,q} = (0)$ if $p < 0$ or $q < 0$ entails that $E_r^{p,q} = (0)$ for each $r \geq 2$ if $p < 0$ or $q < 0$. We shall prove the assertion (1) by induction on $s = k - r$. If $r > p$, then $B_{r+1}(E_r^{p,q}) = \operatorname{Im}(d_r^{p-r,q+r-1}) = (0)$ and $\pi\colon E_r^{p,q} \to E_r^{p,q}/B_{r+1}(E_r^{p,q})$ is the identity homomorphism. By the induction hypothesis, $B_k(E_r^{p,q}) = \pi^{-1}(B_k(E_{r+1}^{p,q})) = (0)$ for each $k > r+1$. If $r > q+1$, then $Z_{r+1}(E_r^{p,q}) = \operatorname{Ker}(d_r^{p,q})$ and $E_r^{p+r,q-r+1} = (0)$, whence $Z_{r+1}(E_r^{p,q}) = E_r^{p,q}$. For each $k > r+1$ the induction hypothesis entails $Z_k(E_r^{p,q}) = \pi^{-1}(Z_k(E_{r+1}^{p,q})) = \pi^{-1}(E_{r+1}^{p,q}) = E_r^{p,q}$ because π is the surjection from $E_r^{p,q}$ onto $E_{r+1}^{p,q}$.

(2) Suppose $p \leq 0$. We have $F^{p-1}(E^n)/F^p(E^n) \cong Z_\infty(E_2^{p-1,q})/B_\infty(E_2^{p-1,q})$ $(p+q = n+1)$, and $Z_\infty(E_2^{p-1,q})$ is an R-submodule of $E_2^{p-1,q}$. Since $p-1 < 0$, we see $E_2^{p-1,q} = (0)$ and, accordingly, $Z_\infty(E_2^{p-1,q})/B_\infty(E_2^{p-1,q}) = (0)$. Therefore, $F^{p-1}(E^n) = F^p(E^n)$. By a similar reasoning, we have $F^{p-1}(E^n) = F^{p-2}(E^n) = \cdots$. Suppose $p > n$. Then $F^p(E^n)/F^{p+1}(E^n) \cong Z_\infty(E_2^{p,q})/B_\infty(E_2^{p,q})(p+q = n)$, and $E_2^{p,q} = (0)$ since $q = n - p < 0$. By the same reasoning, $F^p(E^n) = F^{p+1}(E^n)$. Similarly, we have $F^{p+1}(E^n) = F^{p+2}(E^n) = \cdots$. □

LEMMA 2.26. *If a spectral sequence $E = \{E_r^{p,q}, E^n\}$ is biregular and lies in the first quadrant, then there exists an exact sequence*

$$0 \to E_2^{1,0} \xrightarrow{i_1} E^1 \xrightarrow{\pi_1} E_2^{0,1} \xrightarrow{d_2^{0,1}} E_2^{2,0} \xrightarrow{i_2} E^2,$$

where i_p stands for the natural homomorphism

$$E_2^{p,0} \to E_2^{p,0}/B_3(E_2^{p,0}) \cong E_3^{p,0} \to E_4^{p,0} \to \cdots$$
$$\to E_\infty^{p,0} \cong F^p(E^n) \hookrightarrow E^n = E^p,$$

and π_1 stands for the natural homomorphism

$$E^1 = F^0(E^1) \to F^0(E^1)/F^1(E^1) \cong E_\infty^{0,1} \cong Z_3(E_2^{0,1}) \hookrightarrow E_2^{0,1}.$$

PROOF. Since $E_2^{1,0} = E_3^{1,0} = \cdots = E_\infty^{1,0}$, i_1 is injective. Note that $F^{p+1}(E^p) = (0)$ by (2) of Lemma 2.25. By the definition of π_1, we have also $\operatorname{Ker}\pi_1 \cong E_2^{1,0}$, Similarly, by the definition of π_1, we have $\operatorname{Im}\pi_1 = \operatorname{Ker} d_2^{0,1}$. Since $E_3^{2,0} \cong E_4^{2,0} \cong E_\infty^{2,0}$, we have $\operatorname{Ker} i_2 \cong B_3(E_2^{2,0}) = \operatorname{Im} d_2^{0,1}$. □

LEMMA 2.27. *If a spectral sequence $E = \{E_r^{p,q}, E^n\}$ is biregular and lies in the first quadrant, we have*:

(1) *If $E_2^{p,q} = (0)$ for each $q > 0$, then $E_2^{p,0} \cong E^p$ for each $p \geq 0$.*

(2) *If $E_2^{p,q} = (0)$ for each $p > 0$, then $E_2^{0,q} \cong E^q$ for each $q \geq 0$.*

PROOF. (1) By the hypothesis, $E_r^{p,q} = (0)$ for each $q > 0$ and each $r \geq 2$. Hence, $E_\infty^{p,q} \cong F^p(E^{p+q})/F^{p+1}(E^{p+q}) = (0)$ for each $q > 0$. So $E^p = F^0(E^p) = \cdots = F^p(E^p) = E_\infty^{p,0}$. On the other hand, since $E_2^{p,0} \cong E_3^{p,0} \cong \cdots \cong E_\infty^{p,0}$, we have $E_2^{p,0} \cong E^p$. We can prove the assertion (2) in the same fashion. □

By $E_2^{p,q} \Rightarrow E^n$ we denote a spectral sequence $E = \{E_r^{p,q}, E^n\}$ which is biregular and lies in the first quadrant. This is because all the modules $E_r^{p,q}$ and $E_\infty^{p,q}$, except for the boundary operators $d_r^{p,q}$ and the filtration $\{F^p(E^n)\}$ of E^n, are determined by $E_2^{p,q}$. In Definition 2.24, we can consider a spectral sequence of $\mathscr{A}$-Modules over a ringed space $(X, \mathscr{A})$, where $E_r^{p,q}$ and $d_r^{p,q}$ are $\mathscr{A}$-Modules and $\mathscr{A}$-homomorphisms. Then Lemmas 2.25–2.27 hold as they are. In this book, we make use of the following two spectral sequences.

THEOREM 2.28. *Let $\Phi = (f, \varphi): (X, \mathscr{A}) \to (Y, \mathscr{B})$ be a morphism of ringed spaces, and let $\mathscr{F}$ be an $\mathscr{A}$-Module. Then there exists a spectral sequence*

$$E_2^{p,q} = H^p(Y, R^q f_*\mathscr{F}) \Rightarrow H^n(X, \mathscr{F})$$

which is biregular and lies in the first quadrant.

THEOREM 2.29. *Let $\Phi = (f, \varphi): (X, \mathscr{A}) \to (Y, \mathscr{B})$ and $\Psi = (g, \psi): (Y, \mathscr{B}) \to (Z, \mathscr{C})$ be morphisms of ringed spaces, and let $\mathscr{F}$ be an $\mathscr{A}$-Module. Then there exists a spectral sequence*

$$E_2^{p,q} = R^p g_*(R^q f_*\mathscr{F}) \Rightarrow R^n(gf)_*(\mathscr{F})$$

which is biregular and lies in the first quadrant.

The spectral sequences in Theorems 2.28 and 2.29 are called the *Leray spectral sequences*. In proving the existence of these spectral sequences, we use a more general theorem [2, Theorem 2.4.1] and the following simple fact:

> If $\mathscr{F}$ is a scattered $\mathscr{A}$-Module, then $f_*\mathscr{F}$ is a scattered $\mathscr{B}$-Module.

In the present book, we will not go into further details of the existence proof. Finally, we quote [2] as a general reference related to the contents of this chapter, which is now a fundamental reference concerning abelian categories and their applications. It is now appropriate to call this a classical reference. The readers are advised to have a look at it.

I.2. Problems

In what follows, $(X, \mathscr{A})$ is a ringed space.

1. For an exact sequence of $\mathscr{A}$-Modules

$$0 \to \mathscr{F} \to \mathscr{G} \to \mathscr{H} \to 0$$

verify the following assertions.

(1) If $\mathscr{F}$ is finitely generated and $\mathscr{G}$ is quasicoherent, the $\mathscr{H}$ is also quasicoherent.

(2) If $\mathscr{H}$ is finitely presented, i.e., for each $x \in X$ there exist an open neighborhood U, positive integers p, q, and an exact sequence of $\mathscr{A}_U$-Modules $(\mathscr{A}_U)^q \to (\mathscr{A}_U)^p \to \mathscr{H}_U \to 0$, and if $\mathscr{F}$ is quasicoherent, then $\mathscr{G}$ is also quasicoherent.

2. Find an example of a homomorphism of $\mathscr{A}$-Modules $\varphi: \mathscr{F} \to \mathscr{G}$ for which the presheaf $\mathscr{C}'$, as defined in Lemma 2.6, is not a sheaf. (If we use a result to be explained later, we can find the following easy example. Let C be a nonsingular

projective curve and let P, Q be points of C. Then we have an exact sequence of $\mathscr{O}_C$-Modules

$$0 \to \mathscr{O}_C(-P-Q) \to \mathscr{O}_C \to \mathscr{O}_P \oplus \mathscr{O}_Q \to 0$$

for which $\Gamma(C, \mathscr{O}_C(-P-Q)) = (0)$ and $\Gamma(C, \mathscr{O}_C) = k$ ($=$ the ground field) entail $\Gamma(C, \mathscr{C}') = k$ though ${}^a\mathscr{C}' = \mathscr{O}_P \oplus \mathscr{O}_Q$ and $\Gamma(C, {}^a\mathscr{C}') = k \oplus k$. Hence $\mathscr{C}' \neq {}^a\mathscr{C}'$.)

3. Find an example of $\mathscr{A}$-Modules $\mathscr{F}$, $\mathscr{G}$ for which the presheaf $\mathscr{P}$ defined by $\mathscr{P}(U) = \mathscr{F}(U) \otimes_{\mathscr{A}(U)} \mathscr{G}(U)$ is not a sheaf. (We find the following example again using the results to be explained later. Let P be a point on the projective line $C = \mathbf{P}^1$, let $\mathscr{F} = \mathscr{O}_C(-P)$, and let $\mathscr{G} = \mathscr{O}_C(P)$. Then $\mathscr{F} \otimes \mathscr{G} \cong \mathscr{O}_C$, though $\Gamma(C, \mathscr{P}) = \Gamma(C, \mathscr{O}_C(-P)) \otimes_k \Gamma(C, \mathscr{O}_C(P)) = (0) \otimes_k k = (0)$. Hence, $\mathscr{P} \neq {}^a\mathscr{P}$.)
4. Show that if $\mathscr{F}$ is a scattered $\mathscr{A}$-Module, then each term $\mathscr{C}^n(\mathfrak{U}, \mathscr{F})$ appearing in the Čech resolution of $\mathscr{F}$ is a scattered sheaf as well.
5. Verify the following assertions step by step.
   (1) For an $\mathscr{A}$-Module $\mathscr{F}$, define an $\mathscr{A}$-Module $\mathscr{S}(\mathscr{F})$ by $\mathscr{S}(\mathscr{F})(U) = \prod_{x \in U} \mathscr{F}_x$ and $\rho_{VU}\colon \prod_{x \in U} \mathscr{F}_x \to \prod_{x \in V} \mathscr{F}_x$ (the natural projection). Then $\mathscr{S}(\mathscr{F})$ is a scattered sheaf. Moreover, a homomorphism $\eta\colon \mathscr{F} \to \mathscr{S}(\mathscr{F})$ defined by $s \in \mathscr{F}(U) \mapsto \prod_{x \in U} s_x \in \mathscr{S}(\mathscr{F})(U)$ is injective.
   (2) We can define a scattered resolution of $\mathscr{F}$

$$S^\bullet(\mathscr{F})\colon 0 \to \mathscr{F} \xrightarrow{\eta} \mathscr{S}^0(\mathscr{F}) \xrightarrow{d^0} \mathscr{S}^1(\mathscr{F}) \xrightarrow{d^1} \cdots \xrightarrow{d^{n-1}} \mathscr{S}^n(\mathscr{F}) \xrightarrow{d^n} \cdots$$

   by $\mathscr{S}^0(\mathscr{F}) = \mathscr{S}(\mathscr{F})$, $\mathscr{S}^1(\mathscr{F}) = \mathscr{S}(\mathscr{S}^0(\mathscr{F})/\eta(\mathscr{F})), \ldots, \mathscr{S}^n(\mathscr{F}) = \mathscr{S}(\mathscr{S}^{n-1}(\mathscr{F})/d^{n-2}(\mathscr{S}^{n-2}(\mathscr{F}))), \ldots$. We call this the standard *scattered resolution.* This gives rise to a complex

$$0 \to \Gamma(X, \mathscr{S}^0(\mathscr{F})) \xrightarrow{d^0} \Gamma(X, \mathscr{S}^1(\mathscr{F})) \xrightarrow{d^1} \cdots \xrightarrow{d^{n-1}} \Gamma(X, \mathscr{S}^n(\mathscr{F})) \xrightarrow{d^n} \cdots.$$

   We denote by $\widetilde{H}^n(X, \mathscr{F})$ the cohomology group of this complex.
   (3) Let

$$0 \to \mathscr{F} \xrightarrow{\varepsilon} \mathscr{R}^0 \xrightarrow{\delta^0} \mathscr{R}^1 \xrightarrow{\delta^1} \cdots \xrightarrow{\delta^{n-1}} \mathscr{R}^n \xrightarrow{\delta^n} \cdots$$

   be an arbitrary scattered resolution of $\mathscr{F}$, i.e., an exact sequence such that each term except for $\mathscr{F}$ is a scattered $\mathscr{A}$-Module. Let $\widehat{H}^n(X, \mathscr{F})$ denote the cohomology group of the complex

$$0 \to \Gamma(X, \mathscr{R}^0) \xrightarrow{\delta^0} \Gamma(X, \mathscr{R}^1) \xrightarrow{\delta^1} \cdots \xrightarrow{\delta^{n-1}} \Gamma(X, \mathscr{R}^n) \xrightarrow{\delta^n} \cdots$$

   which the above scattered resolution of $\mathscr{F}$ gives rise to. Then we have $\widetilde{H}^n(X, \mathscr{F}) \cong \widehat{H}^n(X, \mathscr{F})$.

(Hint: We can define naturally the following commutative diagram:

$$
\begin{array}{ccccccccccc}
 & & 0 & & 0 & & & & 0 & & \\
 & & \downarrow & & \downarrow & & & & \downarrow & & \\
0 & \longrightarrow & \mathscr{F} & \xrightarrow{\varepsilon} & \mathscr{R}^0 & \xrightarrow{\delta^0} & \cdots & \xrightarrow{\delta^{n-1}} & \mathscr{R}^n & \xrightarrow{\delta^n} & \cdots \\
 & & \downarrow{\scriptstyle \eta} & & \downarrow{\scriptstyle \eta} & & & & \downarrow{\scriptstyle \eta} & & \\
0 & \longrightarrow & \mathscr{S}^0(\mathscr{F}) & \xrightarrow{\varepsilon} & \mathscr{S}^0(\mathscr{R}^0) & \xrightarrow{\delta^0} & \cdots & \xrightarrow{\delta^{n-1}} & \mathscr{S}^0(\mathscr{R}^n) & \xrightarrow{\delta^n} & \cdots \\
 & & \downarrow{\scriptstyle d^0} & & \downarrow{\scriptstyle d^0} & & & & \downarrow{\scriptstyle d^0} & & \\
0 & \longrightarrow & \mathscr{S}^1(\mathscr{F}) & \xrightarrow{\varepsilon} & \mathscr{S}^1(\mathscr{R}^0) & \xrightarrow{\delta^0} & \cdots & \xrightarrow{\delta^{n-1}} & \mathscr{S}^1(\mathscr{R}^n) & \xrightarrow{\delta^n} & \cdots \\
 & & \downarrow{\scriptstyle d^1} & & \downarrow{\scriptstyle d^1} & & & & \downarrow{\scriptstyle d^1} & & \\
 & & \vdots & & \vdots & & & & \vdots & & \\
 & & \downarrow{\scriptstyle d^{n-1}} & & \downarrow{\scriptstyle d^{n-1}} & & & & \downarrow{\scriptstyle d^{n-1}} & & \\
0 & \longrightarrow & \mathscr{S}^n(\mathscr{F}) & \xrightarrow{\varepsilon} & \mathscr{S}^n(\mathscr{R}^0) & \xrightarrow{\delta^0} & \cdots & \xrightarrow{\delta^{n-1}} & \mathscr{S}^n(\mathscr{R}^n) & \xrightarrow{\delta^n} & \cdots \\
 & & \downarrow{\scriptstyle d^n} & & \downarrow{\scriptstyle d^n} & & & & \downarrow{\scriptstyle d^n} & & \\
 & & \vdots & & \vdots & & & & \vdots & &
\end{array}
$$

where all rows and columns are exact sequences. Applying the functor $\Gamma(X,\cdot)$ to this diagram, we obtain a double complex as we did right before Lemma 2.21. Next by utilizing the arguments in (2) of Lemma 2.19 and Lemma 2.21, show that two cohomology groups $\widetilde{H}^n(X,\mathscr{F})$ and $\widehat{H}^n(X,\mathscr{F})$ coincide with each other.) $\{\widetilde{H}^n(x,\cdot)\}_{n\geq 0}$ is a cohomology functor on a ringed space $(X,\mathscr{A})$. By making use of (1) of Lemma 2.19, show that $\widetilde{H}^n(X,\cdot)\cong H^n(X,\cdot)$ for each $n\geq 0$.

(4) Every $\mathscr{A}$-Module $\mathscr{F}$ can be regarded as a $\mathbf{Z}$-Module, i.e., an abelian sheaf. Denote by $\{H^n_{\mathrm{ab}}(X,\cdot)\}_{n\geq 0}$ the cohomology functor on a ringed space $(X,\mathbf{Z}_X)$ defined by means of injective resolutions. Show that $H^n(X,\mathscr{F})\cong H^n_{\mathrm{ab}}(X,\mathscr{F})$ for an arbitrary $\mathscr{A}$-Module $\mathscr{F}$. (Hereafter we identify these cohomology groups.)

(5) (Hint: Note that a scattered $\mathscr{A}$-Module is a scattered $\mathbf{Z}$-Module. Using this remark, show that $H^n(X,\mathscr{F})\cong\widetilde{H}^n(X,\mathscr{F})\cong\widetilde{H}^n_{\mathrm{ab}}(X,\mathscr{F})\cong H^n_{\mathrm{ab}}(X,\mathscr{F})$. Here $\{\widetilde{H}^n_{\mathrm{ab}}(X,\cdot)\}_{n\geq 0}$ is the cohomology functor defined by means of resolutions by scattered $\mathbf{Z}$-Modules.)

6. Suppose for an $\mathscr{A}$-Module $\mathscr{F}$ there exists a closed set Y such that $\operatorname{Supp}\mathscr{F}:=\{x\in X;\mathscr{F}_x\neq(0)\}\subseteq Y$. Show then that $H^n_{\mathrm{ab}}(X,\mathscr{F})\cong H^n_{\mathrm{ab}}(Y,\mathscr{F}|_Y)$ for each $n\geq 0$.

Hereafter we assume that X is a noetherian space (cf. Definition II.1.5).

7. Let $\{\mathscr{F}_i; i\in I\}$ be an inductive system of $\mathscr{A}$-Modules (or abelian sheaves) indexed by a directed set I. Define a presheaf $\mathscr{P}$ by $\mathscr{P}(U)=\varinjlim_I\mathscr{F}_i(U)$. Show that $\mathscr{P}$ is an $\mathscr{A}$-Module (or an abelian sheaf). We denote $\mathscr{P}$ by $\varinjlim_I\mathscr{F}_i$ and call it the *limit* of the inductive system $\{\mathscr{F}_i; i\in I\}$. Show that if $\mathscr{F}_i$ is a scattered sheaf for

each $i \in I$, then $\varinjlim_I \mathscr{F}_i$ is a scattered sheaf. Show also that $H^n(X, \varinjlim_I \mathscr{F}_i) \cong \varinjlim_I H^n(X, \mathscr{F}_i)$ (for each $n \geq 0$).

(Hint: In order to prove the first assertion, prove and use the following result: A closed set and an open set of a noetherian space are also noetherian spaces. Let U be an open set of a noetherian space X, and let $\mathfrak{U} = \{U_\alpha\}_{\alpha \in A}$ be an open covering of U. Then there is a finite open covering of U consisting of finitely many members of $\mathfrak{U}$. In order to prove the last assertion, use the fact that $\varinjlim_I$ is an exact functor, i.e., the limit of exact sequences of abelian sheaves indexed by I is an exact sequence.)

8. If the Krull dimension of X (cf. II.3.5) equals n, then we have $H^i(X, \mathscr{F}) = (0)$ (all $i > n$) for any abelian sheaf $\mathscr{F}$. Verify this assertion by induction on n following the next steps one by one.
   (1) If $n = 0$, then X is a finite set with discrete topology. Then $H^i(X, \mathscr{F}) = (0)$ for each $i > 0$.
   (2) Let X be a decomposition of X into irreducible components. Let $\varphi_j : X_j \to X$ be the natural embedding for $1 \leq j \leq r$, and let $\mathscr{F}|_{X_j} = \varphi_j^* \mathscr{F}$ be the inverse image of $\mathscr{F}$ by φ_j. Since X_j is a closed set of X, we can extend $\mathscr{F}|_{X_j}$ to a sheaf $\mathscr{F}_j$ on X by setting $\mathscr{F}_j|_{X-X_j} = (0)$. Then there exists a natural injective homomorphism $\psi : \mathscr{F} \to \bigoplus_{j=1}^r \mathscr{F}_j$. Let $\mathscr{G} = \operatorname{Coker} \psi$. Then $\operatorname{Supp} \mathscr{G} \subseteq \bigcup_{j \neq k} X_j \cap X_k (:= Y)$. The Krull dimension of Y is less than n. By the induction hypothesis, $H^i(X, \bigoplus_{i=1}^r \mathscr{F}_j) = \bigoplus_{i=1}^r H^i(X_j, \mathscr{F}_j)$ for each $i > n$. Hence, it suffices to show that $H^i(X_j, \mathscr{F}_j) = (0)$ (for each $i > n$ and each j, $1 \leq j \leq r$). We may, therefore, assume that X is irreducible.
   (3) Let Y be a closed set of X, and let $U = X - Y$. Let $\mathbf{Z}_X$ be a constant sheaf with $(\mathbf{Z}_X)_x = \mathbf{Z}$ (for each $x \in X$), and let $\mathbf{Z}_Y$ denote, by the abuse of notation, the constant sheaf $\mathbf{Z}_Y$ on Y extended to X with $\mathbf{Z}_Y|_U = (0)$. We can define a natural surjective homomorphism $\pi : \mathbf{Z}_X \to \mathbf{Z}_Y$ as follows: Let V be an open set of X. If $V \cap Y \neq \emptyset$, then $\pi(V) = \mathrm{id}_{\mathbf{Z}}$ and if $V \cap Y = \emptyset$, then $\pi(V) = (0)$. Denote by $\mathbf{Z}_U$ the kernel of π. Then $\mathbf{Z}_U(V) = (0)$ if $V \cap Y \neq \emptyset$, and $\mathbf{Z}_U(V) = \mathbf{Z}$ if $V \cap Y = \emptyset$. For an element $s \in \mathscr{F}(U)$ define a homomorphism of abelian sheaves $\varphi_s : \mathbf{Z}_U \to \mathscr{F}$ by setting $\varphi_s(V) = (0)$ if $V \cap Y \neq \emptyset$ and $\varphi_s(V)(1) = \rho_{VU}(s)$ if $V \cap Y = \emptyset$. Let $\mathscr{F}_s = \varphi_s(\mathbf{Z}_U)$. Then $\mathscr{F}_s$ is a subsheaf of $\mathscr{F}$, and $\operatorname{Supp}(\operatorname{Ker} \varphi_s)$ is a proper closed subset of X provided $s \neq 0$. Furthermore, there exists a surjective homomorphism of abelian sheaves $p : \bigoplus_{j \in I} \mathbf{Z}_{U_j} \to \mathscr{F}$ for a suitable set I. Write $\mathscr{F}_j = p(\mathbf{Z}_{U_j})$. Then $\mathscr{F} = \bigcup_{j \in I} \mathscr{F}_j = \varinjlim_I \mathscr{F}_j$. So $H^i(X, \mathscr{F}) = \varinjlim_I H^i(X, \mathscr{F}_j)$. In order to show that $H^i(X, \mathscr{F}) = (0)$ for each $i > n$, it suffices to prove that $H^i(X, \mathbf{Z}_U) = (0)$ for each $i > n$.
   (4) Using the fact that $\mathbf{Z}_X$ is a scattered sheaf on X and using an exact sequence $0 \to \mathbf{Z}_U \to \mathbf{Z}_X \to \mathbf{Z}_Y \to 0$ $(Y := X - U)$, verify that $H^i(X, \mathbf{Z}_U) = (0)$ (for each $i > n$).
9. With the notations of Lemma I.2.9, verify by following the next steps that $R^p f_*(f^* \mathscr{E} \otimes \mathscr{F}) \cong \mathscr{E} \otimes R^p f_* \mathscr{F}$ $(p \geq 0)$ for an $\mathscr{A}$-Module $\mathscr{F}$ and a locally free $\mathscr{B}$-Module $\mathscr{E}$.
   (1) For a $\mathscr{B}$-Module $\mathscr{G}$, there exists a natural $\mathscr{B}$-homomorphism $\alpha : \mathscr{G} \otimes f_* \mathscr{F} \to f_*(f^* \mathscr{G} \otimes \mathscr{F})$ such that α is an isomorphism provided $\mathscr{G} = \mathscr{E}$.
   (Hint: First of all, show the existence of α by making use of Lemma

I.2.9. In the case $\mathscr{G} = \mathscr{E}$, $\alpha|_U$ is an isomorphism if U is an open set of Y such that $\mathscr{E}|_U$ is a free $\mathscr{B}|_U$-Module.)

(2) Let $0 \to \mathscr{F} \to \mathscr{I}^0 \to \mathscr{I}^1 \to \cdots$ be an injective resolution of $\mathscr{F}$. Then $0 \to f^*\mathscr{E} \otimes \mathscr{F} \to f^*\mathscr{E} \otimes \mathscr{I}^0 \to f^*\mathscr{E} \otimes \mathscr{I}_1 \to \cdots$ is an injective resolution of $f^*\mathscr{E} \otimes \mathscr{F}$.

(3) By making use of (1) and (2) above, show that $\mathscr{E} \otimes R^p f_*\mathscr{F} \cong R^p f_*(f^*\mathscr{E} \otimes \mathscr{F})$ for each $p \geq 0$.

Part II

Schemes and Algebraic Varieties

CHAPTER 3

Affine Schemes and Algebraic Varieties

This chapter is an introduction to more general concepts of schemes and algebraic varieties.

Let R be a commutative ring. We denote by $\mathrm{Spec}(R)$ the set of all prime ideals of R and call it an *affine scheme* defined by R (or with *coordinate ring* R). We read $\mathrm{Spec}(R)$ as *spectrum* (or *spec*, for short) of R. For a subset E of R, let $V(E) = \{\mathfrak{p} \in \mathrm{Spec}(R); E \subset \mathfrak{p}\}$, and let $D(E) = \mathrm{Spec}(R) - V(E)$. With the ideal $I(E) = \sum_{f \in E} Rf$ generated by E, clearly $V(E) = V(I(E))$ and $D(E) = D(I(E))$. If E is a set consisting of a single element $E = \{f\}$, then we write $V(\{f\}) = V(f)$ and $D(\{f\}) = D(f)$. Obviously, $V(1) = \emptyset$ and $V(0) = \mathrm{Spec}(R)$. Correspondingly, we have $D(1) = \mathrm{Spec}(R)$ and $D(0) = \emptyset$. We have then the following result.

LEMMA 3.1. (1) *For ideals I, J, I_λ $(\lambda \in \Lambda)$ of R, we have the relations below:*

(i) $V(I) \cup V(J) = V(I \cap J) = V(IJ)$, *where IJ is the ideal of R generated by $\{xy; x \in I, y \in J\}$.*

(ii) $\bigcap_{\lambda \in \Lambda} V(I_\lambda) = V(\sum_{\lambda \in \Lambda} I_\lambda)$, *where $\sum_{\lambda \in \Lambda} I_\lambda$ is the ideal of R generated by I_λ $(\lambda \in \Lambda)$.*

(iii) $V(0) = \mathrm{Spec}(R)$, $V(R) = \emptyset$.

(iv) $V(I) \subseteq V(J)$ *if and only if* $\sqrt{J} \subseteq \sqrt{I}$.

(2) *For the complement $D(I)$ of $V(I)$, we have the relations below:*

(i) $D(I) \cap D(J) = D(I \cap J) = D(IJ)$.

(ii) $\bigcup_{\lambda \in \Lambda} D(I_\lambda) = D(\sum_{\lambda \in \Lambda} I_\lambda)$.

(iii) $D(0) = \emptyset$, $D(R) = \mathrm{Spec}(R)$.

(iv) $D(I) = \bigcup_{f \in I} D(f)$.

(v) *For $\mathfrak{p} \in D(I)$, there is an element $f \in R$ such that $\mathfrak{p} \in D(f) \subseteq D(I)$.*

PROOF. (1) (i) Note that $V(J) \subseteq V(I)$ if $I \subseteq J$. Since $IJ \subseteq I \cap J \subseteq I$ (and also $\subseteq J$), $V(I) \cup V(J) \subseteq V(I \cap J) \subseteq V(IJ)$. If $\mathfrak{p} \in V(IJ)$, then $I \subseteq \mathfrak{p}$ or $J \subseteq \mathfrak{p}$. Hence, $V(IJ) \subseteq V(I) \cup V(J)$.

(ii) Since $I_\lambda \subseteq \sum_{\lambda \in \Lambda} I_\lambda$, $V(\sum_{\lambda \in \Lambda} I_\lambda) \subseteq \bigcap_{\lambda \in \Lambda} V(I_\lambda)$. If $\mathfrak{p} \in \bigcap_{\lambda \in \Lambda} V(I_\lambda)$, $\mathfrak{p} \supseteq I_\lambda$ for each $\lambda \in \Lambda$. Hence, $\mathfrak{p} \supseteq \sum_{\lambda \in \Lambda} I_\lambda$.

(iii) Obvious. (iv) follows from (I.1.24).

(2) (i), (ii), and (iii) are equivalent to (i), (ii) and (iii) of (1), respectively.

(iv) If $f \in I$, then $D(f) \subseteq D(I)$. Hence, $\bigcup_{f \in I} D(f) \subseteq D(I)$. If $\mathfrak{p} \not\supset I$, then $f \notin \mathfrak{p}$ for some $f \in I$. Hence, $\mathfrak{p} \in D(f)$. Namely, $D(I) \subseteq \bigcup_{f \in I} D(f)$.

(v) has been proved in (iv) above. □

DEFINITION 3.2. Lemmas 3.1 shows that $\mathrm{Spec}(R)$ admits a topology with $V(I)$ ($D(I)$, resp.) as a closed set (an open set, resp.) when I ranges over all ideals of R. With respect to this topology, $\{D(f); f \in R\}$ forms an open base. We call this topology the *Zariski topology*, and we consider hereafter that $\mathrm{Spec}(R)$ is given the Zariski topology.

The Zariski topology on $\mathrm{Spec}(R)$ is a T_0-topology, though it is not a T_1-topology. In fact, if $\mathfrak{p}_1, \mathfrak{p}_2 \in \mathrm{Spec}(R)$ satisfy $\mathfrak{p}_1 \subsetneqq \mathfrak{p}_2$ then any open neighborhood $D(I)$ of $\mathfrak{p}_2$ necessarily contains $\mathfrak{p}_1$.

DEFINITION 3.3. Let $\varphi\colon R \to S$ be a homomorphism of commutative rings, let $X = \mathrm{Spec}(R)$, and let $Y = \mathrm{Spec}(S)$. Define a mapping of sets $f\colon Y \to X$ by assigning $f(\mathfrak{q}) := \varphi^{-1}(\mathfrak{q})$ to $\mathfrak{q} \in Y$. We denote f by ${}^a\varphi$ and call it the *morphism of affine schemes* associated with φ.

Since $f^{-1}(V(I)) = V(\varphi(I))$, f is a continuous mapping with respect to the Zariski topology, where $\varphi(I) = \{\varphi(x); x \in I\}$. Furthermore, if $\varphi\colon R_1 \to R_2$ and $\psi\colon R_2 \to R_3$ are homomorphisms of commutative rings, then we have ${}^a(\psi \cdot \varphi) = {}^a\varphi \cdot {}^a\psi$.

LEMMA 3.4. (1) *Let I be an ideal of R, and let $\pi\colon R \to R/I$ be the natural residue homomorphism. Then the mapping ${}^a\pi\colon$ $\mathrm{Spec}(R/I) \to \mathrm{Spec}(R)$ gives rise to a homeomorphism between* $\mathrm{Spec}(R/I)$ *and the closed set $V(I)$ with the induced topology.*

(2) *Let S be a multiplicatively closed subset of R with $1 \in S$ and $0 \notin S$. Then* $\mathrm{Spec}(S^{-1}R) = \bigcap_{f \in S} D(f)$, *and the topology on $\bigcap_{f\in S} D(f)$ induced by the Zariski topology of* $\mathrm{Spec}(R)$ *coincides with the Zariski topology of* $\mathrm{Spec}(S^{-1}R)$.

PROOF. The correspondences of ideals given in the proof of (I.1.13) yield the correspondences of the same kind between prime ideals. It is straightforward to prove the assertions if this remark is taken into account. □

In order to describe topological properties of affine schemes, we have to prepare with some definitions concerning topological spaces.

DEFINITION 3.5. Let X be a topological space.

(1) A closed subset F of X is *reducible* if $F = F_1 \cup F_2$ for proper closed subsets F_1, F_2 of F. We call a closed subset F *irreducible* if it is not reducible. In particular, if F is irreducible, then $F = F_1 \cup F_2$ with closed subsets F_1, F_2 of F implies $F = F_1$ or $F = F_2$.

(2) X is called a *noetherian space* if given an arbitrary descending chain of closed subsets

$$X \supseteq X_0 \supseteq X_1 \supseteq \cdots \supseteq X_n \supseteq \cdots$$

there exists $N \geq 0$ such that $X_n = X_N$ (for each $n \geq N$).

(3) Let

$$Z_0 \subsetneqq Z_1 \subsetneqq \cdots \subsetneqq Z_r$$

be an ascending chain of irreducible closed subsets of X. We define the *length* of the sequence to be r. We define the *Krull dimension* of X to be the maximum of the length of ascending chains of irreducible subsets of the above kind, and denote it by $\dim X$. We could have $\dim X = \infty$.

(4) X is *quasicompact* if given an arbitrary open covering $\mathfrak{U} = \{U_i\}_{i\in I}$ of X, there exist finitely many members $U_{i_1}, \ldots, U_{i_n}$ of $\mathfrak{U}$ such that $X = U_{i_1} \cup U_{i_2} \cup \cdots \cup U_{i_n}$.

LEMMA 3.6. (1) *A closed set and an open set of a noetherian space are noetherian spaces with respect to the induced topologies.*

(2) *A noetherian space is quasicompact.*

(3) $X = \operatorname{Spec}(R)$ *is quasicompact though it is not necessarily a noetherian space.*

PROOF. (1) and (2) are apparent. We shall prove (3). Let $\{D(I_\lambda); \lambda \in \Lambda\}$ be an open covering of X. Then $\sum_{\lambda\in\Lambda} I_\lambda = R$ by Lemma 3.1. Hence, $1 = \sum_{i=1}^n a_i$ with $a_i \in I_{\lambda_i}$ and $\lambda_i \in \Lambda$. This implies that $D(a_i) \subseteq D(I_{\lambda_i})$ and $X = \bigcup_{i=1}^n D(a_i)$. Consequently $\bigcup_{i=1}^n D(I_{\lambda_i}) = X$. □

LEMMA 3.7. *Let $X = \operatorname{Spec}(R)$. Then we have*

(1) *For a closed subset $V(I)$ of X, $V(I)$ is irreducible if and only if $\sqrt{I}$ is a prime ideal.*

(2) *For $\mathfrak{p} \in X$, $V(\mathfrak{p}) = \overline{\{\mathfrak{p}\}}$, where $\overline{\{\mathfrak{p}\}}$ denotes the closure of the point $\mathfrak{p}$. We then say that $\mathfrak{p}$ is the* generic point *of the irreducible closed subset $V(\mathfrak{p})$.*

(3) *$\mathfrak{p} \in X$ is a closed point if and only if $\mathfrak{p}$ is a maximal ideal of R.*

PROOF. (1) We may assume $I = \sqrt{I}$. For the "only if" part, suppose $ab \in I$. Set $J = I + aR$ and $K = I + bR$. Then $JK \subseteq I$. Hence, $V(J) \cup V(K) = V(JK) \supseteq V(I)$, $V(J) \subseteq V(I)$, and $V(K) \subseteq V(I)$. So $V(I) = V(J) \cup V(K)$. Since $V(I)$ is irreducible, either $V(I) = V(J)$ or $V(I) = V(K)$. So $I = \sqrt{J}$ or $I = \sqrt{K}$. Hence, $a \in I$ or $b \in I$. Namely, I is a prime ideal. For the "If" part, suppose there exist ideals J, K such that $J \supseteq I$, $K \supseteq I$, and $V(I) = V(J) \cup V(K)$. Then $V(I) = V(JK)$, whence $JK \subseteq I$. Since I is a prime ideal, $J \subseteq I$ or $K \subseteq I$. So $J = I$ or $K = I$. Namely, $V(J) = V(I)$ or $V(K) = V(I)$. $V(I)$ is therefore irreducible.

(2) By the definition of the closure $\overline{\{\mathfrak{p}\}}$, we know $\overline{\{\mathfrak{p}\}} \subseteq V(\mathfrak{p})$. Moreover, if $\mathfrak{p} \in V(I)$, then $V(\mathfrak{p}) \subseteq V(I)$. Hence, $V(\mathfrak{p}) = \overline{\{\mathfrak{p}\}}$.

(3) $\overline{\{\mathfrak{p}\}} - \mathfrak{p} \neq \varnothing$ if and only if there exists some $\mathfrak{q} \in \operatorname{Spec}(R)$ with $\mathfrak{q} \supsetneqq \mathfrak{p}$. Hence, the assertion follows. □

COROLLARY 3.8. *For $X = \operatorname{Spec}(R)$, $\dim X = \operatorname{K-dim} R$ (see* (I.1.16) *for the definition of* $\operatorname{K-dim} R$).

PROOF. Since the set of irreducible closed subsets of X is in one-to-one correspondence with the set of prime ideals of R, an ascending chain of irreducible closed subsets of X corresponds bijectively to a descending chain of prime ideals of R. The result follows from this fact. □

Recall the one-to-one correspondence between the set of closed subsets of $X = \operatorname{Spec}(R)$ and the set of radical ideals of R (Lemma 1.7). This correspondence is inclusion-reversing. In particular, if R is a noetherian ring, then X is a noetherian space, though the converse does not necessarily hold (Problem II.3.1).

LEMMA 3.9. *A closed subset F of a noetherian space X is uniquely expressed as a finite union of irreducible closed subsets*

$$F = F_1 \cup \cdots \cup F_r, \qquad F_i : \text{ an irreducible closed subset of } F,$$

$$F \supsetneqq F_1 \cup \cdots \cup \check{F}_i \cup \cdots \cup F_r \qquad (\text{for each } i, 1 \le i \le r).$$

Each of $F_1, \dots, F_r$ appearing in the finite union is called an irreducible component of F. When R is a noetherian ring, $X = \operatorname{Spec}(R)$ and $F = V(I)$ with a radical ideal I, the decomposition of F into irreducible components corresponds to the prime divisor decomposition (I.1.23).

PROOF. Let $\mathfrak{S}$ be the set of closed subsets F of X which are not expressed as the finite unions of irreducible closed subsets. We shall show that the assumption $\mathfrak{S} \neq \emptyset$

leads to a contradiction. Introduce in $\mathfrak{S}$ a partial order $F \geq F'$ by $F \subseteq F'$. Since X is a noetherian space, $\mathfrak{S}$ is an inductively ordered set. Then by Zorn's lemma, there exists a maximal element, say F_0, in $\mathfrak{S}$. Since F_0 is an element of $\mathfrak{S}$, F_0 is not irreducible. Hence, F_0 is reducible, and F_0 is expressed as a union of closed subsets $F_0 = F_1 \cup F_2$ with $F_i \subsetneqq F_0$ $(i = 1, 2)$. Since F_0 is a maximal element of $\mathfrak{S}$, $F_i \notin \mathfrak{S}$ $(i = 1, 2)$. So F_i is expressed as a finite union of irreducible closed subsets: $F_i = F_{i1} \cup F_{i2} \cup \cdots \cup F_{ir_i}$ $(i = 1, 2)$. Then $F_0 = \bigcup_{i=1}^{2} \bigcup_{j=1}^{r_i} F_{ij}$, which is a finite union of irreducible closed subsets. This contradicts the choice of F_0. It follows that $\mathfrak{S} = \emptyset$.

Now let F be an arbitrary closed subset and express it as a finite union of irreducible closed subsets $F = F_1 \cup \cdots \cup F_r$, where no inclusion relations exist among $\{F_1, \ldots, F_r\}$; this is always possible. Suppose $F = G_1 \cup \cdots \cup G_s$ is another expression of F as a finite union of irreducible closed subsets among which there are no inclusion relations. Then we have

$$G_1 = (G_1 \cap F_1) \cup \cdots \cup (G_1 \cap F_r).$$

Since G_1 is irreducible, $G_1 = G_1 \cap F_i$ for some i. We may assume $i = 1$. Then $G_1 \subseteq F_1$. Apply the same argument to a decomposition

$$F_1 = (F_1 \cap G_1) \cup \cdots \cup (F_1 \cap G_s)$$

to obtain $F_1 \subseteq G_j$ (for some j). Then $G_1 \subseteq G_j$, whence $j = 1$. So $F_1 = G_1$. The above argument implies that $r = s$ and $G_i = F_{\sigma(i)}$ (for each $i, 1 \leq i \leq r$) for some permutation σ of $\{1, 2, \ldots, r\}$. Namely, we conclude that the way of expressing F as a finite union of irreducible closed subsets is unique.

When $X = \operatorname{Spec}(R)$, $F = V(I)$, and $I = \sqrt{I}$, then each irreducible component F_i is expressed as $V(\mathfrak{p}_i)$ with $\mathfrak{p}_i \in \operatorname{Spec}(R)$, and F being expressed as $F = F_1 \cup \cdots \cup F_r$ is equivalent to I being expressed as $I = \mathfrak{p}_1 \cap \cdots \cap \mathfrak{p}_r$. The last decomposition is nothing but the prime divisor decomposition of I. □

Let X be a noetherian space, and let Z be an irreducible closed subset of X. Then Z is also a noetherian space. Considering an ascending chain of irreducible closed subsets of X which passes through Z so that Z is one of the irreducible closed subsets in the ascending chain, we know that $\dim Z \leq \dim X$. If Z is reducible and $Z = Z_1 \cup \cdots \cup Z_r$ is the decomposition into irreducible components (the *irreducible decomposition*, for short), we have by definition that $\dim Z = \sup_{1 \leq i \leq r} \dim Z_i$ and $\dim Z_i \leq \dim X$ for each i. So $\dim Z \leq \dim X$ again. Suppose anew that Z is irreducible. Consider all possible ascending chains of irreducible closed subsets of X which start with Z,

$$Z = F_0 \subsetneqq F_1 \subsetneqq \cdots \subsetneqq F_s.$$

The maximum of the length s is called the *codimension* of Z in X and is denoted by $\operatorname{codim}_X Z$. If Z is reducible, we define $\operatorname{codim}_X Z = \inf_{1 \leq i \leq r} \operatorname{codim}_X Z_i$, where $Z = Z_1 \cup \cdots \cup Z_r$ is the irreducible decomposition.

When R is a noetherian ring, $X = \operatorname{Spec}(R)$, and $Z = V(I)$, then $\operatorname{codim}_X Z$ is equal to the height $\operatorname{ht}(I)$ of I (cf. (I.1.30)).

Our next purpose is to define a local ringed space structure on $\operatorname{Spec}(R)$. We need one more lemma.

LEMMA 3.10. *Let X be a topological space, and let $\{U_\alpha; \alpha \in A\}$ be an open base of X. Suppose a set (or an abelian group or a commutative ring, resp.) $\mathcal{P}(U_\alpha)$ is* *assigned to each* U_α $(\alpha \in A)$ *and the restriction morphism* $\rho_{\beta\alpha}\colon \mathscr{P}(U_\alpha) \to \mathscr{P}(U_\beta)$, *which is a mapping of sets (a homomorphism of abelian groups or commutative rings, resp.) is defined to every inclusion* $U_\beta \subseteq U_\alpha$ *in such a way that* $\rho_{\alpha\alpha} = \mathrm{id}_{\mathscr{P}(U_\alpha)}$ *and* $\rho_{\gamma\alpha} = \rho_{\gamma\beta} \cdot \rho_{\beta\alpha}$ *whenever* $U_\gamma \subseteq U_\beta \subseteq U_\alpha$. *Define* $\mathscr{P}_x = \varinjlim_{x \in U_\alpha} \mathscr{P}(U_\alpha)$ *for each* $x \in X$. *Then there exists uniquely a sheaf of sets (or abelian groups or commutative rings, resp.)* $\mathscr{F}$ *on* X *such that* $\mathscr{F}_x = \mathscr{P}_x$ *for each* $x \in X$.

PROOF. Set $\widetilde{\mathscr{P}} = \coprod_{x\in X} \mathscr{P}_x$. For each $\alpha \in A$ and each $s \in \mathscr{P}(U_\alpha)$, define a subset $V(\alpha, s)$ of $\widetilde{\mathscr{P}}$ by $\{s_x; x \in U_\alpha\}$, where s_x is the image of s in $\mathscr{P}_x$. Suppose $V(\alpha, s) \cap V(\beta, t) \neq \emptyset$. Then for $s_x (= t_x) \in V(\alpha, s) \cap V(\beta, t)$, there exist U_γ $(\gamma \in A)$ and $u \in \mathscr{P}(U_\gamma)$ such that $x \in U_\gamma \subseteq U_\alpha \cap U_\beta$ and $s_x \in V(\gamma, u) \subseteq V(\alpha, s) \cap V(\beta, t)$. Hence, we can define a topology on $\widetilde{\mathscr{P}}$ for which $\{V(\alpha, s); \alpha \in A, s \in \mathscr{P}(U_\alpha)\}$ is an open base. Define $\pi\colon \widetilde{\mathscr{P}} \to X$ by $\pi(s_x) = x$. Then $\widetilde{\mathscr{P}}$ and X are locally homeomorphic to each other under π. Now define $\mathscr{F}(U) = \{\sigma\colon U \to \widetilde{\mathscr{P}}; \sigma$ is a continuous mapping with $\pi \cdot \sigma = \mathrm{id}_U\}$ for any open set U of X and the restriction morphism $\rho_{VU}\colon \mathscr{F}(U) \to \mathscr{F}(V)$ in a natural fashion. Then $\mathscr{F}$ is a sheaf (cf. (I.2.5)). We shall show that $\mathscr{F}$ is uniquely determined. Let $\mathscr{G}$ be a sheaf as required in the statement. Then the sheafifying spaces $\widetilde{\mathscr{F}}$ and $\widetilde{\mathscr{G}}$ of $\mathscr{F}$ and $\mathscr{G}$ are homeomorphic to $\widetilde{\mathscr{P}}$. Hence, $\widetilde{\mathscr{F}}$ is homeomorphic to $\widetilde{\mathscr{G}}$. So $\mathscr{F}$ is isomorphic to $\mathscr{G}$ as sheaves. □

When we regard $X = \mathrm{Spec}(R)$ as a topological space, we denote its points by $x, y, \ldots$ and the corresponding prime ideals of R by $\mathfrak{p}_x, \mathfrak{p}_y, \ldots$. For $x \in X$, we denote by R_x the quotient ring $R_{\mathfrak{p}_x}$ of R with respect to a multiplicatively closed subset $R - \mathfrak{p}_x$.

Recall that $\{D(f); f \in R\}$ is an open base of $\mathrm{Spec}(R)$. To each $D(f)$ we assign a commutative ring $R_f = R[f^{-1}]$. We then have the following result.

LEMMA 3.11. (1) *If* $D(g) \subseteq D(f)$ *there is a natural ring homomorphism* $\rho_{gf}\colon R_f \to R_g$ *satisfying the conditions*

(i) $\rho_{ff} = \mathrm{id}_{R_f}$.

(ii) $\rho_{hf} = \rho_{hg} \cdot \rho_{gf}$ *provided* $D(h) \subseteq D(g) \subseteq D(f)$.

(2) *For each* $x \in X$, *let* $U_x = \{D(f); f \notin \mathfrak{p}_x\}$. *Then we have*

$$\varinjlim_{D(f)\in U_x} R_f = R_x.$$

PROOF. (1) We have the following equivalent conditions: $D(g) \subseteq D(f) \Leftrightarrow V(g) \supseteq V(f) \Leftrightarrow \sqrt{gR} \subseteq \sqrt{fR} \Leftrightarrow g^n = fa$ for some $n > 0$ and some $a \in R$. So define ρ_{gf} by $\rho_{gf}(c/f^r) = (ca^r)/g^{rn}$. Suppose $D(h) \subseteq D(g) \subseteq D(f)$. Then $g^n = fa$ and $h^m = gb$ for some $n, m > 0$ and some $a, b \in R$. According to the definition, we have $\rho_{hf}(c/f^r) = ca^r b^{rn}/h^{rmn}$ and $\rho_{hg} \cdot \rho_{gf}(c/f^r) = \rho_{hg}((ca^r)/g^{rn}) = ((ca^r)b^{rn})/h^{rmn}$. So $\rho_{hf} = \rho_{hg} \cdot \rho_{gf}$.

(2) If $D(f) \in U_x$, define a ring homomorphism $\psi_f\colon R_f \to R_x$ naturally by $\psi_f(c/f^r) = c/f^r$. If $x \in D(g) \subseteq D(f)$, we have $\psi_f = \psi_g \cdot \rho_{gf}$. Hence, there exists a ring homomorphism $\psi\colon \varinjlim_{D(f)\in U_x} R_f \to R_x$ such that $\psi_f = \psi \cdot \eta_f$, where $\eta_f\colon R_f \to \varinjlim_{D(f)\in U_x} R_f$ is the natural ring homomorphism associated with the inductive limit. Here ψ is surjective because any element of R_x is expressed as a/f with $a, f \in R$ and $f \notin \mathfrak{p}_x$. Take an element of $\varinjlim_{D(f)\in U_x} R_f$ which is represented by an element c/f^r of R_f. Suppose $\psi(c/f^r) = c/f^r = 0$. Then $cg = 0$ for some

$g \notin \mathfrak{p}_x$. Therefore, $\rho_{gf,f}(c/f^r) = (cg^r)/(gf)^r = 0$. So ψ is injective. Hence, ψ is an isomorphism. □

By virtue of Lemmas 3.10 and 3.11 there exists a sheaf of commutative rings $\widetilde{R}$ on X such that $\widetilde{R}_x = R_x$ for each $x \in X$. Since R_x is a local ring, $(X, \widetilde{R})$ is a local ringed space. We call $\widetilde{R}$ the *structure sheaf* and denote it by $\mathcal{O}_X$.

Let M be an R-module. By assigning an R_f-module $M_f := M \otimes_R R_f$ to $D(f)$, we can define by Lemma 3.10 an $\mathcal{O}_X$-Module $\widetilde{M}$ such that $\widetilde{M}_x = M \otimes_R R_x$ for each $x \in X$. Given an R-homomorphism $v: M \to N$, we assign an R_f-homomorphism $v_f: M_f \to N_f$ to $D(f)$ defined by $v_f(x/f^r) = v(x)/f^r$. Hence, we obtain a homomorphism of $\mathcal{O}_X$-Modules $\tilde{v}: \widetilde{M} \to \widetilde{N}$. To an exact sequence of R-modules

(1) $$0 \to L \xrightarrow{u} M \xrightarrow{v} N \to 0$$

there corresponds an exact sequence of $\mathcal{O}_X$-Modules

(2) $$0 \to \widetilde{L} \xrightarrow{\tilde{u}} \widetilde{M} \xrightarrow{\tilde{v}} \widetilde{N} \to 0.$$

In fact, the sequence of stalks at $x \in X$

(3) $$0 \to \widetilde{L}_x \xrightarrow{\tilde{u}_x} \widetilde{M}_x \xrightarrow{\tilde{v}_x} \widetilde{N}_x \to 0$$

is nothing but an exact sequence of R_x-modules

(4) $$0 \to L_x \xrightarrow{u_x} M_x \xrightarrow{v_x} N_x \to 0,$$

where we write $L_x = L \otimes_R R_x$, $u_x = u \otimes_R R_x$, etc. Since the functor $(\cdot) \otimes_R R_x$ is an exact functor, i.e., a functor sending an exact sequence to an exact sequence, we know the sequence (4) is exact. Hence, the sequence (3) is an exact sequence. This implies that the sequence (2) is an exact sequence.

An arbitrary R-module M is a holomorphic image of a free R-module. Namely, there exists a surjective homomorphism $\varphi: R^I \to M$. For example, we take as I the underlying set of M and, with a free basis $\{e_m; m \in M\}$ of R^M, define φ by $\varphi(e_m) = m$. Hence, we have an exact sequence

$$R^J \xrightarrow{\psi} R^I \xrightarrow{\varphi} M \to 0.$$

By the above remark, we obtain an exact sequence of $\mathcal{O}_X$-Modules

$$\mathcal{O}_X^J \xrightarrow{\tilde{\psi}} \mathcal{O}_X^I \xrightarrow{\tilde{\varphi}} \widetilde{M} \to 0.$$

Therefore $\widetilde{M}$ is a quasicoherent $\mathcal{O}_X$-Module. We shall prove the following basic results on $\mathcal{O}_X$-Modules over an affine scheme X.

THEOREM 3.12. *Let $(X, \mathcal{O}_X)$ be an affine scheme defined by a commutative ring R. Then we have*:

(1) *For an R-module M and $f \in R$, $\widetilde{M}(D(f)) = M_f$. In particular, $\widetilde{M}(X) = \widetilde{M}(D(1)) = M$ and $\mathcal{O}_X(X) = R$.*

(2) *For R-modules M and N, the correspondence $u \mapsto \tilde{u}$ gives rise to an isomorphism* $\mathrm{Hom}_R(M, N) \cong \mathrm{Hom}_{\mathcal{O}_X}(\widetilde{M}, \widetilde{N})$.

(3) *For an R-module M, $\widetilde{M}$ is a quasicoherent $\mathcal{O}_X$-Module. Conversely, an arbitrary quasicoherent $\mathcal{O}_X$-Module is isomorphic to an $\mathcal{O}_X$-Module $\widetilde{M}$ for an R-module M. Namely, the category of R-modules and the category of quasicoherent $\mathcal{O}_X$-Modules are equivalent to each other.*

(4) *Suppose R is a noetherian ring. Then for a quasicoherent $\mathcal{O}_X$-Module $\mathcal{F}$, $\mathcal{F}$ is coherent if and only if the R-module $M = \mathcal{F}(X)$ is finitely generated. In particular, $\mathcal{O}_X$ is a coherent $\mathcal{O}_X$-Module.*

(5) *For R-modules M and N, $\widetilde{M} \otimes_{\mathcal{O}_X} \widetilde{N} \cong (M \otimes_R N)^{\sim}$. Furthermore, if M is finitely presented, $\mathcal{H}om_{\mathcal{O}_X}(\widetilde{M}, \widetilde{N}) \cong \mathrm{Hom}_R(M, N)^{\sim}$.*

Proof. (1) Suppose $D(g) \subseteq D(f)$. Then since $g^n = fa$ for some $n > 0$ and some $a \in R$, we have $M_g = (M_f)_g$. So $\widetilde{M}|_{D(f)} \cong \widetilde{(M_f)}$. Moreover, $D(f) = \mathrm{Spec}\, R_f$. Hence, in order to show $\widetilde{M}(D(f)) = M_f$, we may assume $f = 1$ by replacing R and M by R_f and M_f, respectively. By the construction of $\widetilde{M}$ in Lemma 3.10, there exists a natural isomorphism $\varphi\colon M \to \widetilde{M}(X)$. We have only to show that φ is an isomorphism.

(i) *Injectivity of φ*. Suppose $\varphi(z) = 0$ for $z \in M$, i.e., $z_x = 0$ for each $x \in X$. So for each $x \in X$, we have $f_x z = 0$ for some $f_x \notin \mathfrak{p}_x$. Let $\mathfrak{a} = \mathrm{Ann}_R(z) := \{a \in R; az = 0\}$. Then $\mathfrak{a}$ is an ideal of R and $\mathfrak{a} = R$ if and only if $z = 0$. Suppose $z \neq 0$. Then $\mathfrak{p}_y \supseteq \mathfrak{a}$ for some $\mathfrak{p}_y \in \mathrm{Spec}(R)$. Meanwhile, $f_y \in \mathfrak{a}$ and $f_y \notin \mathfrak{p}_y$. This is absurd. So $z = 0$.

(ii) *Surjectivity of φ*. Let $\xi \in \widetilde{M}(X)$. For each $x \in X$, we can express $\xi = z/f_x$ with $z \in M$ and $f_x \notin \mathfrak{p}_x$ because $\widetilde{M}_x = M_x$. Apparently, $\bigcup_{x\in X} D(f_x) = X$. Since X is quasicompact, there is a finite open covering $\bigcup_{i\in I} D(f_i) = X$ (I is a finite set) such that $\xi|_{D(f_i)} = z_i \in M_{f_i}$ for each $i \in I$. For each $i, j \in I$, we have $D(f_i) \cap D(f_j) = D(f_i f_j)$ and a natural homomorphism $\varphi_{ij}\colon M_{f_i f_j} \to \widetilde{M}(D(f_i f_j))$. With $z_i - z_j$ as an element of $M_{f_i f_j}$, $\varphi_{ij}(z_i - z_j) = \xi|_{D(f_i f_j)} - \xi|_{D(f_i f_j)} = 0$. By the injectivity of φ_{ij} as we have shown above, $z_i = z_j$ as elements of $M_{f_i f_j}$. Here write $z_i = m_i/f_i^n$ with $m_i \in M$, where we can take n independently of $i \in I$; this is possible because I is a finite set. For each $i, j \in I$, we have $(f_i f_j)^{r_{ij}}(f_j^n m_i - f_i^n m_j) = 0$, where we may take $r_{ij} = r$ (a constant independent of $i, j \in I$). Replacing then m_i by $f_i^r m_i$ and f_i^n by f_i^{n+r}, we may assume $r = 0$. So we have $f_j^n m_i = f_i^n m_j$ for each $i, j \in I$. On the other hand, since $\bigcup_{i\in I} D(f_i) = X$, we have $\sum_{i\in I} f_i R = R$. Hence, $\sum_{i\in I} f_i^n R = R$. So $\sum_{i\in I} f_i^n g_i = 1$ for $g_i \in R$ ($i \in I$). Let $m = \sum_{j\in I} g_j m_j$. Then for each $i \in I$, we have

$$f_i^n m = \sum_{j\in I} f_i^n g_j m_j = \left(\sum_{j\in I} g_j f_j^n\right) m_i = m_i.$$

Therefore, $\xi|_{D(f_i)} = \varphi(m)|_{D(f_i)}$ for each $i \in I$. Since $\widetilde{M}$ is a sheaf, we have $\xi = \varphi(m)$. Therefore, φ is surjective.

(2) Define two mappings

$$\mathrm{Hom}_R(M, N) \underset{\Psi}{\overset{\Phi}{\rightleftarrows}} \mathrm{Hom}_{\mathcal{O}_X}(\widetilde{M}, \widetilde{N})$$

by $\Phi(u) = \tilde{u}$ and $\Psi(\alpha) = \alpha(X)$. By (1) above, $\alpha(X)$ is an R-homomorphism from M to N. It is apparent that $\Psi \cdot \Phi$ is the identity morphism. In order to show that $\Phi \cdot \Psi(\alpha) = \alpha$, we have only to show it on all stalks. For the stalks, we have $\Phi \cdot \Psi(\alpha)_x = \Psi(\alpha) \otimes_R R_x = \alpha(X) \otimes_R R_x = \alpha_x$ because $\widetilde{M}_x = \widetilde{M}(X) \otimes_R R_x$.

(3) With (1) and (2) above taken into account, we have only to prove that $\mathcal{F} \cong \widetilde{\mathcal{F}(X)}$ for any quasicoherent $\mathcal{O}_X$-Module $\mathcal{F}$. Since $\mathcal{F}$ is quasicoherent, for each

$x \in X$ there exist an open neighborhood $D(f)$ of x and an exact sequence

$$(\mathcal{O}_X|_{D(f)})^J \xrightarrow{\psi} (\mathcal{O}_X|_{D(f)})^I \xrightarrow{\varphi} \mathcal{F}|_{D(f)} \to 0.$$

Noting that $\mathcal{O}_X|_{D(f)} \cong \widetilde{R_f}$, we let $M(f)$ be the cokernel of $\psi(D(f))\colon (R_f)^J \to (R_f)^I$. Then $\mathcal{F}|_{D(f)} \cong \widetilde{M(f)}$. Hence, $\mathcal{F}(D(f)) \cong M(f)$. Since X is quasicompact, there exist a finite open covering $\bigcup_{i \in I} D(f_i) = X$ and an R_{f_i}-module M_i $(i \in I)$ such that $\mathcal{F}|_{D(f_i)} \cong \widetilde{M_i}$. Putting $M = \mathcal{F}(X)$, we shall show that $M_i \cong M_{f_i}$ for each $i \in I$. Since there is a natural homomorphism $\alpha\colon \widetilde{M} \to \mathcal{F}$, we have a natural homomorphism of R_{f_i}-modules $u_i := \alpha(D(f_i))\colon M_{f_i} \to M_i$. We show that u_i is an isomorphism.

Injectivity of u_i. Suppose $u_i(s) = 0$ for $s \in M$, i.e., $s_x = 0$ for each $x \in D(f_i)$. Then $s_x = 0$ for each $j \in I$ and each $x \in D(f_i) \cap D(f_j) = D(f_i f_j)$. Since $\mathcal{F}_{D(f_i f_j)} = (\mathcal{F}|_{D(f_j)})|_{D(f_i f_j)} \cong \widetilde{M}_j|_{D(f_i f_j)} = ((M_j)_{f_i f_j})^{\sim}$, $(f_i f_j)^{n_{ij}} s = 0$ as an element of $M_j = \mathcal{F}(D(f_j))$ for some $n_{ij} > 0$. Since I is a finite set, we may assume $n_{ij} = n$ (= a constant). Moreover, since $(f_j)^{-1} \in \mathcal{O}_X(D(f_j))$, $f_i^n s = 0$ as an element of $\mathcal{F}(D(f_j))$. This holds for each $j \in I$. Hence, $f_i^n s = 0$ as an element of $M = \mathcal{F}(X)$. So $s/1 = 0$ as an element of M_{f_i}.

Surjectivity of u_i. Let $z_i \in M_i$. Since $z_i|_{D(f_i f_j)} \in \mathcal{F}(D(f_i f_j)) = (M_j)_{f_i f_j}$, $(f_i f_j)^{n_{ij}} z_i \in M_j$ for some $n_{ij} > 0$. Since $(f_j)^{-1} \in \mathcal{O}_X(D(f_j))$, $f_i^{n_{ij}} z_i \in M_j$. Take an integer n so that $n \geq \sup_j(n_{ij})$. Then $f_i^n z_i \in M_j$ for each $j \in I$. Let $z = f_i^n z_i$. Then $z \in M$. So $z_i = z/f_i^n$. This shows that u_i is surjective.

By virtue of the isomorphism u_i, we know that $\widetilde{M}|_{D(f_i)} \cong \mathcal{F}|_{D(f_i)}$ for each $i \in I$. Hence, α is an isomorphism of sheaves.

(4) Let $\mathcal{F}$ be a finitely generated, quasi-coherent $\mathcal{O}_X$-Module and let $M = \mathcal{F}(X)$. Then there exists a finite open covering $X = \bigcup_{i \in I} D(f_i)$ such that M_{f_i} is a finitely generated R_{f_i}-module. Let $\{z_{i\lambda}; \lambda \in \Lambda_i\}$ be a system of generators of M_{f_i}. Since $f_i^{n_{i\lambda}} z_{i\lambda} \in M$ for some $n_{i\lambda} > 0$, we may assume $z_{i\lambda} \in M$ for each $i \in I, \lambda \in \Lambda_i$. We shall then show that $\{z_{i\lambda}; i \in I, \lambda \in \Lambda_i\}$ is a system of generators of M. Take an arbitrary element $m \in M$. Then $m|_{D(f_i)} = \sum_{\lambda \in \Lambda_i} (a_{i\lambda}/f_i^{r_{i\lambda}}) z_{i\lambda}$. Hence, with $r \gg \sup_\lambda(r_{i\lambda})$, we may assume that $f_i^r m = \sum_{\lambda \in \Lambda_i} a'_{i\lambda} z_{i\lambda}$ as elements of M, where $a'_{i\lambda} \in R$. Since $X = \bigcup_{i \in I} D(f_i^r)$, we have $\sum_{i \in I} f_i^r g_i = 1$ with $g_i \in R$. So $m = \sum_{i \in I} f_i^r g_i m = \sum_{i \in I} \sum_{\lambda \in \Lambda_i} a'_{i\lambda} g_i z_{i\lambda}$. It follows that M is a finitely generated R-module.

Suppose R is a noetherian ring and M is a finitely generated R-module. Given an open set U and an $\mathcal{O}_U$-homomorphism $\varphi\colon (\mathcal{O}_U)^n \to \mathcal{F}|U$, we shall show that $\operatorname{Ker}\varphi$ is finitely generated. For this, it is sufficient to show that $(\operatorname{Ker}\varphi)|_{D(f)}$ is finitely generated for each $x \in U$ and an open neighborhood $D(f)$ of x with $D(f) \subseteq U$. Let N be the kernel of $\varphi(D(f))\colon (R_f)^n \to M_f$. Then $(\operatorname{Ker}\varphi)|_{D(f)} \cong \widetilde{N}$. Since $R_f = R[f^{-1}]$ is a noetherian ring (I.1.14), N is a finitely generated R_f-module. Hence, by the first half of the proof, $(\operatorname{Ker}\varphi)|_{D(f)}$ is a finitely generated $\mathcal{O}_{D(f)}$-Module. It should be clear that $\mathcal{F}$ itself is a finitely generated $\mathcal{O}_X$-Module. So $\mathcal{F}$ is coherent.

(5) $\widetilde{M} \otimes_{\mathcal{O}_X} \widetilde{N}$ is the sheafification of a presheaf $U \mapsto \widetilde{M}(U) \otimes_{\mathcal{O}_X(U)} \widetilde{N}(U)$. If $U = D(f)$, this correspondence is given by $D(f) \mapsto M_f \otimes_{R_f} N_f \cong (M \otimes_R N)_f$. Hence, $\widetilde{M} \otimes_{\mathcal{O}_X} \widetilde{N} \cong (M \otimes_R N)^{\sim}$ by Lemma 1.10. Next we have

$$\begin{aligned}\mathcal{H}om_{\mathcal{O}_X}(\widetilde{M}, \widetilde{N})(D(f)) &= \operatorname{Hom}_{\mathcal{O}_{D(f)}}(\widetilde{M}|_{D(f)}, \widetilde{N}|_{D(f)}) \cong \operatorname{Hom}_{R_f}(M_f, N_f) \\ &\cong \operatorname{Hom}_R(M, N \otimes_R R_f).\end{aligned}$$

By the hypothesis on M, there is an exact sequence

$$R^s \xrightarrow{u} R^t \xrightarrow{v} M \to 0$$

which entails, by an easy diagram chase,

$$\begin{aligned} &\operatorname{Hom}_R(M, N \otimes_R R_f) \\ &\quad\cong \operatorname{Ker}(\operatorname{Hom}_R(R^t, N \otimes_R R_f) \xrightarrow{u^*} \operatorname{Hom}_R(R^s, N \otimes_R R_f)) \\ &\quad\cong \operatorname{Ker}(\operatorname{Hom}_R(R^t, N) \otimes_R R_f \xrightarrow{u^*} \operatorname{Hom}_R(R^s, N) \otimes_R R_f) \\ &\quad\cong \operatorname{Hom}_R(M, N) \otimes_R R_f. \end{aligned}$$

Therefore, we have $\mathscr{H}om_{\mathscr{O}_X}(\widetilde{M}, \widetilde{N}) \cong \operatorname{Hom}_R(M, N)^\sim$ by Lemma 3.10. □

Following [4], we shall prove the next result.

Lemma 3.13. *Let R be a noetherian ring and let $X = \operatorname{Spec}(R)$. If I is an injective R-module, then the associated $\mathscr{O}_X$-Module $\widetilde{I}$ is a scattered sheaf.*

Proof. Let $\mathscr{I} = \widetilde{I}$. We shall show that the restriction morphism $\mathscr{I}(X) \to \mathscr{I}(U)$ is surjective for any open set U. We note that since X is a noetherian space U is also a noetherian space and U is, therefore, quasicompact (cf. Lemma 3.6). First of all, taking $D(f)(\neq \emptyset)$ contained in U, we show that the restriction morphism $\mathscr{I}(X) \to \mathscr{I}(D(f))$ is surjective, i.e., the natural homomorphism $I \to I_f$ is surjective. Let $\mathfrak{a} = \{a \in R; f^n a = 0 \text{ for some } n > 0\}$. Then $\mathfrak{a}$ is an ideal of R, and $\mathfrak{a} = R$ if and only if $f^n = 0$ (for some $n > 0$) which is equivalent to $D(f) = \emptyset$. Since $D(f) \neq \emptyset$ by the assumption, $\mathfrak{a} \neq R$. Since R is a noetherian ring, $\mathfrak{a}$ is a finitely generated ideal. Hence, $f^N \mathfrak{a} = (0)$ for some $N > 0$. Now let x/f^r ($x \in I$) be an arbitrary element of I_f and let $x' = f^N x$. Define an R-homomorphism $\varphi \colon R \to I$ by $\varphi(1) = x'$. We also let $\alpha \colon R \to R$ be the multiplication by f^{r+N}; $\alpha(a) = f^{r+N} a$. Then we have the implications: $\alpha(a) = 0 \Rightarrow f^{r+N} a = 0 \Rightarrow a \in \mathfrak{a} \Rightarrow f^N a = 0 \Rightarrow \varphi(a) = a x' = f^N a x = 0$. Hence, we obtain the following commutative diagram

$$\begin{array}{ccccc} 0 & \longrightarrow & \alpha(R) & \xrightarrow{\alpha'} & R \\ & & \downarrow{\scriptstyle \varphi'} & \swarrow{\scriptstyle \psi} & \\ & & I & & \end{array}$$

where φ' and α' are the homomorphisms induced naturally by φ and α, respectively. Since I is injective, there exists an R-homomorphism $\psi \colon R \to I$ such that $\varphi' = \psi \cdot \alpha'$. Hence, putting $\psi(1) = y$, we have $x' = f^{r+N} y$. Namely, $x/f^r = x'/f^{r+N} = y/1$.

Here let $\operatorname{Supp}(\mathscr{I}) = \{x \in X; \mathscr{I}_x \neq (0)\}$ and let $Y_0 = \overline{\operatorname{Supp}(\mathscr{I})}$. [If $\mathscr{I}$ is not finitely generated, $\operatorname{Supp}(\mathscr{I})$ is not necessarily a closed set (cf. problem II.3.2).] Now let $\xi \in \mathscr{I}(U)$. We shall show that $\xi = z_0|_U$ for some $z_0 \in \mathscr{I}(X)$. We may assume $\xi \neq 0$. Hence, $Y_0 \cap U \neq \emptyset$. Take an open set $D(f)$ so that $D(f) \subset U$ and $D(f) \cap Y_0 \neq \emptyset$. By virtue of the first remark, $(\xi - z_1|_U)_{D(f)} = 0$ for some $z_1 \in \mathscr{I}(X)$. Since U is quasicompact, $f^n(\xi - z_1|_U) = 0$ (for some $n > 0$) by the reasoning we employed in the proof of (3) of Theorem 3.12 (the injectivity of u_i). We define an R-submodule I_1 of I by $I_1 = \{w \in I; f^n w = 0 \text{ for some } n > 0\}$. Then I_1 is an injective R-module by Lemma 3.13.1 below. Let $\mathscr{I}_1 = \widetilde{I_1}$ and $Y_1 = \overline{\operatorname{Supp}(\mathscr{I}_1)}$. Then $Y_1 \subsetneqq Y_0$. In fact, $Y_1 \subseteq Y_0$ obviously, and $Y_1 \cap D(f) = \emptyset$, and $Y_0 \cap D(f) \neq \emptyset$. Meanwhile,

$\xi - z_1|_U \in \mathscr{I}_1(U)$. If $\xi - z_1|_U \neq 0$, take an open set $D(f_1)$ so that $D(f_1) \subset U$ and $D(f_1) \cap Y_1 \neq \emptyset$. Then $(\xi - (z_1 + z_2)|_U)|_{D(f_1)} = 0$ for some $z_2 \in I_1 = \mathscr{I}_1(X)$. Let $I_2 = \{w \in I_1; f_1^n w = 0 \text{ for some } n > 0\}$, $\mathscr{I}_2 = \widetilde{I_2}$, and $Y_2 = \overline{\operatorname{Supp}(\mathscr{I}_2)}$. Then $Y_2 \subsetneqq Y_1 \subsetneqq Y_0$. Since X is a noetherian space, this process terminates at finitely many steps. Therefore, $\xi = z|_U$ for some $z \in I$. □

LEMMA 3.13.1. *Let R be a noetherian ring, and let $\mathfrak{a}$ be its ideal. Let I be an injective R-module, and let $J = \{w \in I; \mathfrak{a}^n w = 0$ for some $n > 0\}$. Then J is an injective R-module, too.*

PROOF. (1) First of all, note the following result:

Let I be an R-module. Then I is an injective R-module if and only if the natural R-homomorphism $\operatorname{Hom}_R(R, I) \to \operatorname{Hom}_R(\mathfrak{b}, I)$ is surjective for every ideal $\mathfrak{b}$ of R.

The *only if* part is clear. So we shall prove the *if* part. Let N be an R-module, and let M be a submodule. It suffices to show that any R-homomorphism $\varphi: M \to I$ extends to an R-homomorphism $\psi: N \to I$. Let $\mathfrak{S} = \{(M', \varphi'); M \subseteq M' \subseteq N, \varphi'|_M = \varphi\}$ and define in $\mathfrak{S}$ a partial order $(M'', \varphi'') \geq (M', \varphi')$ if $M'' \supseteq M'$ and $\varphi''|_{M'} = \varphi'$. Then $\mathfrak{S}$ is an inductively ordered set. Let (L, ρ) be a maximal element of $\mathfrak{S}$. If $L \neq N$, take $z \in N - L$ and put $\mathfrak{b} = \{a \in R; az \in L\}$. Define an R-homomorphism $\alpha: \mathfrak{b} \to I$ by $\alpha(a) = \rho(az)$ for each $a \in \mathfrak{b}$. Then by the assumption, there exists an R-homomorphism $\beta: R \to I$ such that $\alpha = \beta|_{\mathfrak{b}}$. Now define $\rho': L + Rz \to I$ by $\rho'(\ell + az) = \rho(\ell) + \beta(a)$. Then ρ' is an R-homomorphism which extends ρ. This is a contradiction to the maximality of (L, ρ).

(2) Let $\mathfrak{b}$ be an ideal of R, and let $\varphi: \mathfrak{b} \to J$ be an R-homomorphism. For each $b \in \mathfrak{b}$, $\mathfrak{a}^n \varphi(b) = 0$ for some $n > 0$. Since $\mathfrak{b}$ is a finitely generated ideal, $\mathfrak{a}^N \varphi(\mathfrak{b}) = \varphi(\mathfrak{a}^N \mathfrak{b}) = (0)$ for some $N > 0$. By the lemma of Artin-Rees (I.1.31), there exists $r > 0$ such that $\mathfrak{a}^n \cap \mathfrak{b} = \mathfrak{a}^{n-r}(\mathfrak{a}^r \cap \mathfrak{b}) \subseteq \mathfrak{a}^{n-r}\mathfrak{b}$ for each $n \geq r$. Hence, $\varphi(\mathfrak{a}^n \cap \mathfrak{b}) = (0)$ for each $n \geq N + r$. Therefore, we have the following commutative diagram.

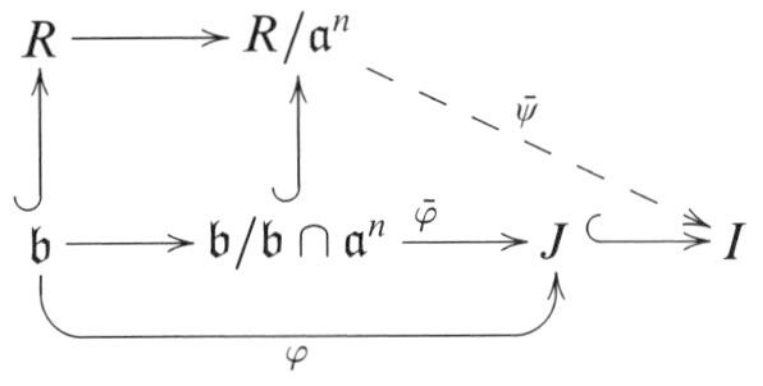

Since I is injective, there exists an R-homomorphism $\overline{\psi}: R/\mathfrak{a}^n \to I$ which extends $\overline{\varphi}: \mathfrak{b}/\mathfrak{b} \cap \mathfrak{a}^n \to J \hookrightarrow I$. Let $\psi = \overline{\psi} \cdot \pi$, where $\pi: R \to R/\mathfrak{a}^n$ is the natural residue homomorphism. Then ψ decomposes as $\psi: R \to J \hookrightarrow I$. □

The theory developed in Chapter 2 of Part I together with Lemma 3.13 yields the following result.

THEOREM 3.14. *Let R be a noetherian ring, and let $X = \operatorname{Spec}(R)$. Then, for any quasicoherent $\mathscr{O}_X$-Module $\mathscr{F}$, we have $H^0(X, \mathscr{F}) = \Gamma(X, \mathscr{F})$ and $H^i(X, \mathscr{F}) = (0)$ for each $i > 0$.*

PROOF. Let $M = \Gamma(X, \mathscr{F})$, and let

$$0 \to M \xrightarrow{\varepsilon} I_0 \xrightarrow{d^0} I_1 \xrightarrow{d^1} \cdots \xrightarrow{d^{n-1}} I_n \xrightarrow{d^n} \cdots$$

be an injective resolution of M. Then

$$0 \to \mathscr{F} \xrightarrow{\tilde{\varepsilon}} \widetilde{I_0} \xrightarrow{\widetilde{d^0}} \widetilde{I_1} \xrightarrow{\widetilde{d^1}} \cdots \xrightarrow{\widetilde{d^{n-1}}} \widetilde{I_n} \xrightarrow{\widetilde{d^n}} \cdots$$

is a scattered resolution of $\mathscr{F}$. Since $H^i(X, \mathscr{F})$ coincides with the cohomology group defined by a scattered resolution of $\mathscr{F}$ (problem I.2.5), we obtain the stated result. □

This theorem holds true without the assumption that R is a noetherian ring. See [3, III.1.3.1] for a proof.

Consider an exact sequence of R-modules

$$(*) \qquad 0 \to L \xrightarrow{\alpha} M \xrightarrow{\beta} N \to 0.$$

The sequence obtained by taking tensor products with an R-module P is right exact, i.e.,

$$L \otimes_R P \xrightarrow{\alpha \otimes \mathbf{1}_P} M \otimes_R P \xrightarrow{\beta \otimes \mathbf{1}_P} N \otimes_R P \to 0$$

is an exact sequence (problem II.3.3). If the homomorphism $\alpha \otimes \mathbf{1}_P$ is injective for an arbitrary exact sequence like $(*)$, then we call P *a flat* R-module.

LEMMA 3.15. *Let R be a noetherian ring, and let P be a finitely generated R-module. Then the following four conditions are equivalent.*

(1) *For each* $\mathfrak{p} \in \operatorname{Spec}(R)$, *there exists* $f \in R - \mathfrak{p}$ *such that* P_f *is a free* R_f*-module.*

(2) *For each* $\mathfrak{p} \in \operatorname{Spec}(R)$, $P_\mathfrak{p}$ *is a free* $R_\mathfrak{p}$*-module.*

(3) P *is a projective* R*-module.*

(4) P *is a flat* R*-module.*

PROOF. (1) implies (2) is clear.

(2) *implies* (3). Since P is finitely presented, we have

$$\operatorname{Hom}_R(P, M)_\mathfrak{p} \cong \operatorname{Hom}_{R_\mathfrak{p}}(P_\mathfrak{p}, M_\mathfrak{p})$$

for any R-module M (cf. Proof of Theorem 3.12 (5)). Hence, if $\pi\colon M \to N$ is a surjective R-homomorphism, then $(\pi_*)_\mathfrak{p}\colon \operatorname{Hom}_{R_\mathfrak{p}}(P_\mathfrak{p}, M_\mathfrak{p}) \to \operatorname{Hom}_{R_\mathfrak{p}}(P_\mathfrak{p}, N_\mathfrak{p})$ is surjective. So $\pi_*\colon \operatorname{Hom}_R(P, M) \to \operatorname{Hom}_R(P, N)$ is surjective. Namely, P is a projective R-module.

(3) *implies* (4). There is a surjective homomorphism $p\colon F \to P$ from a finitely generated free R-module F to P. Then $F \cong P \oplus Q$, where $Q = \operatorname{Ker} p$. Since F is clearly a flat R-module, for an injective homomorphism $\alpha\colon L \to M$, $\alpha \otimes \mathbf{1}_F = (\alpha \otimes \mathbf{1}_P) \oplus (\alpha \otimes \mathbf{1}_Q)$ is injective, whence $\alpha \otimes \mathbf{1}_P\colon L \otimes_R P \to M \otimes_R P$ is injective.

(4) *implies* (2). For each $\mathfrak{p} \in \operatorname{Spec}(R)$, since $P_\mathfrak{p} \cong P \otimes_R R_\mathfrak{p}$, $P_\mathfrak{p}$ is a flat $R_\mathfrak{p}$-module provided P is a flat R-module. So we have only to show that if R is a local ring with maximal ideal $\mathfrak{m}$, P is a free R-module. Since $P/\mathfrak{m}P$ is a vector space over $R/\mathfrak{m}$, choose elements $x_1, \dots, x_n$ of P so that the residue classes $\overline{x_i} = x_i \pmod{\mathfrak{m}P}$ form a basis of $P/\mathfrak{m}P$ over $R/\mathfrak{m}$. Let $Q = \sum_{i=1}^n Rx_i$. Then $P = Q + \mathfrak{m}P$. Hence, $P = Q$ by Nakayama's lemma (I.1.28). We shall show that $\{x_1, \dots, x_n\}$ is an R-free basis of P. We have to show that $a_1x_1 + \cdots + a_nx_n = 0$ $(a_i \in R)$ implies $a_i = 0$ for each i. First of all, we know that $\mathfrak{m}^r \otimes_R P \cong \mathfrak{m}^r P$ for each $r > 0$; this can be seen by taking tensor products of P with terms of an exact sequence $0 \to \mathfrak{m}^r \to R \to R/\mathfrak{m}^r \to 0$. Let $\overline{a_i} = a_i \pmod{\mathfrak{m}}$. Then $\overline{a}_1\overline{x}_1 + \cdots + \overline{a}_n\overline{x}_n = 0$. Since $\{\overline{x}_1, \dots, \overline{x}_n\}$ is a basis over $R/\mathfrak{m}$, we have $\overline{a}_i = 0$ (for each i). Hence, $a_i \in \mathfrak{m}_i$ for each i. Here we show that if $a_i \in \mathfrak{m}^r$ for each i then $a_i \in \mathfrak{m}^{r+1}$ for each i. In fact, we have $\mathfrak{m}^r/\mathfrak{m}^{r+1} \otimes_{R/\mathfrak{m}} P/\mathfrak{m}P \cong \mathfrak{m}^r P/\mathfrak{m}^{r+1}P$. Let $\tilde{a}_i = a_i \pmod{\mathfrak{m}^{r+1}}$. Then $\sum_{i=1}^n a_ix_i = 0$

implies $\sum_{i=1}^{n} \tilde{a}_i \otimes \overline{x}_i = 0$. Since $\mathfrak{m}^r/\mathfrak{m}^{r+1} \otimes_{R/\mathfrak{m}} P/\mathfrak{m}P$ is a tensor product of two vector spaces over $R/\mathfrak{m}$ and $\{\overline{x}_1, \dots, \overline{x}_n\}$ is a basis of $P/\mathfrak{m}P$, we know that each $\tilde{a}_i = 0$. So $a_i \in \mathfrak{m}^{r+1}$ for each i. This implies that $a_i \in \bigcap_{r>0} \mathfrak{m}^r = (0)$ for each i (cf. (I.1.28) and (I.1.31)).

(2) *implies* (1). Choose elements $x_1, \dots, x_n$ of P so that $\{x_1/1, \dots, x_n/1\}$ is an $R_\mathfrak{p}$-free basis of $P_\mathfrak{p}$. Consider an R-free module $F = \sum_{i=1}^{n} Re_i$ of rank n and a homomorphism $\varphi\colon F \to P$ ($\varphi(e_i) = x_i$). Let $K = \operatorname{Ker}\varphi$ and $Q = \operatorname{Coker}\varphi$. Then both K and Q are finitely generated. Furthermore, since $R_\mathfrak{p}$ is R-flat, $K_\mathfrak{p} = Q_\mathfrak{p} = (0)$. Therefore, $K_f = Q_f = (0)$ for an element f of $R - \mathfrak{p}$. Then $P_f \cong F_f$. So P_f is an R_f-free module. □

COROLLARY 3.16. *Let R be a noetherian ring, and let $X = \operatorname{Spec}(R)$. Then the following conditions on a coherent $\mathscr{O}_X$-Module $\mathscr{F}$ are equivalent*:

(1) *$\mathscr{F}$ is locally free (cf.* (I.2.10)).

(2) *$\mathscr{F}_x$ is $\mathscr{O}_{X,x}$-flat for each $x \in X$.*

When R is an integral domain, we can characterize $\Gamma(U, \mathscr{O}_X)$ for an open set U of X as a subring of the quotient field $K = Q(R)$ of R in the following fashion.

LEMMA 3.17. *Let R be an integral domain, let $K = Q(R)$, and let $X = \operatorname{Spec}(R)$. We regard R_x as a subring of K for each $x \in X$. Then $\Gamma(U, \mathscr{O}_X) = \bigcap_{x \in U} R_x$ for an arbitrary open set U of X.*

PROOF. (1) Consider first the case where $U = D(f)$. Note that $\Gamma(D(f), \mathscr{O}_X) = R_f$. Since $R_f \subseteq R_x$ for each $x \in D(f)$, we know $R_f \subseteq \bigcap_{x \in D(f)} R_x$. Let θ be an element of $\bigcap_{x \in D(f)} R_x$. Then for each $x \in D(f)$, there exists $f_x \in R - \mathfrak{p}_x$ such that $D(f_x) \subseteq D(f)$ and $\theta = a_x/f_x$ for some $a_x \in R$. Since $D(f) = \bigcup_{x \in D(f)} D(f_x)$ there exists a finite open covering $D(f) = \bigcup_{i=1}^{n} D(f_i)$ with $f_i = f_{x_i}$. Here by putting $a_i = a_{x_i}$, we have $a_i = \theta \cdot f_i$ ($1 \leq i \leq n$). Meanwhile, $f^r = \sum_{i=1}^{n} f_i b_i$ for some $r > 0$ and $b_i \in R$. Let $c = \sum_{i=1}^{n} b_i a_i$. Then $f^r \theta = \sum_{i=1}^{n} f_i b_i \theta = \sum_{i=1}^{n} a_i b_i = c$. So $\theta = c/f^r \in R_f$. Therefore, $\Gamma(D(f), \mathscr{O}_X) = \bigcap_{x \in D(f)} R_x$.

(2) In the case of a general open set U, take an open covering $U = \bigcup_{i \in I} D(f_i)$ ($D(f_i) \neq \emptyset$ for each i) and look at a sequence

$$\Gamma(U, \mathscr{O}_X) \to \prod_{i \in I} \Gamma(D(f_i), \mathscr{O}_X) \rightrightarrows \prod_{i,j} \Gamma(D(f_i f_j), \mathscr{O}_X).$$

Let $(\xi_i)_{i \in I} \in \prod_{i \in I} \Gamma(D(f_i), \mathscr{O}_X)$ be such that $\xi_i|_{D(f_i f_j)} = \xi_j|_{D(f_i f_j)}$ for each i, j. Then $\xi_i|_{D(f_i f_j)}$ and $\xi_j|_{D(f_i f_j)}$ are equal as elements of $R_{f_i f_j} (\subseteq K)$, where we note that $D(f_i f_j) \neq \emptyset$. Hence, $\xi_i = \xi_j \in \bigcap_{x \in D(f_i) \cap D(f_j)} R_x$. Applying this argument to two arbitrary elements i, j of I, we know that $\xi_i = \xi_j$ for each $i, j \in I$. Let ξ be this element. Then $\xi \in \bigcap_{x \in U} R_x$. Hence, by the definition of a sheaf, $\Gamma(U, \mathscr{O}_X) = \bigcap_{x \in U} R_x$. □

We shall consider the case where R is a finitely generated algebra over a field k.

LEMMA 3.18. *Let R be a finitely generated algebra over a field k, let $X = \operatorname{Spec}(R)$, and let M be the set of all closed points of X. Then M is a dense subset of X.*

PROOF. Let $\overline{M}$ be the closure of M, and let $U = X - \overline{M}$. If $U \neq \emptyset$, then there exists a nonempty open set $D(f)$ such that $D(f) \subseteq U$. Let $\tilde{\mathfrak{m}}$ be a maximal ideal of R_f, and let $\mathfrak{m} = \{a \in R; a/1 \in \tilde{\mathfrak{m}}\}$. Then $k \subseteq R/\mathfrak{m} \subseteq R_f/\tilde{\mathfrak{m}}$, where $R_f/\tilde{\mathfrak{m}}$ is a finite algebraic extension of k because R_f is a finitely generated k-algebra (cf. (I.1.15) and (I.1.10(3))). Hence, $R/\mathfrak{m}$ is a field and $\mathfrak{m}$ is a maximal ideal of R. However, $\mathfrak{m} \in D(f)$ because $f \notin \mathfrak{m}$. This is a contradiction. So $\overline{M} = X$. □

Under the same assumptions as in the above lemma, we introduce the induced topology on M from X. The induced topology on M restores the topology on X. In fact, if I is a radical ideal of R, then $I = \bigcap_{I \subseteq \mathfrak{m}} \mathfrak{m}$ by the Nullstellensatz of Hilbert (I.1.24). So I is restored by $V(I) \cap M$. We also have the following result.

LEMMA 3.19. *Let R be a finitely generated algegbra domain over a field k, and let $X = \text{Spec}(R)$. Then $\Gamma(U, \mathcal{O}_X) = \bigcap_{x \in U \cap M} R_x$, where M is the set of closed points of X.*

PROOF. Suppose $R_f = \bigcap_{x \in D(f) \cap M} R_x$ for $D(f) \subseteq U$. Then Lemma 3.17 implies

$$\Gamma(U, \mathcal{O}_X) = \bigcap_{D(f) \subseteq U} R_f = \bigcap_{D(f) \subseteq U} \bigcap_{x \in D(f) \cap M} R_x = \bigcap_{x \in U \cap M} R_x.$$

Hence, we may assume $U = D(f)$ to prove the assertion. As the maximal ideals $\mathfrak{m}$ of R with $f \notin \mathfrak{m}$ correspond bijectively to the maximal ideals of R_f via $\mathfrak{m} \mapsto \mathfrak{m}R_f$, we have

$$\bigcap_{x \in U \cap M} R_x = \bigcap_{f \notin \mathfrak{m}} R_{\mathfrak{m}} = \bigcap_{f \notin \mathfrak{m}} (R_f)_{\mathfrak{m}R_f}.$$

So by replacing R by R_f, we may assume $f = 1$. Now $R \subseteq \bigcap_{x \in M} R_x$, clearly. We shall next show the opposite inclusion. Let $\theta \in \bigcap_{x \in M} R_x$, and let $\mathfrak{a} = \{a \in R; a\theta \in R\}$. Suppose $\theta \notin R$. Then $\mathfrak{a}$ is a proper ideal of R. Let $\mathfrak{m}$ be a maximal ideal of R containing $\mathfrak{a}$. Then $\theta \in R_{\mathfrak{m}}$. Hence, $f\theta \in R$ for some $f \in R - \mathfrak{m}$. So $f \in \mathfrak{a} \subseteq \mathfrak{m}$. This is absurd. Thus, $\bigcap_{x \in M} R_x = R$. □

We further make the stronger assumption that k is an algebraically closed field and R is a finitely generated k-algebra. Then we can write $R = k[X_1, \ldots, X_n]/I$ as the residue ring of a polynomial ring over k, where $I = (f_1, \ldots, f_m)$ as I is a finitely generated ideal. Let $\mathfrak{m}$ be a maximal ideal of R. Then $R/\mathfrak{m} = k$ because $R/\mathfrak{m}$ is a finite algebraic extension of k and k is algebraically closed. Let $\tilde{\mathfrak{m}}$ be the pullback of $\mathfrak{m}$ on $k[X_1, \ldots, X_n]$. Then $\mathfrak{m} = \tilde{\mathfrak{m}}/I$ and $\tilde{\mathfrak{m}} = (X_1 - \alpha_1, \ldots, X_n - \alpha_n)$, where $(\alpha_1, \ldots, \alpha_n) \in k^n := \underbrace{k \times \cdots \times k}_{n}$ and $f_i(\alpha_1, \ldots, \alpha_n) = 0$ for each $i, 1 \le i \le m$. Conversely, if $(\alpha_1, \ldots, \alpha_n) \in k^n$ satisfies $f_i(\alpha_1, \ldots, \alpha_n) = 0$ (for each $i, 1 \le i \le m$), then the maximal ideal $\tilde{\mathfrak{m}} = (X_1 - \alpha_1, \ldots, X_n - \alpha_n)$ contains I and $\mathfrak{m} = \tilde{\mathfrak{m}}/I$ is a maximal ideal of R. Then we say that $(\alpha_1, \ldots, \alpha_n)$ are the *coordinates* of a point $\mathfrak{m}$ ($\in M$). Now we have the following.

DEFINITION 3.20. Let k be a field and let $A_n = k[X_1, \ldots, X_n]$ be a polynomial ring in n variables. We denote Spec(A_n) by $\mathbf{A}_k^n$ and call it the *affine space* of dimension n. We assume, henceforth, that k is algebraically closed. Then the set of closed points of $\mathbf{A}_k^n$ is identified with k^n. If R is a finitely generated k-algebra, then R is given as $R = A_n/I$ for some $n > 0$ and Spec(R) is identified with a closed set $V(I)$ of $\mathbf{A}_k^n$. Furthermore, the set M of closed points of Spec(R) is identified with $V(I) \cap k^n$. We call $V(I) \cap k^n$ an *affine algebraic set* defined by an ideal I of A_n, I its *defining ideal*, and $R = A_n/I$ its *coordinate ring*. When we write $X = \text{Spec}(R)$, $X(k)$ stands for $M = V(I) \cap k^n$. We have $V(I) \cap k^n = V(\sqrt{I}) \cap k^n$, and if $X = X_1 \cup \cdots \cup X_r$ is the irreducible decomposition, i.e., $\sqrt{I} = \mathfrak{p}_1 \cap \cdots \cap \mathfrak{p}_r$ is the prime divisor decomposition and $X_i = V(\mathfrak{p}_i)$ $(1 \le i \le r)$, then $X(k) = X_1(k) \cup \cdots \cup X_r(k)$ is the irreducible decomposition of $X(k)$. If X is irreducible, we call $X(k)$ an *affine algebraic variety*. Then the coordinate ring R is an integral domain if we take I as a radical ideal $I = \sqrt{I}$, and its quotient field, which we denote by $k(X)$, is called the *rational function field* of $X(k)$ (or X). We call an element of $k(X)$ a rational function on X.

When $M = X(k)$ is an affine algebraic set, we regard the structure sheaf $\mathcal{O}_X$ on X as a sheaf $\mathcal{O}_M$ on M in the following fashion: An open set V of M is written as $V = U \cap M$, where U is an open set of X uniquely determined by V. We define $\Gamma(U \cap M, \mathcal{O}_M) = \Gamma(U, \mathcal{O}_X)$. Then $\mathcal{O}_M$ is a sheaf. We consider M as a local ringed space $(M, \mathcal{O}_M)$.

As the above definitions show, local ringed spaces $(X, \mathcal{O}_X)$ and $(M, \mathcal{O}_M)$ determine each other uniquely. The difference between X and M is that $X - M = \{\mathfrak{p} \in \operatorname{Spec}(R); \mathfrak{p} \neq \text{maximal ideal}\}$ as sets. For $\mathfrak{p} \in X - M$, $V(\mathfrak{p}) = \overline{\{\mathfrak{p}\}}$ is an irreducible closed subset of X of dimension ≥ 1. $V(\mathfrak{p}) \cap M$ is an irreducible closed subset of M of dimension equal to $\dim V(\mathfrak{p})$, but the generic point $\mathfrak{p}$ of $V(\mathfrak{p})$ does not belong to $V(\mathfrak{p}) \cap M$. However, $V(\mathfrak{p})$ is restored from $V(\mathfrak{p}) \cap M$ as the closure of $V(\mathfrak{p}) \cap M$ in X. We call $(X, \mathcal{O}_X)$ an *affine algebraic scheme* and $(M, \mathcal{O}_M)$ an affine algebraic set. These are, of course, distinct objects. However, for the reasons explained just now, we can and shall often treat them as the same.

For an affine scheme $X = \operatorname{Spec}(R)$, we denote by X_{red} an affine scheme $\operatorname{Spec}(R_{\text{red}})$ determined by $R_{\text{red}} := R/\mathfrak{n}$, where $\mathfrak{n}$ is the nilradical $\sqrt{(0)}$ of R. If $X = X_{\text{red}}$ as schemes, we say that X is *reduced*.

We assume, for the moment, that k is algebraically closed. Let $X \subseteq \mathbf{A}_k^n$ be an irreducible and reduced, algebraic affine scheme, let R be its coordinate ring, and let $K := k(X)$ be its rational function field. Any element of R is represented by an element of $A_n = k[X_1, \dots, X_n]$. If $f \in R$ is represented by $F \in A_n$, we write $f = [F]$. For each $x \in X(k)$, we set $f(x) := F(\alpha_1, \dots, \alpha_n)$ with the coordinate expression $x = (\alpha_1, \dots, \alpha_n)$. Then $f(x) \in k$ and this value $f(x)$ is independent of the choice of a representative F. Thus, an element f of R is looked upon as a k-valued function on $X(k)$. If we express an element $\xi \in K$ as $\xi = [F]/[G]$ $(F, G \in A_n)$ and $G(\alpha_1, \dots, \alpha_n) \neq 0$, then $\xi(x) := F(\alpha_1, \dots, \alpha_n)/G(\alpha_1, \dots, \alpha_n)$ is determined independently of the way of expressing $\xi = [F]/[G]$. In fact, if $\xi = [F']/[G']$ and $G'(\alpha_1, \dots, \alpha_n) \neq 0$, then $FG' - F'G \in I$ (:= the defining ideal of X), whence

$$F(\alpha_1, \dots, \alpha_n)/G(\alpha_1, \dots, \alpha_n) = F'(\alpha_1, \dots, \alpha_n)/G'(\alpha_1, \dots, \alpha_n).$$

We then say that a rational function ξ is *regular* at a point x.

In terms of the regularity of a function, Lemma 3.19 is stated as follows.

LEMMA 3.21. *In the above setting, we have*

(1) *For each $x \in X(k)$, $R_x = \{\xi \in K; \xi$ is regular at $x\}$.*

(2) *For $y \in X - X(k)$, let $Y = \overline{\{y\}}$. Then $R_y = \{\xi \in K; \xi$ is regular at some point of $Y \cap X(k)\}$.*

(3) *Let U be an open set of X. Then $\Gamma(U, \mathcal{O}_X) = \{\xi \in K; \xi$ is regular at every point of $U \cap X(k)\}$.*

PROOF. (1) Let $\xi \in R_x$. Then $\xi = f/g$ with $f, g \in R$ and $g \notin \mathfrak{p}_x$. Moreover, $f = [F]$ and $g = [G]$ with $F, G \in A_n$ and $G \notin \mathfrak{P}_x$, where $\mathfrak{P}_x$ is the pullback of $\mathfrak{p}_x$ onto A_n. When we write $x = (\alpha_1, \dots, \alpha_n)$, $G(\alpha_1, \dots, \alpha_n) \neq 0$. Namely, $\xi = [F]/[G]$

is regular at x. Conversely, let $\xi \in K$ be a function regular at x. Thus, we can write $\xi = [F]/[G]$ with $G(\alpha_1, \dots, \alpha_n) \neq 0$. Then $G \notin \mathfrak{P}_x$. Hence, if we put $f = [F]$ and $g = [G]$, then $g \notin \mathfrak{p}_x := \mathfrak{P}_x/I$ and $\xi = f/g$. So $\xi \in R_x$.

(2) Suppose ξ is regular at a point $x \in Y \cap X(k)$. Since $\mathfrak{p}_x \supseteq \mathfrak{p}_y$, R_y is a quotient ring of R_x. By (1) above, $\xi \in R_x$. Hence, $\xi \in R_y$. Conversely, suppose $\xi \in R_y$. Write ξ as $\xi = f/g$ with $f, g \in R$ and $g \notin \mathfrak{p}_y$. Let $\mathfrak{m}$ be a maximal ideal of R_g containing $\mathfrak{p}_y R_g$. Since R_g is a finitely generated k-algebra, $\mathfrak{p} := R \cap \mathfrak{m}$ is a maximal ideal of R (cf. the proof of Lemma 3.18). Let x be a point of $X(k)$ corresponding to $\mathfrak{p}$. Then $\mathfrak{p}_y \subseteq \mathfrak{p}_x := \mathfrak{p}$ and $g \notin \mathfrak{p}_x$. Hence, $x \in Y \cap X(k)$ and $g(x) \neq 0$. So, ξ is regular at x.

(3) By Lemma 3.19, $\Gamma(U, \mathscr{O}_X) = \bigcap_{x \in U \cap M} R_x$. Hence, $\Gamma(U, \mathscr{O}_X)$ consists of elements of K which are regular at every point of $U \cap M$. □

Now coming back to Definition 3.3, we shall look into the properties of morphisms of affine schemes.

LEMMA 3.22. *Let R and S be commutative rings, let $X = \operatorname{Spec}(R)$, and let $Y = \operatorname{Spec}(S)$. Then we have*

(1) *A homomorphism of rings $\varphi\colon R \to S$ gives rise to a morphism of local ringed spaces $({}^a\varphi, \tilde{\varphi})\colon (Y, \mathscr{O}_Y) \to (X, \mathscr{O}_X)$.*

(2) *Conversely, given a morphism of local ringed spaces $(f, \theta)\colon (Y, \mathscr{O}_Y) \to (X, \mathscr{O}_X)$, there exists a ring homomorphism $\varphi\colon R \to S$ such that $(f, \theta) = ({}^a\varphi, \tilde{\varphi})$.*

(3) *Fix a morphism of local ringed spaces $(f, \theta) = ({}^a\varphi, \tilde{\varphi})\colon (Y, \mathscr{O}_Y) \to (X, \mathscr{O}_X)$. If N is an S-module, $f_*(\widetilde{N}) = (N_{[\varphi]})^{\sim}$, where $N_{[\varphi]}$ is the module N regarded as an R-module via φ. Furthermore, if M is an R-module, then $f^*(\widetilde{M}) \cong (M \otimes_R S)^{\sim}$.*

PROOF. (1) Let $f = {}^a\varphi$, and let $\tilde{\varphi}\colon \mathscr{O}_X \to f_*\mathscr{O}_Y$ be a homomorphism defined by the natural ring homomorphism $R_g \to S_{\varphi(g)}$, $a/g^n \mapsto \varphi(a)/\varphi(g)^n$, where we note that $\Gamma(D(g), \mathscr{O}_X) = R_g$ and $\Gamma(D(g), f_*\mathscr{O}_Y) = \Gamma(D(\varphi(g)), \mathscr{O}_Y) = S_{\varphi(g)}$. For each $y \in Y$ and $x = f(y)$, we have $\tilde{\varphi}_x\colon R_x \to (f_*\mathscr{O}_Y)_x = \varinjlim_{x \in D(g)} \Gamma(D(g), f_*\mathscr{O}_Y) = \varinjlim_{x \in D(g)} S_{\varphi(g)}$. Since $\mathfrak{p}_x = \varphi^{-1}(\mathfrak{p}_y)$ and $g \notin \mathfrak{p}_x$ implies $\varphi(g) \notin \mathfrak{p}_y$, we have a ring homomorphism $\varinjlim_{x \in D(g)} S_{\varphi(g)} \to S_y$. This homomorphism composed with $\tilde{\varphi}_x$ is obviously a homomorphism of local rings $(\tilde{\varphi})^{\#}_y\colon R_x \to S_y$. So, $({}^a\varphi, \tilde{\varphi})$ is a morphism of local ringed spaces.

(2) Let $(f, \theta)\colon (Y, \mathscr{O}_Y) \to (X, \mathscr{O}_X)$ be a morphism of local ringed spaces, and let $\varphi = \theta(X)\colon R \to S$. Then φ is a ring homomorphism. We shall show that $(f, \theta) = ({}^a\varphi, \tilde{\varphi})$. For this we shall make use of the following commutative diagram

$$\begin{array}{ccccc}
\mathscr{O}_X(X) & \xrightarrow{\varphi} & \mathscr{O}_Y(Y) & & \\
\downarrow & & \downarrow & & \\
\mathscr{O}_{X,x} & \xrightarrow{\theta_x} & (f_*\mathscr{O}_Y)_x & = \varinjlim_{x \in U} \mathscr{O}_Y(f^{-1}(U)) \xrightarrow{\rho} & \mathscr{O}_{Y,y}
\end{array}$$

where U ranges over the set of open neighborhoods of x. If $x = f(y)$, then $y \in f^{-1}(U)$; whence, there exists a natural ring homomorphism ρ as given in the above diagram. We have $\rho \cdot \theta_x = (\theta^{\#})_y$. Namely, $\rho \cdot \theta_x$ is a homomorphism of local rings.

Hence $\varphi^{-1}(\mathfrak{p}_y) = \mathfrak{p}_x$. So, $f = {}^a\varphi$. Moreover, comparing the definitions of $(\tilde{\varphi})^\#_y$ and $(\theta^\#)_y$, we know that $(\tilde{\varphi})^\#_y = (\theta^\#)_y$ for each $y \in Y$. Hence $(\tilde{\varphi})^\# = \theta^\#$. So, $\tilde{\varphi} = \theta$.

(3) For an open set $D(g)$ of X, $\Gamma(D(g), f_*(\widetilde{N})) = \Gamma(D(\varphi(g)), \widetilde{N}) = N_{[\varphi]} \otimes_R R_g$. If $D(h) \subseteq D(g)$, the restriction morphism $\rho_{hg} := \rho_{D(h)D(g)} \colon \Gamma(D(g), f_*(\widetilde{N})) \to \Gamma(D(h), f_*(\widetilde{N}))$ coincides with the restriction morphism $1_{N_{[\varphi]}} \otimes_R \rho_{hg} \colon N_{[\varphi]} \otimes_R R_g \to N_{[\varphi]} \otimes_R R_h$. Hence, $f_*(\widetilde{N}) = (N_{[\varphi]})^\sim$.

For an R-module M, define a homomorphism of R-modules $j \colon M \to (M \otimes_R S)_{[\varphi]}$ by $m \mapsto m \otimes 1$ which gives rise to a homomorphism of $\mathcal{O}_X$-Modules $\tilde{j} \colon \widetilde{M} \to f_*((M \otimes_R S)^\sim)$ and a homomorphism of $\mathcal{O}_Y$-Modules $(\tilde{j})^\sharp \colon f^*(\widetilde{M}) \to (M \otimes_R S)^\sim$. We shall show that $(\tilde{j})^\#$ is an isomorphism. For each $y \in Y$, we have

$$f^*(\widetilde{M})_y = (f^*\widetilde{M} \otimes_{f^*\mathcal{O}_X} \mathcal{O}_Y)_y = \widetilde{M}_x \otimes_{\mathcal{O}_{X,x}} \mathcal{O}_{Y,y} = (M \otimes_R S) \otimes_S S_y,$$

where $x = f(y)$. This implies that $(\tilde{j})^\sharp_y$ is a homorphism of S_y-modules and the identity morphism when restricted on $M \otimes 1_S$. So, $(\tilde{j})^\sharp_y$ is an isomorphism for each $y \in Y$. Therefore, $f^*(\widetilde{M}) \cong (M \otimes_R S)^\sim$. □

THEOREM 3.23. *With the same assumptions as in Lemma* 3.22, *the following assertions hold*:

(1) *For an exact sequence of scattered $\mathcal{O}_Y$-Modules*

$$0 \to \mathcal{F}_1 \xrightarrow{\alpha} \mathcal{F}_2 \xrightarrow{\beta} \mathcal{F}_3 \to 0,$$

the sequence

$$0 \to f_*\mathcal{F}_1 \xrightarrow{f_*\alpha} f_*\mathcal{F}_2 \xrightarrow{f_*\beta} f_*\mathcal{F}_3 \to 0$$

is an exact sequence of scattered $\mathcal{O}_X$-Modules.

(2) *If S is a noetherian ring, we have $R^i f_*\mathcal{F} = (0)$ (all $i > 0$) for every quasicoherent $\mathcal{O}_Y$-Module $\mathcal{F}$.*

PROOF. (1) It suffices to show that the morphism of stalks $(f_*\beta)_x$ is surjective for each $x \in X$. Let $\xi \in (f_*\mathcal{F}_3)_x$. Then there exist an open neighborhood U of x and $s \in \Gamma(U, f_*\mathcal{F}_3)$ such that $\xi = s_x$. Here $\Gamma(f^{-1}(U), \beta) \colon \Gamma(f^{-1}(U), \mathcal{F}_2) \to \Gamma(f^{-1}(U), \mathcal{F}_3)$ is surjective by (I.2.19). Choose $t \in \Gamma(f^{-1}(U), \mathcal{F}_2)$ such that $s = \Gamma(f^{-1}(U), \beta)(t)$, and let $\eta = t_x$. Then $\xi = (f_*\beta)_x(\eta)$. So $(f_*\beta)_x$ is surjective. It is clear that if $\mathcal{F}$ is a scattered $\mathcal{O}_Y$-Module then $f_*\mathcal{F}$ is a scattered $\mathcal{O}_X$-Module.

(2) $R^i f_*\mathcal{F}$ coincides with the cohomology group defined by a scattered resolution of $\mathcal{F}$. In fact, by making use of the assertion (1) above and the argument in a proof of problem I.2.5 (see the hint), we know, first of all, that the cohomology groups defined by a scattered resolution of $\mathcal{F}$ are independent of the choice of a scattered resolution of $\mathcal{F}$. We denote these cohomology groups by $\widetilde{R}^i f_*\mathcal{F}$. Then $\{\widetilde{R}^i f_*(\cdot)\}_{i \geq 0}$ is a cohomology functor. Here we have to extend the definition of cohomology functor (see Chapter 2 of Part I) as follows. Namely, a functor assigning to an $\mathcal{O}_Y$-Module $\mathcal{F}$ a collection of $\mathcal{O}_X$-Modules $\{K^i(\mathcal{F})\}_{i \geq 0}$ is a cohomology functor if the following conditions are satisfied:

(i) $K^0(\mathcal{F}) = f_*\mathcal{F}$.

(ii) $K^i(\mathcal{J}) = (0)$ (for each $i > 0$) for an injective $\mathcal{O}_Y$-Module $\mathcal{J}$.

(iii) For an exact sequence of $\mathscr{O}_Y$-Modules

$$0 \to \mathscr{F}_1 \xrightarrow{\alpha} \mathscr{F}_2 \xrightarrow{\beta} \mathscr{F}_3 \to 0,$$

there is the following cohomology exact sequence

$$\begin{aligned} 0 \to K^0(\mathscr{F}_1) &\xrightarrow{\alpha^0} K^0(\mathscr{F}_2) \xrightarrow{\beta^0} K^0(\mathscr{F}_3) \xrightarrow{\partial^0} K^1(\mathscr{F}_1) \xrightarrow{\alpha^1} K^1(\mathscr{F}_2) \\ &\xrightarrow{\beta^1} K^1(\mathscr{F}_3) \xrightarrow{\partial^1} K^2(\mathscr{F}_1) \to \cdots \to K^n(\mathscr{F}_1) \xrightarrow{\alpha^n} K^n(\mathscr{F}_2) \\ &\xrightarrow{\beta^n} K^n(\mathscr{F}_3) \xrightarrow{\partial^n} K^{n+1}(\mathscr{F}_1) \to \cdots. \end{aligned}$$

If $\mathscr{I}$ is an injective $\mathscr{O}_Y$-Module, then $\mathscr{I}$ is a scattered sheaf (cf. (I.2.19)). Then $\widetilde{R}^i f_*\mathscr{I} = (0)$ for each $i > 0$ by (1) above. For an exact sequence of $\mathscr{O}_Y$-Modules

$$0 \to \mathscr{F}_1 \xrightarrow{\alpha} \mathscr{F}_2 \xrightarrow{\beta} \mathscr{F}_3 \to 0,$$

the standard scattered resolutions of $\mathscr{F}_j$ $(j = 1, 2, 3)$ (cf. Problem I.2.5) yield by a straightforward argument a cohomology exact sequence

$$\cdots \to \widetilde{R}^n f_*\mathscr{F}_1 \xrightarrow{\alpha^n} \widetilde{R}^n f_*\mathscr{F}_2 \xrightarrow{\beta^n} \widetilde{R}^n f_*\mathscr{F}_3 \xrightarrow{\partial^n} \widetilde{R}^{n+1} f_*\mathscr{F}_1 \to \cdots$$

We conclude that $\widetilde{R}^i f_*\mathscr{F} \cong R^i f_*\mathscr{F}$ (for each $i \geq 0$).

Now let $\mathscr{F}$ be a quasicoherent $\mathscr{O}_Y$-Module. Write $\mathscr{F} = \widetilde{N}$, where N is an S-module. Let

$$0 \to N \xrightarrow{\varepsilon} J^0 \xrightarrow{d^0} J^1 \xrightarrow{d^1} \cdots \to J^n \xrightarrow{d^n} \cdots$$

be an injective resolution of an S-module N. Then

$$0 \to N_{[\varphi]} \xrightarrow{\varepsilon} J^0_{[\varphi]} \xrightarrow{d^0} J^1_{[\varphi]} \xrightarrow{d^1} \cdots \to J^n_{[\varphi]} \xrightarrow{d^n} \cdots$$

is an exact sequence of R-modules. Hence, we obtain an exact sequence of quasicoherent $\mathscr{O}_X$-Modules

$$0 \to f_*\mathscr{F} \xrightarrow{f_*\tilde{\varepsilon}} f_*\mathscr{J}^0 \xrightarrow{f_*\widetilde{d^0}} f_*\mathscr{J}^1 \xrightarrow{f_*\widetilde{d^1}} \cdots \to f_*\mathscr{J}^n \xrightarrow{f_*\widetilde{d^n}} \cdots$$

where $\mathscr{J}^n = \widetilde{J^n}$. If we note that

$$0 \to \mathscr{F} \xrightarrow{\tilde{\varepsilon}} \mathscr{J}^0 \xrightarrow{\widetilde{d^0}} \mathscr{J}^1 \xrightarrow{\widetilde{d^1}} \cdots \to \mathscr{J}^n \xrightarrow{\widetilde{d^n}} \cdots$$

is a scattered resolution of $\mathscr{F}$ (cf. (3.13)), we have $\widetilde{R}^i f_*\mathscr{F} = (0)$ (for each $i > 0$). So $R^i f_*\mathscr{F} = (0)$ for each $i > 0$. □

Let k be an algebraically closed field, and let $X(k)$ and $Y(k)$ be respectively the affine algebraic sets over k with the coordinate rings R and S. A mapping of sets $f: X(k) \to Y(k)$ is called a *morphism of affine algeraic sets* if there exists a k-algebra homomorphism $\varphi: R \to S$ such that the following diagram is commutative:

$$\begin{array}{ccc} \operatorname{Spec}(S) & \xrightarrow{{}^a\varphi} & \operatorname{Spec}(R) \\ \uparrow & & \uparrow \\ Y(k) & \xrightarrow{f} & X(k). \end{array}$$

In this definition, φ is not necessarily determined uniquely by f. However, if $X(k)$

and $Y(k)$ are affine algebraic varieties, φ is determined uniquely by f as shown in the next lemma.

LEMMA 3.24. *Let $X(k)$ and $Y(k)$ be affine algebraic varieties defined over an algebraically closed field k, and let $f\colon Y(k) \to X(k)$ be a mapping of sets. Then the following conditions are equivalent*:

(1) *f is a morphism of affine algebraic varieties.*

(2) (i) *f is a continuous mapping.*

(ii) *If $g \in k(X)$ is regular over $X(k)$, i.e., $g \in R := \Gamma(X, \mathscr{O}_X)$, then $f^*(g)$ is regular over $Y(k)$, i.e., $f^*(g) \in S := \Gamma(Y, \mathscr{O}_Y)$, where $f^*(g)(y) = g(f(y))$ for each $y \in Y(k)$.*

The homomorphism of coordinate rings $\varphi\colon R \to S$ (see the above definition) is nothing but f^*.

PROOF. (1) *implies* (2). By definition, there exists a k-algebra homomorphism $\varphi\colon R \to S$ such that $f = {}^a\varphi|_{Y(k)}$. Obviously, f is continuous. For $g \in R$ and $y \in Y(k)$, $f^*(g)(y) = g(f(y)) = g({}^a\varphi(y)) = \varphi(g)(y)$. Hence, $f^*(g) = \varphi(g) \in S$ as a function on $Y(k)$.

(2) *implies* (1). Express R as $R = k[X_1, \dots, X_n]/I$ with $I = \sqrt{I}$. Let ξ_i be the residue class of $X_i \pmod I$, and let $\Phi\colon k[X_1, \dots, X_n] \to S$ be a k-homomorphism such that $\Phi(X_i) = f^*(\xi_i)$ for each i. For $G \in I$, we have

$$\begin{aligned}\Phi(G)(y) = G(f^*(\xi_1), \dots, f^*(\xi_n))(y) &= G(f^*(\xi_1)(y), \dots, f^*(\xi_n)(y)) \\ &= G(\xi_1(f(y)), \dots, \xi_n(f(y))),\end{aligned}$$

where $\xi_i(f(y)) = \alpha_i$ if $f(y) = (\alpha_1, \dots, \alpha_n) \in k^n$. Since $f(y) \in X(k)$ and $G \in I$, we have $\Phi(G)(y) = G(\alpha_1, \dots, \alpha_n) = 0$. Hence, Φ induces a k-algebra homomorphism $\varphi\colon R \to S$. For a maximal ideal $\mathfrak{p}_y$ of S, $\varphi^{-1}(\mathfrak{p}_y)$ is a maximal ideal of R which corresponds to a point $x = (\alpha'_1, \dots, \alpha'_n)$. Writing $f(y) = (\alpha_1, \dots, \alpha_n)$, we have

$$\alpha'_i = \xi_i(x) = \xi_i({}^a\varphi(y)) = \varphi(\xi_i)(y) = \Phi(X_i)(y) = f^*(\xi_i)(y) = \alpha_i.$$

Hence, it follows that $f = {}^a\varphi|_{Y(k)}$. Suppose f is induced by two k-algebra homomorphisms $\varphi, \varphi'\colon R \to S$. Then for each $y \in Y(k)$ and $g \in R$, we have $\varphi(g)(y) = f^*(g)(y) = \varphi'(g)(y)$. So $\varphi(g) - \varphi'(g) \in \bigcap_{y \in Y(k)} \mathfrak{p}_y = \sqrt{(0)} = (0)$. Namely, $\varphi(g) = \varphi'(g)$ for each $g \in R$. It follows that $\varphi = \varphi'$. □

Here we give some explanations of the notation $X(k)$. Let R be a finitely generated algebra over an algebraically closed field k, and let $X = \operatorname{Spec}(R)$. For a closed point x of X, $R/\mathfrak{p}_x = k$. The residue homomorphism $R \to k$ gives rise to a morphism of affine schemes $\operatorname{Spec}(k) \to \operatorname{Spec}(R)$. Note that $\operatorname{Spec}(k)$ consists of a single point and the structure sheaf is k. Conversely, given a morphism of algebraic sets over k, $f\colon \operatorname{Spec}(k) \to \operatorname{Spec}(R)$, it is given by a k-homomorphism $\varphi\colon R \to k$. $\operatorname{Ker}\varphi$ is a maximal ideal of R and corresponds to a point $f(\operatorname{Spec}(k))$. This point is determined independently of the choice of φ. Therefore, we have a bijection

$$X(k) \leftrightarrow \left\{ \begin{array}{ll} f\colon \operatorname{Spec}(k) \to X = \operatorname{Spec}(R); & \text{a morphism of} \\ & \text{algebraic sets} \end{array} \right\}.$$

We denote the last set by $\operatorname{Hom}_k(\operatorname{Spec}(k), X)$ (or $X(k)$ in a more abbreviated notations).

II.3. Problems

1. Construct an example of an affine scheme $X = \operatorname{Spec}(R)$ for which X is a noetherian space but R is not a noetherian ring. One way of constructing such an example is the following. Let A be a commutative ring, and let M be an A-module. In the direct sum $R = A \oplus M$ we define a ring structure by $(a_1, x_1) + (a_2, x_2) = (a_1 + a_2, x_1 + x_2)$ and $(a_1, x_1) \cdot (a_2, x_2) = (a_1 a_2, a_2 x_1 + a_1 x_2)$. The identity element is $(1, 0)$, and elements x of M are identified with $(0, x)$. Hence $(0, x) \cdot (0, y) = (0, 0)$. Namely, $M^2 = (0)$. Hence $\operatorname{Spec}(R) = \operatorname{Spec}(A)$. We call R the *idealization* of an A-module M. Here we take a noetherian ring A and an A-module M which is not finitely generated. Then R is not noetherian.
2. Let A be a noetherian domain, and let $\{\mathfrak{p}_\lambda\}_{\lambda \in \Lambda}$ be the set of prime ideals of A such that $\operatorname{ht} \mathfrak{p}_\lambda = r$ for each $\lambda \in \Lambda$. Let $K(\mathfrak{p}_\lambda) = Q(A/\mathfrak{p}_\lambda)$ and $I = \oplus_{\lambda \in \Lambda} K(\mathfrak{p}_\lambda)$. Then show that for a quasicoherent Module $\widetilde{I}$ over $X = \operatorname{Spec}(A)$, we have $\operatorname{Supp}(\widetilde{I}) = \bigcup_{\lambda \in \Lambda} V(\mathfrak{p}_\lambda)$. So $\operatorname{Supp}(\widetilde{I})$ is not a closed set of X provided Λ is an infinite set.
3. Verify that for an exact sequence of R-modules

$$0 \to L \xrightarrow{\alpha} M \xrightarrow{\beta} N \to 0$$

and an R-module P, the sequence

$$L \otimes_R P \xrightarrow{\alpha \otimes 1_P} M \otimes_R P \xrightarrow{\beta \otimes 1_P} N \otimes_R P \to 0$$

is an exact sequence. (It is easy to show that $\beta \otimes 1_P$ is surjective. In order to show that $\operatorname{Ker}(\beta \otimes 1_P) = \operatorname{Im}(\alpha \otimes 1_P)$ one needs to go back to the definition of a tensor product $M \otimes_R P$.)

CHAPTER 4

Schemes and Algebraic Varieties

In order to proceed further, we need the concept of a scheme which is more general than that of an affine scheme.

DEFINITION 4.1. Let $(X, \mathcal{O}_X)$ be a local ringed space. $(X, \mathcal{O}_X)$ is called a *scheme* if for every point x of X there exist an open neighborhood U of x and a commutative ring A_x such that $(U, \mathcal{O}_X|_U)$ is isomorphic to $(\mathrm{Spec}(A_x), \widetilde{A_x})$ as local ringed spaces. An open set U of a scheme $(X, \mathcal{O}_X)$ is called an *affine open set* if $(U, \mathcal{O}_X|_U)$ is isomorphic to an affine scheme $(\mathrm{Spec}(A), \widetilde{A})$ as local ringed spaces. For schemes $(X, \mathcal{O}_X)$ and $(Y, \mathcal{O}_Y)$, a morphism of local ringed spaces $(f, \varphi): (Y, \mathcal{O}_Y) \to (X, \mathcal{O}_X)$ is called a *morphism of schemes*. As an abbreviation of (f, φ), we frequently write $f: Y \to X$. If there exists such a morphism $f: Y \to X$, we call Y a scheme over X and call f the *structure morphism*. If $f: Y \to X$ and $g: Z \to X$ are schemes over X, we define

$$\mathrm{Hom}_X(Y, Z) = \{h : Y \to Z;\ \text{a morphism of schemes with } f = g \cdot h\}.$$

In the next lemma, we list some of the elementary properties of schemes.

LEMMA 4.2. *Let $(X, \mathcal{O}_X)$ be a scheme.*

(1) *An affine scheme is a scheme.*

(2) *The set of all affine open sets of $(X, \mathcal{O}_X)$ is an open basis of the topology of X.*

(3) *$(X, \mathcal{O}_X)$ is a T_0-space, but it is not necessarily a T_1-space.*

(4) *An irreducible closed set F of X has a unique generic point. Namely, there exists a unique point $x \in F$ with $F = \overline{\{x\}}$. If $F \cap U \neq \emptyset$ for an open set U of X, then $x \in U$.*

(5) *Let $\mathcal{J}$ be a quasi-coherent Ideal of $\mathcal{O}_X$, i.e., $\mathcal{J}$ is a sheaf of ideals of $\mathcal{O}_X$ which is a quasi-coherent $\mathcal{O}_X$-Module, let $Y := \mathrm{Supp}(\mathcal{O}_X/\mathcal{J})$, and let $\mathcal{O}_Y := \mathcal{O}_X/\mathcal{J}$. Then $(Y, \mathcal{O}_Y)$ is a scheme. (The scheme $(Y, \mathcal{O}_Y)$ expressed in this manner is called a* closed subscheme *of X. If a scheme $(Z, \mathcal{O}_Z)$ is isomorphic to a closed subscheme $(Y, \mathcal{O}_Y)$ of X via a morphism $\sigma: (Z, \mathcal{O}_Z) \to (Y, \mathcal{O}_Y)$, then the morphism $(\sigma, \theta): (Z, \mathcal{O}_Z) \to (X, \mathcal{O}_X)$ is called a* closed immersion *or a* closed embedding, *where $\theta: \mathcal{O}_X|_Y \to \mathcal{O}_X/\mathcal{J} \xrightarrow{\sigma^*} \mathcal{O}_Z$.)*

(6) *For $x \in X$, $\mathrm{Spec}(\mathcal{O}_{X,x}) = \{y \in X; x \in \overline{\{y\}}\}$. (For two points x, y of X, if $x \in \overline{\{y\}}$, we say that x is a* specialization *of y and y is a* generalization *of x.)*

(7) *For an open set U of X, $(U, \mathcal{O}_X|_U)$ is a scheme. (A morphism of schemes $(\sigma, \theta): (Z, \mathcal{O}_Z) \to (X, \mathcal{O}_X)$ is called an* open immersion *if $\sigma(Z)$ is an open set of X, σ induces a homeomorphism between Z and $\sigma(Z)$, and $\theta^{\#}: \sigma^*\mathcal{O}_X \to \mathcal{O}_Z$ induces an isomorphism between $\mathcal{O}_X|_{\sigma(Z)}$ and $\mathcal{O}_Z$.)*

PROOF. (1) and (2) are obvious.

(3) Let x, y be two points of X, and let U be an affine open neighborhood of x. Suppose $y \in U$. Since x and y are two points of an affine scheme, the remark given before Definition 3.3 implies that there exists an open set containing one of x, y and not containing the other. Hence, the topology of X is a T_0-topology.

(4) If U is an open set of X with $U \cap F \neq \emptyset$, then there exists an affine open set V of X such that $V \subseteq U$ and $V \cap F \neq \emptyset$. Since $F = \overline{(V \cap F)} \cup (F \cap (X - V))$ and F is irreducible, $F = \overline{(V \cap F)}$. Namely, $V \cap F$ is dense in F. Suppose $V \cap F = (V \cap F_1) \cup (V \cap F_2)$, $V \cap F_1 \subsetneqq V \cap F$, and $V \cap F_2 \subsetneqq V \cap F$ for closed sets F_1, F_2 of X. Then we have

$$F = (F \cap F_1) \cup (F \cap F_2) \cup (F \cap (X - V)),$$
$$F \cap F_1 \subsetneqq F, \qquad F \cap F_2 \subsetneqq F$$

which contradicts the irreducibility of F. Hence, $V \cap F$ is an irreducible closed subset of V. By Lemma 3.7, there exists a point $x \in V \cap F$ such that $V \cap F = \overline{\{x\}}$ in V. Hence, $F = \overline{\{x\}} \cup (F \cap (X - V))$. So by the irreducibility of F, $F = \overline{\{x\}}$. If $F = \overline{\{x'\}}$, then $x' \in V \cap F$. So by Lemma 3.7, $x = x'$.

(5) Since $\mathscr{O}_X/\mathscr{I}$ is finitely generated, $Y := \operatorname{Supp}(\mathscr{O}_X/\mathscr{I})$ is a closed subset of X. **For each $x \in Y$, let $U = \operatorname{Spec}(A)$ be an affine open neighborhood of x. Then there exists an ideal I of A such that $\mathscr{I}|_U = \tilde{I}$, $Y \cap U = V(I)$ and $\mathscr{O}_{Y \cap U} = \widetilde{(A/I)}$. Hence, $Y \cap U$ is an affine open neighborhood of x in Y.** Thereby, **Y is a scheme.**

(6) Let $V = \operatorname{Spec}(A)$ be an affine open neighborhood of x. Then $\mathscr{O}_{X,x} = A_x$ (the localization of A by a prime ideal $\mathfrak{p}_x$). Suppose $x \in \overline{\{y\}}$. Then $y \in V$ and $\mathfrak{p}_x \supseteq \mathfrak{p}_y$ in A. So $y \in \operatorname{Spec}(A_x)$. The converse also holds. So $\operatorname{Spec}(A_x) = \{y \in X ; x \in \overline{\{y\}}\}$.

(7) For each $x \in U$, we can choose its affine open neighborhood V so that $V \subseteq U$. Then $(U, \mathscr{O}_X|_U)$ is clearly a scheme. □

Define the sheaf of nilradicals $\mathscr{N}$ by

$$U \mapsto \mathscr{N}(U) = \text{the nilradical of } \Gamma(U, \mathscr{O}_X).$$

Then $\mathscr{N}_x$ is the nilradical of $\mathscr{O}_{X,x}$ for each $x \in X$. Moreover, $\mathscr{N}$ is a quasicoherent Ideal of $\mathscr{O}_X$. Hence, $(X, \mathscr{O}_X/\mathscr{N})$ is a closed subscheme and $\operatorname{Supp}(\mathscr{O}_X/\mathscr{N}) = X$. We denote this closed subscheme by X_{red} and call it the *reduced form* of X. (Compare the definition with the one given before Lemma 3.21.) We say that X is *reduced* if $X = X_{\text{red}}$.

If Y is a closed subset of X, there is a unique reduced scheme structure on Y. In fact, let $U = \operatorname{Spec}(A)$ be an arbitrary affine open set of X. Then $Y \cap U = V(I)$ with $I = \sqrt{I}$. For another affine open set $V = \operatorname{Spec}(B)$, write $V \cap Y = V(J)$ with $J = \sqrt{J}$. Then $\tilde{I}|_{U \cap V} = \tilde{J}|_{U \cap V}$. (Compare $\tilde{I}_x$ and $\tilde{J}_x$ for each $x \in U \cap V$.) Hence, there exists a quasicoherent Ideal $\mathscr{I}$ such that $\mathscr{I}|_U = \tilde{I}$. It is clear from the above construction that $Y = \operatorname{Supp}(\mathscr{O}_X/\mathscr{I})$ and $(Y, \mathscr{O}_X/\mathscr{I})$ is a reduced scheme. Suppose $Y = \operatorname{Supp}(\mathscr{O}_X/\mathscr{J})$, $\mathscr{J}|_U = \tilde{J}$, and $J = \sqrt{J}$. Then $U \cap Y = V(I) = V(J)$; whence, $I = J$. Hence, $\mathscr{I} = \mathscr{J}$. So there is a unique reduced scheme structure on Y. We also denote it by Y_{red}.

If X_0 is a connected component of X, then X_0 is also an open set of X. Hence, $(X_0, \mathscr{O}_X|_{X_0})$ is a scheme. If $X = \coprod_{i \in I} X_i$ is the decomposition of X into connected components then X is regarded as a disjoint union of schemes $\{(X_i, \mathscr{O}_X|_{X_i})\}_{i \in I}$. Conversely, given a set of schemes $\{(X_i, \mathscr{O}_{X_i})\}_{i \in I}$, we define on a direct sum of topological spaces $X = \coprod_{i\in I} X_i$ a sheaf $\mathscr{O}_X$ by $\mathscr{O}_X|_{X_i} = \mathscr{O}_{X_i}$. Then $(X, \mathscr{O}_X)$ is a scheme. We call this scheme a *direct sum* of $\{(X_i, \mathscr{O}_{X_i})\}_{i\in I}$ and denote it by $\coprod_{i\in I} X_i$. It is straightforward to verify that the direct sum satisfies the following property:

$$\operatorname{Hom}\left(\coprod_{i\in I} X_i, T\right) \cong \prod_{i\in I} \operatorname{Hom}(X_i, T) \quad \text{for every scheme } T,$$

where $\prod_{i\in I}$ stands for a direct product of sets and $\operatorname{Hom}(\cdot,\cdot)$ is the set of morphisms of schemes.

We shall prove the following lemma concerning local properties of schemes and morphisms of schemes.

LEMMA 4.3. (1) *Let $\{W_i\}_{i\in I}$ be a set of schemes satisfying the following two conditions*:

(i) *For each $i, j \in I$, there exist open sets U_{ij} of W_i and U_{ji} of W_j and an isomorphism of schemes $\theta_{ji}\colon (U_{ij}, \mathscr{O}_{W_i}|_{U_{ij}}) \to (U_{ji}, \mathscr{O}_{W_j}|_{U_{ji}})$ such that $\theta_{ij}\cdot\theta_{ji} = 1$ and $\theta_{ii} = 1$, where 1 stands for the identity morphism.*

(ii) *For each $i, j, k \in I$, $\theta_{ji}(U_{ij}\cap U_{ik}) = U_{ji}\cap U_{jk}$ and $\theta_{kj}\cdot\theta_{ji} = \theta_{ki}$ on $U_{ij}\cap U_{ik}$.*

Then there exist a scheme W and the open immersions $\xi_i\colon W_i \to W$ for each $i\in I$ such that $W = \bigcup_{i\in I} U_i$ with $U_i = \xi_i(W_i)$ and ξ_i induces an isomorphism between U_{ij} and $U_i\cap U_j$ to the effect that $\xi_i|_{U_{ij}} = (\xi_j|_{U_{ji}})\cdot\theta_{ji}$ for each $i, j\in I$.

(2) *Let X and Y be schemes and let $X = \bigcup_{i\in I} U_i$ be an open covering of X. Suppose we are given morphisms of schemes $f_i\colon U_i \to Y$ $(i\in I)$ such that $f_i|_{U_i\cap U_j} = f_j|_{U_i\cap U_j}$ for each $i, j\in I$. Then there exists a morphism of schemes $f\colon X\to Y$ such that $f_i = f|_{U_i}$ for each $i\in I$.*

PROOF. (1) First of all, there exist a topological space W, its open covering $\{U_i\}_{i\in I}$ and homeomorphisms $\xi_i\colon W_i \to U_i$ $(i\in I)$ such that $\xi_i(U_{ij}) = U_i\cap U_j$ and $\theta_{ji} = (\xi_j|_{U_{ji}})^{-1}\cdot(\xi_i|_{U_{ij}})$ for each $i, j\in I$. We define a sheaf of commutative rings $\mathscr{O}_W$ on W as follows: Let U be an open set of W. If $U\subseteq U_i$ (for some i) then $\Gamma(U, \mathscr{O}_W) = \{s\cdot\xi_i^{-1}; s\in\Gamma(\xi_i^{-1}(U), \mathscr{O}_{W_i})\}$. If $U\subseteq U_i\cap U_j$, then $s\cdot\xi_i^{-1} = (s\cdot\theta_{ij})\cdot\xi_j^{-1}$, where $s\mapsto s\cdot\theta_{ij}$ is an isomorphism between $\Gamma(\xi_i^{-1}(U), \mathscr{O}_{W_i})$ and $\Gamma(\xi_j^{-1}(U), \mathscr{O}_{W_j})$. This implies that the definition of $\Gamma(U, \mathscr{O}_W)$ is independent of the choice of $i\in I$ with $U\subseteq U_i$. So we can define the stalk $\mathscr{O}_{W,x}$ for each $x\in W$ and introduce a topology on $\widetilde{\mathscr{O}}_W = \coprod_{x\in W}\mathscr{O}_{W,x}$ such that the natural projection $\pi\colon\widetilde{\mathscr{O}}_W \to W$ is a local homeomorphism. We then define $\mathscr{O}_W$ as the sheaf of local sections of π (cf. (I.2.5)).

It is clear from the above construction that $\xi_i\colon (W_i, \mathscr{O}_{W_i}) \to (U_i, \mathscr{O}_W|_{U_i})$ is an isomorphism of local ringed spaces. Hence, W is a scheme and $\xi_i\colon W_i \xrightarrow{\sim} U_i \hookrightarrow W$ is an open immersion.

(2) Patching $\{f_i\}_{i\in I}$ together, we can define a mapping of topological spaces $f\colon X\to Y$. We can also define a homomorphism of sheaves of commutative rings $\varphi^\#\colon f^*\mathscr{O}_Y \to \mathscr{O}_X$ by patching together homomorphisms $\varphi_i^\#\colon f_i^*\mathscr{O}_Y \to \mathscr{O}_{U_i}$ associated with f_i. In fact, we have only to note that $f^*\mathscr{O}_Y|_{U_i} = f_i^*\mathscr{O}_Y$, and $f_i^*\mathscr{O}_Y|_U = f_j^*\mathscr{O}_Y|_U$ and $\varphi_i^\#|_U = \varphi_j^\#|_U$ provided $U\subseteq U_i\cap U_j$. Then f is a morphism of schemes such that $f_i = f|_{U_i}$. □

The following property of schemes is also important.

LEMMA 4.4. *Let* $(X, \mathscr{O}_X)$ *be a scheme, let* $(S, \mathscr{O}_S) = (\mathrm{Spec}(R), \widetilde{R})$ *be an affine scheme, and let* $(f, \varphi)\colon (X, \mathscr{O}_X) \to (S, \mathscr{O}_S)$ *be a morphism of schemes. Let* $A = \Gamma(X, \mathscr{O}_X)$, *and let* $\sigma = \Gamma(S, \varphi)\colon R \to A$. *Then there exists a unique morphism of schemes* $(g, \psi)\colon (X, \mathscr{O}_X) \to (\mathrm{Spec}(A), \widetilde{A})$ *such that* $(f, \varphi) = ({}^a\sigma, \tilde{\sigma}) \cdot (g, \psi)$.

PROOF. For an affine open set $U = \mathrm{Spec}(A_U)$ of X, the restriction morphism $\rho_{UX}\colon A = \Gamma(X, \mathscr{O}_X) \to A_U = \Gamma(U, \mathscr{O}_X)$ gives rise to a morphism of affine schemes $g_U\colon (U, \mathscr{O}_X|_U) \to (\mathrm{Spec}(A), \widetilde{A})$. We shall show that $g_U|_{U\cap U'} = g_{U'}|_{U\cap U'}$ for another affine open set U'. For this, it suffices to show that $g_U|_V = g_V$ for any affine open set $V = \mathrm{Spec}(B)$ contained in $U \cap U'$. Meanwhile, the restriction morphism $\rho_{VU}\colon A_U \to B = \Gamma(V, \mathscr{O}_X)$ induces a morphism of schemes ${}^a(\rho_{VU})\colon V \to U$, which turns out to be the natural open immersion $V \hookrightarrow U$. Hence, the relation $\rho_{VU} \cdot \rho_{UX} = \rho_{VX}$ implies $g_U|_V = g_V$. Since X has an affine open covering, i.e., a covering consisting of affine open sets, we know by Lemma 4.3(2) that there exists a morphism of schemes $g\colon X \to \mathrm{Spec}(A)$. Let $f\colon X \to S$ be a morphism of schemes as in the statement. The restriction $f|_U\colon U \to S$ of f onto an affine open set U corresponds to a ring homomorphism $\sigma_U\colon R \to A_U$ (Lemma 3.22). For $V \subseteq U \cap U'$ as above, $f|_V$ corresponds to $\rho_{VU} \cdot \sigma_U = \sigma_V = \rho_{VU'} \cdot \sigma_{U'}$. Since $\mathscr{O}_X$ is a sheaf, this gives $\rho_{U\cap U', U} \cdot \sigma_U = \rho_{U\cap U', U'} \cdot \sigma_{U'}$. Hence, by the definition of sheaf again, we know that there exists a ring homomorphism $\sigma\colon R \to A$ such that $\sigma_U = \rho_{UX} \cdot \sigma$. (More precisely, consider an affine open covering $\{U_\lambda\}_{\lambda\in\Lambda}$ of X and apply the above argument.) Hence, $f|_U$ decomposes as

$$U \xrightarrow{g_U} \mathrm{Spec}(A) \xrightarrow{{}^a\sigma} S.$$

Since U is an arbitrary affine open set, we have $f = {}^a\sigma \cdot g$. The uniqueness of g should be clear by the above construction of g. □

Let S be a scheme, and let $f\colon X \to S$ and $g\colon Y \to S$ be schemes over S. A triple (Z, p, q) consisting of a scheme $h\colon Z \to S$ over S and morphisms of S-schemes $p\colon Z \to X$ and $q\colon Z \to Y$ is called a *fiber product* of X and Y over S if the following conditions are satisfied:

For every S-scheme T, a mapping of sets

$$\mathrm{Hom}_S(T, Z) \to \mathrm{Hom}_S(T, X) \times \mathrm{Hom}_S(T, Y), \qquad u \mapsto (p \cdot u, q \cdot u)$$

is a bijection.

We denote Z by $X \times_S Y$ as well. If $X \times_S Y$ exists, then morphisms of S-schemes (S-morphisms, for short) $\alpha\colon T \to X$ and $\beta\colon T \to Y$ determine an S-morphism $T \to X \times_S Y$, which we denote by $(\alpha, \beta)_S$ or (α, β). If Z exists, it is determined uniquely up to an S-isomorphism. More precisely, if an S-scheme $h'\colon Z' \to S$ together with S-morphisms $p'\colon Z' \to X$ and $q'\colon Z' \to Y$ satisfies the same conditions as the triple (Z, p, q) does, then there exists an S-isomorphism $\theta\colon Z \xrightarrow{\sim} Z'$ such that $p = p' \cdot \theta$ and $q = q' \cdot \theta$. This isomorphism θ is uniquely determined.

THEOREM 4.5. *A fiber product* $X \times_S Y$ *of* S*-schemes* (X, f) *and* (Y, g) *exists.*

PROOF. We shall prove the assertion in several steps.

CLAIM 1. Assume that a triple (Z, p, q) consisting of an S-scheme Z and S-morphisms $p\colon Z \to X$ and $q\colon Z \to Y$ gives a fiber product $X \times_S Y$. Let U and V be open sets of X and Y, respectively, and let $W = p^{-1}(U) \cap q^{-1}(V)$. Then $W = U \times_S V$, where U and V are viewed as S-schemes via $f|_U$ and $g|_V$, respectively.

PROOF. Given S-morphisms $v: T \to U$ and $w: T \to V$ with $f|_U \cdot v = g|_V \cdot w$, there exists a unique S-morphism $u: T \to Z$ such that $v = p \cdot u$ and $w = q \cdot u$. Then the morphism u passes through W as $u: T \to W \hookrightarrow Z$. Conversely, if an S-morphism $u: T \to Z$ passes through W, then $p \cdot u$ and $q \cdot u$ pass through U and V, respectively. □

CLAIM 2. Let Z be an S-scheme, and let $p: Z \to X$ and $q: Z \to Y$ be S-morphisms. Let $\mathfrak{U} = \{U_i\}_{i \in I}$ and $\mathfrak{V} = \{V_j\}_{j \in J}$ be open coverings of X and Y, respectively. Let $W_{ij} = p^{-1}(U_i) \cap q^{-1}(V_j)$ for each $(i, j) \in I \times J$. If $W_{ij} = U_i \times_S V_j$ for each $(i, j) \in I \times J$, then $Z = X \times_S Y$.

PROOF. We show that

$$\mathrm{Hom}_S(T, Z) \to \mathrm{Hom}_S(T, X) \times \mathrm{Hom}_S(T, Y), \qquad u \mapsto (p \cdot u, q \cdot u)$$

is a bijection.

Injectivity. Suppose we are given S-morphisms $u, u': T \to Z$ such that $p \cdot u = p \cdot u'$ and $q \cdot u = q \cdot u'$. Since

$$\begin{aligned} u^{-1}(W_{ij}) &= u^{-1}p^{-1}(U_i) \cap u^{-1}q^{-1}(V_j) = (pu)^{-1}(U_i) \cap (qu)^{-1}(V_j) \\ &= (pu')^{-1}(U_i) \cap (qu')^{-1}(V_j) = u'^{-1}(W_{ij}) \end{aligned}$$

and since $W_{ij} = U_i \times_S V_j$, we have $u|_{u^{-1}(W_{ij})} = u'|_{u'^{-1}(W_{ij})}$. Obviously, $\{u^{-1}(W_{ij}); (i, j) \in I \times J\}$ is an open covering of T, whence $u = u'$.

Surjectivity. Let $v: T \to X$ and $w: T \to Y$ be S-morphisms. Set $T_{ij} = v^{-1}(U_i) \cap w^{-1}(V_j)$. Then there exists an S-morphism $u_{ij}: T_{ij} \to W_{ij}$ such that $p \cdot u_{ij} = v|_{T_{ij}}$ and $q \cdot u_{ij} = w|_{T_{ij}}$. If $T_{ij} \cap T_{kl} \neq \emptyset$, then $u_{ij}(T_{ij} \cap T_{kl}) \subseteq p^{-1}(U_k) \cap q^{-1}(V_l) = W_{kl}$. Hence, $u_{ij}(T_{ij} \cap T_{kl}) \subseteq W_{ij} \cap W_{kl}$. We also have $u_{kl}(T_{ij} \cap T_{kl}) \subseteq W_{ij} \cap W_{kl}$. On the other hand, since $W_{ij} \cap W_{kl} = p^{-1}(U_i \cap U_k) \cap q^{-1}(V_j \cap V_l)$, we have $W_{ij} \cap W_{kl} = (U_i \cap U_k) \times_S (V_j \cap V_l)$ by (1) above. Furthermore, since $p \cdot u_{ij}|_{T_{ij} \cap T_{kl}} = v|_{T_{ij} \cap T_{kl}} = p \cdot u_{kl}|_{T_{ij} \cap T_{kl}}$ and $q \cdot u_{ij}|_{T_{ij} \cap T_{kl}} = w|_{T_{ij} \cap T_{kl}} = q \cdot u_{kl}|_{T_{ij} \cap T_{kl}}$, we have $u_{ij}|_{T_{ij} \cap T_{kl}} = u_{kl}|_{T_{ij} \cap T_{kl}}$ by the definition of fiber product. Noting that $T = \bigcup_{i,j} T_{ij}$, we then know that there exists an S-morphism $u: T \to Z$ such that $u_{ij} = u|_{T_{ij}}$ for each $(i, j) \in I \times J$. □

CLAIM 3. Let $\mathfrak{U} = \{U_i\}_{i \in I}$ and $\mathfrak{V} = \{V_j\}_{j \in J}$ be open coverings of X and Y, respectively. If $U_i \times_S V_j$ exists for each $(i, j) \in I \times J$, then $X \times_S Y$ exists.

PROOF. Put $\alpha = (i, j)$, briefly. Let $(Z_\alpha, p_\alpha, q_\alpha)$ denote a fiber product $U_i \times_S V_j$ and its projections. Let $\beta = (k, l)$. By (1), $Z_{\alpha\beta} = p_\alpha^{-1}(U_i \cap U_k) \cap q_\alpha^{-1}(V_j \cap V_l)$ and $Z_{\beta\alpha} = p_\beta^{-1}(U_i \cap U_k) \cap q_\beta^{-1}(V_j \cap V_l)$ are fiber products of $U_i \cap U_k$ and $V_j \cap V_l$, and by the uniqueness of a fiber product, there exists an S-isomorphism $\theta_{\alpha\beta}: Z_{\beta\alpha} \xrightarrow{\sim} Z_{\alpha\beta}$ such that $p_\alpha \cdot \theta_{\alpha\beta} = p_\beta$ and $q_\alpha \cdot \theta_{\alpha\beta} = q_\beta$. Moreover, since $Z_{\gamma\alpha} \cap Z_{\gamma\beta}$ is a fiber product of $U_i \cap U_k \cap U_m$ and $V_j \cap V_l \cap V_n$ for $\gamma = (m, n) \in I \times J$, we have $\theta_{\alpha\beta} \cdot \theta_{\beta\gamma} = \theta_{\alpha\gamma}$ on $Z_{\gamma\alpha} \cap Z_{\gamma\beta}$. Hence, by applying (1) of Lemma 4.3 to $\{Z_\alpha (\alpha \in I \times J), Z_{\alpha\beta}\ (\alpha, \beta \in I \times J)\}$, we know that there exist an S-scheme Z, an open covering $\{W_\alpha\}_{\alpha \in I \times J}$ of Z, and S-isomorphisms $\xi_\alpha: Z_\alpha \xrightarrow{\sim} W_\alpha (\alpha \in I \times J)$ such that $\xi_\alpha(Z_{\alpha\beta}) = W_\alpha \cap W_\beta = \xi_\beta(Z_{\beta\alpha})$ and $\theta_{\alpha\beta} = (\xi_\alpha|_{Z_{\alpha\beta}})^{-1} \cdot (\xi_\beta|_{Z_{\beta\alpha}})$. Here, since

$$\begin{aligned} p_\alpha \cdot (\xi_\alpha^{-1}|_{W_\alpha \cap W_\beta}) &= p_\beta \cdot (\xi_\beta^{-1}|_{W_\alpha \cap W_\beta}) \\ q_\alpha \cdot (\xi_\alpha^{-1}|_{W_\alpha \cap W_\beta}) &= q_\beta \cdot (\xi_\beta^{-1}|_{W_\alpha \cap W_\beta}), \end{aligned}$$

we know by (2) of Lemma 4.3 that there exist S-morphisms $p: Z \to X$ and $q: Z \to Y$ such that $p|_{W_\alpha} = p_\alpha \cdot \xi_\alpha^{-1}$ and $q|_{W_\alpha} = q_\alpha \cdot \xi_\alpha^{-1}$. Then we have only to show that a triple (Z, p, q) is a fiber product of X and Y over S. We will be done by (2) above if we show that Z_α is S-isomorphic to $p^{-1}(U_i) \cap q^{-1}(V_j)$ for each $\alpha = (i, j) \in I \times J$. For $\beta = (k, l)$, we have

$$\begin{aligned} p^{-1}(U_i) \cap q^{-1}(V_j) \cap W_\beta &= \xi_\beta p_\beta^{-1}(U_i \cap U_k) \cap \xi_\beta q_\beta^{-1}(V_j \cap V_l) \\ &= \xi_\beta(p_\beta^{-1}(U_i \cap U_k) \cap q_\beta^{-1}(V_j \cap V_l)) \\ &= \xi_\beta(Z_{\beta\alpha}) = W_\alpha \cap W_\beta. \end{aligned}$$

Since $\beta \in I \times J$ is arbitrary, we have $p^{-1}(U_i) \cap q^{-1}(V_j) = W_\alpha$, which is S-isomorphic to Z_α. Hence, Z is a fiber product of X and Y over S. □

Claim 4. Let $\{S_i\}_{i \in I}$ be an open covering of S, let $X_i = f^{-1}(S_i)$, and let $Y_i = g^{-1}(S_i)$. If a fiber product $X_i \times_{S_i} Y_i$ of $(X_i, f|_{X_i})$ and $(Y_i, g|_{Y_i})$ exists for each $i \in I$, then there exists a fiber product $X \times_S Y$ of (X, f) and (Y, g).

Proof. Since $\{X_i\}_{i \in I}$ and $\{Y_i\}_{i \in I}$ are open coverings of X and Y, respectively, we have only to show by (3) above that a fiber product $X_i \times_S Y_j$ exists for each $(i, j) \in I \times J$. First of all, $X_i \times_{S_i} Y_i$ is a fiber product of X_i and Y_i over S, where X_i and Y_i are regarded as S-schemes via $S_i \hookrightarrow S$. Let $X_{ij} = X_i \cap X_j$ and $Y_{ij} = Y_i \cap Y_j$. By (1) above, there exists a fiber product $X_{ij} \times_S Y_{ij}$ which we denote by Z_{ij}. We can show, by verifying the conditions in the definition of fiber product, that Z_{ij} is S-isomorphic to $X_i \times_S Y_j$. So $X_i \times_S Y_j$ exists. By (3) above, a fiber product $X \times_S Y$ thereby exists. □

Let $\{S_i\}_{i \in I}$ be an affine open covering of S. By (4), it suffices to show that $X_i \times_{S_i} Y_i$ exists. So we may assume that S is an affine scheme. Now let $\{U_i\}_{i \in I}$ and $\{V_j\}_{j \in J}$ be affine open coverings of X and Y, respectively. By (3), it suffices to show that $U_i \times_S V_j$ exists. So we may assume that X and Y are affine schemes as well. Namely, suppose $f: X \to S$ and $g: Y \to S$ are given by ring homomorphisms $\varphi: C \to A$ and $\psi: C \to B$, respectively. With A and B viewed as C-algebras by φ and ψ, we show that $X \times_S Y \cong \operatorname{Spec}(A \otimes_C B)$. Let T be an arbitrary S-scheme. Note that every S-morphism from T to an affine scheme is factorized by $\operatorname{Spec}\Gamma(T, \mathscr{O}_T)$ (Lemma 4.4). Hence, in order to show

$$\operatorname{Hom}_S(T, Z) \cong \operatorname{Hom}_S(T, X) \times \operatorname{Hom}_S(T, Y),$$

where

$$Z = \operatorname{Spec}(A \otimes_C B),$$

we may assume that T is also an affine scheme. Let $T = \operatorname{Spec}(R)$. Then we have only to show that a mapping between the sets of C-algebra homomorphisms

$$\operatorname{Hom}_C(A, R) \times \operatorname{Hom}_C(B, R) \to \operatorname{Hom}_C(A \otimes_C B, R)$$

$$(\alpha, \beta) \mapsto \left(\alpha \otimes \beta : \sum_i a_i \otimes b_i \mapsto \sum_i \alpha(a_i)\beta(b_i)\right)$$

is a bijection. This is a well-known result. The proof is left to the reader. □

The underlying set of $X \times_S Y$ is not necessarily identical with the product of underlying sets $\{(x, y); x \in X, y \in Y\}$ (problem II.4.1). In the last step in the proof of

Theorem 4.5, we saw that the fiber product $X \times_S Y$ of affine schemes corresponds to the tensor product $A \otimes_C B$. So properties which are common to the tensor products are inherited by the fiber products of schemes as shown in the next lemma.

LEMMA 4.6. *Let (X, f) and (Y, g) be S-schemes. Then the following assertions hold*:

(1) *For (X, f) and $(S, 1_S)$, we have $X \times_S S \cong S \times_S X \cong X$.*

(2) *Let (S', u) be an S-scheme, and let $X_{S'} = X \times_S S'$. Let $f_{S'} : X_{S'} \to S'$ and $u_X : X_{S'} \to X$ be the natural projections. Then $u \cdot f_{S'} = f \cdot u_X$. (We call $f_{S'} : X_{S'} \to S'$ the* base change *of $f: X \to S$ by u. We also write $f_{S'} = f \times_S S'$.)*

(3) *$X_{S'} \times_{S'} Y_{S'} \cong (X \times_S Y)_{S'}$.*

(4) *$f^{-1}(U) \cong X \times_S U$ for an open set U of S.*

Each assertion is easy to prove, so we omit the proofs. Base changes which we frequently have to consider include the following four kinds. In the following, $f: X \to Y$ signifies a morphism of schemes.

(1) Let y be a point of Y, and let $k(y)$ be the residue field of a local ring $\mathcal{O}_{Y,y}$. If $V = \mathrm{Spec}(B)$ is an affine open neighborhood of y, then the point y corresponds to a prime ideal $\mathfrak{q}$ of B and $k(y) = Q(B/\mathfrak{q}) = B_\mathfrak{q}/\mathfrak{q}B_\mathfrak{q}$. Hence, the composite of the natural ring homomorphisms $B \to B/\mathfrak{q} \hookrightarrow k(y)$ gives rise to a morphism of schemes $\iota_y : \mathrm{Spec}(k(y)) \to V \hookrightarrow Y$. The base change of f by ι_y is denoted by $f_y : X_y \to \mathrm{Spec}(k(y))$, where $X_y = X \times_Y \mathrm{Spec}(k(y))$ and $f_y = f \times_Y \mathrm{Spec}(k(y))$. This definition of (X_y, f_y) is determined independently of the choice of an affine open neighborhood V. We call (X_y, f_y) the *fiber* of f over y. In order to look into the structure of X_y, consider the inverse image $f^{-1}(y)$ as a set and consider a family of affine open sets $\{U_\lambda\}_{\lambda \in \Lambda}$ of X so that $\bigcup_{\lambda \in \Lambda} U_\lambda \supseteq f^{-1}(y)$. Then $X_y = \bigcup_{\lambda \in \Lambda} U_\lambda \times_Y \mathrm{Spec}(k(y))$ and $U_\lambda \times_Y \mathrm{Spec}(k(y)) = \mathrm{Spec}(A_\lambda \otimes_B k(y))$, where $U_\lambda = \mathrm{Spec}(A_\lambda)$.

(2) Let $(\mathcal{O}, t\mathcal{O})$ be a discrete valuation ring. Consider the case where $Y = \mathrm{Spec}(\mathcal{O})$. Then Y consists of two points η and s, where η corresponds to the ideal (0) of $\mathcal{O}$ and s to the maximal ideal $t\mathcal{O}$ of $\mathcal{O}$. Hence, $f: X \to Y$ consists of two fibers X_η and X_s, where X_η is defined over the field $K = Q(\mathcal{O})$, i.e., X_η is a scheme over $\mathrm{Spec}(K)$, and X_s is defined over the field $k := \mathcal{O}/t\mathcal{O}$. We say that X_s is the *reduction* of X_η. In general, for a scheme Y and its point y such that the local ring $\mathcal{O}_{Y,y}$ is an integral domain, we can find, under some additional conditions, a discrete valuation ring $(\mathcal{O}, t\mathcal{O})$ such that $\mathcal{O}_{Y,y} \le \mathcal{O}$ and $Q(\mathcal{O}_{Y,y}) = Q(\mathcal{O})$ (cf. Lemma 4.12). If we put $X_\mathcal{O} = X \times_Y \mathrm{Spec}(\mathcal{O})$ and $f_\mathcal{O} = f \times_Y \mathrm{Spec}(\mathcal{O})$, then $f_\mathcal{O} : X_\mathcal{O} \to \mathrm{Spec}(\mathcal{O})$ fits in the situation considered above. We call X_s a *specialization* of X_η. We use this situation to observe the extent to which the properties of X_η are inherited by X_s.

(3) Let U be an open set of Y, let $X_U = f^{-1}(U)$, and let $f_U = f \times_Y U$. Then $f_U : X_U \to U$ is the restriction of f onto U. We have the next result.

LEMMA 4.7. *Let $\mathcal{F}$ be a quasicoherent $\mathcal{O}_X$-Module, and let $\mathcal{F}_U$ be the restriction of $\mathcal{F}$ onto an open set $f^{-1}(U)$. Then $(R^i f_* \mathcal{F})_U \cong R^i (f_U)_* \mathcal{F}_U$ for each $i \ge 0$.*

PROOF. An injective $\mathcal{O}_X$-Module $\mathcal{I}$ is a scattered sheaf (I.2.19). Hence, $\mathcal{I}_U$ is a scattered $\mathcal{O}_{X_U}$-Module. Thus, if

$$0 \to \mathcal{F} \xrightarrow{\eta} \mathcal{I}^0 \xrightarrow{\Delta^0} \mathcal{I}^1 \xrightarrow{\Delta^1} \cdots \to \mathcal{I}^n \xrightarrow{\Delta^n} \cdots$$

is an injective resolution of $\mathcal{F}$,

$$0 \to \mathcal{F}_U \xrightarrow{\eta} \mathcal{I}_U^0 \xrightarrow{\Delta^0} \mathcal{I}_U^1 \xrightarrow{\Delta^1} \cdots \mathcal{I}_U^n \xrightarrow{\Delta^n} \cdots$$

is a scattered resolution of $\mathscr{F}_U$. On the other hand, note that $(f_*\mathscr{F})_U = (f_U)_*\mathscr{F}_U$ and $(f_*\mathscr{I}^i)_U = (f_U)_*\mathscr{I}^i_U$. Then the above two complexes yield the isomorphisms as stated. Here we note also that $R^i(f_U)_*\mathscr{F}_U$ is obtained by a scattered resolution of $\mathscr{F}_U$ (cf. Proof of Theorem 3.23). □

(4) We say that a morphism of schemes $v: Z \to Y$ is a *flat* morphism if $\mathscr{O}_{Z,z}$ is a flat $\mathscr{O}_{Y,y}$-module for each $z \in Z$ and $y = v(z)$. The base change $f_Z: X_Z := X \times_Y Z \to Z$ by v behaves in terms of cohomologies in the same fashion as f_U in Lemma 4.7. Namely, we shall state the following result without giving a proof.

LEMMA 4.7.1. *Let $\mathscr{F}$ be a quasicoherent $\mathscr{O}_X$-Module, and let $\mathscr{F}_Z$ be the inverse image of $\mathscr{F}$ on X_Z. Then $(R^if_*\mathscr{F})_Z \cong R^i(f_Z)_*\mathscr{F}_Z$ for each $i \geq 0$.*

Now let $f: X \to S$ be a morphism of schemes. Define the *diagonal morphism* $\Delta_{X/S}: X \to X \times_S X$ as the morphism whose composites with two projections from $X \times_S X$ onto X are the identity morphism of X. As a mapping of sets, $\Delta_{X/S}$ has image $\Delta_{X/S}(X) = \{(x,x); x \in X\}$. For $x \in X$ and $s = f(x)$, choose affine open neighborhoods $U = \operatorname{Spec}(A)$ and $V = \operatorname{Spec}(C)$ of x and s, respectively, so that $U \subseteq f^{-1}(V)$. Then $U \times_V U = \operatorname{Spec}(A \otimes_C A)$ is an open neighborhood of a point (x,x) in $X \times_S X$. Then $\Delta_{X/S}|_U$ coincides with $\Delta_{U/V}: U \to U \times_V U$ and is defined by the ring multiplication $m: A \otimes_C A \to A$, $m(a \otimes a') = aa'$. $\Delta_{U/V}$ induces, therefore, an isomorphism between U and the closed subscheme of $U \times_V U$ defined by the ideal $\operatorname{Ker}(m)$ of $A \otimes_C A$. Namely, $\Delta_{U/V}$ is a closed immersion. Hence, we know that there exist a family of affine open sets $\{W_\lambda\}_{\lambda\in\Lambda}$ of $X \times_S X$ and quasicoherent Ideals $\mathscr{I}_\lambda$ ($\lambda \in \Lambda$) such that $\Delta_{X/S}(X) \subseteq \bigcup_{\lambda\in\Lambda} W_\lambda$ and $(\Delta_{X/S})^{-1}(W_\lambda) \cong (\Delta_{X/S}(X) \cap W_\lambda, \mathscr{O}_{W_\lambda}/\mathscr{I}_\lambda)$ for each $\lambda \in \Lambda$. In particular, $\Delta_{X/S}(X)$ is an open set of the closure $\overline{\Delta_{X/S}(X)}$. (As shown in Problem II.4.2, $\Delta_{X/S}(X)$ does not necessarily coincide with $\overline{\Delta_{X/S}(X)}$.) $\Delta_{X/S}(X)$ is a subscheme of $X \times_S X$ in the following sense.

DEFINITION 4.8. (1) Let X and Y be schemes. Y is called a *subscheme* of X if there exist an open set U and a quasicoherent $\mathscr{O}_U$-Ideal $\mathscr{I}$ such that Y is the closed subscheme of U defined by $\mathscr{I}$. (If $U = X$, then Y is a closed subscheme of X.)

(2) Let $f: X \to S$ be a morphism of schemes. We say that f is a *separated* morphism and X is *separated* over S by f if $\Delta_{X/S}$ is a closed immersion.

We can list the following properties of separated morphisms.

LEMMA 4.9. (1) *Let $f: X \to S$ be a morphism of schemes, let $\{V_\lambda\}_{\lambda\in\Lambda}$ be an open covering of S, and let $U_\lambda = f^{-1}(V_\lambda)$. Then f is separated if and only if so is $f|_{U_\lambda}: U_\lambda \to V_\lambda$ for each $\lambda \in \Lambda$.*

(2) *A morphism $f: X \to S$ with affine schemes X and S is separated.*

(3) *If $f: X \to Y$ and $g: Y \to Z$ are separated, so is the composite $g \cdot f: X \to Z$.*

(4) *If $f: X \to S$ is a separated morphism and $j: Y \to X$ is a closed immersion (or an open immersion), then $f \cdot j: Y \to S$ is separated.*

(5) *If $f: X \to S$ is a separated morphism, then any base change $f_{S'}: X_{S'} \to S'$ by an S-scheme S' is a separated morphism.*

(6) *For morphisms of schemes $f: X \to Y$ and $g: Y \to Z$, if the composite $g \cdot f$ is separated, then so is f.*

PROOF. (1) Let $f^{(2)}: X \times_S X \to S$ be the structure morphism. Then $U_\lambda \times_{V_\lambda} U_\lambda = (f^{(2)})^{-1}(V_\lambda)$. Furthermore, $\{U_\lambda \times_{V_\lambda} U_\lambda\}_{\lambda\in\Lambda}$ is an open covering of $X \times_S X$, and

$\Delta_{X/S}(X) \cap (U_\lambda \times_{V_\lambda} U_\lambda) = \Delta_{U_\lambda/V_\lambda}(U_\lambda)$ for each $\lambda \in \Lambda$. Now the assertion follows from the definition.

(2) Repeat the argument as developed just before Definition 4.8.

(3) By hypothesis, $\Delta_{X/Y}: X \to X \times_Y X$ and $\Delta_{Y/Z}: Y \to Y \times_Z Y$ are closed immersions. On the other hand, $\Delta_{X/Z}: X \to X \times_Z X$ is the composite of the morphism $(\Delta_{Y/Z}) \times_{Y \times_Z Y} (f, f)_Z : X \times_Y X \to X \times_Z X$ obtained as the base change of $\Delta_{Y/Z}$ by $(f, f)_Z : X \times_Z X \to Y \times_Z Y$ and $\Delta_{X/Y}$. Since the base change of a closed immersion and the composite of closed immersions are also closed immersions (Problem II.4.3), $\Delta_{X/Z}$ is a closed immersion. Thus, $g \cdot f$ is a separated morphism.

(4) Suppose j is a closed immersion. For an affine open set $V = \mathrm{Spec}(B)$ of X, $U := j^{-1}(V)$ is an affine open set of Y provided $U \neq \emptyset$. We can write $U = \mathrm{Spec}(A)$ with $A = B/I$, where I is an ideal of B. Then the projection $p_1 : U \times_V U = \mathrm{Spec}(A \otimes_B A) \to U$ is an isomorphism. Hence, we know that the projection $p_1 : Y \times_X Y \to Y$ is an isomorphism. Next suppose j is an open immersion. In this case, we can argue with $V \subseteq j(Y)$ to show that $p_1 : Y \times_X Y \to Y$ is an isomorphism. Since $p_1 \cdot \Delta_{Y/X} = 1_Y$, $\Delta_{Y/X}$ is an isomorphism, too. Namely, we know that j is a separated morphism. Then $f \cdot j$ is a separated morphism by (3) above.

(5) Since $\Delta_{X'/S'} = (\Delta_{X/S}) \times_S S'$, $\Delta_{X_{S'}/S'}$ is a closed immersion.

(6) f is the composite of $\Gamma_f : X \to X \times_Z Y$ and $p_2 : X \times_Z Y \to Y$, where $\Gamma_f = (1_X, f)_Z$ and p_2 is the natural projection. Now the diagonal morphism for Γ_f is an isomorphism; hence, Γ_f is a separated morphism. If we regard $Y = Z \times_Z Y$, then $p_2 = (g \cdot f) \times_Z Y$, so the projection p_2 is a base change of $g \cdot f$. By (5), p_2 is therefore a separated morphism. Now we know by (3) that f is a separated morphism. □

The significance of a morphism being separated will be explained after we define an algebraic variety.

DEFINITION 4.10. Let $f : X \to Y$ be a morphism of schemes.

(1) f is a *quasicompact morphism* if $f^{-1}(V)$ is a quasicompact open set of X for every quasicompact open set V of Y.

(2) f is a *locally finitely generated morphism* if for each point x of X there exist affine open neighborhoods $U = \mathrm{Spec}(A)$ of x and $V = \mathrm{Spec}(B)$ of $f(x)$ such that $U \subseteq f^{-1}(V)$ and A is a finitely generated B-algebra.

(3) f is a *finitely generated morphism* if f is quasicompact and locally finitely generated. We then call X a *finitely generated Y-scheme*. In particular, if $Y = \mathrm{Spec}(k)$ with a field k, we call a finitely generated Y-scheme X an *algebraic scheme* defined over k.

(4) Let X be an algebraic scheme defined over k. We call X an *algebraic variety* defined over k if X satisfies the following two conditions:

  (i) X is irreducible and reduced, and $X \times_{\mathrm{Spec}(k)} \mathrm{Spec}(\bar{k})$ (also denoted by $X \otimes_k \bar{k}$) is also irreducible and reduced, where $\bar{k}$ is an algebraic closure of k.

  (ii) The structure morphism $f : X \to \mathrm{Spec}(k)$ is a separated morphism.

(5) Let Y be a subscheme of an algebraic variety X defined over k. We call Y an *algebraic subvariety* of X if Y itself is an algebraic variety defined over k.

LEMMA 4.11. *Let X be an irreducible reduced algebraic scheme defined over a field k. Then the following assertions hold*:

(1) *X is a noetherian space.*

(2) *Let $U = \operatorname{Spec}(A)$ be an affine open set ($\neq \emptyset$) of X. Then the quotient field $Q(A)$ is a finitely generated extension of k which is determined only by X independently of the choice of U. (We call this field the* function field *of X over k and denote it by $k(X)$.) Then we have $\operatorname{tr.deg}_k k(X) = \dim X$.*

(3) *Let $\bar{k}$ be an algebraic closure of k. $X \otimes_k \bar{k}$ is irreducible and reduced if and only if $k(X) \otimes_k \bar{k}$ is a field, i.e., $k(X)$ is a regular extension of k. Then $\bar{k}(X \otimes_k \bar{k}) = k(X) \otimes_k \bar{k}$.*

(4) *Let x be a point of X. Then x is a closed point of X if and only if the residue field $k(x)$ of $\mathcal{O}_{X,x}$ is a finite algebraic extension of k. (We call x a k-*rational point *if $k(x) = k$.) When k is an algebraically closed field, the set $X(k)$ of k-rational points of X possesses a local-ringed space structure which is induced naturally by X. Conversely, the local-ringed space structure on $X(k)$ restores the local-ringed space structure on X.*

PROOF. (1) There exists a finite affine open covering $\mathfrak{U} = \{U_\lambda\}_{\lambda\in\Lambda}$ such that $A_\lambda := \Gamma(U_\lambda, \mathcal{O}_X)$ is finitely generated over k. Since U_λ is then a noetherian space and since $\mathfrak{U}$ is a finite covering, X is a noetherian space.

(2) Let $U = \operatorname{Spec}(A)$ and $V = \operatorname{Spec}(B)$ be nonempty affine open sets. Then $U \cap V \neq \emptyset$. A point x of $U \cap V$ corresponds to prime ideals $\mathfrak{p}, \mathfrak{q}$ of A, B, respectively, and $\mathcal{O}_{X,x} = A_\mathfrak{p} = B_\mathfrak{q}$. So $Q(A) = Q(\mathcal{O}_{X,x}) = Q(B)$. Since we may take U so that A is finitely generated over k, $Q(A)$ is a finitely generated extension of k. With the notations in (1), $\dim X = \max_{\lambda\in\Lambda} \dim U_\lambda$. Since $\dim U_\lambda = \dim \Gamma(U_\lambda, \mathcal{O}_{U_\lambda}) = \operatorname{tr.deg}_k k(X)$, we have $\dim X = \operatorname{tr.deg}_k k(X)$.

(3) By the construction of $X \otimes_k \bar{k}$, $U \otimes_k \bar{k} = \operatorname{Spec}(A \otimes_k \bar{k})$ is an open set of $X \otimes_k \bar{k}$. Suppose $X \otimes_k \bar{k}$ is irreducible and reduced. Then $Q(A) \subseteq Q(A) \otimes_k \bar{k} \subseteq Q(A \otimes_k \bar{k})$. Since $Q(A) \otimes_k \bar{k}$ is integral over $Q(A)$, $Q(A) \otimes_k \bar{k}$ is a field. Conversely, suppose $k(X) \otimes_k \bar{k}$ is a field. We shall show that $X \otimes_k \bar{k}$ is irreducible and reduced. First of all, take $U = \operatorname{Spec}(A)$ as above. Then $A \otimes_k \bar{k}$ is an integral domain because $A \otimes_k \bar{k}$ is a subring of $k(X) \otimes_k \bar{k}$; in fact, $\bar{k}$ is a flat k-module. Next $X \otimes_k \bar{k}$ is connected. If $X \otimes_k \bar{k}$ is not connected, there exists an affine open set $U = \operatorname{Spec}(A)$ such that the inverse image $p_1^{-1}(U)$ is not connected, where $p_1 \colon X \otimes_k \bar{k} \to X$ is the natural projection. Namely, there is an idempotent decomposition $1 = e_1 + e_2$ in $A \otimes_k \bar{k}$ such that $e_1^2 = e_1, e_2^2 = e_2$, and $e_1e_2 = 0$. (Verify this claim.) This is a contradiction because $A \otimes_k \bar{k}$ is an integral domain. Once we know that $X \otimes_k \bar{k}$ is connected, in order to prove that $X \otimes_k \bar{k}$ is irreducible and reduced, we have only to show that the local ring $\mathcal{O}_z$ for each point z of $X \otimes_k \bar{k}$ is an integral domain. Put $x = p_1(z)$, and let $U = \operatorname{Spec}(A)$ be an affine open neighborhood of x. Then z corresponds to a prime ideal $\mathfrak{q}$ of $A \otimes_k \bar{k}$, and $\mathcal{O}_z = (A \otimes_k \bar{k})_\mathfrak{q}$. Since $A \otimes_k \bar{k}$ is an integral domain as remarked above, so is $\mathcal{O}_z$.

(4) Let x be a point of X and choose an affine open neighborhood $U = \operatorname{Spec}(A)$ of x so that A is a finitely generated k-algebra. Then x is a closed point of X if and only if x is a closed point of U. Moreover, x is a closed point of U if and only if $k(x)$ is a finite algebraic extension of k ((I.1.15) and (I.1.10)). Suppose $k = \bar{k}$. Then $U(k)$ endowed with the induced topology from U and the sheaf of local rings $\mathcal{O}_{U(k)}$ (which we denote by $\mathcal{O}_U|_{U(k)}$) is an affine algebraic variety, and $(U(k), \mathcal{O}_{U(k)})$ restores $(U, \mathcal{O}_U)$ as a local ringed space (I.1.24). Since X has a finite affine open covering as specified in the above proof of (1), the induced topology on $X(k)$ from X restores the topology on X. Define $\mathcal{O}_{X(k)}$ by $\mathcal{O}_{X(k)}|_{U_\lambda(k)} = \mathcal{O}_{U_\lambda(k)}$. Then $(X(k), \mathcal{O}_{X(k)})$ is a local ringed space and restores $(X, \mathcal{O}_X)$. □

In view of (4) of Lemma 4.11, we may confuse deliberately an algebraic variety $(X, \mathscr{O}_X)$ with $(X(k), \mathscr{O}_{X(k)})$ when k is an algebraically closed field. As the sets of points, X differs from $X(k)$ in the point that X contains the generic points of all closed algebraic subvarieties of dimension ≥ 1. Now let X be an algebraic scheme defined over a field k with the structure morphism $f: X \to \mathrm{Spec}(k)$. We are going to explain the significance of f being a separated morphism in terms of discrete valuation rings. For this, we need some preparation.

LEMMA 4.12. *Let A be a finitely generated k-algebra domain, let K be its quotient field, and let L be a finite algebraic extension. Then for an arbitrary prime ideal $\mathfrak{p}$ of A, there exists a discrete valuation ring $\mathscr{O}$ of L such that $\mathscr{O}$ dominates $A_{\mathfrak{p}}$. Namely, $\mathscr{O} \supseteq A_{\mathfrak{p}}$ and $\mathfrak{m} \cap A_{\mathfrak{p}} = \mathfrak{p}A_{\mathfrak{p}}$, where $\mathfrak{m}$ is the maximal ideal of $\mathscr{O}$. We express it by $\mathscr{O} \geq A_{\mathfrak{p}}$.*

PROOF. Let $(x_1, \ldots, x_n)$ be a set of generators of $\mathfrak{p}$, i.e., $\mathfrak{p} = (x_1, \ldots, x_n)$, and let $B = A[x_2/x_1, \ldots, x_n/x_1]$. Then $\mathfrak{p}B = x_1 B$. Let R be the integral closure of B in L. By (I.1.34), R is a finitely generated k-algebra domain. Let $T = A - \mathfrak{p}$. Then R_T is a normal ring, and $\mathfrak{p}R_T = x_1 R_T$. Let $\mathfrak{P}$ be a prime divisor of $x_1 R_T$. Then $\mathfrak{P}$ has height 1 and $(R_T)_{\mathfrak{P}}$ is a discrete valuation ring of L (I.1.33). Since $\mathfrak{P}(R_T)_{\mathfrak{P}} \cap A_{\mathfrak{p}}$ is a proper ideal of $A_{\mathfrak{p}}$ containing $\mathfrak{p}A_{\mathfrak{p}}$, we have $\mathfrak{P}(R_T)_{\mathfrak{P}} \cap A_{\mathfrak{p}} = \mathfrak{p}A_{\mathfrak{p}}$. Hence, $(R_T)_{\mathfrak{P}} \geq A_{\mathfrak{p}}$. Thus, we have only to take $\mathscr{O} = (R_T)_{\mathfrak{P}}$. □

Let $(\mathscr{O}, \mathfrak{m})$ be a discrete valuation ring. The prime ideals of $\mathscr{O}$ are (0) and the maximal ideal $\mathfrak{m}$ only. Namely, $\mathrm{Spec}(\mathscr{O})$ consists of two points, the ideal (0) being the generic point and $\mathfrak{m}$ being the unique closed point. Let $g: \mathrm{Spec}(\mathscr{O}) \to X$ be a morphism of schemes, and let $g((0)) = x$ and $g(\mathfrak{m}) = x'$. Then there is a local homomorphism $\varphi: \mathscr{O}_{X,x'} \to \mathscr{O}$ associated with g. (g is factored by an affine open neighborhood $U = \mathrm{Spec}(A)$ of x'.) A prime ideal $\mathfrak{q} := \varphi^{-1}(0)$ corresponds to the point x, and $\mathscr{O}_{X,x'}/\mathfrak{q} = \mathscr{O}_{Y,x'}$, where $Y := (\overline{\{x\}})_{\mathrm{red}}$. Moreover, $\mathscr{O}_{Y,x'} \leq \mathscr{O}$. Furthermore, φ induces a homomorphism from the residue field $k(x) = \mathscr{O}_{X,x}/\mathfrak{m}_{X,x}$ to the quotient field $Q(\mathscr{O})$ of $\mathscr{O}$. Conversely, the following result holds.

LEMMA 4.13. *Let X be an algebraic scheme over a field k, let $x \in X$, let $Y = (\overline{\{x\}})_{\mathrm{red}}$, and let $x' \in Y$. Let L be a finite algebraic extension of the function field $k(Y)$. Then there exists a discrete valuation ring $\mathscr{O}$ of L such that $\mathscr{O} \geq \mathscr{O}_{Y,x'}$.*

PROOF. Since Y is an algebraic scheme over k, there exists an affine open neighborhood $\mathrm{Spec}(A)$ of x' in Y such that A is a finitely generated k-algebra domain. Let $\mathfrak{p}$ be a prime ideal of A corresponding to x'. Then, applying Lemma 4.12, we find a discrete valuation ring $\mathscr{O}$ of L such that $\mathscr{O} \geq A_{\mathfrak{p}} = \mathscr{O}_{Y,x'}$. □

Under the circumstances described just before Lemma 4.13, we say that x' is a *specialization* of x along $\mathscr{O}$ (or dominated by $\mathscr{O}$), and write it as $x \to x'$. The choice of a discrete valuation ring $\mathscr{O}$ which dominates a specialization $x \to x'$ is not unique. Even worse, if we give a point x of X and a discrete valuation ring $\mathscr{O}$ with $k(x) \subseteq Q(\mathscr{O})$, a specialization $x \to x'$ along $\mathscr{O}$ is not necessarily unique (cf. Theorem 4.15 and Problem II.4.2).

LEMMA 4.14. *Let X be an algebraic scheme over a field k, and let Y be a subscheme of X. Then the following two conditions are equivalent*:

(1) *Y is a closed subscheme.*

(2) *If* $x \in Y$ *and* $x \to x'$ *is a specialization along a discrete valuation ring* $\mathscr{O}$, *then* $x' \in Y$.

Proof. (1) *implies* (2). There exists a local homomorphism $\varphi\colon \mathscr{O}_{X,x'} \to \mathscr{O}$ such that x corresponds to a prime ideal $\varphi^{-1}(0)$. Hence, $x' \in \overline{\{x\}} \subseteq Y$.

(2) *implies* (1). Suppose $x' \in \overline{Y}$. Then there exists a point x of Y such that $x' \in \overline{\{x\}}$. By Lemma 4.13, there exists a discrete valuation ring $\mathscr{O}$ of $k(x)$ and a local homomorphism $\varphi\colon \mathscr{O}_{X,x'} \to \mathscr{O}$. Hence, $x \to x'$. By (2), $x' \in Y$. Hence, $\overline{Y} = Y$. □

With this preparation, we shall prove the following.

Theorem 4.15. *Let* X *be an algebraic scheme over* k, *and let* $f : X \to \mathrm{Spec}(k)$ *be the structure morphism. Then the following conditions are equivalent*:

(1) f *is a separated morphism.*

(2) *Given a discrete valuation ring* $\mathscr{O}$ *and specializations* $x \to x'$ *and* $x \to x''$ *along* $\mathscr{O}$ *such that the induced homomorphisms of the fields* $k(x) \to Q(\mathscr{O})$ *are identical, then we have* $x' = x''$.

Proof. (1) *implies* (2). As explained before Definition 4.8, the image of X by the diagonal morphism $\Delta_{X/k}$ is a closed subscheme of $X \times_k X$. Note here that $X \times_k X$ is an algebraic scheme over k. Suppose two specializations $x \to x'$ and $x \to x''$ along $\mathscr{O}$ are respectively given by morphisms of schemes $g, h\colon \mathrm{Spec}(\mathscr{O}) \to X$. Then we have the morphism $(g, h)\colon \mathrm{Spec}(\mathscr{O}) \to X \times_k X$. Let y be the image of the closed point $\mathfrak{m}$ of $\mathscr{O}$ by (g, h). Then $p_1(y) = x'$ and $p_2(y) = x''$, where p_1 and p_2 are the natural projections of $X \times_k X$ to X. Let $K = Q(\mathscr{O})$, and let $\eta\colon \mathrm{Spec}(K) \to \mathrm{Spec}(\mathscr{O})$ give the generic point of $\mathrm{Spec}(\mathscr{O})$. Then $(g, h) \cdot \eta = \Delta_{X/k} \cdot i_x$, where $i_x\colon \mathrm{Spec}(K) \to X$ is the morphism defined by the homomorphism $\mathscr{O}_{X,x} \to k(x) \to K$. We have $y \in \overline{\{(x, x)\}}$, and $y \in \Delta_{X/k}(X)$ by the hypothesis in (1). So $x' = p_1(y) = p_2(y) = x''$.

(2) *implies* (1). Suppose $y \in \overline{\{(x, x)\}}$. By Lemma 4.13, there exists a discrete valuation ring $\mathscr{O}$ such that $(x, x) \to y$ is a specialization along $\mathscr{O}$. Namely, there exists a morphism $l\colon \mathrm{Spec}(\mathscr{O}) \to X \times_k X$ such that $l((0)) = (x, x)$ and $l(\mathfrak{m}) = y$. Let $g = p_1 \cdot l$, $h = p_2 \cdot l$, $g(\mathfrak{m}) = x'$, and $h(\mathfrak{m}) = x''$. Then $x \to x'$ and $x \to x''$ are specializations along $\mathscr{O}$. By (2), we have $x' = x''$, so $g = h$. Namely, l is factored by $\Delta_{X/k}$. Then $y \in \Delta_{X/k}(X)$. So $\Delta_{X/k}$ is a closed immersion, and X is thus separated over k. □

We have given some explanations on what algebraic schemes and algebraic varieties are. We shall define some of their more specific properties.

Definition 4.16. (1) Let k be a field. A separated algebraic scheme X over k is called *proper over* k if it satisfies the following condition:

Let $\mathscr{O}$ be a discrete valuation ring containing k, and let K be its quotient field. Given a point x of X and a field homomorphism from the residue field $k(x)$ to K, there exists a specialization $x \to x'$ along $\mathscr{O}$.

If we denote the morphism induced by $\mathscr{O} \hookrightarrow K$ by $\eta\colon \mathrm{Spec}(K) \to \mathrm{Spec}(\mathscr{O})$, the above condition is equivalent to saying that a mapping

$$\mathrm{Hom}_k(\mathrm{Spec}(\mathscr{O}), X) \to \mathrm{Hom}_k(\mathrm{Spec}(K), X), \qquad g \mapsto g \cdot \eta$$

is surjective for every discrete valuation ring $\mathscr{O}$.

(2) When X is an algebraic variety defined over k, we call X a *complete algebraic variety* if X is proper over k.

(3) Let $f: X \to Y$ be a morphism of schemes. We say that f is a *closed morphism* if $f(T)$ is a closed set of Y for every closed set T of X. We say that f is a *universally closed morphism* if the base change $f_Z: X_Z \to Z$ of f is a closed morphism for every Y-scheme $g: Z \to Y$.

(4) We call $f: X \to Y$ a *proper morphism* if f is finitely generated, separated and universally closed.

We have then the next result.

THEOREM 4.17. *Let X and Y be separated algebraic schemes over a field k, and let $f: X \to Y$ be a morphism of schemes. If X is proper over k, then f is a universally closed morphism. Hence, f is a proper morphism. In particular, the structure morphism $X \to \mathrm{Spec}(k)$ is also a proper morphism.*

PROOF. (I) We shall prove that $f_Z: X_Z \to Z$ is a closed morphism only in the case where Z is a Y-scheme and an algebraic scheme over k. $X_Z := X \times_Y Z$ is a closed subscheme of $X \times_k Z$. In fact, since Y is separated over k the diagonal morphism $\Delta_{Y/k}: Y \to Y \times_k Y$ is a closed immersion. The natural morphism $X \times_Y Z \to X \times_k Z$ is obtained from $\Delta_{Y/k}$ as the base change by $X \times_k Z \to Y \times_k Y$. So with the structure morphism $p: X \to \mathrm{Spec}(k)$, if we show that $p_Z: X \times_k Z \to Z$ is a closed morphism, then the restriction f_Z of p_Z onto $X \times_Y Z$ is a closed morphism. Hence, we may assume that $Y = \mathrm{Spec}(k)$ in the statement.

(II) Let $f: X \to \mathrm{Spec}(k)$ be anew the structure morphism of X. We shall show that the base change $g := f_Z: X \times_k Z \to Z$ is a closed morphism for an algebraic scheme Z over k. Let T be an irreducible closed subset of $X \times_k Z$, and consider the reduced, closed subscheme structure on T. Let $S = \overline{g(T)}$. We regard S as a reduced, closed subscheme of Z. Let t be the generic point of T, and let $s = g(t)$. Then S is an irreducible scheme with the generic point s. Let s' be an arbitrary point of S. Then there exists a discrete valuation ring $\mathscr{O}$ such that $Q(\mathscr{O}) = k(t)$ and $\mathscr{O} \geq \mathscr{O}_{S,s'}$. In fact, $k(t)$ is a finitely generated extension of $k(s)$. Let $A = \mathscr{O}_{S,s'}[\xi_1, \dots, \xi_r]$, where $\{\xi_1, \dots, \xi_r\}$ is a transcendence basis of $k(t)$ over $k(s)$. Then $k(t)$ is a finite algebraic extension of the quotient field K of A. Let $\mathfrak{p}$ be a prime divisor of $\mathfrak{m}_{S,s'}A$. Applying Lemma 4.12, we find a discrete valuation ring $\mathscr{O}$ of $k(t)$ such that $\mathscr{O} \geq A_{\mathfrak{p}}$. Then $\mathscr{O} \geq \mathscr{O}_{S,s'}$. Let $p_1: X \times_k Z \to X$ be the natural projection, and let $x = p_1(t)$. Then $k(x) \hookrightarrow k(t) = Q(\mathscr{O})$. Hence, by the hypothesis that X is proper over k, there exists a specialization $x \to x'$ along $\mathscr{O}$. So there exists morphisms of schemes $h: \mathrm{Spec}(\mathscr{O}) \to X$ and $l: \mathrm{Spec}(\mathscr{O}) \to S$ such that $h((0)) = x$, $h(\mathfrak{m}) = x'$, $l((0)) = s$, and $l(\mathfrak{m}) = s'$, where $\mathfrak{m}$ is the maximal ideal of $\mathscr{O}$ and is identified with the closed point of $\mathrm{Spec}(\mathscr{O})$. Hence, there exists a morphism $q := (h, l): \mathrm{Spec}(\mathscr{O}) \to X \times_k Z$ such that $q((0)) = t$. Let $t' = q(\mathfrak{m})$. Then $t' \in \overline{\{t\}}$. Since T is a closed subset, $t' \in T$. So $s' = g(t') \in g(T)$. We therefore have $S = g(T)$. Namely, $g(T)$ is a closed subset of Z.

(III) Once we know that $f: X \to Y$ is a universally closed morphism, we know that f is a proper morphism because f is finitely generated and separated (cf. Lemma 4.9 (6)). □

A morphism $f: X \to Y$ between irreducible and reduced schemes is called *dominant* if $\overline{f(X)} = Y$.

THEOREM 4.18. *Let X and Y be separated algebraic schemes over a field k. Suppose X is irreducible and reduced. Let $f: X \to Y$ be a proper morphism. Then $f_*\mathscr{O}_X$*

is a coherent $\mathcal{O}_Y$-Module. If X is a complete algebraic variety defined over k, we have $\Gamma(X, \mathcal{O}_X) = k$. Furthermore, for a coherent $\mathcal{O}_X$-Module $\mathcal{F}$, $R^i f_* \mathcal{F}$ is a coherent $\mathcal{O}_Y$-Module for each $i \geq 0$.

PROOF. (I) Let Z be a closed set $\overline{f(X)}$ in Y endowed with the reduced closed subscheme structure. Then f decomposes to a product of $g: X \to Z$ and a closed immersion $\iota: Z \hookrightarrow Y$, where g is a dominant, proper morphism (cf. Lemma 4.19 below). If $g_* \mathcal{O}_X$ is a coherent $\mathcal{O}_Z$-Module, then it is easy to show that $f_* \mathcal{O}_X$ is a coherent $\mathcal{O}_Y$-Module. Hence, replacing Y by Z, we may assume that Y is an irreducible, reduced scheme and f is a dominant morphism.

(II) Let $k(X)$ and $k(Y)$ be the function fields of X and Y over k, respectively. If ξ is the generic point of X, then $\eta = f(\xi)$ is the generic point of Y because f is dominant. Moreover, since $k(X) = k(\xi)$ and $k(Y) = k(\eta)$, f induces the field homomorphism $k(Y) \hookrightarrow k(X)$ by which we regard $k(Y)$ as a subfield of $k(X)$. Evidently, $k(X)$ is a finitely generated extension of $k(Y)$, and the algebraic closure L of $k(Y)$ in $k(X)$ is a finite algebraic extension (I.1.5). Meanwhile, the property that $f_* \mathcal{O}_X$ is a coherent $\mathcal{O}_Y$-Module is a local property on Y, we may assume that Y is an affine scheme, by replacing Y and X by an affine open set $\mathrm{Spec}(A)$ and $f^{-1}(\mathrm{Spec}(A))$, respectively (cf. Lemma 4.19 below). Furthermore, we may assume that A is a finitely generated k-algebra domain. Note that $Q(A) = k(Y)$. The integral closure B of A in L is a finitely generated A-module (I.1.34). On the other hand, $f_* \mathcal{O}_X$ is a quasicoherent $\mathcal{O}_Y$-Module (problem II.4.9). Hence, $f_* \mathcal{O}_X = (\Gamma(X, \mathcal{O}_X))^\sim$ and $\Gamma(X, \mathcal{O}_X) = \bigcap_{x \in X} \mathcal{O}_{X,x}$. We shall prove in the next step (III) the following two assertions:

(1) Let $\{\mathcal{O}_\lambda\}_{\lambda \in \Lambda}$ exhaust all discrete valuation rings such that $Q(\mathcal{O}_\lambda) = k(X)$ and $A \subseteq \mathcal{O}_\lambda$. Then $B = \bigcap_{\lambda \in \Lambda} \mathcal{O}_\lambda$.

(2) For each $\mathcal{O}_\lambda$, there exists a point x of X with $\mathcal{O}_\lambda \geq \mathcal{O}_{X,x}$.

Suppose these two assertions are proved. Then $\bigcap_\lambda \mathcal{O}_\lambda \supseteq \bigcap_{x \in X} \mathcal{O}_{X,x}$ (cf. Lemma 4.12). Namely, $B \supseteq \Gamma(X, \mathcal{O}_X)$. Since B is a finitely generated A-module and A is a noetherian ring, $\Gamma(X, \mathcal{O}_X)$ is a finitely generated A-module.

(III) We shall prove the above assertions (1) and (2). Since $\mathcal{O}_\lambda$ is integrally closed, we see that $B \subseteq \bigcap_\lambda \mathcal{O}_\lambda$. Take $\xi \in \bigcap_\lambda \mathcal{O}_\lambda$. Suppose $\xi \notin B$. Then $\xi^{-1} A[\xi^{-1}]$ is a proper ideal of $A[\xi^{-1}]$. Here we repeat the argument in the step (II) of the proof of Theorem 4.17 to show that there exists a discrete valuation ring $(\mathcal{O}, \mathfrak{m})$ of $k(X)$ such that $\mathcal{O} \supseteq A[\xi^{-1}]$ and $\mathfrak{m} \supseteq \xi^{-1} A[\xi^{-1}]$. Then $\mathcal{O}$ belongs to $\{\mathcal{O}_\lambda\}_{\lambda \in \Lambda}$, but $\xi \notin \mathcal{O}$. This is a contradiction. Hence, $B = \bigcap_\lambda \mathcal{O}_\lambda$. Next we shall prove the assertion (2). Let $\mathcal{O} = \mathcal{O}_\lambda$, $K = k(X)$, and $S = \mathrm{Spec}(\mathcal{O})$. Since $\mathcal{O} \supseteq A$, we have a morphism $h: S \to Y$. Let $g: Z := X_S \to S$ be the base change of $f: X \to Y$ by h. Let $\eta: \mathrm{Spec}(K) \to S$ be the morphism corresponding to the inclusion $\mathcal{O} \hookrightarrow K$. Since $K = k(X)$, there exists a morphism $\sigma: \mathrm{Spec}(K) \to Z$ such that $g \cdot \sigma = \eta$ and $p_1 \cdot \sigma$ is a dominant morphism, where $p_1: X_S \to X$ is the natural projection. Since f is a universally closed morphism, g is a closed morphism. Let ξ be the image of $\mathrm{Spec}(K)$ (which consists of one point) by σ, and let $T = \overline{\{\xi\}}$. Then $g(T) = S$ because $g(T)$ is a closed subset containing the generic point of S. So there exists a point z of T such that $g(z)$ is the closed point of S. Consider the reduced closed subscheme structure on T induced by Z. Then $\mathcal{O}_{T,z} \geq \mathcal{O}$ and $\mathcal{O}_{T,z}$ is a local domain[1] whose quotient field is K. Hence, $\mathcal{O}_{T,z} = \mathcal{O}$. In fact, if $a \in \mathcal{O}_{T,z} - \mathcal{O}$, then $a^{-1} \in \mathfrak{m}$(=the maximal ideal

[1] A local ring which is an integral domain.

of $\mathscr{O}$), so $a^{-1} \in \mathfrak{m}_{T,z}$ and $1 = a \cdot a^{-1} \in \mathfrak{m}_{T,z}$. This is a contradiction. Let $x = p_1(z)$. Since $p_1|_T : T \to X$ is a dominant morphism, we have $\mathscr{O}_{T,z} \geq \mathscr{O}_{X,x}$. So, $\mathscr{O} \geq \mathscr{O}_{X,x}$. Thus, we proved the assertions (1) and (2).

(IV) Let X be a complete algebraic variety defined over k, and let $p: X \to \operatorname{Spec}(k)$ be the structure morphism. Then $p_*\mathscr{O}_X$ is identified with $\Gamma(X, \mathscr{O}_X)$. We know that $\Gamma(X, \mathscr{O}_X)$ is a finitely generated k-module contained in $k(X)$. Hence, $\Gamma(X, \mathscr{O}_X)$ is a finite algebraic extension of k. Then we conclude that $\Gamma(X, \mathscr{O}_X) = k$ because k is algebraically closed in $k(X)$.

We do not give a proof of the last assertion of the theorem. However, the reader will encounter a related result in Theorem 5.13 later. For a rigorous proof, we refer to [**3**, EGA, Chapter 3]. □

In the above proof, we used the following result.

LEMMA 4.19. (1) *A closed immersion is a proper morphism.*

(2) *If $X \to Y$ is a proper morphism then the base change $f': X' := X_{Y'} \to Y'$ by a morphism of schemes $g: Y' \to Y$ is a proper morphism.*

(3) *If $X \to Y$ and $g: Y \to Z$ are proper morphisms, then the composite $g \cdot f: X \to Z$ is a proper morphism.*

(4) *Let S be a scheme, and let $f_i: X_i \to Y_i$ $(i = 1, 2)$ be a proper morphism of S-schemes. Then $f_1 \times_S f_2: X_1 \times_S X_2 \to Y_1 \times_S Y_2$ is a proper morphism.*

(5) *Suppose the composite $g \cdot f$ of two morphisms of schemes $f: X \to Y$ and $g: Y \to Z$ is a proper morphism. Then f is a proper morphism provided g is a separated morphism.*

PROOF. Suppose (1), (2), and (3) were proved. Then (4) and (5) follow from them. In fact, the morphism $f_1 \times_S f_2$ in (4) is the composite of the two morphisms which are obtained from f_1 and f_2 as the base changes. Hence, $f_1 \times_S f_2$ is a proper morphism. In the case of the morphism f in (5), we have $f = p_2 \cdot \Gamma_f$ as in the proof of Lemma 4.9 (6), where p_2 and Γ_f are the base changes of proper morphisms. So f is a proper morphism. We shall prove (1), (2), and (3). In order to show that a morphism $f: X \to Y$ is a proper morphism, we have to verify all three properties that f is quasicompact, locally finitely generated and universally closed. So we shall show that the morphisms considered in (1), (2), and (3) satisfy each of these properties. However, since the requirement that a morphism be locally finitely generated is easy to check, we omit it.

(1) Let $f: X \to Y$ be a closed immersion. Since a closed subset of a quasicompact set is also quasicompact, f is a quasicompact morphism. Any base change of a closed immersion is a closed immersion (Problem II.4.3), and a closed immersion is clearly a closed morphism. Hence, f is a universally closed morphism.

(2) Let U' be a quasicompact, open set of Y'. For a point $y' \in U'$ and $g(y') \in Y$, we may take affine open neighborhoods U of $g(y')$ and W of y' so that $W \subseteq U' \cap g^{-1}(U)$. U' is covered by finitely many W's of this kind. So we have only to show that $f'^{-1}(W)$ is a quasicompact, open set. Hence, it suffices to show that X' is quasicompact if Y' and Y are affine schemes. By the proof of Theorem 4.5 concerning the existence of fiber product, $\{V_\lambda \times_Y Y'\}_{\lambda \in \Lambda}$ is a finite affine open covering of X' if $\{V_\lambda\}_{\lambda \in \Lambda}$ is a finite affine open covering of X, which exists because X is quasicompact. Since an affine scheme is quasicompact, a finite union of affine schemes $X' = \bigcup_\lambda (V_\lambda \times_Y Y')$ is also quasicompact. Thus, $f': X' \to Y'$ is a quasicompact morphism. On the other hand, it follows readily from the definition

that f' is a universally closed morphism.

(3) It is easy to verify that $g \cdot f$ is a quasicompact morphism as well as a universally closed morphism. □

DEFINITION 4.20. Let $f: X \to Y$ be a morphism of schemes. f is said to be an *affine morphism* if there exists an affine open covering $\{V_\lambda\}_{\lambda\in\Lambda}$ such that $f^{-1}(V_\lambda)$ is an affine open set of X for each $\lambda \in \Lambda$. If we write $V_\lambda = \mathrm{Spec}(A_\lambda)$ and $f^{-1}(V_\lambda) = \mathrm{Spec}(B_\lambda)$, B_λ is an A_λ-algebra. So we may view B_λ naturally as an A_λ-module. If we choose the covering $\{V_\lambda\}_{\lambda\in\Lambda}$ so that B_λ is a finitely generated A_λ-module, we say that f is a *finite morphism*.

We now have the following.

THEOREM 4.21. *Let X and Y be separated algebraic schemes over a field k. For a morphism $f: X \to Y$, the following two conditions are equivalent to each other*:

(i) *f is a finite morphism.*

(ii) *f is a proper and affine morphism.*

PROOF. (ii) *implies* (i). There is an affine open covering $\{V_\lambda\}_{\lambda\in\Lambda}$ of Y such that $f^{-1}(V_\lambda)$ is an affine open set of X for each $\lambda \in \Lambda$. The base change $f_\lambda = f \times_Y V_\lambda: f^{-1}(V_\lambda) \to V_\lambda$ is a proper morphism (Lemma 4.19). Hence, we have only to show by the condition (ii) that A is a finitely generated B-module if $X = \mathrm{Spec}(A)$ and $Y = \mathrm{Spec}(B)$. But this is immediate from Theorem 4.18 because $f_*\mathscr{O}_X = \widetilde{A}$ is a coherent $\widetilde{B}$-Module.

(i) *implies* (ii). There exists an affine open covering $\{V_\lambda\}_{\lambda\in\Lambda}$ such that $f^{-1}(V_\lambda)$ is an affine open set of X for each $\lambda \in \Lambda$ and A_λ is a finitely generated B_λ-module, where $V_\lambda = \mathrm{Spec}(B_\lambda)$ and $f^{-1}(V_\lambda) = \mathrm{Spec}(A_\lambda)$. If $f_\lambda = f \times_Y V_\lambda: f^{-1}(V_\lambda) \to V_\lambda$ is a proper morphism for each $\lambda \in \Lambda$, then f is a proper morphism. Since f_λ is quasicompact and separated (Lemma 4.9), it suffices to show that f_λ is universally closed. Namely, we have only to show that if $X = \mathrm{Spec}(A)$, $Y = \mathrm{Spec}(B)$, and A is a finitely generated B-module, then f is a universally closed morphism. Let $g: Z \to Y$ be any morphism of schemes, and let $\{Z_i\}_{i\in I}$ be an affine open covering of Z. Then the base change $f_i = f \times_Y Z_i: X \times_Y Z_i \to Z_i$ is a finite morphism. In fact, if $Z_i = \mathrm{Spec}(C_i)$, then $X \times_Y Z_i = \mathrm{Spec}(A \otimes_B C_i)$ and $A \otimes_B C_i$ is a finitely generated C_i-module. Moreover, if f_i is a closed morphism, then $f_Z = f \times_Y Z: X \times_Y Z \to Z$ is a closed morphism. So all in all, it suffices to show that if X and Y are affine schemes as above and A is a finitely generated B-module, then f is a closed morphism. Let T be a closed subset of X. T is an affine scheme, and if $T = \mathrm{Spec}(C)$, then C is a finitely generated B-module. Hence, replacing X by T we have only to show that $f(X)$ is a closed set of Y. Since $\overline{f(X)} = \{\mathfrak{q} \in \mathrm{Spec}(B);$ for some $\mathfrak{p} \in f(X), \mathfrak{p} \subseteq \mathfrak{q}\}$, it suffices to show that if $\mathfrak{q} \in \mathrm{Spec}(B)$ satisfies the condition $\mathfrak{p} \subseteq \mathfrak{q}$ with $\mathfrak{p} = \varphi^{-1}\mathfrak{P}$ for some $\mathfrak{P} \in \mathrm{Spec}(A)$, then $\mathfrak{q} = \varphi^{-1}(\mathfrak{Q})$ with $\mathfrak{Q} \in \mathrm{Spec}(A)$, where $\varphi: B \to A$ is a ring homomorphism with $f = {}^a\varphi$. Replace A and B by $A/\mathfrak{P}$ and $B/\mathfrak{p}$, respectively. Then the induced ring homomorphism $\bar{\varphi}: B/\mathfrak{p} \to A/\mathfrak{P}$ is injective, and $A/\mathfrak{P}$ is a finitely generated $B/\mathfrak{p}$-module. The prime ideal $\mathfrak{Q}$ which we require corresponds to $\overline{\mathfrak{Q}} \in \mathrm{Spec}(A/\mathfrak{P})$ such that $\bar{\varphi}^{-1}(\overline{\mathfrak{Q}}) = \mathfrak{q}/\mathfrak{p}$. Hence, we may assume from the beginning that A and B are integral domains and B is a subring of A. Then the prime ideal $\mathfrak{Q}$ exists by (I.1.18). □

If $f: X \to Y$ is a finite and dominant morphism of algebraic varieties defined over a field k, we say that X is a *finite covering space* (or a *finite covering*, for short) of

Y. As an example of finite morphism, we shall explain the normalization morphism of an algebraic variety.

DEFINITION 4.22. We call a scheme X a *locally noetherian scheme* if each point x of X has an affine open neighborhood $\mathrm{Spec}(A_x)$ such that A_x is a noetherian ring. Furthermore, if X is quasicompact, we call X a *noetherian scheme*. A locally noetherian scheme X is called a *normal scheme* if the local ring $\mathcal{O}_{X,x}$ of each point x is a normal ring, i.e., a noetherian integral domain which is integrally closed. An algebraic variety X defined over a field k, which is a normal scheme, is called a *normal algebraic variety*.

We have the following result.

THEOREM 4.23. *Let X be an algebraic variety defined over a field k, and let K be its function field. For a finite algebraic extension L of K, there exist a normal algebraic scheme Z defined over the field k and a dominant finite morphism $f: Z \to X$ satisfying the following conditions*:

(1) $L = k(Z)$.

(2) *For a normal algebraic scheme Z' over k with $L = k(Z')$ and a dominant finite morphism $f': Z' \to X$, there exists an isomorphism $g: Z \to Z'$ such that $f = f' \cdot g$.*

PROOF. (1) We can take an affine open covering $\{U_\lambda\}_{\lambda\in\Lambda}$ such that $A_\lambda := \Gamma(U_\lambda, \mathcal{O}_X)$ is a domain which is finitely generated over k.[2] Note that since X is separated over k, $U_{\lambda\mu} := U_\lambda \cap U_\mu$ is also an affine open set (cf. (II.3.12)). Note also that $K = Q(A_\lambda)$. Let R_λ be the integral closure of A_λ in L. By (I.1.34), R_λ is then a finitely generated k-domain and a finitely generated A_λ-module. Let $f_\lambda: W_\lambda \to U_\lambda$ be the finite morphism associated with the inclusion $A_\lambda \hookrightarrow R_\lambda$, where $W_\lambda = \mathrm{Spec}(R_\lambda)$. If $\mu \neq \lambda$, then the coordinate ring $A_{\lambda\mu} := \Gamma(U_{\lambda\mu}, \mathcal{O}_X)$ is given as $A_{\lambda\mu} = \bigcap_{x\in U_{\lambda\mu}} \mathcal{O}_{X,x}$.

Let $R_{\lambda\mu}$ be the integral closure of $A_{\lambda\mu}$ in L. We claim that $\mathrm{Spec}(R_{\lambda\mu})$ is naturally identified with $f_\lambda^{-1}(U_{\lambda\mu})$. Since $f_\lambda^{-1}(U_{\lambda\mu}) \cong W_\lambda \times_{U_\lambda} U_{\lambda\mu} \cong \mathrm{Spec}(R_\lambda \otimes_{A_\lambda} A_{\lambda\mu})$, $f_\lambda^{-1}(U_{\lambda\mu})$ is an affine open set of W_λ. Hence, the coordinate ring $R_\lambda \otimes_{A_\lambda} A_{\lambda\mu}$ is an integrally closed, integral domain $\bigcap_{w\in f_\lambda^{-1}(U_{\lambda\mu})} \mathcal{O}_{W,w}$, and $R_\lambda \otimes_{A_\lambda} A_{\lambda\mu}$ is a finitely generated $A_{\lambda\mu}$-module because R_λ is a finitely generated A_λ-module. Thus, as a subring of L, $R_{\lambda\mu}$ is identified with $R_\lambda \otimes_{A_\lambda} A_{\lambda\mu}$. Under this identification, we have $f_\lambda^{-1}(U_{\lambda\mu}) = \mathrm{Spec}(R_{\lambda\mu})$.

Similarly, $f_\mu^{-1}(U_{\lambda\mu})$ is identified with $\mathrm{Spec}(R_{\lambda\mu})$. Hence, there exists an isomorphism $s_{\mu\lambda}: f_\lambda^{-1}(U_{\lambda\mu}) \to f_\mu^{-1}(U_{\lambda\mu})$. Furthermore, $U_{\lambda\mu\nu} = U_\lambda \cap U_\mu \cap U_\nu$ ($\lambda, \mu, \nu \in \Lambda$) is an affine open set, and if $A_{\lambda\mu\nu}$ and $R_{\lambda\mu\nu}$ denote respectively the coordinate ring of $U_{\lambda\mu\nu}$ and the integral closure of $A_{\lambda\mu\nu}$ in L, then $f_\lambda^{-1}(U_{\lambda\mu\nu})$, $f_\mu^{-1}(U_{\lambda\mu\nu})$, and $f_\nu^{-1}(U_{\lambda\mu\nu})$ are identified with $\mathrm{Spec}(R_{\lambda\mu\nu})$. Since these identifications are given by the natural identifications of $R_\lambda \otimes_{A_\lambda} A_{\lambda\mu\nu}$, $R_\mu \otimes_{A_\mu} A_{\lambda\mu\nu}$, and $R_\nu \otimes_{A_\nu} A_{\lambda\mu\nu}$ with the subring $R_{\lambda\mu\nu}$ in L, we have a relation $s_{\nu\lambda} = s_{\nu\mu} \cdot s_{\mu\lambda}$. Since $s_{\lambda\lambda} = \mathrm{id}$ ($\lambda \in \Lambda$), there exists by Lemma 4.3 a scheme Z and a morphism $f: Z \to X$ such that for each $\lambda \in \Lambda$, W_λ and f_λ are identified with an open set $f^{-1}(U_\lambda)$ of Z and $f|_{W_\lambda}$, respectively. Then by the construction, Z is a normal algebraic scheme over k and f is a dominant finite morphism.

(2) Let $\{U_\lambda\}_{\lambda\in\Lambda}$ be an affine open covering of X as above. Then $f'^{-1}(U_\lambda)$ is an affine open set of Z' by Lemma 4.24. Furthermore, the coordinate ring R'_λ

[2] We call it a finitely generated k-domain.

of $f'^{-1}(U_\lambda)$ is given as $R'_\lambda = \bigcap_{z\in f'^{-1}(U_\lambda)} \mathcal{O}_{Z',z}$ and is an integrally closed, integral domain which is a finitely generated A_λ-module. If we view R'_λ as a subring of L, then we have $R_\lambda = R'_\lambda$ because both R_λ and R'_λ are the integral closure of A_λ in L. So there exists an isomorphism $g_\lambda : f^{-1}(U_\lambda) \xrightarrow{\sim} f'^{-1}(U_\lambda)$ such that $f = f' \cdot g_\lambda$ on $f^{-1}(U_\lambda)$. Let $R'_{\lambda\mu}$ be the coordinate ring of $f'^{-1}(U_{\lambda\mu})$. Then $R'_{\lambda\mu}$, as a subring of L, coincides with the integral closure $R_{\lambda\mu}$ of $A_{\lambda\mu}$. This implies that the restrictions of g_λ and g_μ onto $f^{-1}(U_{\lambda\mu})$ are equal. By virtue of Lemma 4.3 (2), we conclude the existence of an isomorphism $g: Z \to Z'$ such that $g_\lambda = g|_{f^{-1}(U_\lambda)}$ for each $\lambda \in \Lambda$ and $f = f' \cdot g$. □

In the above proof, we made use of the result below.

LEMMA 4.24. *Let $f: Z \to X$ be an affine morphism. Then $f^{-1}(U)$ is an affine open set for every affine open set U of X. If f is a finite morphism, then $\Gamma(f^{-1}(U), \mathcal{O}_X)$ is a finitely generated $\Gamma(U, \mathcal{O}_X)$-module.*

PROOF. We readily see that $f|_{f^{-1}(U)}: f^{-1}(U) \to U$ is an affine morphism. In fact, let $\{U_\lambda\}_{\lambda\in\Lambda}$ be an affine open covering of X such that $\{f^{-1}(U_\lambda)\}_{\lambda\in\Lambda}$ is an affine open covering of Z. Then for an affine open set V with $V \subseteq U_\lambda \cap U$ (for some $\lambda \in \Lambda$), $f^{-1}(V)$ is an affine open set of Z and U is covered by such affine open sets V's. If f is a finite morphism and $\Gamma(f^{-1}(U_\lambda), \mathcal{O}_Z)$ is a finitely generated $\Gamma(U_\lambda, \mathcal{O}_X)$-module for each $\lambda \in \Lambda$, we can argue as above that $f|_{f^{-1}(U)}$ is also a finite morphism. Hence, it suffices to prove the lemma under the hypothesis $U = X$.

Let $X = \operatorname{Spec}(A)$, $B = \Gamma(Z, \mathcal{O}_Z)$, and $Y = \operatorname{Spec}(B)$. Then the morphism f is the composite of the two morphisms $h: Z \to Y$ and $g: Y \to X$ (Lemma 4.4). Meanwhile, if $\{U_\lambda\}_{\lambda\in\Lambda}$ is an affine open covering of X as above, $W_\lambda = f^{-1}(U_\lambda)$, and $f_\lambda = f|_{W_\lambda}$, then $f_*\mathcal{O}_Z|_{U_\lambda} = (f_\lambda)_*\mathcal{O}_{W_\lambda}$ (Lemma 4.7). If we put $A_\lambda = \Gamma(U_\lambda, \mathcal{O}_X)$ and $B_\lambda = \Gamma(W_\lambda, \mathcal{O}_Z)$, then $(f_\lambda)_*\mathcal{O}_{W_\lambda} = \widetilde{B}_\lambda$ and $(f_\lambda)_*\mathcal{O}_{W_\lambda}$ is thus a quasicoherent $\mathcal{O}_{U_\lambda}$-Module. So $f_*\mathcal{O}_Z$ is a quasicoherent $\mathcal{O}_X$-Module (cf. Problem II.4.9). Therefore, $f_*\mathcal{O}_Z = \widetilde{B}$ (Theorem 3.12). Since $g^{-1}(U_\lambda) = \operatorname{Spec}(B \otimes_A A_\lambda)$ and $(B \otimes_A A_\lambda)^\sim = f_*\mathcal{O}_Z|_{U_\lambda}$ (Lemma 3.22 (3)), and since W_λ is an affine scheme and $f_*\mathcal{O}_Z|_{U_\lambda} = (f_\lambda)_*\mathcal{O}_{W_\lambda}$, we know that the morphism h induces an isomorphism between $W_\lambda = f^{-1}(U_\lambda)$ and $g^{-1}(U_\lambda)$. So $h: Z \to Y$ is an isomorphism, and thus, Z is an affine scheme.

We may assume that for the affine open covering $\{U_\lambda\}_{\lambda\in\Lambda}$, the set Λ is a finite set, $U_\lambda = D(t_\lambda)$ with $t_\lambda \in A$, and B_λ is a finitely generated A_λ-module. Take a finite system of generators $\{b_{i\lambda}; i \in I_\lambda\}$ of the A_λ-module B_λ with $b_{i\lambda} \in B$. Then $\{b_{i\lambda}; i \in I_\lambda, \lambda \in \Lambda\}$ is a finite system of generators of the A-module B. The proof is similar to the proof of Theorem 3.12 (4). □

The scheme Z and the finite morphism $f: Z \to X$, whose existence was proved in Theorem 4.23, are called the *normalization* of X in L and the *normalization morphism*, respectively. If $L = K$, then Z is an algebraic variety defined over k. We then call Z simply the *normalization* of X.

In algebraic geometry, rational mappings of schemes, which we discuss below, are as significant as morphisms of schemes.

DEFINITION 4.25. Let X and Y be S-schemes. Consider the set R consisting of pairs (U, f), where U is a dense open subset of X and an S-morphism $f: U \to Y$. Two elements (U, f) and (V, g) of R are equivalent to each other, denoted $(U, f) \sim (V, g)$, if there exists a dense open subset $W \subseteq U \cap V$ such that $f|_W = g|_W$. This is an equivalence relation on R. A pair (U, f) or its equivalence class is called an

S-rational mapping from X to Y and expressed by $f: X \cdots \to Y$. We say that f is defined on U. If there is no fear of confusion, we denote it also by $f: X \to Y$. For a point x of X, we say that f is *defined* at x if there is a pair (V, g) equivalent to (U, f) such that $x \in V$. The set of points x of X where f is defined is a dense open subset of X, which we call the *domain of definition* of $f: X \cdots \to Y$.

LEMMA 4.26. *Let X be a reduced scheme, let Y be a scheme separated over S, and let $f: X \cdots \to Y$ be an S-rational mapping. Let U_0 be the domain of definition of f. Then there exists an S-morphism $f_0: U_0 \to Y$ such that (U_0, f_0) represents the equivalence class of f.*

PROOF. If $f_1: U \to Y$ and $f_2: U_2 \to Y$ are S-morphisms representing the class of f, then there exists a dense open set $V \subseteq U_1 \cap U_2$ such that $f_1|_V = f_2|_V$. Put $X' = U_1 \cap U_2$ and $f_i' = f_i|_{X'}$ $(i = 1, 2)$, where $f_i': X' \to Y$ are S-morphisms. We claim that $f_1' = f_2'$. Put $g = (f_1', f_2'): X' \to Y \times_S Y$ and $h = f_1|_V = f_2|_V$. Then $g|_V = \Delta_{Y/S} \cdot h$. Since Y is separated over S, $\Delta_{Y/S}$ is a closed immersion and the scheme $(X', g) \times_{Y \times_S Y} (Y, \Delta_{Y/S})$ is, therefore, a closed subscheme of X' which contains a dense open set V. Here we used the notations (X', g) and $(Y, \Delta_{Y/S})$ to emphasize that X' and Y are schemes over $Y \times_S Y$ by the respective morphisms g and $\Delta_{Y/S}$. Since X' is reduced, $(X', g) \times_{Y \times_S Y} (Y, \Delta_{Y/S})$ is, thus, identified with X'. This means that the S-morphism $h: V \to Y$ is extended onto X' and $q = \Delta_{Y/S} \cdot h$. So $h = f_1' = f_2'$ as claimed above. By Lemma 4.3, f_1 and f_2 are then extended to an S-morphism $f_3: U_1 \cup U_2 \to Y$ and $(U_1 \cup U_2, f_3)$ represents the class of f. Repeating this argument, we derive the existence of an S-morphism (U_0, f_0) which represents the class of f. □

Hereafter, we are mainly interested in the case $S = \mathrm{Spec}(k)$, where k is a field.

LEMMA 4.27. *Let k be a field, let X be an irreducible reduced k-scheme, and let Y be an algebraic k-scheme. Then there is a one-to-one correspondence between the following two sets: $\{k$-rational mapping $f: X \cdots \to Y\} \to \{k$-morphism $f_\eta: \mathrm{Spec}\, k(X) \to Y\}$. The correspondence assigns to f the composite $f_\eta: \mathrm{Spec}\, k(X) \xrightarrow{i_\eta} X \cdots \xrightarrow{f} Y$, where η is the generic point of X and $i_\eta: \mathrm{Spec}\, k(X) \to X$ is the natural morphism which maps the unique point of $\mathrm{Spec}\, k(X)$ to η.*

PROOF. Suppose (U, f) represents the class of $f: X \cdots \to Y$. Then i_η decomposes as $\mathrm{Spec}\, k(X) \xrightarrow{i_{\eta,U}} U \hookrightarrow X$ and $f_\eta = f \cdot i_{\eta,U}$. If $(U_1, f_1) \sim (U_2, f_2)$, we know readily that $f_1 \cdot i_{\eta,U_1} = f_2 \cdot i_{\eta,U_2}$. Hence, the k-morphism $f_\eta: \mathrm{Spec}\, k(X) \to Y$ is determined by f. Conversely, given a k-morphism $g: \mathrm{Spec}\, k(X) \to Y$, let y be the image of the unique point of $\mathrm{Spec}\, k(X)$ by g. Let $V = \mathrm{Spec}(B)$ be an affine open neighborhood of y such that B is a finitely generated k-algebra. Then g is given by a k-algebra homomorphism $\varphi: B \to k(X)$. Write $B = k[b_1, \ldots, b_n]$ and let $a_i = \varphi(b_i)$. Then there exists an affine open set $U = \mathrm{Spec}(A)$ of X such that $a_i \in A$ for each i. Thereby, g decomposes as

$$g: \mathrm{Spec}\, k(X) \xrightarrow{i_{\eta,U}} U \xrightarrow{h} V \overset{j}{\hookrightarrow} Y,$$

where h is the morphism associated with $\varphi: B \to A$ and j is the natural open immersion. Then $g = f_\eta$, where we put $f = j \cdot h$. □

COROLLARY 4.28. *Let k be a field, and let X be an irreducible reduced k-scheme. Then there is a one-to-one correspondence between the set of k-rational mappings $f: X \cdots \to \mathbf{A}_k^1$ and the set of the elements of the field $k(X)$.*

PROOF. f_η: $\operatorname{Spec} k(X) \to \mathbf{A}_k^1 = \operatorname{Spec} k[t]$ is determined by a k-algebra homomorphism $\varphi: k[t] \to k(X)$ which is determined by the image $\varphi(t)$ of t. □

Now let X and Y be algebraic varieties defined over a field k, and let $f: X \cdots \to Y$ be a k-rational mapping. Suppose f is represented by a pair of an open set U of X and a morphism $f_U: U \to Y$. Since Y is separated over k, the morphism $(1_U, f_U): U \to U \times_k Y$ is a closed immersion. So its image Γ_{f_U} is viewed as a closed subset of $U \times_k Y$. Let Γ_f be the closure of Γ_{f_U} in $X \times_k Y$. We call Γ_f the *graph* of the rational mapping f. Since X and Y are algebraic varieties, $X \times_k Y$ is an irreducible reduced scheme. (Let $U = \operatorname{Spec}(A)$ and $V = \operatorname{Spec}(B)$ be affine open sets of X and Y, respectively. Then $U \times_k V$ is an affine open set of $X \times_k Y$ and $A \otimes_k B$ is a subring of $k(X) \otimes_k k(Y)$. Since $k(X)$ and $k(Y)$ are regular extensions of k, $k(X) \otimes_k k(Y)$ is an integral domain. So $A \otimes_k B$ is an integral domain. Compare the proof of Lemma 4.11 (3).) If one considers on Γ_f the reduced closed subscheme structure of $X \times_k Y$, Γ_f is an algebraic variety defined over k. Let $p: \Gamma_f \to X$ and $q: \Gamma_f \to Y$ be the morphisms obtained by restricting onto Γ_f the projections from $X \times_k Y$ to X and Y. The sets Γ_{f_U} and U are respective open sets of Γ_f and X and isomorphic to each other by p. Hence, we can define a rational mapping $p^{-1}: X \cdots \to \Gamma_f$ by $U \xrightarrow{\sim} \Gamma_{f_U} \hookrightarrow \Gamma_f$. The composite of rational mappings $q \cdot p^{-1}$ is defined in the natural fashion, and we have $q \cdot p^{-1} = f$.

If $f_U: U \to Y$ is a dominant morphism, we call f a *dominant rational mapping*. Then $f_U(\eta)$ is the generic point of Y if η is the generic point of X. So the field homomorphism $f_U^*: k(Y) \to k(X)$ is determined. This homomorphism is independent of the choice of a pair (U, f_U) which represents the class of f. So we denote it by $f^*: k(Y) \to k(X)$. Conversely, let $\varphi: k(Y) \to k(X)$ be a field homomorphism. Choose an affine open set $V = \operatorname{Spec}(B)$ of Y so that B is a finitely generated k-algebra. Then $Q(B) = k(Y)$, and there exists a k-rational mapping $f_V: X \cdots \to V$ by Lemma 4.27, so that $f_V^* = \varphi$. We may consider the composite $f = j \cdot f_V: X \cdots \to Y$ instead of f_V, where $j: V \hookrightarrow Y$ is the natural open immersion. Hence, there is a one-to-one correspondence between the set $\{f: X \cdots \to Y$; a dominant k-rational mapping$\}$ and the set $\{f^*: k(Y) \to k(X)$; a field homomorphism$\}$. As a special case, if $f^*: k(Y) \to k(X)$ is a field isomorphism over k, then there exists a dominant k-rational mapping $g: Y \cdots \to X$ such that $g \cdot f = 1_X$ and $f \cdot g = 1_Y$. If f is represented by (U, f_U), the composite $g \cdot f$ of rational mappings is defined if the domain of definition of g has nonempty intersection with $f_U(U)$. We say that the rational mapping f is a *birational mapping* if $f^*: k(Y) \to k(X)$ is an isomorphism. We also say that X and Y are birational to each other if there exists a birational mapping $f: X \cdots \to Y$.

EXAMPLE. Let $X = \mathbf{A}_k^2 = \operatorname{Spec} k[x, y]$, and let $Y = \mathbf{A}_k^2 = \operatorname{Spec} k[t, u]$. Define a rational mapping $f: X \cdots \to Y$ by the field isomorphism $\varphi: k(t, u) \to k(x, y)$ such that $\varphi(t) = x$ and $\varphi(u) = y/x$. Then the domain of definition of f is $\mathbf{A}_k^2 - \{(0, b); b \in k\}$. The rational mapping $f^{-1}: Y \cdots \to X$ is given by $\psi(x) = t$ and $\psi(y) = tu$, and f^{-1} is a morphism.

In the case where $f: X \cdots \to Y$ is a dominant rational mapping, we consider $k(Y)$ as a subfield of $k(X)$ through f^*, where we also consider $k(X) = k(\Gamma_f)$. For points $x \in X$ and $y \in Y$, we say that x *corresponds* to y by f if there exists a point z of Γ_f such that $x = p(z)$ and $y = q(z)$. We denote this relation temporarily by $x \sim_f y$. Let F be a closed subset of X, and let

$$G = \{y \in Y; x \sim_f y \text{ for some } x \in F\},$$

which we call the *total transform* of F by f. It is apparent that $G = q(p^{-1}(F))$. If X is a complete algebraic variety, then $q\colon \Gamma_f \to Y$ is a proper morphism and G is a closed subset of Y. Conversely, if G is a closed subset of Y, we call $F := p(q^{-1}(G))$ the total transform of G by f. If Y is complete, then F is a closed set.

THEOREM 4.29. *Let X and Y be algebraic varieties over a field k, and let $f\colon X \cdots \to Y$ be a dominant rational mapping. With $k(Y)$ viewed as a subfield of $k(X)$ through f^*, we have the following assertions:*

(1) *Suppose $x \sim_f y$ for $x \in X$ and $y \in Y$. Then f is defined at x if and only if $\mathcal{O}_{X,x} \geq \mathcal{O}_{Y,y}$.*

(2) *If X is normal and Y is complete, then f is defined at every point of codimension 1*[3] *of X. Hence,* $\operatorname{codim}_X(X - U_0) \geq 2$, *where U_0 is the domain of definition of f.*

PROOF. (1) If $x \sim_f y$, then $x = p(z)$ and $y = p(z)$ for $z \in \Gamma_f$. Let $\mathcal{O}_z = \mathcal{O}_{\Gamma_f, z}$, $\mathcal{O}_x = \mathcal{O}_{X,x}$, and $\mathcal{O}_y = \mathcal{O}_{Y,y}$. Then we have $\mathcal{O}_z \geq \mathcal{O}_x$ and $\mathcal{O}_z \geq \mathcal{O}_y$ as subrings of $k(X)$. If x belongs to the domain of definition U_0 of f, then $p\colon \Gamma \to X$ is isomorphic near the point x, whence $\mathcal{O}_z = \mathcal{O}_x$. So, $\mathcal{O}_x \geq \mathcal{O}_y$. Conversely, suppose $\mathcal{O}_x \geq \mathcal{O}_y$. We choose an affine open neighborhood $\operatorname{Spec}(B)$ of y so that B is finitely generated over k. Then $\mathcal{O}_y = B_{\mathfrak{q}}$ for a prime ideal $\mathfrak{q}$ of B. Similarly, $\mathcal{O}_x = A_{\mathfrak{p}}$ for an affine open neighborhood $\operatorname{Spec}(A)$ and a prime ideal $\mathfrak{p}$ of A. Write $B = k[b_1, \ldots, b_n]$. Since $b_i \in \mathcal{O}_x$, we may write $b_i = a_i/s_i$ ($a_i, s_i \in A$, $s_i \notin \mathfrak{p}$). By replacing A by $A[1/\prod_{i=1}^n s_i]$, we may assume that $B \subset A$. Then $\mathfrak{p} \cap B = \mathfrak{q}$. So the rational mapping f is represented by the morphism $f_0\colon \operatorname{Spec}(A) \to \operatorname{Spec}(B) \hookrightarrow Y$ associated with the inclusion $B \hookrightarrow A$, and $f_0(x) = y$. Thus, f is defined at the point x.

(2) Set $Z = \Gamma_f$. Then $p\colon Z \to X$ is a morphism which is a birational mapping. Let x be a point of codimension 1 of X. Namely, x is the generic point of an irreducible closed subscheme $\overline{\{x\}}$ which has codimension 1. Since X is normal, the local ring $\mathcal{O}_x$ of x is a discrete valuation ring of $k(X)$. Then $\mathcal{O} := \mathcal{O}_x \cap k(Y)$ is a discrete valuation ring of $k(Y)$. Since Y is complete, there exists by Definition 4.16 a point y of Y such that $\mathcal{O} \geq \mathcal{O}_y$. Then $\mathcal{O}_x \geq \mathcal{O}_y$ clearly. Hence f is defined at x, and $y = f(x)$. □

Let X and Y be normal, complete algebraic varieties, and let $f\colon X \cdots \to Y$ be a birational mapping. The mapping f is defined at a point $x \in X$ of codimension 1. The point x is the generic point of an irreducible reduced closed subscheme $F = \overline{\{x\}}$, and the point $y = f(x)$ is also the generic point of an irreducible reduced closed subscheme $G_0 = \overline{\{y\}}$. We call G_0 the *proper transform* of F by f. G_0 is a subset of the total transform G of F, but G_0 is not always equal to G. We can argue similarly with $f^{-1}\colon Y \cdots \to X$ and a point $y \in Y$ of codimension 1. If we put $x = f^{-1}(y)$, then $\overline{\{x\}}$ is the proper transform of $\overline{\{y\}}$ by f^{-1}. But we often call $\overline{\{x\}}$ the proper transform of $\overline{\{y\}}$ by f. Though it may appear that we use f and f^{-1} confusedly, in fact, we regard $f\colon X \cdots \to Y$ as a correspondence relation (without orientations)

[3] x is a point of codimension 1 of X if $\overline{\{x\}}$ has codimension 1 in X.

between the sets of points of X and Y. Moreover, when we speak of the proper transform G_0 of F, we mostly consider the case $\operatorname{codim}_Y G_0 = 1$.

Finally, we state a result concerning the dimension of an algebraic scheme defined over a field k.

THEOREM 4.30. *Let X and Y be irreducible algebraic schemes over k. Then we have the following*:

(1) *For a closed point x of X, we have*

$$\dim X = \text{K-}\dim(\mathcal{O}_{X,x}) = \operatorname{tr.deg}_k k(X_{\text{red}}).$$

(2) *For a dominant morphism $f: X \to Y$ and a closed point y of Y, we have $\dim X_y \geq e$, where $e = \dim X - \dim Y$.*

(3) *If f is a flat dominant morphism in the assertion* (2) *above, then we have $\dim X_y = e$.*

PROOF. (1) Since $\dim X = \dim X_{\text{red}}$, we may assume that $X = X_{\text{red}}$. Then X is an irreducible, reduced algebraic scheme. Let $F_0 \subsetneqq F_1 \subsetneqq \cdots \subsetneqq F_n$ be an ascending chain of irreducible closed subsets, where $n = \dim X$. Then F_0 consists of a single point z, and the generic points of the irreducible closed subsets containing z correspond bijectively to the prime ideals of $\mathcal{O}_{X,z}$ (Lemma 4.2 (6)). Hence, $K\text{-}\dim(\mathcal{O}_{X,z}) = n$. By problem I.1.9, we have $\text{K-}\dim(\mathcal{O}_{X,z}) = \operatorname{tr.deg}_k Q(\mathcal{O}_{X,z})$. (Note that $Q(\mathcal{O}_{X,z}) = k(X)$.) Now let x be any closed point of X. Then $\text{K-}\dim(\mathcal{O}_{X,x}) = \operatorname{tr.deg}_k k(X)$ in the same fashion as above by problem I.1.9. So we have $\dim X = \text{K-}\dim(\mathcal{O}_{X,x})$.

(2) Let x be any closed point of X_y. By problem I.1.9, we have

$$\text{K-}\dim(\mathcal{O}_{X,x}) \leq \text{K-}\dim(\mathcal{O}_{Y,y}) + \text{K-}\dim(\mathcal{O}_{X_y,x}).$$

By (1) above, we have

$$\text{K-}\dim(\mathcal{O}_{X,x}) = \dim X, \qquad \text{K-}\dim(\mathcal{O}_{Y,y}) = \dim Y.$$

So we have $\text{K-}\dim(\mathcal{O}_{X_y,x}) \geq e$. Since $\dim X_y = \max\{\text{K-}\dim(\mathcal{O}_{X_y,x});\, x \in X_y\}$, we have $\dim X_y \geq e$.

(3) By the hypothesis, $\mathcal{O}_{X,x}$ is a flat $\mathcal{O}_{Y,y}$-module for any closed point x of X_y. Since $\text{K-}\dim(\mathcal{O}_{X_y,x}) = e$ by problem I.1.10, we have $\dim X_y = e$. □

We state the following result without proof.

THEOREM 4.31. *Let $f: X \to Y$ be a dominant morphism between irreducible algebraic schemes defined over a field k, and let $e = \dim X - \dim Y$. Then for any integer $r \geq e$, $Z := \{y \in Y; \dim X_y \geq r\}$ is a closed subset of Y.*

Summarizing the statement of this theorem, we say that the dimension of fibers of f is *upper semicontinuous*.

II.4. Problems.

1. The fiber product $X \times_S Y$ of schemes does not necessarily coincide (as sets) with the set $\{(x, y); x \in X, y \in Y\}$. Explain this by making use of the following example:
   Let K be a field, let L/K be a finite, separable, algebraic extension, and let K'/K be a decomposition field of L/K. Put $X = \operatorname{Spec}(L)$, $S = \operatorname{Spec}(K)$, and $Y = \operatorname{Spec}(K')$. Then $X \times_S Y = \operatorname{Spec}(L \otimes_K K') = \coprod \operatorname{Spec}(K')$ (a direct sum of $[L : K]$ copies of $\operatorname{Spec}(K')$).

2. Let t be a coordinate of the affine line $\mathbf{A}_k^1$, let P be the point $t = 0$, and let $U = \mathbf{A}_k^1 - \{P\}$. Let X be a local ringed space which is obtained by patching two copies of $\mathbf{A}_k^1$ along the open set U. Then X is a scheme. Show that $\Delta_{X/k}(X) = \{(Q, Q); Q \in U\} \cup \{(P, P), (P', P')\}$ and $\overline{\Delta_{X/k}(X)} = \Delta_{X/k}(X) \cup \{(P', P), (P, P')\}$. So X is not separated over $\mathrm{Spec}(k)$.
3. Prove the following two assertions on closed immersions relative to the proof of Lemma 4.9.
(1) Let $f: X \to Y$ be a closed immersion, and let $f': X' \to Y'$ be the base change of f by a morphism $g: Y' \to Y$. Then f' is a closed immersion as well.
(2) If $f: X \to Y$ and $g: Y \to Z$ are closed immersions, then the composite morphism $g \cdot f: X \to Z$ is a closed immersion.
4. Let k be a field of characteristic $p \geq 0$.
(1) Let n be a positive integer prime to p, and let $a \in k$ such that $a^{1/m} \notin k$ for each $m, 1 < m \leq n$, with $m \mid n$. Let C be an affine plane curve $\mathrm{Spec}\, k[x, y]/(y^n - ax^n)$. Prove that C is irreducible and reduced, but $C \otimes_k \bar{k}$ decomposes into the union of n lines passing through the origin of $\mathbf{A}_{\bar{k}}^2$.
(2) If $n = p > 0$, in the example (1) above, then show that $C \otimes_k \bar{k}$ is a nonreduced scheme such that $(C \otimes_k \bar{k})_{\mathrm{red}}$ is a single line, though C is irreducible and reduced. Namely, $C \otimes_k \bar{k}$ is the line $y = a^{1/n}x$ counted n-times.
5. Let k be an algebraically closed field. Let Y be the scheme obtained by patching two affine lines $\mathbf{A}_k^1 = \mathrm{Spec}\, k[t]$ and $\mathbf{A}_k^1 = \mathrm{Spec}\, k[u]$ together along the open sets $U_0 = D(t)$ and $U_1 = D(u)$ by $t = u^{-1}$. Verify the following assertions.
(1) Y is an algebraic k-scheme whose function field is $k(t)$.
(2) A discrete valuation ring of $k(t)$ containing k is equal to either $k[t]_{(t-\alpha)}$ $(\alpha \in k)$ or $k[u]_{(u)}$ (cf. (I.1.40)).
(3) Y is separated over k. (Use Theorem 4.15.)
(4) Y is a complete algebraic curve. (Compare Definition 4.17.)
(5) The scheme X in problem 2 above is not complete. The scheme Y is the *projective line* $\mathbf{P}_k^1$, which we define in the next chapter.
6. An algebraic variety of dimension 1 is called an *algebraic curve*. Let X be a normal algebraic curve defined over a field k, let Y be a complete algebraic variety, and let $f: X \cdots \to Y$ be a rational mapping. Prove that f is then a morphism. (Suppose f is represented by a pair of an open set U of X and a morphism $g: U \to Y$. Consider $Z = \overline{g(U)}$. If Z is a closed point of Y, then f is a constant morphism. If Z is not a closed point, then Z is a complete algebraic curve if Z is provided with the irreducible reduced closed subscheme structure. So replacing Y by Z, we may assume that f is dominant. Use Theorem 4.29.)
7. Let X be a normal complete algebraic curve. Show that there is a one-to-one correspondence between the set of closed points of X and the set of discrete valuation rings of $k(X)$ containing k. The correspondence is to assign the local ring $\mathcal{O}_{X,x}$ to a closed point x of X. (Use Theorems 4.15 and 4.17.)
8. Let $f: X \to S$ be a finitely generated morphism between two affine schemes X and S. Prove that $\Gamma(X, \mathcal{O}_X)$ is a finitely generated $\Gamma(S, \mathcal{O}_S)$-algebra.
9. Let X and Y be separated algebraic schemes defined over a field k, let $f: X \to Y$ be a k-morphism, and let $\mathcal{F}$ be a quasicoherent $\mathcal{O}_X$-Module. Following the next steps, prove that $f_*\mathcal{F}$ is a quasicoherent $\mathcal{O}_Y$-Module.
(1) Replacing Y and X by an affine open set V and $f^{-1}(V)$, respectively, we may assume that Y is an affine scheme. (We shall make this assumption.)

(2) If X is an affine algebraic scheme, then $f_*\mathscr{F}$ is quasicoherent.
(3) Let U and U' be affine open sets of X. If $U \cap U' \neq \emptyset$, then $U \cap U'$ is an affine open set.
(4) Let $\{U_i\}_{i\in I}$ be a finite affine open covering and set $U_{ij} = U_i \cap U_j$. By (2) above, $(f|_{U_i})_*(\mathscr{F}|_{U_i})$ and $(f|_{U_{ij}})_*(\mathscr{F}|_{U_{ij}})$ are quasicoherent $\mathscr{O}_Y$-Modules. Moreover, we have the natural exact sequence

$$0 \to f_*\mathscr{F} \to \prod_i (f|_{U_i})_*(\mathscr{F}|_{U_i}) \rightrightarrows \prod_{i,j} (f|_{U_{ij}})_*(\mathscr{F}|_{U_{ij}}).$$

(5) $f_*\mathscr{F}$ is a quasicoherent $\mathscr{O}_Y$-Module.

CHAPTER 5

Projective Schemes and Projective Algebraic Varieties

In this chapter we define projective algebraic varieties over a field k that play central roles in algebraic geometry, and we state and prove results relevant to them.

A commutative ring $A = \sum_{n \in \mathbf{Z}} A_n$ is a *graded ring* if A is a direct sum of abelian groups A_n and $A_n \cdot A_m \subseteq A_{n+m}$ $(n, m \in \mathbf{Z})$ with respect to the multiplication. We call elements of A_n *homogeneous* elements of degree n and denote the degree of an element $a \in A_n$ by $n = \deg a$. The unit element 1 of A belongs to A_0, and A_0 is a subring of A. An A-module $M = \sum_{n \in \mathbf{Z}} M_n$ is a *graded A-module* if M is a direct sum of abelian groups M_n and $A_n \cdot M_m \subseteq M_{n+m}$ for each $n, m \in \mathbf{Z}$. An ideal I of A is called a *homogeneous ideal* if $I = \sum_{n \in \mathbf{Z}} I_n$ with $I_n = I \cap A_n$. (See problem II.5.1.)

Hereafter, we treat graded rings of various kinds and consider, among others, those graded rings $A = \sum_{n \in \mathbf{Z}} A_n$ with $A_n = 0$ $(n < 0)$. Then $A_+ := \sum_{n > 0} A_n$ is an ideal of A, which we call the *irrelevant ideal* of A.

LEMMA 5.1. *Let $A = \sum_{n \geq 0} A_n$ be a graded ring. Then we have*

(1) *A is a noetherian ring if and only if A_0 is a noetherian ring and A is a finitely generated A_0-algebra.*

(2) *Suppose A is a noetherian ring. A graded A-module $M = \sum_{n \in \mathbf{Z}} M_n$ is a finitely generated A-module if and only if the following three conditions are satisfied*:

(i) *M_n is a finitely generated A_0-module for each $n \in \mathbf{Z}$.*

(ii) *for some $n_0 \in \mathbf{Z}$, $M_n = (0)$ for each $n < n_0$.*

(iii) *for some n_1, and some $d \in \mathbf{Z}$, $d > 0$, $M_{n+d} = A_d M_n$ (for all $n \geq n_1$).*

PROOF. (1) Suppose A is a noetherian ring. Since $A_0 = A/A_+$, A_0 is then a noetherian ring. Since A_+ is a finitely generated ideal, there exist homogeneous elements $a_1, \ldots, a_r$ such that $A_+ = \sum_{i=1}^r A a_i$. For a homogeneous element b of degree N in A, we prove by induction on N that $b \in A_0[a_1, \ldots, a_r]$. Obviously, we may assume $N > 0$. Then $b = \sum_{i=1}^r c_i a_i$ with homogeneous elements c_i of degree $N - \deg a_i$. Applying the induction hypothesis to c_i's, we have that $c_i \in A_0[a_1, \ldots, a_r]$. So $b \in A_0[a_1, \ldots, a_r]$. A is, thus, a finitely generated A_0-algebra. The converse follows from (I.1.14).

(2) Suppose A is generated over A_0 by homogeneous elements $a_1, \ldots, a_r$ and M is a finitely generated A-module. Then M is generated as an A-module by finitely many homogeneous elements $m_1, \ldots, m_s$. Let $d_i = \deg a_i$ and $e_j = \deg m_j$. Then any element of M_n is expressed as a linear combination of elements of the form $a_1^{\alpha_1} \cdots a_r^{\alpha_r} m_j$ with coefficients in A_0, where $n = \sum_i \alpha_i d_i + e_j$ and $\alpha_i \geq 0$. For each n, there are only finitely many $(r+1)$-tuples $(\alpha_1, \ldots, \alpha_r, j)$ satisfying this condition. Hence, M_n is a finitely generated A_0-module. If we put $n_0 = \min\{e_j; 1 \leq j \leq s\}$, then

$M_n = (0)$ for each $n < n_0$. Next let d be the least common multiple of $d_1, \ldots, d_r$, and let $b_i = (a_i)^{d/d_i}$. We let $\{x_\mu\}$ stand for the set of all elements $a_1^{\alpha_1} \cdots a_r^{\alpha_r} m_j$ with $0 \leq \alpha_i < d/d_i$, $1 \leq i \leq r$, and $1 \leq j \leq s$. Let n_1 be the greatest one of $\deg x_\mu$'s when x_μ ranges over all elements of $\{x_\mu\}$. If $n \geq n_1$, then every element of M_{n+d} is then expressed as $\sum_\mu f_\mu(b_1, \ldots, b_r)x_\mu$. So $M_{n+d} = A_d M_n$. Conversely, if the conditions (i), (ii), and (iii) are satisfied, then we can readily show that M is a finitely generated A-module. The proof is left to the reader as an exercise. □

In the same way as for the affine scheme $\mathrm{Spec}(A)$ for a ring A, we define the *homogeneous spectrum* $\mathrm{Proj}(A)$ for a graded ring $A = \sum_{n \geq 0} A_n$ as the set of all homogeneous prime ideals of A which does not contain A_+. For a subset E of A, define $V_+(E) = \{\mathfrak{P} \in \mathrm{Proj}(A); \mathfrak{P} \supseteq E\}$ and $D_+(E) = \mathrm{Proj}(A) - V_+(E)$. Denote by E' the set of all homogeneous parts[1] of elements of E, and by I the homogeneous ideal of A generated by E'. Then we have $V_+(E) = V_+(E') = V_+(I)$.

LEMMA 5.2. *$\mathrm{Proj}(A)$ is given a topology for which the subsets of the form $V_+(E)$ are closed subsets. This topology is called the* Zariski topology *of* $\mathrm{Proj}(A)$.

PROOF. We have only to verify the following assertions:
(1) $V_+(0) = \mathrm{Proj}(A)$, $V_+(A_+) = \emptyset$;
(2) $V_+(E_1) \cup V_+(E_2) = V_+(E_1 E_2)$;
(3) $\bigcap_{\lambda \in \Lambda} V_+(E_\lambda) = V_+(\bigcup_{\lambda \in \Lambda} E_\lambda)$.
The proof of (1)–(3) is left to the reader. □

We shall show next that $\mathrm{Proj}(A)$ is a scheme which is obtained as affine schemes patched together. Let a be a homogeneous element of degree d. In the quotient ring $A[a^{-1}]$ we define the degree of an element b/a^r ($b \in A_n$, $r \geq 0$) to be $\deg(b/a^r) = n - dr$. Then $A[a^{-1}]$ is a graded ring which admits homogeneous elements of negative degree. The set of all homogeneous elements of degree 0 is the subring $A[a^{-1}]_0$. Furthermore, if $b \in A_e$ then $A[(ab)^{-1}]_0 = A[a^{-1}]_0[(b^d/a^e)^{-1}]$. In fact, every element of $A[(ab)^{-1}]_0$ is written as $x/(ab)^k$ with $\deg x = k(d+e)$. If we choose integers $l, h > 0$ so that $k + l = dh$, then $x/(ab)^k = (xb^l/a^k a^{eh}) \cdot (a^e/b^d)^h$. So $A[(ab)^{-1}]_0 \subseteq A[a^{-1}]_0[(b^d/a^e)^{-1}]$. The opposite inclusion is apparent. We shall prove the following.

LEMMA 5.3. (1) *For a homogeneous element a of degree d, there is a bijection φ between $D_+(a)$ and* $\mathrm{Spec}\, A[a^{-1}]_0$ *which is given by $\mathfrak{P} \mapsto \mathfrak{P}A[a^{-1}] \cap A[a^{-1}]_0$.*

(2) *If $a \in A_d$ and $b \in A_e$, then $D_+(ab)$ corresponds to $D(b^d/a^e)$ under the bijection in (1) above.*

(3) *If we introduce the topology on $D_+(a)$ induced by the Zariski topology on* $\mathrm{Proj}(A)$, *the bijection in (1) gives rise to a homeomorphism between $D_+(a)$ and* $\mathrm{Spec}\, A[a^{-1}]_0$. *We can therefore regard $D_+(a)$ as a scheme by translating the scheme structure on* $\mathrm{Spec}\, A[a^{-1}]_0$ *onto $D_+(a)$ via this homeomorphism. Then the local ring $\mathscr{O}$ at a point $\mathfrak{P}$ of $D_+(a)$ is equal to $(A_{\mathfrak{P}})_0$, where $S = \{z;\ z$ is a homogeneous element of A and $z \notin \mathfrak{P}\}$ is a multiplicatively closed subset of A and $A_{\mathfrak{P}}$ is the quotient ring of A with respect to S. $A_{\mathfrak{P}}$ is a graded ring admitting homogeneous elements of negative degree.*

(4) $\mathrm{Proj}(A)$ *is a scheme separated over* $\mathrm{Spec}(A_0)$.

[1] If we write $x = x_r + x_{r+1} + \cdots + x_s$ with $x_j \in A_j$, then each x_j is called the *homogeneous part* of degree j of x.

PROOF. (1) It is apparent that $\mathfrak{p} := \mathfrak{P}A[a^{-1}] \cap A[a^{-1}]_0$ is a prime ideal of $A[a^{-1}]_0$. We shall show that $\varphi(\mathfrak{P}) \neq \varphi(\mathfrak{P}')$ for $\mathfrak{P}, \mathfrak{P}' \in D_+(a)$ with $\mathfrak{P} \neq \mathfrak{P}'$. Let $\mathfrak{p} = \varphi(\mathfrak{P})$ and $\mathfrak{p}' = \varphi(\mathfrak{P}')$. Since $\mathfrak{P} \neq \mathfrak{P}'$ by hypothesis, there exists a homogeneous element x such that $x \in \mathfrak{P}$ and $x \notin \mathfrak{P}'$. Replacing x by x^d if necessary, we may assume $x \in A_{nd}$. Then $x/a^n \in \mathfrak{p}$ and $x/a^n \notin \mathfrak{p}'$. (If $x/a^n \in \mathfrak{p}'$, then $x/a^n = y/a^m$ for $y \in A_{md} \cap \mathfrak{P}'$. Hence, $a^{s+m}x = a^{s+n}y \in \mathfrak{P}'$ $(s \geq 0)$. This implies $x \in \mathfrak{P}'$, which is a contradiction.) So $\mathfrak{p} \neq \mathfrak{p}'$. Next we shall show that φ is surjective. Let $\mathfrak{p}$ be a prime ideal of $A[a^{-1}]_0$. For each $n > 0$, let $\mathfrak{P}_n = \{x \in A_n; x^d/a^n \in \mathfrak{p}\}$, and for $n = 0$, let $\mathfrak{P}_0 = \{x \in A_0; x/1 \in \mathfrak{p}\}$. We claim that $\mathfrak{P} = \sum_{n \geq 0} \mathfrak{P}_n$ is a homogeneous prime ideal in $D_+(a)$ and $\mathfrak{p} = \varphi(\mathfrak{P})$. By definition, $\mathfrak{P}$ is a homogeneous ideal. In order to show that $\mathfrak{P}$ is a prime ideal, it suffices to verify the condition: $xy \in \mathfrak{P}$, $x \notin \mathfrak{P}$ implies $y \in \mathfrak{P}$. Since $\mathfrak{P}$ is a homogeneous ideal, we may assume that $x \in A_n$, $y \in A_m$. By definition, $(xy)^d/a^{n+m} \in \mathfrak{p}$ and $x^d/a^n \notin \mathfrak{p}$. (By convention, $a^0 = 1$.) Since $\mathfrak{p}$ is a prime ideal, we have $y^d/a^m \in \mathfrak{p}$. Hence, $y \in \mathfrak{P}_m \subset \mathfrak{P}$. Meanwhile, every element of $\mathfrak{p}$ is written as x/a^n with $x \in A_{nd}$, and $x/a^n \in \mathfrak{p}$ if and only if $x^d/a^{nd} \in \mathfrak{p}$. Then $x \in \mathfrak{P}_{nd}$, and $x/a^n \in \mathfrak{P}A[a^{-1}] \cap A[a^{-1}]_0$. So $\mathfrak{p} = \varphi(\mathfrak{P})$. Thus, φ is a bijection.

(2) We have $D_+(ab) = D_+(a) \cap D_+(b)$, and for $\mathfrak{P} \in D_+(ab)$,

$$\begin{aligned}\mathfrak{P}A[(ab)^{-1}] \cap A[(ab)^{-1}]_0 &= \mathfrak{P}A[(ab)^{-1}] \cap A[a^{-1}]_0[(b^d/a^e)^{-1}] \\ &= \mathfrak{p}A[a^{-1}]_0[(b^d/a^e)^{-1}],\end{aligned}$$

where $\mathfrak{p} = \varphi(\mathfrak{P})$. Hence, $\mathfrak{p}$ belongs to the open set $D(b^d/a^e)$ of $\operatorname{Spec} A[a^{-1}]_0$. Conversely, if $\mathfrak{p} = \varphi(\mathfrak{P}) \in D(b^d/a^e)$, then $a^d/a^d \notin \mathfrak{p}$ and $b^d/a^e \notin \mathfrak{p}$. So by the definition of $\mathfrak{P}$, we have $ab \notin \mathfrak{P}$. Thus, φ induces a bijection between $D_+(ab)$ and $D(b^d/a^e)$.

(3) Note that $\{D_+(ab); b$ is a homogeneous element of $A\}$ is an open basis for the Zariski topology on $D_+(a)$ and that an open set $D(x/a^n)(\deg x = nd)$ of $\operatorname{Spec} A[a^{-1}]_0$ corresponds to $D_+(ax)$ under φ. So φ is a homeomorphism by (2). Thus, the local ringed space $(D_+(a), \varphi^* A[a^{-1}]_0^{\sim})$ is isomorphic to the affine scheme $\operatorname{Spec} A[a^{-1}]_0$. The local ring at the point $\mathfrak{P}$ is equal to $(A[a^{-1}]_0)_{\mathfrak{p}}$, where $\mathfrak{p} = \varphi(\mathfrak{P})$, which is nothing but $(A_{\mathfrak{P}})_0$. It can be verified by a straightforward computation.

(4) Let $X = \operatorname{Proj}(A)$. Then $\{D_+(a)\}_{a \in A_+}$ is an affine open covering of X. The coordinate ring $A[a^{-1}]_0$ of $D_+(a)$ is viewed as an A_0-algebra in the natural fashion. For a homogeneous element $b \in A_+$, denote by $\sigma_{ab,a}$ the natural ring homomorphism $A[a^{-1}]_0 \to A[(ab)^{-1}]_0$. Then $A[(ab)^{-1}]_0$ is generated over A_0 by the images $\sigma_{ab,a}(A[a^{-1}]_0)$ and $\sigma_{ab,b}(A[b^{-1}]_0)$. So $A[a^{-1}]_0 \otimes_{A_0} A[b^{-1}]_0 \to A[(ab)^{-1}]_0$, $x \otimes y \mapsto \sigma_{ab,a}(x) \cdot \sigma_{ab,b}(y)$, is a surjective ring homomorphism. This gives rise to a closed immersion $\Delta_{a,b}\colon D_+(ab) \to D_+(a) \times_{A_0} D_+(b)$. Since $D_+(ab) = D_+(a) \cap D_+(b)$, $\Delta_{a,b}$ turns out to be the restriction of the diagonal morphism Δ of X onto $D_+(ab)$. So we know that Δ is a closed immersion. $\square$

Note that the closed set $V_+(I)$ of $\operatorname{Proj}(A)$ is identified with $\operatorname{Proj}(A/I)$ as sets. We summarize the properties of $\operatorname{Proj}(A)$ in the following theorem.

THEOREM 5.4. *For a graded ring $A = \sum_{n \geq 0} A_n$, let $X = \operatorname{Proj}(A)$, and let $S = \operatorname{Spec}(A_0)$. Let $\pi\colon X \to S$ be the structure morphism with X viewed naturally as an S-scheme. Then the following assertions hold*:

(1) *Let $\mathfrak{N}$ be the nilradical of A, and let $\mathfrak{N}_+ = A_+ \cap \mathfrak{N}$. Then $\mathfrak{N}$ and $\mathfrak{N}_+$ are homogeneous Ideals and* $\operatorname{Proj} A/\mathfrak{N}_+ = X_{\mathrm{red}}$.

(2) *Suppose* $\mathfrak{N}_+ = (0)$. *Then* X *is irreducible if and only if* A_+ *has no zero divisors in* A_+.

(3) *If* A *is a noetherian ring, then* X *is a noetherian scheme and* $\pi\colon X \to S$ *is a finitely generated morphism.*

(4) *Suppose* A *is a noetherian ring and is generated by* A_1 *as an* A_0*-algebra. Then the structure morphism* $\pi\colon X \to S$ *is a proper morphism.*

PROOF. (1) By problem II.5.1, $\mathfrak{N}$ and $\mathfrak{N}_+$ are homogeneous ideals. Let $\overline{A} = A/\mathfrak{N}_+$. Then $\overline{A}$ is a graded ring. Let $\rho\colon A \to \overline{A}$ be the residue homomorphism. We have $\rho(A_n) = \overline{A}_n$. For a homogeneous element a of degree $d > 0$, define a homomorphism $\rho_a\colon A[a^{-1}]_0 \to \overline{A}[\bar{a}^{-1}]_0$ by $\rho_a(x/a^r) = \bar{x}/\bar{a}^r$, where $\bar{a} = \rho(a)$ and $\bar{x} = \rho(x)$. We claim that $\overline{A}[\bar{a}^{-1}]_0 \cong A[a^{-1}]_0/N$ provided $a \notin \mathfrak{N}_+$, where N is the nilradical of $A[a^{-1}]_0$. Suppose $x/a^r \in A[a^{-1}]_0$ is a nilpotent element. Then $(x/a^r)^t = 0$ (for some $t > 0$). Hence, $a^s x^t = 0$ for an integer $s \geq 0$. So $a^s x \in \mathfrak{N}_+$ and $\rho_a(x/a^r) = \bar{a}^s\bar{x}/\bar{a}^{s+r} = 0$. Namely, $N \subseteq \operatorname{Ker}\rho_a$. Conversely, suppose $\rho_a(x/a^r) = 0$. Then $a^s x \in \mathfrak{N}_+$ for some $s \geq 0$. So $(a^s x)^t = 0$. Then $(x/a^r)^t = (a^s x)^t/(a^{r+s})^t = 0$. Thus, $\operatorname{Ker}\rho_a \subseteq N$. The claim is proved. In other words, ${}^a(\rho_a)$ induces an isomorphism between $\operatorname{Spec}\overline{A}[\bar{a}^{-1}]_0 \cong D_+(\bar{a})$ and $(\operatorname{Spec} A[a^{-1}]_0)_{\mathrm{red}} \cong D_+(a)_{\mathrm{red}}$. Furthermore, we can show that ${}^a(\rho_{ab}) = {}^a(\rho_a)|_{D_+(\bar{a}\bar{b})}$ for a homogeneous element b of degree $e > 0$. Hence, patching $\{{}^a(\rho_a)\}_{a\in A_+}$ together, we obtain an isomorphism between $\operatorname{Proj}(\overline{A})$ and X_{red}.

(2) To prove the "only if" part, suppose there are homogeneous elements a, b of A_+ such that $ab = 0$, $a \neq 0$, and $b \neq 0$. If $D_+(a) \cong \operatorname{Spec} A[a^{-1}]_0 = \emptyset$, then $A[a^{-1}]_0$ is the zero ring, where $1 = 0$. Hence, a is nilpotent, and this contradicts the hypothesis $\mathfrak{N}_+ = (0)$. So $D_+(a) \neq \emptyset$, $D_+(b) \neq \emptyset$, and $D_+(a) \cap D_+(b) = D_+(ab) = \emptyset$. This contradicts the assumption that X is irreducible.

The "if" part. If a ranges over homogeneous elements of A_+, $\{D_+(a)\}$ is an affine open covering of X. If we show that all $D_+(a)$ are irreducible and X is connected, then X is irreducible. Moreover, $D_+(a)$ is irreducible if $A[a^{-1}]_0$ is an integral domain. Suppose $(x/a^r)\cdot(y/a^s) = 0$. Since $x/a^r = 0$ if and only if $a^n x/a^{r+n} = 0$ $(n > 0)$, we may assume that $x, y \in A_+$. Then $a^m xy = 0$. Since A_+ has no zero divisors, either $x = 0$ or $y = 0$. So $x/a^r = 0$ or $y/a^s = 0$. We shall next show that X is connected. Suppose $X = X_1 \coprod X_2$. Since X_1 and X_2 are open sets and since $\{D_+(a)\}$ is an open basis of X, there exist nonzero homogeneous elements a, b such that $D_+(a) \subseteq X_1$ and $D_+(b) \subseteq X_2$. Let $d = \deg a$ and $e = \deg b$. We have $b^d/a^e \neq 0$ in $A[a^{-1}]_0$. So $D_+(ab) \cong D(b^d/a^e) \neq \emptyset$. This contradicts the assumption that $D_+(a) \cap D_+(b) = \emptyset$.

(3) For a positive integer d, define a graded subring $A^{(d)}$ of A by $A^{(d)} = \sum_{n\geq 0} A_{dn}$, for which the homogeneous part of degree n in $A^{(d)}$ is A_{dn}. By virtue of Lemma 5.5 below, we have $A[a^{-1}]_0 \cong A^{(d)}/(a-1)$ for a homogeneous element a of degree d. Suppose A is a noetherian ring. Then by Lemma 5.1, A_0 is a noetherian ring and A is a finitely generated A_0-algebra. We may assume that A is generated over A_0 by homogeneous elements $a_1, \ldots, a_r$ in A_+. Let $d_i = \deg a_i$. In order to show that $X = \operatorname{Proj}(A)$ is a noetherian scheme and X is finitely generated over S, it suffices to show that $A[a^{-1}]_0$ is a finitely generated A_0-algebra if a is a homogeneous element of degree $d > 0$. Let $E = \{a_1^{\alpha_1}\cdots a_r^{\alpha_r}; 0 \leq \alpha_i \leq d, \sum_{i=1}^r \alpha_i d_i \equiv 0 \pmod{d}\}$. Then E is a finite set consisting of homogeneous elements of $A^{(d)}$. Note that each element of $(A^{(d)})_n = A_{dn}$ is expressed as $\sum c a_1^{\beta_1}\cdots a_r^{\beta_r}$ $(c \in A_0,\ \beta_i \geq 0,\ \sum_{i=1}^r \beta_i d_i = nd)$, where $a_1^{\beta_1}\cdots a_r^{\beta_r}$ is written as a product of elements in E. Thus, E generates the A_0-algebra

$A^{(d)}$. Hence, $A[a^{-1}]_0 \cong A^{(d)}/(a-1)$ is a finitely generated A_0-algebra.

(4) Since $\pi\colon X \to S$ is a separated, finitely generated morphism, it suffices to show that π is a universally closed morphism. Namely, we have only to show that the base change $\pi_T\colon X \times_S T \to T$ is a closed morphism for an arbitrary morphism of schemes $T \to S$. Replacing T by an affine open set, we may assume that T is an affine scheme Spec(B). Then since $X = \bigcup D_+(a)$, the construction of $X \times_S T$ implies that $X \times_S T = \mathrm{Proj}(A \otimes_{A_0} B)$, where $A \otimes_{A_0} B = \sum_{n\geq 0} A_n \otimes_{A_0} B$. A closed set of $X \times_S T$ is of the form $V_+(I) = \mathrm{Proj}(A \otimes_{A_0} B/I)$, where $A \otimes_{A_0} B/I$ is a graded ring which is generated by $A_1 \otimes_{A_0} B/I \cap (A_1 \otimes_{A_0} B)$ over $B/I \cap B$. It suffices therefore to prove that the image $\pi(X)$ of the structure morphism $\pi\colon X \to S$ is a closed set under the assumption that A_0 is not necessarily noetherian, A_1 is a finitely generated A_0-module and A is a graded ring which is generated by A_1 over A_0. For a point y of S, let $k(y) = \mathscr{O}_y/\mathfrak{m}_y$ be the residue field. Then $\pi^{-1}(y) \cong \mathrm{Proj}(A \otimes_{A_0} k(y))$, and $y \notin \pi(X)$ if and only if $\pi^{-1}(y) = \emptyset$. Let $a_1, \ldots, a_r$ be a set of generators of the A_0-module A_1, and let $\bar{a}_i$ be the image of a_i in $A_1 \otimes_{A_0} k(y)$. We have the equivalent conditions:

$$\begin{aligned}
\pi^{-1}(y) = \emptyset &\Leftrightarrow k(y)[\bar{a}_1/\bar{a}_i, \ldots, \bar{a}_r/\bar{a}_i] = (0), \qquad 1 \leq i \leq r;\\
&\Leftrightarrow \text{ for some } N > 0,\ \bar{a}_i^N = 0, \qquad 1 \leq i \leq r;\\
&\Leftrightarrow A_n \otimes_{A_n} k(y) = (0), \qquad n \gg 0;\\
&\Leftrightarrow A_n \otimes_{A_0} \mathscr{O}_y = (0), \qquad n \gg 0,
\end{aligned}$$

where, in order to show the last equivalence, we use the hypothesis that $A_n \otimes_{A_0} \mathscr{O}_y$ is a finitely generated $\mathscr{O}_y$-module. (Compare this with the proof of Nakayama's Lemma (I.1.28).] Let I_n be the annihilator ideal of a finitely generated A_0-module A_n, i.e., $I_n := \{c \in A_0;\, cx = 0, \text{ for each } x \in A_n\}$. Then $A_n \otimes_{A_0} \mathscr{O}_y = (0)$ if and only if $y \notin V(I_n)$. In fact, write $A_n = A_0 b_1 + \cdots + A_0 b_t$ and $\mathscr{O}_y = (A_0)_\mathfrak{p}$. If $A_n \otimes_{A_0} \mathscr{O}_y = (0)$, then for some $s \notin \mathfrak{p}$ such that $sb_j = 0$ for each j. Hence, $s \in I_n - \mathfrak{p}$, i.e., $y \notin V(I_n)$. Conversely, if $y \notin V(I_n)$, then there exists some $s \in I_n - \mathfrak{p}$, whence, $A_n \otimes_{A_0} \mathscr{O}_y = (0)$. On the other hand, $I_n \subseteq I_{n+1}$ because $A_1 \cdot A_n = A_{n+1}$. Let $I = \bigcup_{n\geq 0} I_n$. Then I is an ideal of A_0, and $V(I) = \bigcap_{n\geq 0} V(I_n)$. Summarizing the arguments, we know that $y \notin \pi(X)$ if and only if $y \notin V(I)$. Hence, $\pi(X) = V(I)$. So $\pi(X)$ is a closed subset of S.

Consider, in particular, the case A_0 is a field k. Then $\pi\colon X \to S$ is an algebraic scheme over $S = \mathrm{Spec}(k)$. In order to show that π is a proper morphism, we may replace X by X_{red} and then X_{red} by its irreducible component. So we may assume that X is irreducible and reduced. There is no loss of generality through these substitutions nor by assuming that X is given as $X = \mathrm{Proj}(A)$, where A is a finitely generated, graded k-algebra which is generated by A_1 (cf. (1) of this theorem and problem II.5.2). By Theorem 4.17, we have only to show that given a discrete valuation ring $(\mathscr{O}, \mathfrak{m})$ of the function field $k(X)$ of X there exists a point x' of X such that $\mathscr{O} \geq \mathscr{O}_{x'}$. (To verify that the condition in (1) of Definition 4.16 is satisfied by X, we have to consider an irreducible and reduced closed subscheme $\overline{\{x\}}$ and a discrete valuation ring $k(x) \cap \mathscr{O}$ of the function field $k(x)$. However, since $\overline{\{x\}}$ is again of the form Proj(A) we may assume from the beginning that $X = \overline{\{x\}}$.) Let $\{a_1, \ldots, a_r\}$ be a k-basis of the k-vector space A_1. Then $X = \bigcup_{i=1}^r D_+(a_i)$, and $D_+(a_i) \cong \mathrm{Spec}\, k[a_1/a_i, \ldots, a_r/a_i]$. Let v be the valuation associated with $\mathscr{O}$. Suppose that $\min\{v(a_i/a_1);\, 1 \leq i \leq r\}$ is attained by $v(a_t/a_1)$. Since $v(a_i/a_t) = v(a_i/a_1) - v(a_t/a_1) \geq 0$ (for each i, $1 \leq i \leq r$), we have $k[a_1/a_t, \ldots, a_r/a_t] \subseteq \mathscr{O}$. Let $\mathfrak{p} = \mathfrak{m} \cap k[a_1/a_t, \ldots, a_r/a_t]$, and let x' be the point of $D_+(a_t)$ corresponding to $\mathfrak{p}$. Then $\mathcal{O} \geq k[a_1/a_t, \ldots, a_r/a_t]_{\mathfrak{p}} = \mathcal{O}_{x'}$. Hence, X is proper over k. **By Theorem 4.17, we conclude that the structure morphism π is a proper morphism.** □

In the above proof, we made use of the following lemma.

LEMMA 5.5. *Let $A = \sum_{n\geq 0} A_n$ be a graded ring, and let $A^{(d)} = \sum_{n\geq 0} A_{dn}$ for a positive integer d. Then for a homogeneous element a of degree d, we have*

$$A[a^{-1}]_0 \cong A^{(d)}/(a-1).$$

PROOF. Define a ring homomorphism $\rho\colon A^{(d)}/(a-1) \to A[a^{-1}]_0$ by $x \in A_{dn} \mapsto x/a^n$. Evidently, ρ is surjective. We shall show that ρ is injective. Suppose $\rho(x_1 + \cdots + x_s) = 0$ ($x_i \in A_{dn_i}$). For $n \geq n_i$ (for each i), $\rho(x_1 + \cdots + x_s) = x_1/a^{n_1} + \cdots + x_s/a^{n_s} = (a^{n-n_1}x_1 + \cdots + a^{n-n_s}x_s)/a^n$. So $a^l(a^{n-n_1}x_1 + \cdots + a^{n-n_s}x_s) = 0$ for some $l \geq 0$. Hence, $x_1 + \cdots + x_s = (x_1 - a^{l+n-n_1}x_1) + \cdots + (x_s - a^{l+n-n_s}x_s) \in (a-1)A^{(d)}$. □

DEFINITION 5.6. When A is a noetherian graded ring which is generated by A_1 as an A_0-algebra, then $X = \mathrm{Proj}(A)$ is called a *projective scheme* over $S = \mathrm{Spec}(A_0)$. The structure morphism is then a proper morphism (Theorem 5.4 (4)). When A_0 is a field k and $X = \mathrm{Proj}(A)$ is an algebraic variety, then X is called a *projective algebraic variety*.

A basic example of projective scheme is given by the polynomial ring $A = R[T_0, T_1, \ldots, T_n]$ in $n+1$ variables over a ring R which we view as a graded ring by putting $A_0 = R$ and $\deg T_i = 1$ $(0 \leq i \leq n)$. Then $\mathrm{Proj}(A) = \bigcup_{i=0}^n D_+(T_i)$ and $D_+(T_i) = \mathrm{Spec}\, R[T_0/T_i, \ldots, T_n/T_i] = \mathbf{A}_R^n$ (the affine space of dimension n over R). If $i \neq j$, then $D_+(T_i)$ and $D_+(T_j)$ are patched up in $\mathrm{Proj}(A)$ along the respective open sets $D(T_j/T_i)$ and $D(T_i/T_j)$ by the isomorphism which is associated with an $R[T_i/T_j, T_j/T_i]$-algebra isomorphism

$$R[T_0/T_j, \ldots, T_n/T_j, T_j/T_i] \to R[T_0/T_i, \ldots, T_n/T_i, T_i/T_j]$$
$$T_l/T_j \mapsto T_l/T_j = T_l/T_i \cdot T_i/T_j \qquad (l \neq i, j).$$

We then denote $\mathrm{Proj}(A)$ by $\mathbf{P}_R^n$ and call it the *projective space* of dimension n. We call $(T_0, T_1, \ldots, T_n)$ its *homogeneous coordinates*. If R is a field, $\mathbf{P}_k^n$ is an algebraic variety over k. We shall consider the set of closed points $\mathbf{P}^n(k)$ when k is an algebraically closed field. Let $P \in \mathbf{P}^n(k)$. Then $P \in D_+(T_i)$ for some i. In order to simplify the situation we assume $i = 0$ in the subsequent argument. Let $t_i = T_i/T_0$ $(1 \leq i \leq n)$. Then P corresponds to a maximal ideal $\mathfrak{m} = (t_1 - \alpha_1, \ldots, t_n - \alpha_n)$ $(\alpha_i \in k)$. So, the homogeneous prime ideal $\mathfrak{P}$ which corresponds to P is $\mathfrak{P} = (T_1 - \alpha_1 T_0, \ldots, T_n - \alpha_n T_0)$. This is considered as the defining ideal of a line $(T_0, \alpha_1 T_0, \ldots, \alpha_n T_0)$ on $\mathbf{A}_k^{n+1} = \mathrm{Spec}\, k[T_0, \ldots, T_n]$ which passes through the origin $(0, \ldots, 0)$. If $\alpha_i \neq 0$, then the line is written also as $((1/\alpha_i)T_0, (\alpha_1/\alpha_i)T_0, \ldots, (\alpha_n/\alpha_i)T_0)$. Conversely, given a line $(\beta_0 T_0, \beta_1 T_0, \ldots, \beta_n T_0)$ $(\beta_i \in k)$ passing through the origin, we have $\beta_i \neq 0$ for some i. Then the line defines a point $(\beta_0/\beta_i, \ldots, \beta_{i-1}/\beta_i, \beta_{i+1}/\beta_i, \ldots, \beta_n/\beta_i)$ of $D_+(T_i)$. Namely, there is a one-to-one correspondence between $\mathbf{P}^n(k)$ and the set of lines on $\mathbf{A}_k^{n+1}$ passing through the origin. A line on $\mathbf{A}_k^{n+1}$ passing through the origin is determined by its slope $(\beta_0, \beta_1, \ldots, \beta_n)$, and the slope is uniquely determined up to the equivalence relation $(\beta_0, \beta_1, \dots, \beta_n) \sim (\lambda\beta_0, \lambda\beta_1, \dots, \lambda\beta_n)$ $(\lambda \in k^* := k - (0))$. Thereby, we obtain a one-to-one correspondence

$$\mathbf{P}^n(k) \leftrightarrow k^{n+1} - (0)/\sim,$$

where $(\alpha_0, \dots, \alpha_n) \sim (\beta_0, \dots, \beta_n)$ if and only if $\beta_i = \lambda\alpha_i$ (for each i) for some $\lambda \in k^*$. To this effect, we denote a point $(\alpha_0, \dots, \alpha_n)$ of $\mathbf{P}^n(k)$ by $(\alpha_0 : \alpha_1 : \cdots : \alpha_n)$.

Let I be a homogeneous ideal of $A = k[T_0, \dots, T_n]$. Then $V_+(I)$ is a closed set of $\mathbf{P}^n_k$ and the closed subsets of $\mathbf{P}^n_k$ are exhausted by those of the form $V_+(I)$. The residue ring $B = A/I$ is a graded ring which is generated by $B_1 = A_1/A_1 \cap I$ over $B_0 (= k)$. Since every homogeneous prime ideal of B is expressed as $\mathfrak{P}/I$ with $\mathfrak{P} \in V_+(I)$, the topological space $V_+(I)$ is identified with $\operatorname{Proj}(B)$. Let $X = \operatorname{Proj}(B)$. X is then an algebraic scheme which is separated over k. By Theorem 5.4, X is reduced if $I = \sqrt{I}$ and an algebraic variety over k if I is a prime ideal. (The hypothesis that k is algebraically closed is still in force.) As a homogeneous ideal of the polynomial ring $k[T_0, \dots, T_n]$, I is generated by finitely many homogeneous polynomials

$$f_j = f_j(T_0, \dots, T_n), \qquad 1 \le j \le N.$$

If $P = (\alpha_1, \dots, \alpha_n)$ is a point of $\mathbf{P}^n(k)$ and $\mathfrak{P}$ is the corresponding homogeneous prime ideal of A, then we have the equivalence

$$P \in X(k) \quad \text{iff} \quad \mathfrak{P} \supset I \quad \text{iff} \quad f_j(\alpha_0, \dots, \alpha_n) = 0, \qquad 1 \le j \le N.$$

The first equivalence is apparent. We shall show the second equivalence. For the sake of simplicity, we assume $\alpha_0 \neq 0$. Then $P \in D_+(T_0)$, and $X \cap D_+(T_0)$ is the closed subset in $\operatorname{Spec} k[t_1, \dots, t_n]$ defined by the ideal I_0 of $k[t_1, \dots, t_n]$ which is generated by $\{f_j(1, t_1, \dots, t_n); 1 \le j \le N\}$. Hence, if $P \in X \cap D_+(T_0)$, then

$$(*) \quad f_j\left(1, \frac{\alpha_1}{\alpha_0}, \dots, \frac{\alpha_n}{\alpha_0}\right) = \alpha_0^{-\deg f_j} f_j(\alpha_0, \alpha_1, \dots, \alpha_n) = 0, \qquad 1 \le j \le N.$$

Thus, we know that the "only if" part holds. Conversely, if $(*)$ holds, then $P \in X \cap D_+(T_0)$, whence the the "if" part follows.

Since an irreducible reduced algebraic scheme defined over an algebraically closed field is an algebraic variety, X is therefore an algebraic variety. As we explained after Lemma 4.11, we confuse $(X, \mathcal{O}_X)$ and $(X(k), \mathcal{O}_{X(k)})$ and call $X(k)$ a projective algebraic variety *defined by a system of equations* $f_j(T_0, \dots, T_n) = 0$ $(1 \le j \le N)$.

When the ideal I is generated by a single homogeneous polynomial $f = f(T_0, T_1, \dots, T_n)$, we call X a *hypersurface* defined by $f = 0$ without caring whether or not X is reduced (or irreducible). We call $\deg f$ the *degree* of the hypersurface X. In particular, if f is a linear polynomial

$$f = a_0T_0 + a_1T_1 + \cdots + a_nT_n, \qquad (a_0, \dots, a_n) \in k^{n+1} - (0),$$

then we call X a *hyperplane*. Suppose the linear polynomials $f = \sum_{i=0}^n a_iT_i$ and $g = \sum_{i=0}^n b_iT_i$ define the hyperplanes $H(f)$ and $H(g)$, respectively. Then we have

$$H(f) = H(g) \text{ if and only if for some } \lambda \in k^*,\ b_i = \lambda a_i,\ 0 \le i \le n.$$

We shall show "only if" part. For the sake of simplicity, assume that $H(f) \cap D_+(T_0) = H(g) \cap D_+(T_0) \neq \emptyset$. Then $H(f) \cap D_+(T_0)$ is defined on $\operatorname{Spec} k[t_1, \dots, t_n]$ by a principal ideal $(a_0 + a_1t_1 + \cdots + a_nt_n)$ and $H(g) \cap D_+(T_0)$ by $(b_0 + b_1t_1 + \cdots + b_nt_n)$. So the two ideals $(a_0 + a_1t_1 + \cdots + a_nt_n)$ and $(b_0 + b_1t_1 + \cdots + b_nt_n)$ coincide with each other, which occurs if and only if for some $\lambda \in k^*$, $b_0 + b_1 t_1 + \cdots + b_n t_n = \lambda(a_0 + a_1 t_1 + \cdots + a_n t_n)$. We have thus shown the "only if" part. The converse is apparent. Consequently, the set of hyperplanes on $\mathbf{P}_k^n$ is in one-to-one correspondence with the set of k-rational points of another projective space $(\mathbf{P}_k^n)'$, the correspondence being the assignment $\sum_{i=0}^n a_i T_i = 0 \mapsto (a_0, \dots, a_n)$. In the case where k is an algebraically closed field, we call $(\mathbf{P}_k^n)'$ the *dual projective space* of $\mathbf{P}_k^n$ in the above sense. The dual projective space of $(\mathbf{P}_k^n)'$ is the $\mathbf{P}_k^n$ which we started with.

The previous observations are quite similar to the ones we made on affine schemes $\mathrm{Spec}(R)$ corresponding to rings R. We constructed morphisms of affine schemes, which correspond to ring homomorphisms $R \to S$, and Modules $\widetilde{M}$ corresponding to R-module M. We shall observe below that similar objects are constructed for homogeneous spectrums as well. Whenever we consider a graded ring $A = \sum_{n \geq 0} A_n$, we assume that A is generated by A_1 as an A_0-algebra.

Let $A = \sum_{n \geq 0} A_n$ and $B = \sum_{n \geq 0} B_n$ be graded rings. A ring homomorphism $\varphi\colon A \to B$ is said to be a *homomorphism of degree* 0 if $\varphi(A_n) \subseteq B_n$ for each $n \geq 0$. For a homogeneous prime ideal $\mathfrak{Q}$ of B, $\varphi^{-1}(\mathfrak{Q})$ is then a homogeneous prime ideal. Note that $\varphi^{-1}(\mathfrak{Q}) \supseteq A_+$ if and only if $\mathfrak{Q} \supseteq \varphi(A_+)$. Let $G(\varphi) = D_+(\varphi(A_+))$. Then we can define a mapping of sets $f\colon G(\varphi) \to \mathrm{Proj}(A)$ by $\mathfrak{Q} \mapsto \varphi^{-1}(\mathfrak{Q})$. Since $f^{-1}(D_+(a)) = D_+(\varphi(a)) \subseteq G(\varphi)$ for a homogeneous element a of A_+, f is a continuous mapping if the open set $G(\varphi)$ is given the induced topology on $\mathrm{Proj}(B)$.

We claim that f is a morphism of schemes. For a homogeneous element $a \in A_+$, we can define the natural ring homomorphism $\varphi_{(a)}\colon A[a^{-1}]_0 \to B[b^{-1}]_0$ by $\varphi_{(a)}(x/a^n) = \varphi(x)/b^n$ for $x/a^n \in A[a^{-1}]_0$, where $b = \varphi(a)$. This induces a morphism ${}^a(\varphi_{(a)})\colon D_+(b) \to D_+(a)$, where we note $D_+(b) \subseteq G(\varphi)$. If a ranges over all homogeneous elements of A_+, $\{D_+(\varphi(a))\}$ is an affine open covering of $G(\varphi)$. For homogeneous elements a, a' of A_+, the restrictions of ${}^a(\varphi_{(a)})$ and ${}^a(\varphi_{(a')})$ onto $D_+(\varphi(aa')) = D_+(\varphi(a)) \cap D_+(\varphi(a'))$ are identical. So in view of Lemma 4.3, we get a morphism of schemes ${}^a\varphi\colon G(\varphi) \to \mathrm{Proj}(A)$, which coincides with f as the mappings of sets. So f is a morphism of schemes. By the above construction, we know that ${}^a\varphi$ is an affine morphism (cf. Definition 4.20).

As an example, take $A = k[T_0, \dots, T_n]$. For a matrix $P = (p_{ij})$ belonging to the general linear group $\mathrm{GL}(n+1, k)$, define an isomorphism $\varphi_P\colon A \to A$ of degree 0 by $\varphi_P(T_i) = \sum_{j=0}^n p_{ij} T_j$. If we note that $\varphi_P(A_+) = A_+$, we see that $G(\varphi_P) = \mathrm{Proj}(A)$. Let $f_P = {}^a(\varphi_P)$. Then f_P is a k-automorphism of $\mathbf{P}_k^n$, and $f_P \cdot f_Q = f_{PQ}$. Moreover, if λP denotes a scalar product with $\lambda \in k^*$, then we have $f_{\lambda P} = f_P$. Meanwhile, the center of $\mathrm{GL}(n+1, k)$ is $\{\lambda I_{n+1}; \lambda \in k^*\} \cong k^*$, where I_{n+1} is the identity matrix of size $n+1$. Let $\mathrm{PGL}(n, k) = \mathrm{GL}(n+1, k)/k^*$. Then the mapping $P \mapsto f_P$ is a group homomorphism $f\colon \mathrm{PGL}(n, k) \to \mathrm{Aut}(\mathbf{P}_k^n)$, where $\mathrm{Aut}(\mathbf{P}_k^n)$ is the group of all k-automorphisms of $\mathbf{P}_k^n$, the multiplication being the composite of morphisms. In fact, it is known that f induces an isomorphism of groups $\mathrm{PGL}(n, k) \cong \mathrm{Aut}(\mathbf{P}_k^n)$. We call f_P the *projective transformation* on $\mathbf{P}_k^n$ defined by P and $\mathrm{PGL}(n, k)$ the *projective transformation group* in dimension n.

Let $M = \sum_{n \in \mathbf{Z}} M_n$ be a graded A-module. For a homogeneous element a of A_+, define an $A[a^{-1}]$-module $M[a^{-1}]$ by $M[a^{-1}] = M \otimes_A A[a^{-1}]$. Then $M[a^{-1}]$ is a graded module. If $x \in M_n$ and $a \in A_d$, then $\deg(x/a^m) = n - dm$. The set $M[a^{-1}]_0$ of elements of degree 0 is an $A[a^{-1}]_0$-module. So we can define a quasicoherent sheaf $M[a^{-1}]_0^\sim$. For $a \in A_d$ and $b \in A_e$, $M[(ab)^{-1}]_0^\sim$ is identified with $(M[a^{-1}]_0[a^e/b^d])^\sim$ if we identify $D_+(ab) = D_+(a) \cap D_+(b)$ with the open set $D(b^d/a^e)$ of $\mathrm{Spec}\, A[a^{-1}]_0$.

For example, an element $x/a^l b^m \in M[(ab)^{-1}]_0$ is written as $x/a^l b^m = (x'/a^{l+e\beta})\cdot(a^e/b^d)^\beta$ which belongs to $M[a^{-1}]_0[a^e/b^d]$, where we choose β so that $d\beta > m$ and put $x' = b^{d\beta-m}x$. Namely, $M[(ab)^{-1}]_0 \subseteq M[a^{-1}]_0[a^e/b^d]$. The opposite inclusion is apparent. Hence, if a ranges over all homogeneous elements of A_+, then the $\{M[a^{-1}]_0^\sim\}$ get patched together to give a quasicoherent Module on $\mathrm{Proj}(A)$, which we denote by $\widetilde{M}$.

Let $f: M \to N$ be a *degree* 0 *homomorphism* of graded A-modules, i.e., $f(M_n) \subseteq N_n$ for each n. For $a \in A_d$, we can define a homomorphism $f_a^\sim: M[a^{-1}]_0^\sim \to N[a^{-1}]_0^\sim$ by $f_a(x/a^n) = f(x)/a^n$ and patch $\{f_a^\sim\}$ together to give a homomorphism $\tilde{f}: \widetilde{M} \to \widetilde{N}$ of quasicoherent Modules. We shall observe in Theorem 5.9 that a quasicoherent Module on $\mathrm{Proj}(A)$ is written as $\widetilde{M}$.

Given graded A-modules M and N, we define a grading in $M \otimes_A N$ by $\deg(x \otimes y) = p+q$, $(x \in M_p, y \in N_q)$ which makes $M \otimes_A N$ a graded A-module. For $a \in A_d$, define the natural $A[a^{-1}]_0$-homomorphism

$$\lambda_a: M[a^{-1}]_0 \otimes_{A[a^{-1}]_0} N[a^{-1}]_0 \to (M \otimes_A N)[a^{-1}]_0$$

by $\lambda_a((x/a^r)\otimes(y/a^s)) = (x \otimes y)/a^{r+s}$. If a ranges over all homogeneous elements of A_+, we can patch $\{\lambda_a^\sim\}$ together to give a homomorphism of quasicoherent Modules $\lambda: \widetilde{M} \otimes_{\tilde{A}} \widetilde{N} \to (M \otimes_A N)^\sim$.

An A-homomorphism $f: M \to N$ is a *degree n homomorphism* if $f(M_r) \subseteq N_{n+r}$ for each r. Let $\mathrm{Hom}_A(M, N)_n$ denote the set of all degree n homomorphisms from M to N, and let $\mathrm{Hom}_A(M, N) = \sum_{n\in\mathbf{Z}} \mathrm{Hom}_A(M, N)_n$. Then $\mathrm{Hom}_A(M, N)$ is a graded A-module. For $a \in A_d$, define an $A[a^{-1}]_0$-homomorphism

$$\mu_a: \mathrm{Hom}_A(M, N)[a^{-1}]_0 \to \mathrm{Hom}_{A[a^{-1}]_0}(M[a^{-1}]_0, N[a^{-1}]_0)$$

by $\mu_a(f/a^n)(x/a^r) = f(x)/a^{n+r}$ $(f \in \mathrm{Hom}_A(M, N)_{nd}, x \in A_{rd})$. If a ranges over homogeneous elements of A_+, we can patch $\{\mu_a^\sim\}$ together to give a homomorphism of quasicoherent Modules

$$\tilde{\mu}: \mathrm{Hom}_A(M, N)^\sim \to \mathscr{H}om_{\tilde{A}}(\widetilde{M}, \widetilde{N}).$$

LEMMA 5.7. *Let A be a noetherian graded ring such that A is generated by A_1 as an A_0-algebra, and let $X = \mathrm{Proj}(A)$. For graded A-modules M and N, the following assertions hold*:

(1) *If M is a finitely generated A-module, then $\widetilde{M}$ is a coherent $\mathscr{O}_X$-Module.*

(2) *$\tilde{\lambda}: \widetilde{M} \otimes_{\tilde{A}} \widetilde{N} \to (M \otimes_A N)^\sim$ is an isomorphism.*

(3) *If M is a finitely generated A-module, the homomorphism $\tilde{\mu}$: $\mathrm{Hom}_A(M, N)^\sim \to \mathscr{H}om_{\tilde{A}}(\widetilde{M}, \widetilde{N})$ is an isomorphism.*

PROOF. (1) For $a \in A_1$, $A[a^{-1}]_0$ is a noetherian ring (cf. the proof of Theorem 5.4 (3)). Moreover, X is a noetherian scheme and is covered by a finite number of open sets $D_+(a)$ $(a \in A_1)$. So in order to show that $\widetilde{M}$ is coherent, it suffices to prove that $M[a^{-1}]_0$ is a finitely generated $A[a^{-1}]_0$-module. Since $a \in A_1$, we have $A[a^{-1}]_0 \cong A/(a-1)A$ and $M[a^{-1}]_0 \cong M/(a-1)M$ by the same argument as in Lemma 5.5. Then $M[a^{-1}]_0$ is a finitely generated $A[a^{-1}]_0$-module because M is a finitely generated A-module.

(2) Since $X = \bigcup_{a\in A_1} D_+(a)$, we have only to show that λ_a is an isomorphism for each $a \in A_1$. Clearly, λ is surjective. Suppose $\lambda_a(\sum_i (x_i/a^{m_i}) \otimes (y_i/a^{n_i})) = 0$. Let $m = \max_i(m_i)$ and $n = \max_i(n_i)$. Replacing x_i and y_i by $a^{m-m_i}x_i$ and $a^{n-n_i}y_i$, we

may assume that $x_i \in M_m$ and $y_i \in N_n$. Since $(\sum_i x_i \otimes y_i)/a^{m+n} = 0$, $a^l \sum_i x_i \otimes y_i = \sum_i a^l x_i \otimes y_i = 0$ in $M \otimes_A N$ for some $l > 0$. If we recall the definition of $M \otimes_A N$, $\sum_i a^l(x_i, y_i)$ is an element of the A-submodule R of the free A-module F generated by the elements of $M \times N$, where R is generated by such elements of F as

$$(u_1 + u_1', v_1) - (u_1, v_1) - (u_1', v_1), \qquad (u_2, v_2 + v_2') - (u_2, v_2) - (u_2, v_2'),$$
$$(bu_3, v_3) - (u_3, bv_3), \quad \text{and} \quad c(u_4, v_4) - (cu_4, v_4),$$

where u_i, v_j, b, c are homogeneous elements of M, N, A, respectively. Namely, we have a relation: $\sum_i a^l(x_i, y_i) =$ a linear combination of the elements as above in R. Noting that $\deg a = 1$, divide both sides of the linear relation by a suitable power of a. Namely, if $\deg u = r$, $\deg v = s$, and $\deg b = t$, then replace u, v, b by u/a^r, v/a^s, b/a^t, respectively. Then $\sum_i (a^l x_i/a^{l+m}, y_i/a^n)$ belongs to the subgroup R_0 of the free $A[a^{-1}]_0$-module F_0 generated by the elements of $M[a^{-1}]_0 \times N[a^{-1}]_0$, such that $F_0/R_0 \cong M[a^{-1}]_0 \otimes_{A[a^{-1}]_0} N[a^{-1}]_0$. This implies that λ_a is injective.

(3) To prove the assertion (3), we need the following definition.

DEFINITION 5.8. Let A be a graded ring, and let l be an integer. Define a graded A-module $A(l)$ by $A(l) = \sum_{n \in \mathbf{Z}} A(l)_n$ and $A(l)_n = A_{l+n}$. $A(l)$ is then a free, graded A-module with generator $1 \in A(l)_{-l}$. For a graded A-module M, define a graded A-module $M(l)$ by $M(l) = \sum_{n \in \mathbf{Z}} M(l)_n$ and $M(l)_n = M_{l+n}$. Clearly, $M(l+m) = M(l)(m)$.

We resume the proof of (3). Since M is a finitely generated A-module, it is generated by finitely many homogeneous elements $\{x_i;\ 1 \le i \le n\}$. Let $l_i = \deg x_i$, and let $P = \bigoplus_{i=1}^n A(-l_i)$ be a free A-module. We then define a surjective A-homomorphism $u\colon P \to M$ of degree 0 by $1 (\in A(-l_i)_{l_i}) \mapsto x_i$. Since A is a noetherian ring, $\operatorname{Ker} u$ is a finitely generated A-module. So we find a surjective A-homomorphism $v\colon Q \to \operatorname{Ker} u$ of degree 0, where $Q = \bigoplus_{j=1}^r A(-m_j)$ is a free A-module. Thus, we obtain an exact sequence of graded A-modules

$$Q \xrightarrow{v} P \xrightarrow{u} M \to 0,$$

where P and Q are finitely generated, free graded A-modules. For $a \in A_1$, the exact sequence yields an exact sequence of $A[a^{-1}]_0$-modules

$$Q[a^{-1}]_0 \xrightarrow{v_a} P[a^{-1}]_0 \xrightarrow{u_a} M[a^{-1}]_0 \to 0.$$

Employing the abbreviations $R = A[a^{-1}]_0$ and $P_a = P[a^{-1}]_0$, we have a commutative diagram

$$\begin{array}{ccccccc}
0 \longrightarrow & \operatorname{Hom}_A(M, N)_a & \xrightarrow{u_a^*} & \operatorname{Hom}_A(P, N)_a & \xrightarrow{v_a^*} & \operatorname{Hom}_A(Q, N)_a \\
& \downarrow{\scriptstyle \mu_a} & & \downarrow{\scriptstyle \mu_a} & & \downarrow{\scriptstyle \mu_a} \\
0 \longrightarrow & \operatorname{Hom}_R(M_a, N_a) & \xrightarrow{(u_a)^*} & \operatorname{Hom}_R(P_a, N_a) & \xrightarrow{(v_a)^*} & \operatorname{Hom}_R(Q_a, N_a),
\end{array}$$

where the upper and lower rows are exact sequences. If μ_a is an isomorphism for free A-modules P and Q, then $\mu_a\colon \operatorname{Hom}_A(M, N)_a \to \operatorname{Hom}_R(M_a, N_a)$ is an isomorphism. Here we have $\operatorname{Hom}_A(P, N) = \bigoplus_{i=1}^n \operatorname{Hom}_A(A(-l_i), N) \cong \bigoplus_{i=1}^n N(l_i)$, where the isomorphism $\operatorname{Hom}_A(A(-l_i), N) \cong N(l_i)$ is obtained by assigning to $f \in \operatorname{Hom}_A(A(-l_i), N)_k$ the image $f(1) (\in N_{l_i+k} = N(l_i)_k)$ of $1 \in A(-l_i)_{l_i}$. If we show that μ_a is an isomorphism for $M = A(-l)$, then μ_a is an isomorphism for P and Q

as well. Since $A(-l)_a = A(-l)[a^{-1}]_0 = R(1/a^l)$, $\mu_a \colon N(l)_a \to \mathrm{Hom}_R(A(-l)_a, N_a)$ is given by $\mu_a(x/a^k)(1/a^l) = x/a^{k+l}$ $(x \in N_{k+l})$. Suppose $\mu_a(x/a^k) = 0$. Then $a^s x = 0$ for some $s > 0$, and hence, $x/a^k = a^s x/a^{k+s} = 0$. So μ_a is injective. Given $\varphi \in \mathrm{Hom}_R(A(-l)_a, N_a)$, let $\varphi(1/a^l) = x/a^k$ $(x \in N_k)$. Then $\mu_a(x/a^{k-l}) = \varphi$. So μ_a is surjective. □

Let A be a noetherian graded ring such that A is generated by A_1 as an A_0-algebra, and let $X = \mathrm{Proj}(A)$. Put $\mathscr{O}_X(l) = A(l)^\sim$ for an integer l. Since $A(l)[a^{-1}]_0 = A[a^{-1}]_0(a^l \cdot 1)$ for $a \in A_1$, we have $\mathscr{O}_X(l)|_{D_+(a)} \cong \mathscr{O}_X|_{D_+(a)}$. Hence, $\mathscr{O}_X(l)$ is a locally free $\mathscr{O}_X$-Module of rank 1 (cf. (I.2.10)). By Lemma 5.7, we have $\mathscr{O}_X(l) \otimes_{\mathscr{O}_X} \mathscr{O}_X(m) \cong (A(l) \otimes_A A(m))^\sim \cong A(l+m)^\sim \cong \mathscr{O}_X(l+m)$ and $\mathscr{H}om_{\mathscr{O}_X}(\mathscr{O}_X(l), \mathscr{O}_X(m)) \cong \mathrm{Hom}_A(A(l), A(m))^\sim \cong A(m-l)^\sim \cong \mathscr{O}_X(m-l)$. In particular, if we denote by $[\mathscr{O}_X(l)]$ the isomorphism class of $\mathscr{O}_X(l)$ as $\mathscr{O}_X$-Modules, the set $\{[\mathscr{O}_X(l)]; l \in \mathbf{Z}\}$ becomes an infinite cyclic group with the multiplication defined by $[\mathscr{O}_X(l)] \cdot [\mathscr{O}_X(m)] = [\mathscr{O}_X(l) \otimes_{\mathscr{O}_X} \mathscr{O}_X(m)]$. We will see later that $\mathscr{O}_X(l)$ is an example of *invertible sheaf*.

Now let $\Gamma_*(\mathscr{O}_X) = \sum_{n\in\mathbf{Z}} \Gamma(X, \mathscr{O}_X(n))$. Then $\Gamma_*(\mathscr{O}_X)$ is a graded ring with the elements of $\Gamma(X, \mathscr{O}_X(n))$ viewed as homogeneous elements of degree n. For $b \in A_n$, $b/1 \in A(n)[a^{-1}]_0 = \Gamma(D_+(a), \mathscr{O}_X(n))$, where $a \in A_1$. Hence, there is the natural homomorphism of abelian groups (or modules over a field k) $\alpha_n \colon A_n \to \Gamma(X, \mathscr{O}_X(n))$, $b \mapsto b/1$. Then $\alpha = \sum_{n\in\mathbf{Z}} \alpha_n \colon A \to \Gamma_*(\mathscr{O}_X)$ is a homomorphism of graded rings.

Let $\mathscr{F}$ be an $\mathscr{O}_X$-Module. Let $\mathscr{F}(n) = \mathscr{F} \otimes_{\mathscr{O}_X} \mathscr{O}_X(n)$, and let

$$\Gamma_*(\mathscr{F}) = \sum_{n\in\mathbf{Z}} \Gamma(X, \mathscr{F}(n)).$$

Then $\Gamma_*(\mathscr{F})$ is a graded $\Gamma_*(\mathscr{O}_X)$-module by the natural mapping

$$\Gamma(X, \mathscr{F}(n)) \otimes \Gamma(X, \mathscr{O}_X(m)) \to \Gamma(X, \mathscr{F}(n+m)).$$

Hence, we can regard $\Gamma_*(\mathscr{F})$ as a graded A-module via the homomorphism α. We then define a homomorphism of $\mathscr{O}_X$-Modules $\beta_{\mathscr{F}} \colon \Gamma_*(\mathscr{F})^\sim \to \mathscr{F}$ as follows.

For $a \in A_d$ and $x \in \Gamma_*(\mathscr{F})_{nd}$, we have $x/a^n \in \Gamma_*(\mathscr{F})[a^{-1}]_0$ and $(x|_{D_+(a)})/(\alpha_d(a)|_{D_+(a)})^n \in \Gamma(D_+(a), \mathscr{F})$. Define a homomorphism of $A[a^{-1}]_0$-modules

$$(\beta_{\mathscr{F}})_a \colon \Gamma_*(\mathscr{F})[a^{-1}]_0 = \Gamma(D_+(a), \Gamma_*(\mathscr{F})^\sim) \to \Gamma(D_+(a), \mathscr{F})$$

by $x/a^n \mapsto (x|_{D_+(a)})/(\alpha_d(a)|_{D_+(a)})^n$. For $b \in A_e$, we have $(\beta_{\mathscr{F}})_{ab} = (\beta_{\mathscr{F}})_a|_{D_+(ab)}$. Then $\{(\beta_{\mathscr{F}})_a\}$ are patched together to give $\beta_{\mathscr{F}} \colon \Gamma_*(\mathscr{F})^\sim \to \mathscr{F}$.

We have now the following result.

THEOREM 5.9. *Let A be a noetherian graded ring such that A is generated by A_1 as an A_0-algebra, and let $X = \mathrm{Proj}(A)$.*

(1) *If A is an integral domain, then $\alpha \colon A \to \Gamma_*(\mathscr{O}_X)$ is injective. If $A_1 = \sum_{i=1}^t A_0 a_i$ and all the a_i's are prime elements of A, then α is an isomorphism.*

(2) *If $\mathscr{F}$ is a quasicoherent $\mathscr{O}_X$-Module, then $\beta_{\mathscr{F}} \colon \Gamma_*(\mathscr{F})^\sim \to \mathscr{F}$ is an isomorphism of $\mathscr{O}_X$-Modules.*

PROOF. (1) Let $b \in A_n$ $(n > 0)$. If $\alpha_n(b) = 0$, then $\alpha(b)|_{D_+(a_i)} = (b/a_i^n) \cdot a_i^n = 0$ for each i. Hence, $b/a_i^n = 0$ for each i. Since A is an integral domain and A_+ is generated by A_1, we have $b = 0$. So α is injective. We shall prove the rest of (1). Let $s \in \Gamma(X, \mathscr{O}_X(n))$. Then we can express $s|_{D_+(a_i)} = (b_i/a_i^{n_i}) \cdot a_i^n$ with $b_i \in A_{n_i}$ with $n_i \geq n$. Since $(b_i/a_i^{n_i}) \cdot a_i^n = (b_j/a_j^{n_j}) \cdot a_j^n$ on $D_+(a_i a_j)$, we have $b_i a_j^{n_j - n} = b_j a_i^{n_i - n}$. Since a_i is a prime element, $a_i \mid b_i$ or $a_i \mid a_j$ provided $n_i > n$. If $a_i \mid a_j$, $a_j = c a_i$ with

$c \in A_0$. Since a_j is also a prime element and $a_j \nmid c$, we have $a_j \mid a_i$. So $c \in (A_0)^* =$ {invertible elements of A_0}. Thus, we may assume $a_i \mid b_i$. This implies that if $n_i > n$ we may replace b_i by b_i/a_i. So we may assume $n_i = n$. Similarly, we may assume $n_j = n$. If we put $b = b_i$, then we have $\alpha_n(b) = s$.

(2) $X = \bigcup_{i=1}^t D_+(a_i)$ is an affine open covering of X. Since $\{D_+(a); a$ is a homogeneous element of $A_+\}$ is an open basis of the topology on X, in order to prove that $\beta_{\mathscr{F}}$ is an isomorphism, it suffices to show that $(\beta_{\mathscr{F}})_a : \Gamma_*(\mathscr{F})[a^{-1}]_0 \to \Gamma(D_+(a), \mathscr{F})$ is an isomorphism. Let $a \in A_d$. Assume that $(s|_{D_+(a)})/(\alpha_d(a)|_{D_+(a)})^n = 0$ for $s \in \Gamma(X, \mathscr{F}(nd))$. This implies $(s|_{D_+(aa_i)}/(\alpha_d(a)|_{D_+(aa_i)})^n = 0$. Considering $s|_{D_+(a_i)} \in \Gamma(D_+(a_i), \mathscr{F}(nd))$, we then have $(\alpha_d(a)|_{D_+(a_i)})^m \cdot (s|_{D_+(a_i)}) = (\alpha_d(a)^m s)|_{D_+(a_i)} = 0$ for some $m \geq 0$ (for each i). Hence, considering $\alpha_d(a)^m \cdot s \in \Gamma(X, \mathscr{F}((n+m)d))$, we have $\alpha_d(a)^m s = 0$. In particular, $s/a^n = \alpha_d(a)^m s/a^{n+m} = 0$. That is to say, $(\beta_{\mathscr{F}})_a$ is injective. Conversely, let $f \in \Gamma(D_+(a), \mathscr{F})$. Since $f|_{D_+(aa_i)} \in \Gamma(D_+(aa_i), \mathscr{F}) = \Gamma(D_+(a_i), \mathscr{F})[(a/a_i^d)^{-1}]$, $(f|_{D_+(aa_i)}) \cdot (a|_{D_+(aa_i)})^n$ is extended to an element $s_i \in \Gamma(D_+(a_i), \mathscr{F}(nd))$ for an integer $n > 0$. We can choose $n \gg 0$ so that n is independent of i. Then the restrictions of $s_i|_{D_+(aa_i)}$ and $s_j|_{D_+(aa_j)}$ onto $D_+(aa_ia_j)$ are identical. Hence, there exists an integer $m > 0$ such that $(s_i \cdot a^m - s_j \cdot a^m)|_{D_+(a_ia_j)} = 0$ in $\Gamma(D_+(a_ia_j), \mathscr{F}((n+m)d))$. Since we can choose m independently of i, j, we have shown that $f \cdot a^{n+m}$ is extended to an element x of $\Gamma(X, \mathscr{F}((n+m)d))$. It is then apparent that $(\beta_{\mathscr{F}})_a(x/a^{n+m}) = f$. (Compare the proof of (2) with the proof of (I.1.12).) □

COROLLARY 5.10. *Let A be the same graded ring as in Theorem 5.9. Let $\mathscr{F}$ be a coherent $\mathscr{O}_X$-Module. Then there exists a finitely generated A-module M such that $\mathscr{F} \cong \widetilde{M}$.*

PROOF. By Theorem 5.9, $\mathscr{F} \cong \widetilde{N}$, where $N = \Gamma_*(\mathscr{F})$. Write $A_1 = \sum_{i=1}^t Aa_i$ and $X = \bigcup_{i=1}^t D_+(a_i)$. Over an affine open set $D_+(a_i) = \operatorname{Spec} A[a_i^{-1}]_0$, $\mathscr{F}|_{D_+(a_i)} \cong N[a_i^{-1}]_0^{\sim}$ and $N[a_i^{-1}]_0$ is, hence, a finitely generated $A[a_i^{-1}]_0$-module. Let $\{x_{ij}/a_i^d; 1 \leq j \leq r_i\}$ be its system of generators, where x_{ij} is a homogeneous element of degree d in N, d being independent of i, j. Let $M = \sum_{i,j} Ax_{ij}$. Then M is a finitely generated, graded A-submodule of N. Since $M[a_i^{-1}]_0 = N[a_i^{-1}]_0$, we infer that $\widetilde{M} = \mathscr{F}$. □

Hereafter, k is a field and $R = k[T_0, \ldots, T_n]$ is a polynomial ring in $n+1$ variables. We consider a graded ring A which is the residue ring of R by a homogeneous ideal I of R ($I \not\supset R_+$). Then A is a noetherian k-algebra, $A_0 = k$, and A is generated by A_1 as a k-algebra. A is an integral domain if and only if I is a homogeneous prime ideal. Proj(R) is the projective space of dimension n, which we simply denote by $\mathbf{P}$. We set $X = \operatorname{Proj}(A)$ as above. X is a closed subscheme of $\mathbf{P}$ defined by the ideal sheaf $\widetilde{I}$. Denoting $\widetilde{I}$ by $\mathscr{I}_X$, we have an exact sequence of $\mathscr{O}_{\mathbf{P}}$-Modules,

$$0 \to \mathscr{I}_X \to \mathscr{O}_{\mathbf{P}} \to \mathscr{O}_X \to 0.$$

For an integer m, define invertible sheaves $\mathscr{O}_{\mathbf{P}}(m)$ and $\mathscr{O}_X(m)$ as above. Then $\mathscr{O}_X(m) \cong \mathscr{O}_{\mathbf{P}}(m) \otimes_{\mathscr{O}_{\mathbf{P}}} \mathscr{O}_X$. Hence, we have an exact sequence of $\mathscr{O}_{\mathbf{P}}$-Modules

$$0 \to \mathscr{I}_X(m) \to \mathscr{O}_{\mathbf{P}}(m) \to \mathscr{O}_X(m) \to 0$$

which yields an exact sequence of k-modules

$$0 \to \Gamma(\mathbf{P}, \mathscr{I}_X(m)) \to \Gamma(\mathbf{P}, \mathscr{O}_{\mathbf{P}}(m)) \to \Gamma(X, \mathscr{O}_X(m)).$$

By virtue of Theorem 5.9 (1), we have

$$\Gamma(\mathbf{P}, \mathscr{O}_{\mathbf{P}}(m)) = \begin{cases} 0 & (m < 0), \\ k[T_0, \ldots, T_n]_m & (m \geq 0). \end{cases}$$

If $m \geq 0$, an element f of $\Gamma(\mathbf{P}, \mathscr{I}_X(m))$ is a homogeneous polynomial of degree m in $T_0, \ldots, T_n$ such that $f/T_i^m \in \Gamma(D_+(T_i), \mathscr{I}_X) = IR[T_i^{-1}] \cap R[T_i^{-1}]_0$. So $T_i^r f \in I$ for $r \geq 0$, where we may assume r to be independent of i. Since $I \not\supset R_+$, we have $T_i \notin I$ for some i. If I is a prime ideal (i.e., A is an integral domain), then $f \in I$. Thus, $\Gamma(\mathbf{P}, \mathscr{I}_X(m)) = I_m$. Hence, we know that $A_m \hookrightarrow \Gamma(X, \mathscr{O}_X(m))$ provided A is an integral domain. By virtue of the cohomology exact sequence (I.2.16), $A_m \cong \Gamma(X, \mathscr{O}_X(m))$ provided $H^1(\mathbf{P}, \mathscr{I}_X(m)) = (0)$.

Let $\mathscr{F}$ be a coherent $\mathscr{O}_X$-Module. Then by Corollary 5.10, $\mathscr{F} \cong \widetilde{M}$ for a finitely generated graded A-module M. Since $A = R/I$, we can view M naturally an R-module which we denote by M_R. Then the $\mathscr{O}_{\mathbf{P}}$-Module $(M_R)^\sim$ is coherent (Lemma 5.7) and equal to $\iota_*\mathscr{F}$, where $\iota\colon X \hookrightarrow \mathbf{P}$ is the natural closed immersion. Since M_R is a finitely generated graded R-module, we obtain, as in the proof of Lemma 5.7 (3), a surjective homomorphism of $\mathscr{O}_{\mathbf{P}}$-Modules

$$\bigoplus_{i=1}^{r} \mathscr{O}_{\mathbf{P}}(m_i) \xrightarrow{\eta} \iota_*\mathscr{F} \to 0.$$

Let $\mathscr{F}_1 = \operatorname{Ker} \eta$. By (I.2.12), $\mathscr{F}_1$ is a coherent $\mathscr{O}_{\mathbf{P}}$-Module. By the same reasoning as above, we have an exact sequence of $\mathscr{O}_{\mathbf{P}}$-Modules

$$0 \to \mathscr{F}_2 \to \bigoplus_{i=1}^{r_1} \mathscr{O}_{\mathbf{P}}(n_{1i}) \xrightarrow{\delta_1} \mathscr{F}_1 \to 0.$$

We can repeat the above argument to construct coherent $\mathscr{O}_{\mathbf{P}}$-Modules $\mathscr{F}_2, \mathscr{F}_3, \ldots$. Namely, we have an exact sequence of $\mathscr{O}_{\mathbf{P}}$-Modules for $j \geq 1$,

$$0 \to \mathscr{F}_{j+1} \to \bigoplus_{i=1}^{r_j} \mathscr{O}_{\mathbf{P}}(n_{ji}) \xrightarrow{\delta_j}, \mathscr{F}_j \to 0.$$

Then the exact sequence of $\mathscr{O}_{\mathbf{P}}$-Modules

$$\begin{aligned} &\to \bigoplus_{i=1}^{r_j} \mathscr{O}_{\mathbf{P}}(n_{ji}) \to \bigoplus_{i=1}^{r_{j-1}} \mathscr{O}_{\mathbf{P}}(n_{j-1i}) \to \cdots \to \bigoplus_{i=1}^{r_1} \mathscr{O}_{\mathbf{P}}(n_{1i}) \\ &\to \bigoplus_{i=1}^{r} \mathscr{O}_{\mathbf{P}}(m_i) \to \iota_*\mathscr{F} \to 0 \end{aligned}$$

corresponds to a resolution of M_R by free, graded R-modules

$$\begin{aligned} &\to \bigoplus_{i=1}^{r_j} R(n_{ji}) \to \bigoplus_{i=1}^{r_{j-1}} R(n_{j-1i}) \to \cdots \to \bigoplus_{i=1}^{r_1} R(n_{1i}) \\ &\to \bigoplus_{i=1}^{r} R(m_i) \to M_R \to 0. \end{aligned}$$

Now we utilize the following result.

LEMMA 5.11. *Let A_0 be a noetherian ring, and let $X \longrightarrow \mathrm{Spec}(A_0)$ be a separated, finitely generated morphism. Then for a quasicoherent $\mathscr{O}_X$-Module $\mathscr{F}$, we have $\check{H}^n(X,\mathscr{F}) \cong H^n(X,\mathscr{F})$ for each $n > 0$. If we have a finite affine open covering $\mathfrak{U} = \{U_i\}_{i=1}^N$ of X, then $H^n(X,\mathscr{F}) = (0)$ for each $n > N$.*

PROOF. For an arbitrary open covering of X, we can choose its refinement which is an affine open covering. So if $\mathfrak{U} = \{U_i\}_{i\in I}$ is an affine open covering of X, we have only to verify that $H^n(U_s,\mathscr{F}) = (0)$ for each $n > 0$, $m \geq 0$, and $s = (i_0,\ldots,i_m) \in I^{m+1}$ (cf. (I.2.22)). Here $U_s = U_{i_0} \cap \cdots \cap U_{i_n}$ is an affine open set, and its coordinate ring R_s is a finitely generated A_0-algebra. (If U and V are affine open sets, $U \cap V \cong (\Delta_{X/S})^{-1}(U \times_S V)$ ($S = \mathrm{Spec}(A_0)$), and since $U \times_S V$ is an affine scheme and $\Delta_{X/S}$ is a closed immersion, $U \cap V$ is an affine open set of X. From this we find U_s to be an affine open set. On the other hand, if U is an affine open set of X, the structure morphism $U \to \mathrm{Spec}(A_0)$ is a finitely generated morphism. By problem II.4.8, $\Gamma(U,\mathscr{O}_U)$ is then a finitely generated algebra over A_0. It follows that $R_s = \Gamma(U_s,\mathscr{O}_X)$ is a noetherian ring.) By means of Theorem 3.14, we conclude $H^n(U_s,\mathscr{F}) = (0)$ for each $n > 0$, and so, $\check{H}^n(X,\mathscr{F}) \cong H^n(X,\mathscr{F})$ for $n > 0$.

Let $\mathfrak{U} = \{U_i\}_{i=1}^N$ be a finite affine open covering of X. By (I.2.22), $H^n(X,\mathscr{F}) \cong H^n(\mathfrak{U},\mathscr{F})$ for each $n \geq 0$. For $n > N$, an element of $H^n(\mathfrak{U},\mathscr{F})$ is represented by a Čech cocycle α which assigns to each $s = (i_0,\ldots,i_n) \in I^{n+1}$ an element $\alpha(s) \in \Gamma(U_s,\mathscr{F})$. Since $n > N$, there is an index appearing repeatedly in s. So $\alpha(s) = (0)$ by the definition of Čech cochains. So $H^n(\mathfrak{U},\mathscr{F}) = (0)$ for each $n > N$. □

Now going back to $\mathbf{P} = \mathbf{P}_k^n$, we have an affine open covering $\mathfrak{U} = \{U_i\}_{i=0}^n$ of $\mathbf{P}$, where $U_i = D_+(T_i)$. We shall prove the following lemma.

LEMMA 5.12. *For an invertible sheaf $\mathscr{O}_{\mathbf{P}}(m)$ ($m \in \mathbf{Z}$) on $\mathbf{P}$, the following assertions hold*:

(1) $H^0(\mathbf{P},\mathscr{O}_{\mathbf{P}}(m)) = (0)$ *for each* $m < 0$; $H^0(\mathbf{P},\mathscr{O}_{\mathbf{P}}(m)) = k[T_0,\ldots,T_n]_m$ *for each* $m \geq 0$.

(2) $H^l(\mathbf{P},\mathscr{O}_{\mathbf{P}}(m)) = (0)$ *for each* l, $0 < l < n$, *and* $m \in \mathbf{Z}$.

(3) $H^n(\mathbf{P},\mathscr{O}_{\mathbf{P}}(m)) = (0)$ *for* $m > -(n+1)$; *If* $m \leq -(n+1)$, $H^n(\mathbf{P},\mathscr{O}_{\mathbf{P}}(m))$ *is a k-vector space of dimension* $\binom{-m-1}{n}$.

PROOF. (1) follows from Theorem 5.9 (1) and the definitions.

(2) Let $\mathfrak{U} = \{U_i\}_{i=0}^n$ be the affine open covering as given before Lemma 5.12. Then $H^l(\mathbf{P},\mathscr{O}_{\mathbf{P}}(m)) \cong H^l(\mathfrak{U},\mathscr{O}_{\mathbf{P}}(m))$. Following the definition of Čech cohomologies, we compute $H^l(\mathfrak{U},\mathscr{O}_{\mathbf{P}}(m))$. Set $I = \{0,1,\ldots,n\}$. For $(i_0,\ldots,i_l) \in I^{l+1}$, let $U_{i_0,\ldots,i_l} = \bigcap_{j=0}^l U_{i_j}$. Then $\Gamma(U_{i_0,\ldots,i_l},\mathscr{O}_{\mathbf{P}}(m)) = k[T_0,\ldots,T_n,T_{i_0}^{-1},\ldots,T_{i_l}^{-1}]_m$. A Čech cochain $\alpha \in C^l(\mathfrak{U},\mathscr{O}_{\mathbf{P}}(m))$ is viewed as a function which assigns to each $(i_0,\ldots,i_l) \in I^{l+1}$ an element $\alpha(i_0,\ldots,i_l) = f_{i_0\cdots i_l}/T_{i_0}^{\alpha_{i_0}}\cdots T_{i_l}^{\alpha_{i_l}}$, where $f_{i_0\cdots i_l}$ is a homogeneous polynomial in $k[T_0,\ldots,T_n]$ of degree $\deg f_{i_0\cdots i_l} = m + \alpha_{i_0} + \cdots + \alpha_{i_l}$ ($\alpha_{i_j} \geq 0$ for each j). Here we have $f_{i_0\cdots i_l} = 0$ if $i_j = i_k$ (for some $j,k, j \neq k$) and $f_{\sigma(i_0)\cdots\sigma(i_l)} = \mathrm{sgn}(\sigma)f_{i_0\cdots i_l}$ for any permutation σ of $\{0,1,\ldots,n\}$. Since I^{l+1} is a finite set, we may express $\alpha(i_0,\ldots,i_l) = f_{i_0\cdots i_l}/(T_{i_0}\cdots T_{i_l})^r$ for $r \geq 0$ which is independent of $(i_0,\ldots,i_l)$. Then α is uniquely determined if $f_{i_0\cdots i_l}$ is given for every $(i_0,\ldots,i_l)$ with $i_0 < i_1 < \cdots < i_l$. Furthermore, $\alpha \in Z^l(\mathfrak{U},\mathscr{O}_{\mathbf{P}}(m))(:= \mathrm{Ker}\, d^l)$ if and only if we have

$$\sum_{j=0}^{l+1}(-1)^j f_{i_0\cdots\check{i}_j\cdots i_{l+1}}/(T_{i_0}\cdots\check{T}_{i_j}\cdots T_{i_{l+1}})^r = 0$$

for any $(i_0 < i_1 < \cdots < i_{l+1})$, i.e., the equality

$$T_{i_0}^r f_{i_1\cdots i_{l+1}} = \sum_{j=1}^{l+1}(-1)^{j-1} T_{i_j}^r f_{i_0\cdots \check{i}_j \cdots i_{l+1}}$$

holds. Here $f_{i_0\cdots \check{i}_j\cdots i_{l+1}}$ is a homogeneous polynomial of degree $m + r(l+1)$, which we regard as a polynomial in T_{i_0} with coefficients in $k[T_0, \ldots, \check{T}_{i_0}, \ldots, T_n]$ and express

$$f_{i_0\cdots\check{i}_j\cdots i_{l+1}} = T_{i_0}^r h_{i_0\cdots\check{i}_j\cdots i_{l+1}} + g_{i_0\cdots\check{i}_j\cdots i_{l+1}},$$
$$\deg_{T_{i_0}} g_{i_0\cdots\check{i}_j\cdots i_{l+1}} \le r-1.$$

Hence, if $\alpha \in Z^l(\mathfrak{U}, \mathcal{O}_{\mathbf{P}}(m))$, we necessarily have

$$\sum_{j=1}^{l+1}(-1)^{j-1} T_{i_j}^r g_{i_0\cdots\check{i}_j\cdots i_r} = 0,$$

and

$$f_{i_1\cdots i_{l+1}} = \sum_{j=1}^{l+1}(-1)^{j-1} T_{i_j}^r h_{i_0\cdots\check{i}_j\cdots i_{l+1}}.$$

The last equality is rewritten as

$$\alpha(i_0, \ldots, i_{l+1}) = \sum_{j=1}^{l+1}(-1)^{j-1}(h_{i_0\cdots\check{i}_j\cdots i_{l+1}}/(T_{i_1}\cdots \check{T}_{i_j}\cdots T_{i_{l+1}})^r).$$

Let $\beta_{j_0\cdots j_{l-1}} = h_{i_0 j_0\cdots j_{l-1}}/(T_{j_0}\cdots T_{j_{l-1}})^r$ and let β be a Čech cochain in $C^{l-1}(\mathfrak{U}, \mathcal{O}_{\mathbf{P}}(m))$ given by $\{\beta_{j_0\cdots j_{l-1}}\}_{(j_0<\cdots<j_{l-1})}$. Then $\alpha = d\beta$ if $\alpha \in Z^l(\mathfrak{U}, \mathcal{O}_{\mathbf{P}}(m))$. So $H^l(\mathfrak{U}, \mathcal{O}_{\mathbf{P}}(m)) = (0)$.

(3) Note that $C^n(\mathfrak{U}, \mathcal{O}_{\mathbf{P}}(m)) = Z^n(\mathfrak{U}, \mathcal{O}_{\mathbf{P}}(m)) = k[T_0, \ldots, T_n, (T_0\cdots T_n)^{-1}]_m$. Then any Čech n-cocycle α is expressed as $f/(T_0\cdots T_n)^r$, where f is a homogeneous polynomial of degree $m + r(n+1)$ with $r \ge 0$. A Čech coboundary ($\in B^n(\mathfrak{U}, \mathcal{O}_{\mathbf{P}}(m))$ is written as $\sum_{i=0}^n (-1)^i f_i T_i^r/(T_0\cdots T_n)^r$, where f_i is a homogeneous polynomial of degree $m + rn$ and $r \ge 0$. If $m + r(n+1) > (r-1)(n+1)$, each monomial in f is divisible by T_i^r for some i . Hence, we can write $f = \sum_{i=0}^n (-1)^i T_i^r f_i$ by choosing f_i's in a suitable way. Thus, $H^n(\mathbf{P}, \mathcal{O}_{\mathbf{P}}(m)) = (0)$ if $m > -(n+1)$. Suppose $m \le -(n+1)$. In view of the above observations, we know that $H^n(\mathbf{P}, \mathcal{O}_{\mathbf{P}}(m))$ is a k-vector space isomorphic to

$$\left\{ \frac{f}{(T_0\cdots T_n)^r};\ \begin{array}{l} f \text{ is a homogeneous polynomial of degree} \\ m + r(n+1),\ \text{none of whose monomials} \\ \text{is divisible by } T_i^r \text{ (for each } i);\ r \ge 0 \end{array} \right\}.$$

As its k-basis, we can choose

$$\left\{ \frac{1}{T_0^{\alpha_0}\cdots T_n^{\alpha_n}};\ \forall \alpha_i > 0,\ \sum_i \alpha_i = -m \right\}.$$

This implies $\dim H^n(\mathbf{P}, \mathcal{O}_{\mathbf{P}}(m)) = \binom{-m-1}{n}$. □

Let us go back to the setting prior to Lemma 5.11. Since $\iota \colon X \hookrightarrow \mathbf{P}$ is a closed immersion, $H^i(X, \mathcal{F}) \cong H^i(\mathbf{P}, \iota_*\mathcal{F})$ for each i, $i \ge 0$ (problem II.5.3).

$H^i(X,\mathscr{F})$ is a k-vector space. We shall show that $\dim_k H^i(X,\mathscr{F}) < \infty$. By Lemma 5.12, $\dim_k H^i(X,\mathscr{F}) < \infty$ if and only if $\dim_k H^{i+1}(\mathbf{P},\mathscr{F}_1) < \infty$. Similarly, $\dim_k H^{i+j}(\mathbf{P},\mathscr{F}_j) < \infty$ if and only if $\dim_k H^{i+j+1}(\mathbf{P},\mathscr{F}_{j+1}) < \infty$. Meanwhile, $H^{i+j}(\mathbf{P},\mathscr{F}) = (0)$ $(j \gg 0)$ by Lemma 5.11. Hence, $\dim_k H^i(X,\mathscr{F}) < \infty$. By similar reasoning, we obtain $H^i(X,\mathscr{F}(N)) \cong H^i(\mathbf{P},\iota_*\mathscr{F}(N)) \cong H^{i+j}(\mathbf{P},\mathscr{F}_j(N)) = (0)$ for $i > 0$ and $N \gg 0$. These observations are summarized in the following fundamental theorem.

THEOREM 5.13. *Let X be a closed subscheme of $\mathbf{P}^n_k$, and let $\mathscr{F}$ be a coherent $\mathscr{O}_X$-Module. Then $H^i(X,\mathscr{F})$ is a k-vector space of finite dimension for each $i \geq 0$. Furthermore, $H^i(X,\mathscr{F}(N)) = (0)$ for each $i > 0$ and each $N \gg 0$.*

Henceforth, we let k be an algebraically closed field, and let X be an algebraic variety defined over k. We shall give more details on invertible sheaves on X. A coherent $\mathscr{O}_X$-Module $\mathscr{L}$ is called a *locally free sheaf* of rank n if there exists an open covering $\mathfrak{U} = \{U_i\}_{i\in I}$ such that $\mathscr{L}|_{U_i} \cong (\mathscr{O}_{U_i})^{\oplus n}$ (a direct sum of n copies of $\mathscr{O}_{U_i}$) (cf. (I.2.10)). In particular, if $n = 1$, we call $\mathscr{L}$ an *invertible sheaf* on X. If $\mathscr{L}$ and $\mathscr{M}$ are invertible sheaves, then $\mathscr{L} \otimes_{\mathscr{O}_X} \mathscr{M}$ is also an invertible sheaf. If we put $\mathscr{L}^{-1} := \mathscr{H}om_{\mathscr{O}_X}(\mathscr{L},\mathscr{O}_X)$, $\mathscr{L}^{-1}$ is also an invertible sheaf. It is clear that if $\mathscr{L} \cong \mathscr{L}'$ and $\mathscr{M} \cong \mathscr{M}'$, then $\mathscr{L} \otimes_{\mathscr{O}_X} \mathscr{M} \cong \mathscr{L}' \otimes_{\mathscr{O}_X} \mathscr{M}'$ and $\mathscr{L}^{-1} \cong \mathscr{L}'^{-1}$. (Compare the definition of $\mathscr{O}_X(l)$ in this chapter.) Denote by $[\mathscr{L}]$ the isomorphism class of $\mathscr{L}$. Then the set of these isomorphism classes becomes an abelian group with respect to the multiplication $[\mathscr{L}]\cdot[\mathscr{M}] = [\mathscr{L} \otimes_{\mathscr{O}_X} \mathscr{M}]$, the inverse $[\mathscr{L}]^{-1} = [\mathscr{L}^{-1}]$ and the identity element $[\mathscr{O}_X]$. Denote this group by $\mathrm{Pic}(X)$ and call it the *Picard group* of X.

Let $\mathscr{L}$ be an invertible sheaf on X, and let $\mathfrak{U} = \{U_i\}_{i\in I}$ be an open covering of X such that $\mathscr{L}|_{U_i} \cong \mathscr{O}_{U_i}$ $(i \in I)$. We say that the open covering $\mathfrak{U}$ *trivializes* $\mathscr{L}$. Let $\varphi_i : \mathscr{L}|_{U_i} \xrightarrow{\sim} \mathscr{O}_{U_i}$ be an isomorphism. Since $\mathscr{L}|_{U_i}$ is a free $\mathscr{O}_{U_i}$-Module, we may write $\mathscr{L}|_{U_i} = \mathscr{O}_{U_i}e_i$ with a free basis e_i. Then φ_i is a mapping $ae_i \mapsto a$. The isomorphism $\varphi_j \cdot \varphi_i^{-1} : \mathscr{O}_{U_i\cap U_j} \to \mathscr{O}_{U_i\cap U_j}$, which is obtained by restricting φ_i, φ_j onto $U_i \cap U_j$, is determined by the image θ_{ji} of $1 \in \Gamma(U_i \cap U_j, \mathscr{O}_X)$, where $\theta_{ji} \in \Gamma(U_i \cap U_j, \mathscr{O}_X)^* =$ the multiplicative group consisting of all invertible elements of $\Gamma(U_i \cap U_j, \mathscr{O}_X)$. We have the equality $\theta_{ki} = \theta_{kj} \cdot \theta_{ji}$ on $U_i \cap U_j \cap U_k$, where $\theta_{ji}|_{U_i\cap U_j\cap U_k}$ is abbreviated by θ_{ji}. Moreover, we have $\theta_{ii} = 1$ for each i. If we alter the isomorphism φ_i to $\psi_i : \mathscr{L}|_{U_i} \xrightarrow{\sim} \mathscr{O}_{U_i}$ $(i \in I)$, the isomorphism $\psi_i \cdot \varphi_i^{-1} : \mathscr{O}_{U_i} \xrightarrow{\sim} \mathscr{O}_{U_i}$ is determined by the image $\sigma_i \in \Gamma(U_i, \mathscr{O}_X)^*$ of $1 \in \Gamma(U_i, \mathscr{O}_X)$. Hence, if $\psi_j \cdot \psi_i^{-1} : \mathscr{O}_{U_i\cap U_j} \xrightarrow{\sim} \mathscr{O}_{U_i\cap U_j}$ gives rise to $\rho_{ji} \in \Gamma(U_i \cap U_j, \mathscr{O}_X)^*$, ρ_{ji} is related to θ_{ji} as

$$\rho_{ji} = (\sigma_j|_{U_i\cap U_j})^{-1} \cdot \theta_{ji} \cdot (\sigma_i|_{U_i\cap U_j})$$

which we abbreviate as $\rho_{ji} = \sigma_j^{-1} \cdot \theta_{ji} \cdot \sigma_i$.

Replace the open covering $\mathfrak{U}$ by a refinement $\mathfrak{V} = \{V_\lambda\}_{\lambda\in\Lambda}$. Choose a mapping $\alpha : \Lambda \to I$ so that $V_\lambda \subset U_{\alpha(\lambda)}$ for each $\lambda \in \Lambda$. If $i = \alpha(\lambda)$, the isomorphism $\varphi_i : \mathscr{L}|_{U_i} \xrightarrow{\sim} \mathscr{O}_{U_i}$ induces an isomorphism $\varphi_{\lambda i} : \mathscr{L}|_{V_\lambda} \xrightarrow{\sim} \mathscr{O}_{V_\lambda}$. If $j = \alpha(\mu)$, $\varphi_{\mu j} \cdot \varphi_{\lambda i}^{-1} : \mathscr{O}_{V_\lambda\cap V_\mu} \xrightarrow{\sim} \mathscr{O}_{V_\lambda\cap V_\mu}$ is given by the restriction $\theta_{ji}|_{V_\lambda\cap V_\mu}$.

As explained above, an open covering $\mathfrak{U} = \{U_i\}_{i\in I}$ and the choice of isomorphisms $\varphi_i : \mathscr{L}|_{U_i} \xrightarrow{\sim} \mathscr{O}_{U_i}$ $(i \in I)$ give rise to a family of functions $\{\theta_{ji}\}_{i,j\in I}$ which we call a *family of transition functions*. The family $\{\theta_{ji}\}_{i,j\in I}$ defines an element $\theta_{\mathfrak{U}}$ of the cohomology group $H^1(\mathfrak{U}, \mathscr{O}_X^*)$, where $\mathscr{O}_X^*$ is the sheaf of multiplicative groups associated with $U \mapsto \Gamma(U, \mathscr{O}_X)^*$. A different choice of isomorphisms $\{\psi_i\}_{i\in I}$ alters the family of transition functions $\{\theta_{ji}\}_{i,j\in I}$ only by a coboundary element as shown above. If $\mathfrak{U}$ ranges over all open coverings of X which trivialize $\mathscr{L}$, then the elements $\theta_{\mathfrak{U}}$ define an element θ in the Čech cohomology group $\check{H}^1(X,\mathscr{O}_X^*) = \varinjlim_{\mathfrak{U}} H^1(\mathfrak{U},\mathscr{O}_X^*)$.

Conversely, an element θ of $\check{H}^1(X,\mathscr{O}_X^*)$ is given in terms of an open covering $\mathfrak{U}$ of X and an element $\theta_{\mathfrak{U}} \in H^1(\mathfrak{U},\mathscr{O}_X^*)$. Represent $\theta_{\mathfrak{U}}$ by a cocycle $\{\theta_{ji}\}_{i,j\in I}$ with $\theta_{ji} \in \Gamma(U_i \cap U_j, \mathscr{O}_X)^*$. Patch $\mathscr{O}_{U_i}$'s $(i \in I)$ together to define an $\mathscr{O}_X$-Module $\mathscr{L}$ by the following identification:

> $f_i \sim f_j$ if and only if $f_j = (\theta_{ji}|_U) \cdot f_i$ for $U \subseteq U_i \cap U_j$, $f_i \in \Gamma(U,\mathscr{O}_{U_i})$, and $f_j \in \Gamma(U,\mathscr{O}_{U_j})$.

Then $\mathscr{L}$ is an invertible sheaf. Different choices of $\mathfrak{U}$ and different ways of representing θ by cocycles $\{\theta_{ji}\}$ give rise to the same invertible sheaf up to isomorphisms. We have, therefore, proved assertion (1) of the following lemma.

LEMMA 5.14. (1) *A mapping $\mathscr{L} \mapsto \{\theta_{ji}\}$ gives rise to a one-to-one correspondence between the abelian groups* $\mathrm{Pic}(X)$ *and* $\check{H}^1(X,\mathscr{O}_X^*)$.

(2) *Let $\mathscr{L}$ and $\mathscr{M}$ be invertible sheaves on X, let $\mathfrak{U} = \{U_i\}_{i\in I}$ be an open covering of X which trivializes $\mathscr{L}$ and $\mathscr{M}$, and let $\{\theta_{ji}\}$ and $\{\tau_{ji}\}$ be families of transition functions of $\mathscr{L}$ and $\mathscr{M}$, respectively. Then $\{\theta_{ji}\cdot\tau_{ji}\}$ and $\{\theta_{ji}^{-1}\}$ are families of transition functions of $\mathscr{L} \otimes_{\mathscr{O}_X} \mathscr{M}$ and $\mathscr{L}^{-1}$, respectively. The correspondence in* (1) *is therefore an isomorphism of groups.*

A proof of the assertion (2) is straightforward. In order to define a family of transition functions $\{\theta_{ji}\}$ of $\mathscr{L}$, we made use of the isomorphisms $\varphi_i : \mathscr{L}|_{U_i} \xrightarrow{\sim} \mathscr{O}_{U_i}$, where φ_i is a mapping $ae_i \mapsto a$ if $\mathscr{L}|_{U_i} = \mathscr{O}_{U_i}e_i$ with a free basis e_i. Since $\mathscr{L}|_{U_{ij}} = \mathscr{O}_{U_{ij}}e_i = \mathscr{O}_{U_{ij}}e_j$ $(U_{ij} = U_i \cap U_j)$, we have $e_j = \alpha_{ji}e_i$ with $\alpha_{ji} \in \Gamma(U_{ij},\mathscr{O}_X)^*$ and $\alpha_{ki} = \alpha_{kj}\cdot\alpha_{ji}$. $\{\alpha_{ji}\}$ is related to $\{\theta_{ji}\}$ determined by $\{\varphi_i\}$ as $\alpha_{ji} = \theta_{ij} = \theta_{ij}^{-1}$. We say that $\{\alpha_{ji}\}$ is also a *family of transition functions*. The readers should be careful not to confuse the transition functions by free bases (i.e., $\{\alpha_{ji}\}$) with those by coefficients (coordinates) (i.e., $\{\theta_{ji}\}$).

Next we assume that X is a normal algebraic variety. We consider all (irreducible and reduced) closed subvarieties of codimension 1 of X and the free abelian group $\mathrm{Div}(X)$ generated by them as free basis. An element of $\mathrm{Div}(X)$ is written as a finite sum $\sum_i n_i Y_i$, where $n_i \in \mathbf{Z}$ and Y_i is a subvariety of codimension 1. We call an element of $\mathrm{Div}(X)$ a *Weil divisor* (or simply a *divisor*). If $n_i \geq 0$ for each i, we call $D = \sum_i n_i Y_i$ an *effective divisor*, $D \geq 0$ by notation. If $D = Y_i$ for some i, we call D an *irreducible divisor*. When $D \geq 0$, we call D a *reduced divisor* if $n_i = 1$ for each i. Given a nonzero element $f \in k(X)$ we define a divisor (f) associated with f as follows.

Let Y be a subvariety of codimension 1 of X, and let η be the generic point of Y. We denote the local ring $\mathscr{O}_{X,\eta}$ by $\mathscr{O}_{X,Y}$. Since X is normal by hypothesis, $\mathscr{O}_{X,Y}$ is a discrete valuation ring of $k(X)$. Let v_Y be the associated discrete valuation of $k(X)$. v_Y is uniquely determined if we put $v_Y(t) = 1$ for a generator t of the maximal ideal $\mathfrak{m}_{X,Y}$ of $\mathscr{O}_{X,Y}$. We then put $(f) = \sum_Y v_Y(f)Y$, where Y ranges over all subvarieties of codimension 1 of X. We have to verify that $\sum_Y v_Y(f)Y$ is a finite sum as follows. Let $U = \mathrm{Spec}(A)$ be an affine open set of X. Since $X - U$ is a closed subset of codimension ≥ 1, there are only finitely many irreducible components of codimension 1 in $X - U$. On the other hand, since $k(X) = Q(A)$, $f = b/a$ with

$a, b \in A$. Replacing A by $A[a^{-1}]$, we may assume that A is a finitely generated k-algebra and $f \in A$. Let Y be a subvariety of codimension 1 of X, let η be its generic point, and let $\mathscr{O} = \mathscr{O}_{X,\eta} = \mathscr{O}_{X,Y}$. If $\eta \notin U$, then Y is an irreducible component of $X - U$. Suppose $\eta \in U$. Then $\mathscr{O} = A_{\mathfrak{p}}(\mathrm{ht}(\mathfrak{p}) = 1)$. If $f \in (A_{\mathfrak{p}})^*$, then $v_Y(f) = 0$, and if $f \in \mathfrak{p}A_{\mathfrak{p}}$, then $v_Y(f) > 0$ and $\mathfrak{p}$ is a prime divisor of fA. Conversely, if $\mathfrak{p}$ is a prime divisor of fA, then $\mathrm{ht}\,\mathfrak{p} = 1$ and $A_{\mathfrak{p}}$ is a discrete valuation ring (I.1.33). Let $Y = \overline{\{\mathfrak{p}\}}$. Then $v_Y(f) > 0$. By this observation, we know that $\sum_Y v_Y(f)Y$ is a finite sum. We call Y a *zero divisor* of f if $v_Y(f) > 0$ and a *polar divisor* of f if $v_Y(f) < 0$. The absolute value $|v_Y(f)|$ if called the *index* of a zero divisor or a polar divisor. Set $(f)_0 = \sum_{v_Y(f)>0} v_Y(f)Y$ and $(f)_\infty = -\sum_{v_Y(f)<0} v_Y(f)Y$. We call $(f)_0$ and $(f)_\infty$ the *zero part* and the *polar part* of f, respectively. It is clear that $(f)_0$ and $(f)_\infty$ are effective divisors and $(f) = (f)_0 - (f)_\infty$. If we emphasize that (f) is considered on X, we denote it by $(f)_X$. By the definition, it is apparent that $(fg) = (f) + (g)$ and $(f^{-1}) = -(f)$ for $f, g \in k(X)^*$. We therefore obtain a group homomorphism $\varphi\colon k(X)^* \to \mathrm{Div}(X)$, $f \mapsto (f)$. By definition, two divisors D and D' are *linearly equivalent*, written $D \sim D'$, if $D' - D = (f)$ for $f \in k(X)^*$. (Verify that $D' \sim D$ is an equivalence relation.) We put $Cl(X) = \mathrm{Div}(X)/\varphi(k(X)^*)$ and call $Cl(X)$ the *divisor class group* X. We have the following result.

LEMMA 5.15. *Let X be a normal algebraic variety defined over k. Then* $\mathrm{Ker}\,\varphi = \Gamma(X, \mathscr{O}_X)^*$ *for the above homomorphism* $\varphi\colon k(X)^* \to \mathrm{Div}(X)$. *In particular, if X is complete, then* $\mathrm{Ker}\,\varphi = k^*$.

PROOF. Suppose $(f) = 0$ for $f \in k(X)^*$. Let x be a point of X, and let $U = \mathrm{Spec}(A)$ be an affine open neighborhood of x. Then $A = \bigcap A_{\mathfrak{p}}$, where $\mathfrak{p}$ ranges over all prime ideals of height 1 of A (cf. (I.1.33)). For such a prime ideal $\mathfrak{p}$, let $Y = \overline{\{\mathfrak{p}\}}$. Since $v_Y(f) = 0$ by hypothesis, $f \in \mathscr{O}_{X,Y}^* = A_{\mathfrak{p}}^* \subseteq A_{\mathfrak{p}}$. So $f \in A$. Similarly, $f^{-1} \in A$. Hence, $f \in A^*$. Since x is an arbitrary point of X, we know that $f \in \Gamma(X, \mathscr{O}_X)^*$. It is clear that $\Gamma(X, \mathscr{O}_X)^* \subseteq \mathrm{Ker}\,\varphi$. If X is complete, we have $\Gamma(X, \mathscr{O}_X) = k$ by Theorem 4.18. Hence, the last assertion follows. □

Suppose X is a normal algebraic variety. Given an invertible sheaf $\mathscr{L}$ on X, take an open covering $\mathfrak{U} = \{U_i\}_{i\in I}$, isomorphisms $\varphi_i\colon \mathscr{L}|_{U_i} \xrightarrow{\sim} \mathscr{O}_{U_i}$, and a family of transition functions as above. Fix an index $i_0 \in I$ and denote it simply by 0. Put $\theta_{ii_0} = \theta_{i0} = f_i$. Then we can regard f_i, θ_{ji} as elements of $k(X)$ satisfying the relation $f_j = \theta_{ji} f_i$. The function f_i may have zeros or poles on $U_i - U_i \cap U_0$. Define a divisor D_i on U_i by $D_i = (f_i)_{U_i}$. Since $\theta_{ji} \in \Gamma(U_i \cap U_j, \mathscr{O}_X)^*$, we have $D_j = D_i$ on $U_i \cap U_j$. Hence, there exists a divisor D on X such that $D_i = D|_{U_i}$ for each $i \in I$. Replace the index i_0 by i_1 and set $g_i = \theta_{i1}$ and $h = \theta_{i_0 i_1}$. We have $g_i = f_i h$ as elements of $k(X)$. Let D' be the divisor given by $\{g_i\}_{i\in I}$. Then $D' = D + (h)$. So $D' \sim D$ (linear equivalence). Alter the isomorphisms $\varphi_i\colon \mathscr{L}|_{U_i} \xrightarrow{\sim} \mathscr{O}_{U_i}$ to isomorphisms $\psi_i\colon \mathscr{L}|_{U_i} \xrightarrow{\sim} \mathscr{O}_{U_i}$. According to the previous notations, $\rho_{ji} = \sigma_j^{-1} \cdot \theta_{ji} \cdot \sigma_i$. Fixing an index i_0, put anew $g_i = \rho_{ii_0}$. Then as rational functions on U_i, $g_i = \sigma_i^{-1} f_i \sigma_0$ with $\sigma_0 = \sigma_{i_0} \in k(X)$. Since $\sigma_i \in \Gamma(U_i, \mathscr{O}_X)^*$, we have $(g_i) = (f_i) + (\sigma_0)$ on U_i. So $D' = D + (\sigma_0)$ if D' denotes the divisor given by $\{g_i\}_{i\in I}$. That is to say, $D' \sim D$. If we replace the open covering $\mathfrak{U}$ by its refinement $\mathfrak{V}$, the divisors given in the above way by means of $\mathfrak{V}$ from $\mathscr{L}$ are linearly equivalent to D. Thus $\mathscr{L}$ defines the linear equivalence class $[D]$ of Weil divisors. We call its representative D "the" Weil divisor defined by $\mathscr{L}$. We denote D also by $D(\mathscr{L})$.

It is easily ascertained that the mapping w: $\mathrm{Pic}(X) \to Cl(X)$, $[L] \mapsto [D]$, is a group homomorphism. Suppose $[D] = 0$. Then $D = (h)$ with $h \in k(X)^*$. According to the above notations, $f_i h^{-1} \in \Gamma(U_i, \mathscr{O}_X)^*$ for each $i \in I$. Set $s_i = f_i \cdot h^{-1}$. Then $\theta_{ji} = s_j \cdot s_i^{-1}$. This implies $\mathscr{L} \cong \mathscr{O}_X$. Hence, the homomorphism w is injective. In general, $\mathrm{Im}(w) \subsetneqq Cl(X)$. In this respect, we call a divisor D a *Cartier divisor* if D is linearly equivalent to the divisor $D(\mathscr{L})$ which is defined by an invertible sheaf $\mathscr{L}$.

Let R be a normal ring. We can consider the free abelian group generated by all irreducible and reduced closed subschemes $V(\mathfrak{p})$ of codimension 1 of $\mathrm{Spec}(R)$, where $\mathfrak{p} \in \mathrm{Spec}(R)$ and $\mathrm{ht}(\mathfrak{p}) = 1$. To $f \in Q(R)^*$ we associate $(f) = \sum_{\mathfrak{p}} v_{\mathfrak{p}}(f) V(\mathfrak{p})$, where $\mathfrak{p}$ ranges over all prime ideals of height 1 of R and $v_{\mathfrak{p}}$ is the discrete valuation of $Q(R)$ associated with a discrete valuation ring $R_{\mathfrak{p}}$. We can show as follows that $\sum_{\mathfrak{p}} v_{\mathfrak{p}}(f) V(\mathfrak{p})$ is a finite sum. Suppose firstly that $f \in R$. Then $v_{\mathfrak{p}}(f) \geq 0$ for each $\mathfrak{p}$, and $v_{\mathfrak{p}}(f) > 0$ if and only if $\mathfrak{p}$ is a prime divisor of fR. Hence, (f) is a finite sum provided $f \in R$. If $f \notin R$, write $f = a/b$ $(a, b \in R)$ and $(f) = (a) - (b)$. Thus, (f) is a finite sum in view of the first case. In the same way as we define the group $Cl(X)$, we can define the linear equivalence of divisors and the abelian group $Cl(\mathrm{Spec}(R))$ of all equivalence classes of divisors. We abbreviate $Cl(\mathrm{Spec}(R))$ as $Cl(R)$. The ring R is a unique factorization domain (UFD, for short) if and only if $Cl(R) = (0)$ (problem II.5.5), that is to say, every prime ideal of height 1 is a principal ideal.

Now assume that every local ring $\mathscr{O}_{X,x}$ of an algebraic variety X is a UFD. There are plenty of algebraic varieties satisfying this condition. If we employ a definition of the next chapter, we can refer to the following result of Auslander.

LEMMA 5.16. *A regular local ring* $(R, \mathfrak{m})$ (*cf. Definition* 6.10) *is a unique factorization domain.*

Every local ring of a nonsingular algebraic variety defined in the next chapter is a regular local ring; hence, a UFD. Every local ring of X is by hypothesis a UFD. So it is a normal ring. X is therefore a normal algebraic variety. Let D be a Weil divisor on X and write $D = n_1 Y_1 + \cdots + n_r Y_r$ (Y_i: irreducible, $n_i \in \mathbf{Z}$). Let x be a point of X. Since the local ring $\mathscr{O}_{X,x}$ is a UFD, each Y_i is defined at x by a principal ideal $a_i \mathscr{O}_{X,x}$, where $a_i \in \mathscr{O}_{X,x}^*$ if $x \notin Y_i$. Put $f_x = \prod_{i=1}^r a_i^{n_i}$ which is in general a rational function. We can consider that f_x defines in an open neighborhood U_x of x the divisor D with the multiplicity n_i of each irreducible component Y_i counted in. $\{U_x : x \in X\}$ is an open covering of X. We denote by $\mathfrak{U} = \{U_i\}_{i \in I}$ this open covering and by f_i the defining equation of D corresponding to U_i. Then $f_j \cdot f_i^{-1} \in \Gamma(U_i \cap U_j, \mathscr{O}_X)^*$. Let $\theta_{ji} = f_j \cdot f_i^{-1}$, and let $\mathscr{L}$ be the invertible sheaf defined in terms of $\mathfrak{U}$ and $\{\theta_{ji}\}$. It suffices, for example, to set $\mathscr{L}|_{U_i} = \mathscr{O}_{U_i} \cdot f_i^{-1}$. We call this $\mathscr{L}$ the invertible sheaf defined by D and denote it by $\mathscr{O}_X(D)$. If we choose another family of local defining equations instead of $\{f_i\}$, we obtain an invertible sheaf which is isomorphic to $\mathscr{O}_X(D)$. We have thus proved the following lemma.

LEMMA 5.17. *Let X be an algebraic variety whose local rings are all unique factorization domains. Then the mapping $\mathscr{L} \mapsto D(\mathscr{L})$ is an isomorphism between the abelian groups* $\mathrm{Pic}(X)$ *and* $Cl(X)$.

EXAMPLE 5.17.1. For $\mathbf{P} = \mathbf{P}_k^n$, we have $\mathrm{Pic}(\mathbf{P}) = \mathbf{Z}[\mathscr{O}_{\mathbf{P}}(1)]$.

It suffices to show that $\mathscr{O}_{\mathbf{P}}(D) = \mathscr{O}_{\mathbf{P}}(d)$ $(d \in \mathbf{Z}_+)$ for every irreducible closed subvariety D of codimension 1 on $\mathbf{P}$. D is defined by a homogeneous prime ideal $\mathfrak{P}$ of height 1 of the homogeneous coordinate ring $k[T_0, \ldots, T_n]$ of $\mathbf{P}$. Since $k[T_0, \ldots, T_n]$ is a UFD, there exists a homogeneous polynomial F such that $\mathfrak{P} = (F)$. Consider the canonical open covering $\mathbf{P} = \bigcup_{i=0}^n U_i$ with $U_i = D_+(T_i)$. D is defined by $F(T_0/T_i, \ldots, T_n/T_i) = F \cdot T_i^{-d}$ ($d = \deg F$) on U_i. Hence, $\mathscr{O}_{\mathbf{P}}(D)|_{U_i} = \mathscr{O}_{U_i} \cdot (T_i^d/F)$. So the transition function on U_{ij} is $(T_j/T_i)^d$. It follows that $\mathscr{O}_{\mathbf{P}}(D) \cong \mathscr{O}_{\mathbf{P}}(d)$.

Let X be a normal projective algebraic variety, let $\mathscr{L}$ be an invertible sheaf on X, and let D be the divisor defined by $\mathscr{L}$. Let σ be a nonzero element of $H^0(X, \mathscr{L})$. Take an open covering $\mathfrak{U} = \{U_i\}_{i \in I}$, isomorphisms $\varphi_i : \mathscr{L}|_{U_i} \xrightarrow{\sim} \mathscr{O}_{U_i}$ and a family of transition functions $\{\theta_{ji}\}$ as specified as above. Let $s_i = \varphi_i(\sigma|_{U_i})$. Then $s_i \in \Gamma(U_i, \mathscr{O}_X)$, and $s_j = \theta_{ji}s_i$ on $U_i \cap U_j$. Hence, $s_j f_j^{-1} = s_i f_i^{-1}$, where $f_i = \theta_{ii_0}$ according to the previous notations. Denote this element by h. Then $h \in k(X)$ and $s_i = f_i \cdot h$ for each $i \in I$. We have an effective divisor (s_i) on U_i and patch $\{(s_i)\}_{i \in I}$ together to give an effective divisor $D' \geq 0$ on X, where $D'|_{U_i} = (s_i)$ and $D' = D + (h)$. We write $D' = D(\sigma)$. The divisor $D(\sigma)$ is determined only by $\mathscr{L}$ and σ independently of the choice of D. We denote $D(\sigma)$ also by $(\sigma)_0$.

Suppose $D(\sigma) = D(\tau)$ for $\sigma, \tau \in H^0(X, \mathscr{L})$. For $t_i = \varphi_i(\tau|_{U_i})$, we have $t_j = \theta_{ji}t_i$. Since $D(\sigma)|_{U_i} = D(\tau)|_{U_i}$, $t_i \cdot s_i^{-1} \in \Gamma(U_i, \mathscr{O}_X)^*$ for each $i \in I$ (Lemma 5.15). $t_i \cdot s_i^{-1}$ is an element of $\Gamma(X, \mathscr{O}_X)^* (= k^*)$ which is independent of i. Namely, $t_i = \alpha s_i$ with $\alpha \in k^*$. Hence, $\tau = \alpha\sigma$.

Conversely, let D' be an effective divisor on X such that $D' = D + (h)$ with $h \in k(X)$. Since $f_i h = 0$ is a defining equation of $D'|_{U_i}$, we have $f_i h \in \Gamma(U_i, \mathscr{O}_X)$ for each $i \in I$. On $U_i \cap U_j$, we have

$$\varphi_j \cdot \varphi_i^{-1}(f_i h) = \theta_{ji} \cdot f_i h = f_j h = \varphi_j \cdot \varphi_j^{-1}(f_j h).$$

Hence, $\varphi_i^{-1}(f_i h) = \varphi_j^{-1}(f_j h)$ (for each $i, j \in I$). So there exists $\sigma \in \Gamma(X, \mathscr{L})$ such that $\varphi_i(\sigma|_{U_i}) = f_i h$. Through these observations, we have proved the next result.

LEMMA 5.18. *Let X be a normal, projective algebraic variety, let $\mathscr{L}$ be an invertible sheaf on X, and let D be the Cartier divisor defined by $\mathscr{L}$. Under the mapping $\sigma \mapsto D(\sigma)$, the set $H^0(X, \mathscr{L}) - (0)/(\sim)$ is then in one-to-one correspondence with the set $\{D'; D' \geq 0, D' = D + (h)$ for some $h \in k(X)\}$, where $\sigma \sim \tau$ if and only if $\tau = \alpha\sigma$ (for some $\alpha \in k^*$) for $\sigma, \tau \in H^0(X, \mathscr{L}) - (0)$.*

$H^0(X, \mathscr{L})$ is a finite-dimensional k-vector space. Choosing a basis $\{\sigma_0, \ldots, \sigma_n\}$ ($n + 1 = \dim_k H^0(X, \mathscr{L})$), we have $H^0(X, \mathscr{L}) \cong k^{n+1}$. Thus, the set $H^0(X, \mathscr{L}) - (0)/(\sim)$ is identified with the projective space $\mathbf{P}^n$ of dimension n. Let $D = D(\mathscr{L})$ and let $|D| := \{D'; D' \geq 0, D' = D + (h)$ for some $h \in k(X)\}$. We call $|D|$ the *complete linear system* of the divisor D. $|D|$ is identified with $\mathbf{P}^n$ by the above lemma. We call $H^0(X, \mathscr{L})$ the *k-module* associated with $|D|$. For a vector subspace M of $H^0(X, \mathscr{L})$, define a subset L of $|D|$, which we also denote by $L(M)$, by $L = \{D' \in |D|; D' = D(\sigma), \sigma \in M - (0)\}$. As a set, L is isomorphic to $M - (0)/(\sim)$ which is a linear subspace of the projective space $\mathbf{P}^n$. Conversely, take a linear subspace L' of $\mathbf{P}^n = |D|$. Then there exists a vector subspace M' of $H^0(X, \mathscr{L})$ such that $L' = L(M')$. Since M' is uniquely determined by L', we denote M' also by $M(L')$. We call L a *linear subsystem* (or simply a *linear system*) of $|D|$ and $M = M(L)$ *the associated k-module* of L. The set $\{h \in k(X);\ (h) = D(\sigma) - D,\ \sigma \in M - (0)\} \cup (0)$ is a subset of $k(X)$, which is a k-vector space isomorphic to M. We call this space also the associated k-module of L. We put $\dim_k L = \dim_k M - 1$ and call it the *dimension* of L.

Suppose $H^0(X, \mathscr{L}) \neq (0)$. Write $\mathscr{L} = \mathscr{O}_X(D)$. We shall consider a linear subsystem L of $|D|$ and its associated k-module M. We assume $\dim_k M = r+1 > 0$ which is equivalent to the condition $L \neq \emptyset$. We regard M as contained in $k(X)$ and take its k-basis $\{f_0, \dots, f_r\}$, where each f_i is a rational function on X. We then define a rational mapping $\Phi_L \colon X \cdots \to \mathbf{P}^r$ by $P \mapsto (f_0(P), \dots, f_r(P)) \in \mathbf{P}^r$, where P is a closed point of X. We can ascertain as follows that Φ_L is a rational mapping. Let $U = \mathrm{Spec}(A)$ be an affine open set such that for each i, $f_i \in A = \Gamma(U, \mathscr{O}_X)$. Moreover, we may assume that $f_0 \neq 0$ everywhere on U. If $T_0, \dots, T_r$ are homogeneous coordinates of $\mathbf{P}^r$, the restriction of Φ_L onto U is the morphism of schemes $U \to \mathbf{A}^r = D_+(T_0) \hookrightarrow \mathbf{P}^r$ attached to a ring homomorphism $k[T_1/T_0, \dots, T_r/T_0] \to A$, $T_i/T_0 \mapsto f_i/f_0$. Thus, Φ_L is a rational mapping. We call Φ_L the *rational mapping associated with L*.

Take a different k-basis $\{g_0, \dots, g_r\}$. Then $g_i = \sum_{j=0}^{r} \alpha_{ij} f_j$ $(0 \leq i \leq r)$, where $(\alpha_{ij}) \in \mathrm{GL}(r+1, k)$. If we use $\{g_0, \dots, g_r\}$ instead of $\{f_0, \dots, f_r\}$, the associated rational mapping is $f_\alpha \cdot \Phi_L$, where f_α is the projective transformation of $\mathbf{P}^r$ defined by the matrix $\alpha = (\alpha_{ij})$.

The k-basis $\{f_0, \dots, f_r\}$ is a k-basis of M which is identified with the k-module $M_D := \{h \in k(X); (h) = D(\sigma) - D, \sigma \in M - (0)\} \cup (0)$. If D' is a divisor linearly equivalent to D, then $|D| = |D'|$. If we write $D' = D + (u)$ with $u \in k(X)$, then the k-module $M_{D'} := \{g \in k(X); (g) = D(\sigma) - D', \sigma \in M - (0)\} \cup (0)$ is isomorphic to M_D via $g \mapsto gu$. Hence, if $\{g_0, \dots, g_r\}$ is a k-basis of $M_{D'}$, then $\{g_0 u, \dots, g_r u\}$ is a k-basis of M_D. The associated rational mappings $P \mapsto (g_0(P), \dots, g_r(P))$ and $P \mapsto (g_0(P)u(P), \dots, g_r(P)u(P))$ are the same.

The above observations show that the rational mapping $\Phi_L \colon X \cdots \to \mathbf{P}^r$ is uniquely determined by the linear system L up to projective transformations of $\mathbf{P}^r$.

For two divisors D_1, D_2, we write $D_1 ge D_2$ if $D_1 - D_2 \geq 0$. For a linear system $L (\subseteq |D|)$ and an irreducible divisor A, we say that A is a *fixed component* of L if $D' \geq A$ for each $D' \in L$. If $L \neq \emptyset$, it is apparent that we can determine an effective divisor F in a unique way so that $D' \geq F$ for each $D' \in L$ and F is the largest (with respect to $\geq$) among those effective divisors with this property. We call F the *fixed part* of L. Then $L - F := \{D' - F; D' \in L\}$ is a linear system again, and $\dim(L - F) = \dim L$. (In fact, since $|D| = |D_0|$ for an element D_0 of L, by replacing D by D_0, we may assume from the beginning that $D \geq 0$ and $D \in L$. Let $M(L) := \{f \in k(X); D + (f) \in L\} \cup (0)$ be the associated k-module of L. Then $D' - F = (D - F) + (f)$ for $D' \in L$. Hence, $L - F \subseteq |D - F|$ and $M(L - F) = M(L)$.) We call $L - F$ the *variable part* of L. Even if L has no fixed components, i.e., if $F = 0$, there may still exist a point $P \in D'$ for each $D' \in L$. (In general, when we write an effective divisor D as a sum of irreducible components $D = \sum_i n_i Y_i$ with each $n_i > 0$, we denote $\bigcup_i Y_i$ by $\mathrm{Supp}\, D$ and call it the *support* of D. We write $P \in D'$ to mean $P \in \mathrm{Supp}\, D'$.) We call P a *base point* of L if $P \in D'$ for each $D' \in L$. Set $\mathrm{Bs}\, L = \{P \in X; P \text{ is a base point of } L\}$. Then $\mathrm{Bs}\, L = \bigcap_{D' \in L} \mathrm{Supp}\, D'$. This relation holds in the case $F > 0$ as well if we regard the points of fixed components as the base points of L. $\mathrm{Bs}\, L$ is a closed set of X, and $\mathrm{codim}_X \mathrm{Bs}\, L \geq 2$ provided $F = 0$.

Suppose a rational function f satisfies the condition $D + (f) \geq 0$ for an effective divisor $D = \sum_i n_i Y_i$ with each $n_i > 0$. If Y is a polar divisor of f, then $Y = Y_i$ and $v_Y(f) \geq -n_i$ for some i. So the index of Y as a polar divisor of f is at most n_i. We shall prove the following lemma.

LEMMA 5.19. *Let X be a normal, projective algebraic variety. Then we have*:

(1) *Let D be a Cartier divisor, let $L \subseteq |D|$ be a linear system with* $\dim L > 0$, *and let Φ_L be the rational mapping associated with L. Then Φ_L is defined on $X - \mathrm{Bs}(L - F)$, where F is the fixed part of L.*

(2) *Let $\rho\colon X \cdots \to Y$ be a dominant rational mapping from X to a projective algebraic variety Y. Then there exists a linear system L such that $\rho = \Phi_L$.*

PROOF. (1) As explained above, $M(L) = M(L - F)$, and $\Phi_L = \Phi_{L-F}$. We may as well assume $D_0 \in L$ and $L \subseteq |D_0|$. Accordingly, we may assume that $1 \in M(L)$ and $\{1, f_1, \dots, f_r\}(r = \dim L)$ is a k-basis of $M(L)$. If $P \notin \mathrm{Supp}\, D_0$, we claim that the rational functions $f_1, \dots, f_r$ are regular at P. Set $f = f_i$ and $\mathscr{O} = \mathscr{O}_{X,P}$. Suppose $f \notin \mathscr{O}$. Since $\mathscr{O} = \bigcap_{\mathfrak{p}} \mathscr{O}_{\mathfrak{p}}$ with $\mathfrak{p}$ ranging over all prime ideals of height 1 of $\mathscr{O}$, there exists some $\mathfrak{p} \in \mathrm{Spec}(\mathscr{O})$ such that $\mathrm{ht}(\mathfrak{p}) = 1$ and $f \notin \mathscr{O}_{\mathfrak{p}}$. Since $\mathscr{O}_{\mathfrak{p}}$ is a discrete valuation ring, then $f^{-1} \in \mathfrak{p}\mathscr{O}_{\mathfrak{p}}$. Let Y be the irreducible divisor $\overline{\{\mathfrak{p}\}}$ on X. Then $v_Y(f) < 0$ and P is in a polar divisor Y of f. However, the hypothesis $D_0 + (f) \geq 0$ implies that every polar divisor of f is an irreducible component of D_0. This contradicts the assumption $P \notin \mathrm{Supp}\, D_0$. Hence, for each i, $f_i \in \mathscr{O}_{X,P}$. This means that Φ_L is defined at the point P. Suppose $P \notin \mathrm{Bs}\, L$. Then $P \notin \mathrm{Supp}\, D_i$ for some i, where $D_i = D_0 + (f_i)$ $(1 \leq i \leq r)$. (Since D is a Cartier divisor by hypothesis, D is defined at every point by a single equation. This is the case for a divisor D_0 linearly equivalent to D. Let $g = 0$ be a defining equation of D_0 is an open neighborhood of the point P. Then D_i is defined by $gf_i = 0$, and $P \in \mathrm{Supp}\, D_i$ If and only if $(gf_i)(P) = 0$. Suppose $P \in \mathrm{Supp}\, D_i$ for each i. Then $(gf)(P) = 0$ for any element f of $M(L)$ because f is expressed as $f = \alpha_0 + \alpha_1 f_1 + \cdots + \alpha_r f_r$ $(\alpha_i \in k)$. Namely, if $P \notin \mathrm{Bs}\, L$, then $P \notin \mathrm{Supp}\, D_i$ for some i.] Then $\{1/f_i, f_1/f_i, \dots, f_r/f_i\}$ is a k-basis of the k-module $\{g \in k(X); (g) = D - D_i,\ D \in L\}$. By the above prescription, we know that Φ_L is defined at the point P. So, $X - \mathrm{Bs}(L - F)$ is contained in the domain of definition of Φ_L.

(2) Y is a closed, algebraic subvariety of a projective space, say $\mathbf{P}^n$. Replacing $\mathbf{P}^n$ by a linear subspace if necessary, we may assume that Y is not contained in any hyperplane. Let $\mathscr{O}_Y(1) = \mathscr{O}_{\mathbf{P}}(1) \otimes \mathscr{O}_Y$. From the description given after Corollary 5.10, it follows that the homomorphism $i : H^0(\mathbf{P}, \mathscr{O}_{\mathbf{P}}(1)) \to H^0(Y, \mathscr{O}_Y(1))$ induced by the closed immersion $\iota\colon Y \to \mathbf{P}^n$ is injective. On the other hand, let U be the domain of definition of ρ, and let $\varphi = \rho|_U$. $\mathscr{L} = \varphi^*\mathscr{O}_Y(1)$ is then an invertible sheaf on U. Let $j\colon H^0(Y, \mathscr{O}_Y(1)) \to H^0(U, \mathscr{L})$ be the natural homomorphism. (Compare the definition of the inverse image in Part I, Chapter 2.) $M = \mathrm{Im}(j \cdot i)$ is a finite-dimensional k-module of $H^0(U, \mathscr{L})$. A nonzero element σ of M defines an effective divisor $D'(\sigma)$ on U. If we write $D'(\sigma) = \sum_i n_i Z_i'$, then define $D(\sigma)$ by $D(\sigma) = \sum_i n_i \overline{Z_i'}$, where $\overline{Z}_i'$ is the closure of Z_i' in X. We also write $D(\sigma) = \overline{D'(\sigma)}$. Then $L = \{D(\sigma); \sigma \in M - (0)\}$ is a linear system on X and the associated k-module of L is equal to M. In fact, fix $D_0' = D(\sigma_0)$. Then $D'(\sigma) = D_0' + (f_\sigma)$, $f_\sigma \in k(U) = k(X)$. Since $\mathrm{codim}_X(X - U) \geq 2$, we have $D(\sigma) = D_0 + (f)$, where $D_0 = D(\sigma_0)$. So L is a linear subsystem of $|D_0|$ and $M(L) := \{f_\sigma; \sigma \in M - (0)\} \cup (0)$ is k-isomorphic to M. Let $T_0, \dots, T_n$ be homogeneous coordinates of $\mathbf{P}^n$, and let $\sigma_0, \dots, \sigma_n$ be the images of $T_0, \dots, T_n$ by $j \cdot i$. Choose f_i $(1 \leq i \leq n)$ in such a way that $D(\sigma_i) = D(\sigma_0) + (f_i)$. Then ρ is the rational mapping given by $P \mapsto (1, f_1(P), \dots, f_n(P))$. If we prove that $1, f_1, \dots, f_n$ are linearly independent, we conclude $\rho = \Phi_L$. Suppose $\alpha_0 + \alpha_1 f_1 + \cdots + \alpha_n f_n = 0$ $(\alpha_i \in k)$. Then $\rho(U)$ (accordingly, $Y = \overline{\rho(U)}$) is contained in the hyperplane $\alpha_0 T_0 + \alpha_1 T_1 + \cdots + \alpha_n T_n = 0$. By the initial hypothesis that Y is not contained in any hyperplane of $\mathbf{P}^n$, we must

have $\alpha_0 = \cdots = \alpha_n = 0$. Namely, $1, f_1, \ldots, f_n$ are linearly independent. □

With the notations in the above proof (2), $M \cong H^0(\mathbf{P}, \mathscr{O}_{\mathbf{P}}(1))$. An element σ of $M - (0)$, viewed as an element of $H^0(\mathbf{P}, \mathscr{O}_{\mathbf{P}}(1))$, defines a hyperplane $H(\sigma)$. We then say that $D(\sigma)$ is the *pullback* of $H(\sigma)$ by ρ. We write $D(\sigma) = X \cdot H(\sigma)$ to simplify the notation.

COROLLARY 5.20. *With the notations of Lemma* 5.19 (1), $\mathrm{Bs}(L - F) = X - U_0$, *where* U_0 *is the domain of definition of* Φ_L.

PROOF. We have shown $\mathrm{Bs}(L - F) \supseteq X - U_0$. Let $\rho = \Phi_L \colon X \to \mathbf{P}^n$ $(n = \dim L)$ and let $Y = \overline{\rho(U_0)}$, $\rho \colon X \cdots \to Y$ is then a dominant rational mapping. Furthermore, $L - F = \{X \cdot H(\sigma); \sigma \in M - (0)\}$ by Lemma 5.19 (2), $\rho|_{U_0} \colon U_0 \to \rho(U_0)$ is a morphism of schemes, and the linear system of hyperplanes on $\mathbf{P}^n$, $\{H(\sigma); \sigma \in M - (0)\}$, has no base points on $\rho(U_0)$. Hence, any common point of $\{\mathrm{Supp}\, D(\sigma); \sigma \in M - (0)\}$ lies outside U_0 even if such a point exists at all. Namely, $\mathrm{Bs}(L - F) \subseteq X - U_0$. □

DEFINITION 5.21. Let $\mathscr{L}$ be an invertible sheaf on a normal, projective algebraic variety X. When $H^0(X, \mathscr{L}) \neq (0)$, we denote by $\Phi_{\mathscr{L}}$ the rational mapping $\Phi_\Lambda \colon X \cdots \to \mathbf{P}^N$ $(N = \dim \Lambda)$ defined by the complete linear system $\Lambda := \{D(\sigma); \sigma \in H^0(X, \mathscr{L}) - (0)\}$. We say that $\mathscr{L}$ is a *very ample* invertible sheaf if $\mathrm{Bs}\, \Lambda = \emptyset$, and $\Phi_{\mathscr{L}}$ is a closed immersion. We say that $\mathscr{L}$ is an *ample* invertible sheaf if $\mathscr{L}^{\otimes r} (= \underbrace{\mathscr{L} \otimes \cdots \otimes \mathscr{L}}_{r})$ is very ample for some positive integer r.

EXAMPLE 5.21.1. Let X be a closed algebraic subvariety of $\mathbf{P}^n$ which is normal, and let $\mathscr{L} = \mathscr{O}_{\mathbf{P}}(1) \otimes \mathscr{O}_X$. Then $\mathscr{L}$ is a very ample invertible sheaf.

With the notations of Lemma 5.19, set $X = Y$ and $\rho = \mathrm{id}_X$. M is a k-submodule of $H^0(X, \mathscr{L})$. Replacing $\mathbf{P}^n$ by a linear subspace if necessary, we may assume that X is not contained in any hyperplane. Then $M \cong H^0(\mathbf{P}, \mathscr{O}_{\mathbf{P}}(1))$ though $M \subsetneqq H^0(X, \mathscr{L})$ in general. So if L is the linear system determined by M, $\Phi_L = \pi \cdot \Phi_{\mathscr{L}}$, where π is the projection from the projective space $\mathbf{P}^N$ $(N = \dim H^0(X, \mathscr{L}) - 1 \geq n)$ to $\mathbf{P}^n$, $(T_0, \ldots, T_N) \mapsto (T_0, \ldots, T_n)$. Since $\mathrm{Bs}\, L = \emptyset$, the complete linear system Λ that contains L has no base points. Hence, $\Phi_{\mathscr{L}}$ is a morphism. If Φ_L is a closed immersion, then $\Phi_{\mathscr{L}}$ is a closed immersion, too (problem II.5.6).

As a final topic of this chapter, we shall discuss the normalization of a projective algebraic variety. Let A be a graded ring such that A_0 is a field k (not necessarily an algebraically closed field) and A is a finitely generated k-algebra domain, and let L be its quotient field.

LEMMA 5.22. *Let A be as above. Then there exists a positive integer N such that* $\mathrm{Proj}(A)$ *is isomorphic to* $\mathrm{Proj}(B)$, *where B is a graded subalgebra of A that is generated by A_N over A_0.*

PROOF. Noting that A is finitely generated over k, take generators $\{x_1, \ldots, x_n\}$ of A which are homogeneous elements. Let $d_i = \deg x_i$. For each i, $A[x_i^{-1}]_0$ is finitely generated over k (Lemma 5.5 and the proof of Theorem 5.4 (3)), and we can take generators of the form $\prod_{j \neq i} x_j^{\alpha_j} / x_i^{\beta}$ $(\alpha_j \geq 0, \beta \geq 0, \beta d_i = \sum_{j \neq i} \alpha_j d_j)$. With i fixed, let e_i be the least common multiple of the βd_i when all generators are counted in. Let N be the least common multiple of $d_1, \ldots, d_n, e_1, \ldots, e_n$. Let $B := k[A_N]$. Then B is a graded subalgebra of A, and the natural injection $\varphi \colon B \to A$ gives rise to a morphism of schemes $f: G(\varphi) \to \text{Proj}(B)$. Since $x_i^{N/d_i} \in A_N$ for each i, we know that $G(\varphi) = \text{Proj}(A)$. Furthermore, $\text{Proj}(B) = \bigcup_{i=1}^n D_+(x_i^{N/d_i})$, $D_+(x_i) = f^{-1}(D_+(x_i^{N/d_i}))$ and $\text{Proj}(A) = \bigcup_{i=1}^n D_+(x_i)$. Hence, in order to show that f is an isomorphism, it suffices to prove that the homomorphism $\varphi_i: B[(x_i^{N/d_i})^{-1}]_0 \to A[x_i^{-1}]_0$ induced by φ is a k-isomorphism. Since φ_i is clearly an injection, φ_i is an isomorphism if the generators of $A[x_i^{-1}]_0$ as a k-algebra are contained in $B[(x_i^{N/d_i})^{-1}]_0$. As remarked already, such a generator is of the form $\prod_{j \neq i} x_j^{\alpha_j}/x_i^{\beta}$. Since $\beta d_i \mid N$, we have

$$\prod_{j \neq i} x_j^{\alpha_j}/x_i^{\beta} = \left(\prod_{j \neq i} x_j^{\alpha_j}\right) x_i^{N/d_i - \beta}/x_i^{N/d_i} \in B[(x_i^{N/d_i})^{-1}]_0.$$

φ_i is, therefore, an isomorphism. □

LEMMA 5.23. *Let A be as above. If A is integrally closed, then* Proj(A) *is a normal scheme.*

PROOF. As in the proof of Lemma 5.22, let $A = k[x_1, \ldots, x_n]$. In order to show that $\text{Proj}(A)$ is a normal scheme, it suffices to prove that $A[x_i^{-1}]_0$ is an integrally closed, integral domain for each i. Let ξ be an element of the quotient field $K = Q(A[x_i^{-1}]_0)$. We can write $\xi = u/v$ ($u, v \in A_n$ (for some $n \geq 0$), $v \neq 0$). Suppose ξ is integral over $A[x_i^{-1}]_0$. Then there exist an integer $r \geq 0$ and a monic relation

$$(x_i^r \xi)^N + a_1 (x_i^r \xi)^{N-1} + \cdots + a_N = 0, \qquad a_i \in A.$$

Since A is integrally closed, $w := x_i^r \xi \in A$. From the equality $vw = x_i^r u$, we see that w is a homogeneous element of A of degree $r \cdot \deg x_i$. So $\xi = w/x_i^r \in A[x_i^{-1}]_0$. □

We assume below that A is generated by A_1 over k. An element ξ of the quotient field L of A is said to be a homogeneous element of degree $p - q$ if ξ is written as $\xi = f/g$, $f \in A_p$, $g \in A_q$, $g \neq 0$. Let $L_r = \{\xi \in L; \xi \text{ is a homogeneous element of degree } r\}$. Then the relation $L_r \cdot L_s \subseteq L_{r+s}$ holds. Hence, $\widetilde{L} := \sum_{r \in \mathbf{Z}} L_r$ is a graded ring which has homogeneous elements of negative degree even if A does not.

LEMMA 5.24. *With the above assumptions and notations, we have*

(1) *Let x be a nonzero element of A_1. Then x is algebraically independent over L_0, $\widetilde{L} = L_0[x, x^{-1}]$, and $L = L_0(x)$.*

(2) *Let $\widetilde{A}$ be the integral closure of A in L. Then $\widetilde{A}$ is a graded ring such that $\widetilde{A}_i = 0$ for each $i < 0$. Moreover, $\widetilde{A}_0$ is a finite algebraic extension of k and $\widetilde{A}$ is finitely generated over k.*

PROOF. (1) First of all, note that L_0 is a field. Suppose x is algebraic over L_0. Then there exists a relation

$$a_0 x^m + a_1 x^{m-1} + \cdots + a_m = 0, \ a_i \in A_r \quad \text{for some } r \geq 0.$$

Since $\deg a_i x^{m-i} = m - i + r$, every monomial $a_i x^{m-i}$ must be 0. Since A is an integral domain, each $a_i = 0$. This contradicts the hypothesis that x be algebraic over L_0. x is, therefore, algebraically independent over L_0. Let $f \in A_p$. Then $f/x^p \in L_0$. Hence, $f \in L_0[x]$. Suppose $f/g \in L_r$ ($f \in A_p, g \in A_q$). Then $f/g = (f/x^p) \cdot (x^q/g) \cdot x^{p-q} \in L_0[x, x^{-1}]$. So $\widetilde{L} \subseteq L_0[x, x^{-1}]$. The opposite inclusion is clear. If we note that $A \subseteq \widetilde{L}$, we know $L = L_0(x)$.

(2) By (1) above, $L_0[x]$ is a polynomial ring in one variable over the field L_0. In particular, $L_0[x]$ and $L_0[x, x^{-1}]$ are normal rings. Since $A \subseteq L_0[x]$, we have $\widetilde{A} \subseteq L_0[x]$. Write an arbitrary element $\xi \in \widetilde{A}$ as

$$\xi = \xi_s + \xi_{s+1} + \cdots + \xi_t, \qquad \xi_j \in L_0 x^j, \ s \geq 0.$$

If each $\xi_j \in \widetilde{A}$, we know that $\widetilde{A}$ is a graded ring. Since ξ is integral over A, $A[\xi]$ is a finitely generated A-module (I.1.10). Hence, there exists $z \in A_d$ ($z \neq 0$) such that $zA[\xi] \subseteq A$. So $z \cdot \xi^i \in A$ for each $i > 0$. Write $z \cdot \xi^i = z \cdot \xi_s^i + \cdots$. Comparing this with the decomposition of $z \cdot \xi^i$ into homogeneous elements in A, we deduce that $z \cdot \xi_s^i \in A$. Namely, $A[\xi_s] \subseteq A \cdot (1/z)$. Since A is a noetherian ring, $A[\xi_s]$ is a finitely generated A-module. This implies $\xi_s \in \widetilde{A}$. Then $\xi - \xi_s = \xi_{s+1} + \cdots + \xi_t \in \widetilde{A}$. Repeating the above argument, we know that each $\xi_j \in \widetilde{A}$. Meanwhile, $\widetilde{A}$ is a finitely generated k-algebra by (I.1.34). If we note that $\widetilde{A}_0$ is integral over k, (I.1.10) implies that $\widetilde{A}_0$ is a finite algebraic extension of k. From $\widetilde{A} \subseteq L_0[x]$, we conclude that $\widetilde{A}_i = 0$ for each $i < 0$. □

Combining the above results, we obtain the following result.

THEOREM 5.25. *Let X be a projective algebraic variety over a field k. Then its normalization $\widetilde{X}$ (cf. (4.23)) is a projective algebraic variety, too.*

PROOF. We can write $X = \text{Proj}(A)$ for a graded ring A over a field k which is a finitely generated k-algebra domain. We may assume $A_0 = k$ and $A = k[A_1]$. Let $\widetilde{A}$ be the integral closure of A in $Q(A)$. By Lemma 5.24, $\widetilde{A}$ is a graded ring which is a finitely generated k-algebra domain, $\widetilde{A}_0 \subseteq L_0 = k(X)$, and $\widetilde{A}_0$ is an algebraic extension of k. Since $k(X)$ is a regular extension of k, we have $\widetilde{A}_0 = k$. $\widetilde{A}$ is, however, not necessarily generated by $\widetilde{A}_1$ over k. But, by Lemma 5.22, there exists a graded subring $\widetilde{B}$ of $\widetilde{A}$ such that $\widetilde{B}$ is generated by $\widetilde{A}_N$ over k, which itself is a finitely generated k-module, and $\text{Proj}(\widetilde{B}) = \text{Proj}(\widetilde{A})$. By Lemma 5.23, $\text{Proj}(\widetilde{B})$ is a normal scheme. If we can show that $\widetilde{X} \cong \text{Proj}(\widetilde{B})$, then we know that $\widetilde{X}$ is a projective algebraic variety over k. (Since $\widetilde{B} = k[\widetilde{B}_N]$, we have only to alter the grading of $\widetilde{B}$ so that the elements of $\widetilde{B}_N$ have degree 1.) We show that $\widetilde{X} \cong \text{Proj}(\widetilde{B})$. The function field of $\text{Proj}(\widetilde{B})$ is equal to the quotient field of $\text{Proj}(\widetilde{A})$, and the function field of $\text{Proj}(\widetilde{A})$ is contained in $L_0 = k(X)$ because $\widetilde{A} \subseteq L_0[x]$. The opposite inclusion also holds. So we have $k(\text{Proj}(\widetilde{B})) = k(X)$. Write $A_1 = kx_1 + \cdots + kx_n$. Let $\widetilde{\mathfrak{P}}$ be a homogeneous prime ideal of $\widetilde{A}$ such that each $x_i \in \widetilde{\mathfrak{P}}$. Then $\widetilde{\mathfrak{P}} \supset A_+$. Since A_+ is a maximal ideal of A, we have $A_+ = \widetilde{\mathfrak{P}} \cap A$. Hence, $\widetilde{\mathfrak{P}}$ is a maximal ideal of $\widetilde{A}$ as well. So $\widetilde{\mathfrak{P}} = \widetilde{A}_+$. Moreover, we have $\text{Proj}(\widetilde{A}) = \bigcup_{i=1}^n D_+(x_i)$. If we show that $\widetilde{A}[x_i^{-1}]_0$ is integral over $A[x_i^{-1}]_0$, it follows that $\text{Proj}(\widetilde{A}) \to \text{Proj}(A)$ is a finite morphism. But, $\widetilde{A}[x_i^{-1}]_0$ is integral over $A[x_i^{-1}]_0$ because $\widetilde{A}$ is integral over A. Then Theorem 4.23 implies $\widetilde{X} \cong \text{Proj}(\widetilde{A}) \cong \text{Proj}(\widetilde{B})$. □

II.5. Problems

1. For a graded ring $A = \sum_{n \geq 0} A_n$ and an ideal I of A, show the following assertions:

   (1) The condition that I is a homogeneous ideal is equivalent to the condition that for each $x \in I$, if $x = x_0 + x_1 + \cdots$ with $x_i \in A_i$, then $x_i \in I \cap A_i := I_i$ for each i.

   (2) If I is a homogeneous ideal, then so is the radical $\sqrt{I}$.

2. Suppose a graded ring $A = \sum_{n \geq 0} A_n$ is a noetherian ring. Applying the arguments in Part I, Chapter 1 and following the subsequent steps, show that each homogeneous ideal has a homogeneous primary ideal decomposition.
(1) A proper, homogeneous ideal I of A is written as the intersection of finitely many, irreducible homogeneous ideals $I = I_1 \cap \cdots \cap I_n$.
(2) An irreducible homogeneous ideal is a primary, homogeneous ideal.
(3) An arbitrary homogeneous ideal $I(\neq A)$ has a homogeneous primary ideal decomposition $I = \mathfrak{Q}_1 \cap \cdots \cap \mathfrak{Q}_n$, as in (I.1.23), satisfying the following two conditions:
   (i) $\sqrt{\mathfrak{Q}_i} \neq \sqrt{\mathfrak{Q}_j}$ if $i \neq j$.
   (ii) $I \subsetneqq \mathfrak{Q}_1 \cap \cdots \cap \check{\mathfrak{Q}}_i \cap \cdots \cap \mathfrak{Q}_n$ for each i.
(4) Let $\{\mathfrak{P}_1, \ldots, \mathfrak{P}_r\}$ exhaust all minimal elements in $\{\sqrt{\mathfrak{Q}_1}, \ldots, \sqrt{\mathfrak{Q}_n}\}$ for the decomposition in (3). Then $\sqrt{I} = \mathfrak{P}_1 \cap \cdots \cap \mathfrak{P}_r$.
(5) $V_+(I) = V_+(\mathfrak{P}_1) \cup \cdots \cup V_+(\mathfrak{P}_r)$ is the irreducible decomposition of $V_+(I)$.
3. Let X be a locally noetherian scheme, let $f: X \to Y$ be an affine morphism, and let $\mathscr{F}$ be a quasicoherent $\mathscr{O}_X$-Module. Follow the next steps to show that

$$H^i(X, \mathscr{F}) \cong H^i(Y, f_*\mathscr{F}) \quad \text{for each } i \geq 0.$$

(1) $R^p f_*\mathscr{F} = (0)$ for each $p > 0$. (Let $\{V_\lambda\}_{\lambda \in \Lambda}$ be an affine open covering of Y such that $f^{-1}(V_\lambda)$ is an affine open set of X for each λ. Then $(R^p f_*\mathscr{F})_{V_\lambda} \cong R^p(f_{V_\lambda})_*\mathscr{F}_{V_\lambda}$ for each $p \geq 0$ and λ. By virtue of Theorem 3.23 (2), $R^p(f_{V_\lambda})_*\mathscr{F}_{V_\lambda} = (0)$ for each $p > 0$ and λ. Hence, $R^p f_*\mathscr{F} = (0)$ for each $p > 0$.)
(2) Applying the spectral sequence in (I.2.28)

$$E_2^{p,q} = H^p(Y, R^q f_*\mathscr{F}) \Rightarrow H^n(X, \mathscr{F}),$$

we have $H^p(Y, f_*\mathscr{F}) \cong H^p(X, \mathscr{F})$ for each $p \geq 0$.
4. Let X and Y be separated algebraic schemes over a field k, and let $f: X \to Y$ be an affine morphism. By making use of Čech cohomologies, show that $H^i(X, \mathscr{F}) \cong H^i(Y, f_*\mathscr{F})$ for each $i \geq 0$ for a quasicoherent $\mathscr{O}_X$-Module $\mathscr{F}$.
5. Let R be a normal ring. Prove that R is a unique factorization domain if and only if the divisor class group $\mathrm{Cl}(R)$ vanishes.
6. Let X be a normal, projective algebraic variety, let $\psi: X \to \mathbf{P}^N$ be a morphism, let $\pi: \mathbf{P}^N \to \mathbf{P}^n$ be a projection, and let $\varphi = \pi \cdot \psi: X \to \mathbf{P}^n$. Show that ψ is a closed immersion if φ is a closed immersion.
7. Let $f: X \to Y$ be a surjective morphism between normal, projective algebraic varieties, and let $\mathscr{L}$ be an invertible sheaf on Y. Verify the following assertions:
(1) $f^*\mathscr{L}$ is an invertible sheaf on X. Let $\mathfrak{U} = \{U_i\}_{i \in I}$ be an open covering of Y which trivializes $\mathscr{L}$, and let $\{\theta_{ji}\}$ be a family of transition functions of $\mathscr{L}$ with respect to $\mathfrak{U}$. Then $f^{-1}(\mathfrak{U}) = \{f^{-1}(U_i)\}_{i \in I}$ is an open covering of X which trivializes $f^*\mathscr{L}$, and $\{f^*(\theta_{ji})\}$ is a family of transition functions of $f^*\mathscr{L}$ with respect to $f^{-1}(\mathfrak{U})$, where $f^*(\theta_{ji})$ is the image of θ_{ji} via the homomorphism of the function fields $f^*: k(Y) \hookrightarrow k(X)$.
(2) Obtain the injective homomorphism $\mathscr{L} \hookrightarrow \mathscr{L} \otimes_{\mathscr{O}_Y} f_*\mathscr{O}_X \cong f_*(f^*\mathscr{L})$ (cf. Problem I.2.9) by tensoring the injection of the structure sheaves $\mathscr{O}_Y \hookrightarrow f_*\mathscr{O}_X$ with $\mathscr{L}$. Obtain from this injection an injective homomorphism $f^*: H^0(Y, \mathscr{L}) \hookrightarrow H^0(X, f^*\mathscr{L})$. Show that the last f^* is an isomorphism provided $\mathscr{O}_Y \cong f_*\mathscr{O}_X$.
(3) Assume that all local rings of X and Y are unique factorization domains. Let

D be a Weil divisor on Y such that, with respect to an open covering $\mathfrak{U} = \{U_i\}_{i \in I}$ of Y, D is defined by an equation $t_i = 0$ on U_i, where $t_i \in k(Y)$. Then show that the local divisors $(f^*(t_i))$ on $f^{-1}(U_i)$ with $f^*(t_i) \in k(X)$ get patched together to define a divisor f^*D on X. Furthermore, show that $f^*D \sim f^*D'$ if $D \sim D'$. (We call f^*D the *total transform* of D by f.)

(4) With the assumptions of (3) above, show that $f^*D(\sigma) = D(f^*(\sigma))$ for each $\sigma \in H^0(Y, \mathscr{L})$, $\sigma \neq 0$.

CHAPTER 6

Nonsingular Algebraic Varieties

Let A be a ring. Consider a family of ideals $\{I_n\}_{n\geq 0}$ of A satisfying the condition that $I_n \subseteq I_m$ whenever $n \geq m$. For example, if we set $I_n = I^n$ for an ideal I, the family $\{I^n\}_{n\geq 0}$ satisfies the condition. We can then define a topology on the set A with an open basis $\{a + I_n; a \in A, n \geq 0\}$. Indeed, we have only to show that if $(a + I_n) \cap (b + I_m) \neq \emptyset$, for every $c \in (a + I_n) \cap (b + I_m)$, there exists $r \geq 0$ such that $c + I_r \subseteq (a + I_n) \cap (b + I_m)$. Write $c = a + u = b + v$ with $u \in I_n$ and $v \in I_m$. Take r so that $r \geq \max(n, m)$. Then $c + I_r = (a + u + I_r) \subseteq a + I_n$ and $c + I_r = b + v + I_r \subseteq b + I_m$, so $c + I_r \subseteq (a + I_n) \cap (b + I_m)$. With respect to this topology on A, the addition and the multiplication of the ring A are continuous mappings. In fact, for $m \leq n$, $(a + I_n) + (b + I_m) \subseteq (a + b) + I_m$ and $(a + I_n) \cdot (b + I_m) \subseteq ab + I_n + I_m + I_n \cdot I_m \subseteq ab + I_m$. We call this topology the *linear topology* defined by a family of ideals $\{I_n\}_{n\geq 0}$.

An infinite sequence $\{x_n\}_{n\geq 0}$ of elements of A is called a *Cauchy sequence* if, for each $n \geq 0$, there exists an integer $N = N(n)$ such that $x_r - x_s \in I_n$ for all $r, s \geq N$. Define the sum and the product of two Cauchy sequences $\{x_n\}_{n\geq 0}$ and $\{y_n\}_{n\geq 0}$ by $\{x_n + y_n\}_{n\geq 0}$ and $\{x_n \cdot y_n\}_{n\geq 0}$, respectively. Then the sum and product are also Cauchy sequences. We denote by $C\{A\}$ the ring of all Cauchy sequences. Two Cauchy sequences $\{x_n\}_{n\geq 0}$ and $\{y_n\}_{n\geq 0}$ are *cofinal* with each other, by definition, if, for each $n \geq 0$, there exists an integer $N = N(n)$ such that $x_r - y_r \in I_n$ for all $r \geq N$. We denote it by $\{x_n\} \sim \{y_n\}$. The set J consisting of all Cauchy sequences which are cofinal with the zero sequence $\{0\}$ is an ideal of $C\{A\}$. Let $\widehat{A} = C\{A\}/J$.

On the other hand, there exists the natural ring homomorphism $f_{mn}\colon A/I_n \to A/I_m$ whenever $n \geq m$, and $f_{mr} = f_{mn} \cdot f_{nr}$ if $r \geq n \geq m$. Namely, the set $\{A/I_n, f_{mn}; n \geq m \geq 0\}$ is a projective system. So we may consider its limit $\varprojlim_n A/I_n$, which is identified with a subset $\{(\overline{x}_n)_{n\geq 0}; f_{mn}(\overline{x}_n) = \overline{x}_m\ (n \geq m)\}$ of the product set $\prod_{n\geq 0} A/I_n$. This subset is also a subring of the product of rings $\prod_{n\geq 0} A/I_n$. We define a ring homomorphism $\varphi\colon \widehat{A} \to \varprojlim_n A/I_n$ as follows. Let $\{x_n\}_{n\geq 0}$ be a Cauchy sequence. By definition, for each $n \geq 0$, there exists $N(n) \geq 0$ such that $x_r - x_s \in I_n$ for all $r, s \geq N(n)$. We put $y_n = x_{N(n)}$. We may assume $N(m) < N(n)$ if $m < n$. Then $\{y_n\}_{n\geq 0}$ is a Cauchy sequence such that $\{y_n\}_{n\geq 0}$ and $\{x_n\}_{n\geq 0}$ are cofinal with each other and that $y_n - y_m \in I_m$ whenever $m \leq n$. So denoting by $[\{x_n\}]$ the equivalence class of $\{x_n\}_{n\geq 0}$ under the cofinality relation, we define $\varphi([\{x_n\}]) = (\overline{y}_n)$, where $\overline{y}_n = y_n \pmod{I_n}$. The cofinality class J is mapped by φ to the zero element of $\varprojlim_n A/I_n$. φ is a ring homomorphism. If $(\overline{x}_n)$ is an arbitrary element of $\varprojlim_n A/I_n$, we have $f_{mn}(\overline{x}_n) = \overline{x}_m$ whenever $m \leq n$. If we choose $x_n \in A$ so that $\overline{x}_n = x_n \pmod{I_n}$, then $x_r - x_s \in I_n$ for all $r, s \geq n$. Hence, $\{x_n\}$ is a Cauchy sequence. This shows that φ is surjective. Similarly, we can show that if the cofinality class of a

Cauchy sequence $\{x_n\}$ is mapped to 0 by φ, then $\{x_n\} \in J$. So φ is injective as well. This way we obtain the ring isomorphism $\varphi\colon \widehat{A} \xrightarrow{\sim} \varprojlim_n A/I_n$.

Let M be an A-module. $\{I_n M\}_{n\geq 0}$ is a family of submodules of M such that $I_n M \subseteq I_m M$ whenever $m \leq n$. As in the previous case for A, M is given a topology with an open basis $\{\xi + I_n M; \xi \in M, n \geq 0\}$, and the addition and the multiplication by elements of A in M are continuous mappings. We can also define Cauchy sequences $\{\xi_n\}_{n\geq 0}$ and the abelian group $C\{M\}$ of Cauchy sequences. Defining the multiplication $\{x_n\} \cdot \{\xi_n\}$ by $\{x_n \xi_n\}$ for $\{x_n\} \in C\{A\}$ and $\{\xi_n\} \in C\{M\}$, we can make $C\{M\}$ a $C\{A\}$-module. Furthermore, we can define the cofinality relation on $C\{M\}$ as in the previous case and set $\widehat{M} = C\{M\}/J_M$, where J_M is the set of Cauchy sequences in $C\{M\}$ which are cofinal with the zero sequence $\{0\}$. Since $C\{A\} \cdot J_M + J \cdot C\{M\} \subseteq J_M$, $\widehat{M}$ is regarded as an $\widehat{A}$-module. As in the case for A, we can also obtain an isomorphism of the abelian groups $\varphi_M\colon \widehat{M} \xrightarrow{\sim} \varprojlim_n M/I_n M$. Let $(\overline{\xi}_n) \in \varprojlim_n M/I_n M$ and $(\overline{x}_n) \in \varprojlim_n A/I_n$. Noting that $M/I_n M$ is an A/I_n-module, we define the product $(\overline{x}_n) \cdot (\overline{\xi}_n)$ by $(\overline{x}_n \cdot \overline{\xi}_n)$, which is an element of $\varprojlim_n M/I_n M$. Thereby, $\varprojlim_n M/I_n M$ is a $\varprojlim_n A/I_n$-module. The isomorphism φ_M is compatible with the ring isomorphism $\varphi_A (= \varphi)$. Namely, we have $\varphi_M(\hat{x} \cdot \hat{\xi}) = \varphi(\hat{x}) \cdot \varphi_M(\hat{\xi})$ for $\hat{x} \in \widehat{A}$ and $\hat{\xi} \in \widehat{M}$.

Define a ring homomorphism $\sigma\colon A \to \widehat{A}$ by $a \mapsto [\{a_n\}]$, where $a_n = a$ for each $n \geq 0$. Similarly, we can define a homomorphism of modules $\sigma_M\colon M \to \widehat{M}$ which is compatible with σ. Namely, $\sigma_M(a\xi) = \sigma(a)\sigma_M(\xi)$ for $a \in A$ and $\xi \in M$. Clearly, $\operatorname{Ker}\sigma = \bigcap_{n\geq 0} I_n$ and $\operatorname{Ker}\sigma_M = \bigcap_{n\geq 0} I_n M$. We often denote $\sigma(a)$ and $\sigma_M(\xi)$ by the same notations a and ξ, respectively, where $a \in A$ and $\xi \in M$.

Since $\{I_n \widehat{A}\}_{n\geq 0}$ is a family of ideals of $\widehat{A}$, we can define $\widehat{\widehat{A}}$ and the ring homomorphism $\tau\colon \widehat{A} \to \widehat{\widehat{A}}$ with respect to this family. An element of $I_m \widehat{A}$ is represented by a Cauchy sequence $\{a_n\}_{n\geq 0}$ such that $a_n \in I_m$ for all $n \gg 0$. Let $\hat{b} \in \bigcap_{m\geq 0} I_m \widehat{A}$. Then there exists a Cauchy sequence $\{a_n^{(m)}\}_{n\geq 0}$ for each $m > 0$ such that $\{a_n^{(r)}\}_{n\geq 0}$ and $\{a_n^{(s)}\}_{n\geq 0}$ are cofinal Cauchy sequences for all $r, s \geq 0$. Consider then a Cauchy sequence $\{a_n^{(n)}\}_{n\geq 0}$, which is cofinal with $\{a_n^{(m)}\}_{n\geq 0}$ for each $m > 0$. On the other hand, $\{a_n^{(n)}\}_{n\geq 0}$, as a Cauchy sequence in $C\{A\}$, is cofinal with the zero sequence. Hence, $\operatorname{Ker}\tau = \bigcap_{m\geq 0} I_m \widehat{A} = (0)$. Meanwhile, a Cauchy sequence $\{\{a_n^{(m)}\}_{n\geq 0}\}_{m\geq 0}$ of $\widehat{A}$ is cofinal with a Cauchy sequence $\{\{b_n^{(m)}\}_{n\geq 0}\}_{m\geq 0}$, where $b_n^{(m)} = a_n^{(n)}$ for all $n, m \geq 0$. This implies that the ring homomorphism $\tau\colon \widehat{A} \to \widehat{\widehat{A}}$ is an isomorphism. Similarly, we obtain an isomorphism $\tau_M\colon \widehat{M} \xrightarrow{\sim} \widehat{\widehat{M}}$.

Let us consider the case where $\bigcap_{n\geq 0} I_n = (0)$. The linear topology on A then satisfies the first axiom of separation "$a, b \in A, a \neq b$ implies that there exists some $n > 0$, such that $a \notin b + I_n$, $b \notin a + I_n$". Then we simply say that the linear topology on A is *separating* or A is *separated* with respect to the linear topology. A Cauchy sequence $\{a_n\}_{n\geq 0}$ in A is said to *converge* to an element a of A if $\{a_n\}_{n\geq 0}$ is cofinal with the Cauchy sequence $\sigma(a) = \{a\}_{n\geq 0}$. If the topology on A is separating, then the element a is uniquely determined. Furthermore, since the ring homomorphism $\sigma\colon A \to \widehat{A}$ is injective, we can identify A with a subring of $\widehat{A}$ by σ. For a Cauchy sequence $\{a_n\}_{n\geq 0}$ in A, $\{\sigma(a_n)\}_{n\geq 0}$ is a Cauchy sequence in $\widehat{A}$ which converges to the element $\{a_n\}_{n\geq 0}$ of $\widehat{A}$. In the case where $\bigcap_{n\geq 0} I_n M = (0)$, we can show similar results for M. We say that $\widehat{A}$ and $\widehat{M}$ are the *completions* of A and M, respectively. Summarizing a part of the above observations, we obtain the following lemma.

LEMMA 6.1. *Let A be a ring and let $\{I_n\}_{n\geq 0}$ be a family of ideals of A such that $I_n \subseteq I_m$ whenever $n \geq m$. Let M be an A-module. Then we have:*

(1) *Let $\widehat{M}$ be the completion of M with respect to $\{I_n M\}_{n\geq 0}$. Then $\widehat{M} \cong \varprojlim_n M/I_n M$. There exists a natural homomorphism of A-modules $\sigma_M : M \to \widehat{M}$ such that* $\operatorname{Ker}\sigma_M = \bigcap_{n\geq 0} I_n M$. *$\widehat{M}$ is an $\widehat{A}$-module, and σ_M is compatible with the ring homomorphism $\sigma : A \to \widehat{A}$.*

(2) *If $\bigcap_{n\geq 0} I_n M = (0)$, M is separated with respect to the topology given by $\{I_n M\}_{n\geq 0}$. Moreover,* $\operatorname{Im}(\sigma_M)$ *is a dense subset of $\widehat{M}$ with respect to the topology given by $\{I_n \widehat{M}\}_{n\geq 0}$.*

(3) *$\widehat{M}$ is separated with respect to the topology defined by $\{I_n \widehat{M}\}_{n\geq 0}$, and $\tau_M : \widehat{M} \to \widehat{\widehat{A}}$ is an isomorphism.*

We shall prove the following result.

LEMMA 6.2. *Let A be a noetherian ring. Let $\{I_n\}_{n\geq 0}$ be a family of ideals of A such that, for every finitely generated A-module M and every A-submodule N of M, there exists some $p > 0$ such that $I_n M \cap N = I_{n-p}(I_p M \cap N)$ for each $n > p$. Then we have:*

(1) *The functor assigning to a finitely generated A-module M the $\widehat{A}$-module $\widehat{M}$ is an exact functor.*

(2) *For a finitely generated A-module M, there exists an isomorphism of $\widehat{A}$-modules $M \otimes_A \widehat{A} \cong \widehat{M}$.*

PROOF. (1) For an exact sequence of A-modules

$$0 \to M_1 \xrightarrow{f} M_2 \xrightarrow{g} M_3 \to 0$$

we can define a sequence of $\widehat{A}$-modules in the natural fashion

$$\widehat{M_1} \xrightarrow{\hat{f}} \widehat{M_2} \xrightarrow{\hat{g}} \widehat{M_3}.$$

Let $\{\xi_n\}_{n\geq 0}$ be a Cauchy sequence in M_1. Suppose the Cauchy sequence $\{f(\xi_n)\}_{n\geq 0}$ in M_2 is cofinal with the zero sequence. Namely, suppose that for each $n > 0$, there is an integer N such that $f(\xi_r) \in I_n M_2$ for each $r \geq N$. By the hypothesis applied to M_2 and a submodule $f(M_1)$, there exists $p > 0$ such that $I_n M_2 \cap f(M_1) = I_{n-p}(I_p M_2 \cap f(M_1))$ for each $n > p$. For $n > p$, we have $f(\xi_r) \in I_{n-p}(I_p M_2 \cap f(M_1)) \subseteq f(I_{n-p} M_1)$. Hence, $\xi_r \in I_{n-p} M_1$ for each r, $r \gg n > p$. Namely, $\{\xi_n\}_{n\geq 0}$ is cofinal with the zero sequence in M_1. Next let $\{\eta_n\}_{n\geq 0}$ be a Cauchy sequence in M_2 such that $\{g(\eta_n)\}_{n\geq 0}$ is cofinal with the zero sequence in M_3. Namely, for each $n > 0$, there is $N = N(n)$ such that $g(\eta_r) \in I_n M_3 = g(I_n M_2)$ each $r \geq N$. We may here assume $N(1) < N(2) < \cdots < N(n) < N(n+1) < \cdots$. Then since $\{\eta_n\}_{n\geq 0}$ is cofinal with a Cauchy sequence $\{\eta_{N(n)}\}_{n\geq 0}$, we may replace $\{\eta_n\}_{n\geq 0}$ by $\{\eta_{N(n)}\}_{n\geq 0}$ and assume from the beginning that for each $n > 0$, $g(\eta_r) \in g(I_n M_2)$ whenever $r \geq n$. Then for each $n > 0$, there is $\varepsilon_n \in I_n M_2$ and $\xi_n \in M_1$ such that $f(\xi_n) = \eta_n - \varepsilon_n$. Here $\{\eta_n - \varepsilon_n\}_{n\geq 0}$ is a Cauchy sequence in M_2 which is cofinal with $\{\eta_n\}_{n\geq 0}$, and $\{\xi_n\}_{n\geq 0}$ is a Cauchy sequence in M_1 by the hypothesis applied to M_2 and $f(M_1)$. Hence,

$\operatorname{Ker}\hat{g} = \operatorname{Im}\hat{f}$. We shall show that $\hat{g}$ is surjective. Let $\{\zeta_n\}_{n\geq 0}$ be a Cauchy sequence in M_3. Replacing it by a Cauchy sequence in the same cofinality class, we may assume that, for each $n > 0$, $\zeta_r - \zeta_n \in I_n M_3$ for each $r \geq n$. Choose $\eta_0 \in M_2$ so that $g(\eta_0) = \zeta_0$ and $\eta_r^{(0)} \in M_2$ for each $r > 0$ so that $g(\eta_r^{(0)}) = \zeta_r$ and $\eta_r^{(0)} - \eta_0 \in I_0 M_2$. This choice is possible because $\zeta_r - \zeta_0 \in I_0 M_3 = g(I_0 M_2)$. We obtain thus a sequence $\{\eta_r^{(0)}\}_{r\geq 0}$ in M_2 with $\eta_0^{(0)} = \eta_0$. Next set $\eta_1^{(1)} = \eta_1^{(0)}$ and choose $\eta_r^{(1)}$ for each $r \geq 2$ so that $g(\eta_r^{(1)}) = \zeta_r$ and $\eta_r^{(1)} - \eta_1^{(1)} \in I_1 M_2$ to obtain a sequence $\{\eta_r^{(1)}\}_{r\geq 1}$. Next, set $\eta_2^{(2)} = \eta_2^{(1)}$ and choose $\eta_r^{(2)}$ for each $r \geq 3$ so that $g(\eta_r^{(2)}) = \zeta_r$ and $\eta_r^{(2)} - \eta_2^{(2)} \in I_2 M_2$ to obtain a sequence $\{\eta_r^{(2)}\}_{r\geq 2}$. Repeat this choice inductively and obtain a sequence $\{\eta_r^{(i)}\}_{r\geq i}$ such that $\eta_i^{(i)} = \eta_i^{(i-1)}$, $g(\eta_r^{(i)}) = \zeta_r$, and $\eta_r^{(i)} - \eta_i^{(i)} \in I_i M_2$ for each $r > i$. Then if we put $\eta_n = \eta_n^{(n-1)}$ for each $n > 0$, the sequence $\{\eta_n\}_{n>0}$ is a Cauchy sequence in M_2. In fact, $\eta_{n+1} - \eta_n = \eta_{n+1}^{(n)} - \eta_n^{(n-1)} = \eta_{n+1}^{(n)} - \eta_n^{(n)} + \eta_n^{(n)} - \eta_n^{(n-1)} \in I_n M_2$. Furthermore, $g(\eta_n) = \zeta_n$. Hence $\hat{g}$ is surjective.

(2) For an A-module M, define a homomorphism of $\widehat{A}$-modules $h_M : M \otimes_A \widehat{A} \to \widehat{M}$ by $(\xi, \{a_n\}) \mapsto \{a_n \xi\}$, where $\xi \in M$ and $\{a_n\}$ is a Cauchy sequence in A. For a homomorphism of A-modules $f : M \to N$, we have $h_N \cdot (f \otimes 1_A) = \hat{f} \cdot h_M$. In the case where F is a finitely generated free A-module, it is easy to show that h_F is an isomorphism. Since A is a noetherian ring, we have an exact sequence for every finitely generated A-module M:

$$F_1 \xrightarrow{p} F_0 \xrightarrow{q} M \to 0,$$

where F_0 and F_1 are finitely generated free A-modules. One then obtains the following commutative diagram:

$$\begin{array}{ccccccc}
F_1 \otimes_A \widehat{A} & \xrightarrow{p\otimes 1_A} & F_0 \otimes_A \widehat{A} & \xrightarrow{q\otimes 1_A} & M \otimes_A \widehat{A} & \longrightarrow & 0 \\
\downarrow{\scriptstyle h_{F_1}} & & \downarrow{\scriptstyle h_{F_2}} & & \downarrow{\scriptstyle h_M} & & \\
\widehat{F_1} & \xrightarrow{\hat{p}} & \widehat{F_2} & \xrightarrow{\hat{q}} & \widehat{M} & \longrightarrow & 0,
\end{array}$$

where the two rows are exact sequences and h_{F_1} and h_{F_2} are isomorphisms. Then h_M is an isomorphism as well. □

Choose a proper ideal I of A and consider a family of ideals $\{I^n\}_{n\geq 0}$, where $I^n \subseteq I^m$ if $n \geq m$. The linear topology on A defined by this family of ideals is called the *I-adic topology*. Similarly, $\{I^n M\}_{n\geq 0}$ defines the I-adic topology on an A-module M. If A is a noetherian ring, the family of ideals $\{I^n\}_{n\geq 0}$ satisfies the hypothesis of Lemma 6.2 as shown in the following lemma.

LEMMA 6.3. *Let A be a noetherian ring, and let I be a proper ideal of A. Let M be a finitely generated A-module, and let N be an A-submodule. Then there exists an integer $p > 0$ such that $I^n M \cap N = I^{n-p}(I^p M \cap N)$ for each $n > p$. In particular, $IL = L$, where $L = \bigcap_{n\geq 0} I^n M$.*

PROOF. Let $R := A \oplus M$ be a direct sum of A-modules. Define the multiplication on R by $(a, x) \cdot (b, y) = (ab, bx + ay)$. Then $(1, 0)$ is the identity element and M, identified with $(0) \oplus M$, satisfies $M^2 = (0)$. R is thus a noetherian ring (compare Problem II.3.1), and M and N, identified respectively with $(0) \oplus M$ and $(0) \oplus N$, are ideals of R. Furthermore, if we set $\mathfrak{a} = I \oplus M$, $\mathfrak{a}$ is an ideal of R. By virtue of Lemma of Artin-Rees (I.1.31), there is $p > 0$ such that for each $n \geq p$, $\mathfrak{a}^n M \cap N =$

$\mathfrak{a}^{n-p}(\mathfrak{a}^p M \cap N)$. By a straightforward computation, $\mathfrak{a}^n M \cap N = I^n M \cap N$ and $\mathfrak{a}^{n-p}(\mathfrak{a}^p M \cap N) = I^{n-p}(I^p M \cap N)$. By (I.1.31) again, we have $IL = L$. □

The following are the results we often refer to in the present book.

THEOREM 6.4. *Let $(A, \mathfrak{m})$ be a noetherian local ring, and let $\widehat{A}$ be the completion of A with respect to the $\mathfrak{m}$-adic topology (the* $\mathfrak{m}$-adic-completion *of A, for short). Then we have:*

(1) *A is separated with respect to the $\mathfrak{m}$-adic topology.*
(2) *$(\widehat{A}, \mathfrak{m}\widehat{A})$ is a local ring, and $\widehat{A}/\mathfrak{m}\widehat{A} \cong A/\mathfrak{m}$.*
(3) *$\widehat{A}$ is a flat A-module.*
(4) *$\widehat{M} \cong M \otimes_A \widehat{A}$ for a finitely generated A-module.*

PROOF. (1) By Lemma 6.3, $\mathfrak{m}J = J$, where $J = \bigcap_{n>0} \mathfrak{m}^n$. Then $J = (0)$ by Nakayama's lemma (I.1.28). Hence, Lemma 6.1 shows that A is separated with respect to the $\mathfrak{m}$-adic topology.

(2) $(\widehat{A}, \mathfrak{m}\widehat{A})$ is a local ring if and only if every element of $\widehat{A} - \mathfrak{m}\widehat{A}$ is invertible. (Prove this as an exercise.) Take an element x of $\widehat{A} - \mathfrak{m}\widehat{A}$, which is represented by a Cauchy sequence $\{a_n\}_{n\geq 0}$ in A, where we may assume $a_{n+1} - a_n \in \mathfrak{m}^n$. Hence, $a_0 \notin \mathfrak{m}$. Then $a_n \notin \mathfrak{m}$ for each n, and $\{a_n^{-1}\}_{n\geq 0}$ is easily seen to be a Cauchy sequence in A. This sequence converges to x^{-1}. It is apparent that the ring homomorphism $\sigma\colon A \to \widehat{A}$ induces a homomorphism of fields $\overline{\sigma}\colon A/\mathfrak{m}A \to \widehat{A}/\mathfrak{m}\widehat{A}$. On the other hand, if $\{a_n\}_{n\geq 0}$ is a Cauchy sequence in A, $a_n \pmod{\mathfrak{m}} \in A/\mathfrak{m}A$ $(n \gg 0)$ is determined independently of n. So, we obtain a homomorphism $\widehat{A}/\mathfrak{m}\widehat{A} \to A/\mathfrak{m}A$ which establishes, together with $\overline{\sigma}$, an isomorphism $A/\mathfrak{m} \cong \widehat{A}/\mathfrak{m}\widehat{A}$.

(3) $\widehat{A}$ is a flat A-module if and only if $j \otimes_A \widehat{A}\colon J \otimes_A \widehat{A} \to A \otimes_A \widehat{A} \cong \widehat{A}$ is an injection for an ideal J of A and the natural inclusion $j\colon J \to A$. (Try to prove this as an exercise. Compare [6, Theorem 7.7].) If we note that A is a noetherian ring, then this assertion together with the next (4) follow from Lemma 6.2. □

EXAMPLE 6.5. Let $A = k[x_1, \ldots, x_n]$ be a polynomial ring in n variables over k and let $I = (x_1, \ldots, x_n)$. The I-adic topology is separating. (In fact, $IL = L$ by Lemma 6.3, where $L = \bigcap_{n\geq 0} I^n$. L is a finitely generated ideal of A. In view of the proof of Nakayama's lemma (I.1.28), $dL = 0$ for $d \in A$, $d \neq 0$. Since A is an integral domain, we conclude $L = (0)$.) The completion $\widehat{A}$ of A with respect to the I-adic topology is a formal power series ring in n variables over k, which is the set of (formal) infinite series $\sum c_{i_1\cdots i_n} x_1^{i_1} \cdots x_n^{i_n}$ $(c_{i_1\cdots i_n} \in k; i_1, \ldots, i_n \geq 0)$ with coefficients in k subject to the addition and the multiplication as defined below

$$\left(\sum c_{i_1\cdots i_n} x_1^{i_1} \cdots x_n^{i_n}\right) + \left(\sum d_{i_1\cdots i_n} x_1^{i_1} \cdots x_n^{i_n}\right) = \sum (c_{i_1\cdots i_n} + d_{i_1\cdots i_n}) x_1^{i_1} \cdots x_n^{i_n},$$

$$\left(\sum c_{i_1\cdots i_n} x_1^{i_1} \cdots x_n^{i_n}\right) \cdot \left(\sum d_{i_1\cdots i_n} x_1^{i_1} \cdots x_n^{i_n}\right)$$
$$= \sum_{(i_1\cdots i_n)} \left(\sum_{j_\alpha + k_\alpha = i_\alpha} c_{j_1\cdots j_n} d_{k_1\cdots k_n} \right) x_1^{i_1} \cdots x_n^{i_n}.$$

Replacing the field k by a ring R, we can also define a formal power series ring $R[[x_1, \ldots, x_n]]$ with coefficient ring R. Let $(S, \mathfrak{m})$ be the localization of A with respect to I. Then the $\mathfrak{m}$-adic completion of S coincides with $\widehat{A}$. We have also

$k[[x_1, \dots, x_n]] = k[[x_1, \dots, x_{n-1}]][[x_n]]$. The ring $k[[x_1, \dots, x_n]]$ is a noetherian ring by the following lemma.

LEMMA 6.6. *Let R be a noetherian ring. Then $R[[x]]$ is a noetherian ring.*

PROOF. An element g of $R[[x]]$ is expressed as a formal power series

$$g = a_d x^d + a_{d+1} x^{d+1} + \cdots, \qquad a_d \neq 0,$$

where we call $a_d x^d$ the term of the lowest degree of g and denote this term by $LF(g)$; we also write $d = \deg g$. Clearly, $LF(g)$ is an element of the polynomial ring $R[x]$. Now let I be an ideal of $R[[x]]$, and let $I^* = \{LF(g); g \in I\}$. Let $\mathfrak{a}$ be the ideal of $R[x]$ generated by I^*. Since $R[x]$ is a noetherian ring, there are finitely many elements $\xi_1, \dots, \xi_n$ of I^* such that $\mathfrak{a} = \sum_{i=1}^n R[x]\xi_i$. For each i, $\xi_i = LF(g_i)$ with $g_i \in I$. We shall show that $I = \sum_{i=1}^n R[[x]]g_i$. Choose any element g of I. Since $LF(g) \in I^* \subset \mathfrak{a}$, we have $LF(g) = \sum_{i=1}^n \xi_i h_{i0}$ with homogeneous elements h_{i0} of $R[x]$ $(1 \leq i \leq n)$. Then $\deg(g - \sum_{i=1}^n g_i h_{i0}) > \deg g$. Since $g - \sum_{i=1}^n g_i h_{i0} \in I$, we find homogeneous elements h_{i1} $(1 \leq i \leq n)$ by the above argument such that

$$\deg\left(g - \sum_{i=1}^n g_i(h_{i0} + h_{i1})\right) > \deg\left(g - \sum_{i=1}^n g_i h_{i0}\right), \qquad \deg h_{i1} > \deg h_{i0} \text{ (for each } i\text{)}.$$

Repeating this argument, we find homogeneous elements $\{h_{ij}; 1 \leq i \leq n,\ j \geq 0\}$ such that

$$\deg h_{ij} > \deg h_{ij-1} \quad \text{(for each } i\text{)}$$

and

$$\deg\left(g - \sum_{i=1}^n g_i(h_{i0} + h_{i1} + \cdots + h_{ij})\right) > \deg\left(g - \sum_{i=1}^n g_i(h_{i0} + h_{i1} + \cdots + h_{ij-1})\right) \quad \text{(for all } j \geq 1\text{)}.$$

Then $h_i := \sum_{j \geq 0} h_{ij}$ is an element of $R[[x]]$ and $g = \sum_{i=1}^n g_i h_i$. □

COROLLARY 6.7. *Let $(R, \mathfrak{m})$ be a noetherian local ring, and let $\widehat{R}$ be the $\mathfrak{m}$-adic completion of R. Then the following assertions hold:*

(1) *Let $\xi_1, \dots, \xi_n$ be elements of $\mathfrak{m}$ such that the residue classes $\overline{\xi}_1, \dots, \overline{\xi}_n$ of $\xi_1, \dots, \xi_n$ modulo $\mathfrak{m}^2$ constitute a basis of the finite-dimensional vector space $\mathfrak{m}/\mathfrak{m}^2$ over the field $R/\mathfrak{m}$. Then $\mathfrak{m} = (\xi_1, \dots, \xi_n)$.*

(2) *Suppose R is an algebra over a field k and the natural homomorphism $k \to R \to R/\mathfrak{m}$ induces an isomorphism between k and $R/\mathfrak{m}$; we then say that R contains the residue field. Then there exists a surjective homomorphism of rings $\rho\colon k[[x_1, \dots, x_n]] \to \widehat{R}$ from the formal power series ring to $\widehat{R}$. In particular, $\widehat{R}$ is a noetherian ring.*

PROOF. (1) Let $\mathfrak{n} = \sum_{i=1}^n R\xi_i$. The $\mathfrak{m} = \mathfrak{n} + \mathfrak{m}^2$. Let $M = \mathfrak{m}/\mathfrak{n}$ which is a finitely generated R-module and satisfies the condition $\mathfrak{m}M = M$. So $M = (0)$ by Nakayama's lemma. Hence, $\mathfrak{m} = \mathfrak{n}$.

(2) Note that R is a subring of $\widehat{R}$. Define $\rho\colon k[[x_1, \dots, x_n]] \to \widehat{R}$ by $f = \sum_{j \geq 0} f_j(x_1, \dots, x_n) \mapsto \sum_{j \geq 0} f_j(\xi_1, \dots, \xi_n)$. It is readily shown that ρ is well defined and that ρ is a ring homomorphism. We shall show that ρ is surjective. For each $r > 0$ and every element b_r of $\mathfrak{m}^r$, there exists a homogeneous polynomial $f_r(x_1, \dots, x_n)$

of degree r and with coefficients in k such that $b_r - f_r(\xi_1, \dots, \xi_r) \in \mathfrak{m}^{r+1}$. Every element of $\widehat{R}$ is represented by a Cauchy sequence $\{a_r\}_{r\ge 0}$ with $a_{r+1} - a_r \in \mathfrak{m}^{r+1}$ for each $r \ge 0$. Then choose $f_r(x_1, \dots, x_r) \in k[x_1, \dots, x_n]_r$ so that

$$a_r - \sum_{j=0}^{r} f_j(\xi_1, \dots, \xi_n) \in \mathfrak{m}^{r+1} \quad (\text{for each } r \ge 0).$$

Set $f = \sum_{j\ge 0} f_j$. Then the Cauchy sequence $\{a_r\}_{r\ge 0}$ converges to $\rho(f)$ in $\widehat{R}$. So ρ is surjective. □

The next result is called the *altitude theorem of Krull*. We refer to [7, p. 26] for a proof, though the proof is not hard.

LEMMA 6.8. *Let R be a noetherian ring. Let I be an ideal of R which is generated by n elements. Then every minimal prime divisor $\mathfrak{p}$ of I has* $\operatorname{ht}(\mathfrak{p}) \le n$. *In particular, if $(R, \mathfrak{m})$ is a noetherian local ring, we have* $\dim R \le \dim_{R/\mathfrak{m}}(\mathfrak{m}/\mathfrak{m}^2)$. (*Henceforth, we denote K-*$\dim R$ *also by* $\dim R$.)

The next result is a significant one in the theory of commutative algebras.

LEMMA 6.9. *Let $(R, \mathfrak{m})$ be a noetherian local ring with $d = \dim R > 0$. Then there exist d elements $a_1, \dots, a_d$ of $\mathfrak{m}$ such that the ideal $(a_1, \cdots, a_d)$ is a primary ideal belonging to $\mathfrak{m}$.*

PROOF. Let $\mathfrak{p}_{01}, \dots, \mathfrak{p}_{0r_0}$ exhaust minimal prime ideals of R. Then $\mathfrak{m} \supsetneqq \bigcup_{i=1}^{r_0} \mathfrak{p}_{0i}$. (In general, for prime ideals $\mathfrak{p}_1, \dots, \mathfrak{p}_t$ and $\mathfrak{p}, \mathfrak{p}_i \not\subset \mathfrak{p}_j$ $(i \ne j)$ and $\mathfrak{p} \subseteq \bigcup_{i=1}^{t} \mathfrak{p}_i$ imply $\mathfrak{p} \subseteq \mathfrak{p}_i$ (for some i). In fact, if $\mathfrak{p} \not\subset \mathfrak{p}_i$ for each i, $\mathfrak{p} \cap \mathfrak{p}_1 \cdots \cap \check{\mathfrak{p}}_i \cap \cdots \cap \mathfrak{p}_t \not\subset \mathfrak{p}_i$ for each i. So there is some $x_i \in \mathfrak{p} \cap \mathfrak{p}_1 \cap \cdots \cap \check{\mathfrak{p}}_i \cap \cdots \cap \mathfrak{p}_t$ and $x \notin \mathfrak{p}_i$. Set $y = x_1 + \cdots + x_t$. Then $y \notin \bigcup_{i=1}^{t} \mathfrak{p}_i$ and $y \in \mathfrak{p}$. This is absurd.) Let a be an element of $\mathfrak{m}$, not in $\bigcup_{i=1}^{r_0} \mathfrak{p}_{0i}$, and let $\mathfrak{p}_{11}, \dots, \mathfrak{p}_{1r_1}$ exhaust minimal prime divisors of $a_1 R$. Then $\operatorname{ht}(\mathfrak{p}_{1i}) = 1$ for each i. In fact, $\operatorname{ht}(\mathfrak{p}_{1i}) \le 1$ by the altitude theorem. If $\operatorname{ht}(\mathfrak{p}_{1i}) = 0$, then $\mathfrak{p}_{1i}$ is a minimal prime ideal. This contradicts the hypothesis $a \notin \bigcup_{i=1}^{r_0} \mathfrak{p}_{0i}$. For $s < d$, suppose we have chosen elements $a_1, \dots, a_s$ in such a way that $\operatorname{ht}(\mathfrak{p}_{sj}) = s$ for any one of minimal prime divisors $\mathfrak{p}_{s1}, \dots, \mathfrak{p}_{sr_s}$ of the ideal $(a_1, \dots, a_s)$. We choose an element a_{s+1} of $\mathfrak{m}$, not in $\bigcup_{i=1}^{r_s} \mathfrak{p}_{si}$. (If $\mathfrak{m} = \bigcup_{i=1}^{r_s} \mathfrak{p}_{si}$, then $\mathfrak{m} = \mathfrak{p}_{sj}$ (for some j) by the above reasoning, and this contradicts the hypothesis that $d = \operatorname{ht}(\mathfrak{m})$.) Let $\mathfrak{p}_{s+1.1}, \dots, \mathfrak{p}_{s+1.r_s+1}$ exhaust minimal prime divisors of the ideal $(a_1, \dots, a_{s+1})$. Then $\operatorname{ht}(\mathfrak{p}_{s+1.i}) = s + 1$ for each i. In fact, $\operatorname{ht}(\mathfrak{p}_{s+1.i}) \le s + 1$ by the altitude theorem. Since $(a_1, \dots, a_s) \subseteq \mathfrak{p}_{s+1.i}$, we have $\mathfrak{p}_{s+1.i} \supseteq \mathfrak{p}_{s.j}$ for some j. Hence, $\mathfrak{p}_{s+1.i} \ge s$. If $\operatorname{ht}(\mathfrak{p}_{s+1.i}) = s$, then $\mathfrak{p}_{s+1.i} = \mathfrak{p}_{s.j}$, which contradicts the choice of a_{s+1}. Thus, if we choose $a_1, \dots, a_d$ inductively as above, then $\mathfrak{m}$ is the unique minimal prime divisor of the ideal $(a_1, \dots, a_d)$. Hence, if we consider a primary ideal decomposition of $(a_1, \dots, a_d)$, we see that $(a_1, \dots, a_d)$ is a primary ideal belonging to $\mathfrak{m}$. □

DEFINITION 6.10. Let $(R, \mathfrak{m})$ be a noetherian local ring. A collection $\{a_1, \dots, a_d\}$ of elements of $\mathfrak{m}$ is called a *system of parameters* of R if $d = K\text{-}\dim R$ and $\mathfrak{m} = \sqrt{(a_1, \dots, a_d)}$. By Lemma 6.9, there exists a system of parameters. If we can choose a system of parameters $\{a_1, \dots, a_d\}$ so that $\mathfrak{m} = (a_1, \dots, a_d)$, we call R a *regular local ring*, and we call $\{a_1, \dots, a_d\}$ a *regular system of parameters* of R.

By a result of Auslander (Lemma 5.16), a regular local ring is a unique factorization domain, and hence, a normal ring.

LEMMA 6.11. *Let* $(R, \mathfrak{m})$ *be a noetherian local domain, and let* $\widehat{R}$ *be the* $\mathfrak{m}$*-adic completion of* R. *If* $\widehat{R}$ *is noetherian (this is, in fact, always the case* [7, (17.6)]), *we have* $\text{K-dim}\,\widehat{R} = \text{K-dim}\,R$.

PROOF. Our proof proceeds by induction on $d := \text{K-dim}\,R$. If $d = 0$, the zero ideal (0) is a primary ideal belonging to $\mathfrak{m}$. Hence, $\mathfrak{m}^N = (0)$ for some $N > 0$. So the $\mathfrak{m}$-adic topology on R is nothing but the discrete topology. So $\widehat{R} = R$. Suppose $d > 0$, and let $\{a_1, \dots, a_d\}$ be a system of parameters of R. Then $\mathfrak{m}^N \subseteq I := (a_1, \dots, a_d)$ for some $N > 0$. Since $\hat{\mathfrak{m}} = \mathfrak{m}\widehat{R}$ (Theorem 6.4), we have $\hat{\mathfrak{m}}^N \subseteq I\widehat{R}$. So by the altitude theorem of Krull, we have $\text{K-dim}\,\widehat{R} \leq d$. Next note that a_1 is not a zero divisor of $\widehat{R}$. In fact, $a_1 \colon R \to R$ $(x \mapsto a_1 x)$ is an injection because R is an integral domain. Since $\widehat{R}$ is a flat R-module (Theorem 6.4), we infer that $a_1 \colon \widehat{R} \to \widehat{R}$ is an injection as well. Hence, a_1 is a nonzero divisor of $\widehat{R}$. This implies that every minimal prime divisor of $a_1\widehat{R}$ has height 1. (In fact, if $\mathfrak{P}$ is a minimal prime divisor of $a_1\widehat{R}$ with $\text{ht}(\mathfrak{P}) = 0$, then $\mathfrak{P} = ((0) \colon \hat{x})$ (I.1.23). Hence, a_1 becomes a zero divisor which is a contradiction.) It follows that $\text{K-dim}\,\widehat{R}/a_1\widehat{R} \leq \text{K-dim}\,\widehat{R} - 1$. Suppose $\text{K-dim}\,\widehat{R}/a_1\widehat{R} \leq \text{K-dim}\,\widehat{R} - 2$. Then we can choose elements $\widehat{a_2}, \dots, \widehat{a_s}$ $(s = \text{K-dim}\,\widehat{R}/a_1\widehat{R} + 1)$ of $\hat{\mathfrak{m}}$ so that their residue classes modulo $a_1\widehat{R}$ constitute a system of parameters of $\widehat{R}/a_1\widehat{R}$. The ideal $(a_1, \hat{a}_2, \dots, \hat{a}_s)$ is then a primary ideal belonging to $\hat{\mathfrak{m}}$. By virtue of the altitude theorem, we have $\text{K-dim}\,\widehat{R} \leq s$ while $s = \text{K-dim}\,\widehat{R}/a_1\widehat{R} + 1 \leq \text{K-dim}\,\widehat{R} - 1$ by the hypothesis. This is a contradiction. So we know that $\text{K-dim}\,\widehat{R}/a_1\widehat{R} = \text{K-dim}\,\widehat{R} - 1$. By means of Theorem 6.4 (4), $\widehat{R}/a_1\widehat{R}$ is the $(\mathfrak{m}/a_1R)$-adic completion of R/a_1R. We can show by the argument above that $\text{K-dim}\,R/a_1R = d - 1$. The induction hypothesis implies that $\text{K-dim}\,\widehat{R}/a_1\widehat{R} = \text{K-dim}\,R/a_1R = d - 1$. Hence, $\text{K-dim}\,\widehat{R} = \text{K-dim}\,R$. □

As a conclusion of the above arguments, we obtain the following result.

THEOREM 6.12. *Let* $(R, \mathfrak{m})$ *be a noetherian local domain such that* R *contains the residue field* $k = R/\mathfrak{m}$ *and* $d = \text{K-dim}\,R$. *Then the following conditions are equivalent to each other*:

(1) R *is a regular local ring.*

(2) $\widehat{R} \cong k[[x_1, \dots, x_d]]$.

PROOF. (1) *implies* (2). Let $\{a_1, \dots, a_d\}$ be a regular system of parameters of R. By Corollary 6.7 there exists a surjective ring homomorphism $\rho \colon k[[x_1, \dots, x_d]] \to \widehat{R}$ such that $\rho(x_i) = a_i$ $(1 \leq i \leq d)$. In particular, $\widehat{R}$ is a noetherian ring. By Lemma 6.11, $\widehat{R}$ and $k[[x_1, \dots, x_d]]$ have the same Krull dimension d. So ρ must be an injection.

(2) *implies* (1). $\widehat{R}/\mathfrak{m}\widehat{R} = k$, and $\mathfrak{m}/\mathfrak{m}^2 \cong \mathfrak{m}\widehat{R}/(\mathfrak{m}\widehat{R})^2$ as k-vector spaces. Hence, $\dim_k \mathfrak{m}/\mathfrak{m}^2 = d$. By virtue of Corollary 6.7 (1), we know that R has a regular system of parameters. □

We now consider the case where $(R, \mathfrak{m})$ is a local ring of an algebraic variety. Let X be an irreducible reduced algebraic scheme defined over a field k, let P be a k-rational point of X, let $R = \mathcal{O}_{X,P}$ and let $\mathfrak{m} = \mathfrak{m}_{X,P}$. R is then a noetherian local domain which contains the residue field k. We say that P is a *nonsingular* (or *smooth*) *point* of X if R is a regular local ring, and a *singular point* of X otherwise. If k is an algebraically closed field, then X is an algebraic variety defined over k and every closed point of X is a k-rational point. If every closed point is a nonsingular point, then we say that X is a *nonsingular algebraic variety*. Otherwise, we set $\operatorname{Sing} X = \{P \in X(k); P \text{ is a singular point of } X\}$ and call it the *singular locus* of X. We quote the next result without giving a proof (cf. [7, (28.3)]).

LEMMA 6.13. *Let $(R, \mathfrak{m})$ be a regular local ring, and let $\mathfrak{p}$ be a prime ideal. Then $R_{\mathfrak{p}}$ is a regular local ring.*

Let us go back again to the set-up before Lemma 6.13. Replacing X by an affine open neighborhood of P, we assume that X is a closed subscheme of the affine space $\mathbf{A}^n_k$. Choose the coordinate functions $x_1, \dots, x_n$ of $\mathbf{A}^n_k$ so that the point P is given by $(0, \dots, 0)$. Set $\mathscr{O} = \mathscr{O}_{\mathbf{A}^n, P}$. We have the natural surjective ring homomorphism

$$\rho \colon \widehat{\mathscr{O}} = k[[x_1, \dots, x_n]] \to \widehat{R} \to 0$$

which is induced by the natural ring homomorphism

$$\sigma \colon k[x_1, \dots, x_n] \to \Gamma(X, \mathscr{O}_X).$$

So if we set $I = \operatorname{Ker} \sigma$, then we have $\operatorname{Ker} \rho = I\widehat{\mathscr{O}}$. Let $\{f_i; 1 \le i \le N\}$ be a system of generators of I. Since $f_i(0, \dots, 0) = 0$ for each i, f_i, viewed as an element of $\widehat{\mathscr{O}}$, is expressed as

$$f_i = \sum_{j=1}^{n} \alpha_{ij} x_j + (\text{terms of degree } \ge 2).$$

We let M the $(N \times n)$-matrix (α_{ij}).

LEMMA 6.14. *If $r = \operatorname{rank} M$, there exists a surjective ring homomorphism from a formal power series ring to $\widehat{R}$*

$$\pi \colon k[[y_1, \dots, y_{n-r}]] \to \widehat{R} \to 0.$$

Let $d = \dim R$. If $r = n - d$, then R is a regular local ring. Conversely, if R is a regular local ring, we have $r = n - d$.

PROOF. After a suitable change of indices, we may assume that $S := (\alpha_{ij})_{1 \le i, j \le r}$ is an invertible matrix. Then replacing ${}^t(f_1, \dots, f_r)$ by $(S^{-1})^t (f_1, \dots, f_r)$, we may assume that S is the identity matrix. Let $y_i = x_{r+i}$ $(1 \le i \le n - r)$ and $y_{n-r+i} = f_i$ $(1 \le i \le r)$. Then we have $y_{n-r+i} = x_i +$ (terms of degree ≥ 2) for $1 \le i \le r$. These relations entail

$$x_i - y_{n-r+i} - g_i \in ((x_1, \dots, x_n)\widehat{\mathscr{O}})^{c+1}$$

for an arbitrary integer $c \gg 0$, where g_i is a polynomial in $y_1, \dots, y_n$ and $g_i = g_{i2} + \dots + g_{ic}$ with g_{ij} the homogeneous part of g_i of degree j. Hence, $\widehat{\mathscr{O}} = k[[y_1, \dots, y_n]]$. In particular, $I\widehat{\mathscr{O}} = (y_{n-r+1}, \dots, y_n, f_{r+1}, \dots, f_N)\widehat{\mathscr{O}}$. So we obtain the natural surjective ring homomorphism $\pi \colon k[[y_1, \dots, y_{n-r}]] \to \widehat{R}$. Let $\mathfrak{n} = (x_1, \dots, x_n)\widehat{\mathscr{O}}$. The existence of π implies $n - r \ge d$. If $r < n - d$, then the above argument implies $\dim_k \mathfrak{n}/I\widehat{\mathscr{O}} + \mathfrak{n}^2 = n - r > d$. Meanwhile, $\mathfrak{m}/\mathfrak{m}^2$ is isomorphic to $\mathfrak{n}/I\widehat{\mathscr{O}} + \mathfrak{n}^2$. Hence, $\dim_k \mathfrak{m}/\mathfrak{m}^2 > d$. So R does not have a regular system of parameters. So $r \ge n - d$ provided R is a regular local ring. Therefore, $r = n - d$. □

If we regard f_i $(1 \le i \le N)$ as the elements of $k[x_1, \ldots, x_n]$, then the matrix $M = (\alpha_{ij})$ is equal to the following matrix:

$$M = \begin{pmatrix} \frac{\partial f_1}{\partial x_1}(P) & \cdots & \frac{\partial f_1}{\partial x_n}(P) \\ \cdots & \cdots & \cdots \\ \frac{\partial f_N}{\partial x_1}(P) & \cdots & \frac{\partial f_N}{\partial x_n}(P) \end{pmatrix},$$

where $\frac{\partial f_i}{\partial x_j}(P)$ is the partial derivative of f_i with respect to x_j evaluated at the point P. Let $Q = (c_1, \ldots, c_n)$ be another k-rational point of X. Then $\{x_1 - c_1, \ldots, x_n - c_n\}$ is a regular system of parameters of $\mathscr{O}_{\mathbf{A}^n, Q}$, and the following is an exact sequence

$$0 \to I\widehat{\mathscr{O}}_{\mathbf{A}^n, Q} \to \widehat{\mathscr{O}}_{\mathbf{A}^n, Q} \xrightarrow{\rho_Q} \widehat{\mathscr{O}}_{X, Q} \to 0,$$

where $\widehat{\mathscr{O}}_{\mathbf{A}^n, Q} = k[[z_1, \ldots, z_n]]$ $(z_i = x_i - c_i)$. The system of generators $\{f_i; 1 \le i \le N\}$ of I is expressed as $\{g_i; 1 \le i \le N\}$ after the change of variables $g_i(z_1, \ldots, z_n) = f_i(z_1 + c_1, \ldots, z_n + c_n)$. Consider then the $(N \times n)$ matrix $(\frac{\partial g_i}{\partial z_j}(Q))$. By a simple computation, we have

$$\frac{\partial g_i}{\partial z_j} = \frac{\partial f_i(z_1 + c_1, \ldots, z_n + c_n)}{\partial z_j} = \frac{\partial f_i}{\partial x_j}(z_1 + c_1, \ldots, z_n + c_n),$$

where

$$\frac{\partial g_i}{\partial z_j}(0, \ldots, 0) = \frac{\partial f_i}{\partial x_j}(c_1, \ldots, c_n) = \frac{\partial f_i}{\partial x_j}(Q).$$

Hence, $\mathscr{O}_{X, Q}$ is a regular local ring if and only if

$$\operatorname{rank}\left(\frac{\partial g_i}{\partial z_j}(0, \ldots, 0)\right) = \operatorname{rank}\left(\frac{\partial f_i}{\partial x_j}(Q)\right) = n - d.$$

Let J be the ideal of $k[x_1, \ldots, x_n]$ generated by all $(n-d) \times (n-d)$-minors of the $(N \times n)$-matrix $(\frac{\partial f_i}{\partial x_j})$. If k is an algebraically closed field, then the set of singular points (called the *singular locus*) of X is a closed subscheme of X defined by the ideal $I + J$. Summarizing the above observations, we obtain the following result.

THEOREM 6.15. *Let X be an algebraic variety of dimension d defined over an algebraically closed field k. Then the following assertions hold*:

(1) *Suppose X is defined by an ideal $(f_1, \ldots, f_N)$ as a closed subscheme of the affine space $\mathbf{A}_k^n = \operatorname{Spec} k[x_1, \ldots, x_n]$. Then a closed point P of X is a nonsingular point if and only if* $\operatorname{rank}((\frac{\partial f_i}{\partial x_j}(P)) = n - d$.

(2) *The singular locus* $\operatorname{Sing} X$ *of X is a closed subset. Furthermore,* $\operatorname{Sing}(X)_{\text{red}} = \{P \in X; \mathscr{O}_{X,P}$ *is not a regular local ring*$\}$ *as a closed subscheme. Hence* $\operatorname{codim}_X \operatorname{Sing}(X) \ge 2$ *provided X is a normal algebraic variety.*

We omit the proof of the latter half of the assertion (2). If X is normal the local ring $\mathscr{O}_{X,\xi}$ of a point ξ of codimension 1 is a discrete valuation ring, so $\xi \notin \operatorname{Sing}(X)_{\text{red}}$. Hence, $\operatorname{codim}_X \operatorname{Sing}(X) \ge 2$. The result given in the assertion (1) is called the *Jacobian criterion of nonsingularity*.

Hereafter in the present chapter, we shall define the sheaf of differential forms $\Omega_{X/k}$ attached to an algebraic variety X and discuss the nonsingularity of X in terms of $\Omega_{X/k}$. Let B be a ring, and let A be a B-algebra. Let M be an A-module. A homomorphism $\delta\colon A \to M$ of B-modules is called a B*-derivation* of A (with values in M) if it satisfies the condition that

$$\delta(xy) = x\delta(y) + y\delta(x), \quad \text{for all } x, y \in A.$$

This condition implies $\delta(b) = 0$ for each $b \in B$. We denote by $\mathrm{Der}_B(A, M)$ the set of B-derivations of A with values in M. If we define $a\delta + a'\delta'\colon A \to M$ by $(a\delta + a'\delta')(x) = a\delta(x) + a'\delta'(x)$ for $\delta, \delta' \in \mathrm{Der}_B(A, M)$ and $a, a' \in A$, then we have $a\delta + a'\delta' \in \mathrm{Der}_B(A, M)$. With this operation, $\mathrm{Der}_B(A, M)$ is an A-module. For an A-module homomorphism $f\colon M \to N$, define an A-module homomorphism $f_*\colon \mathrm{Der}_B(A, M) \to \mathrm{Der}_B(A, N)$ by $f_*(\delta)(x) = f(\delta(x))$ ($\delta \in \mathrm{Der}_B(A, M)$, $x \in A$). Clearly, $(g \cdot f)_* = g_* \cdot f_*$ for $f\colon M \to N$ and $g\colon N \to P$, and $(1_M)_*$ is the identity morphism. In other words, the correspondence $M \mapsto \mathrm{Der}_B(A, M)$ is a covariant functor from the category of A-modules into itself. We shall show that there exist an A-module (denoted by $\Omega_{A/B}$) and a B-derivation $d\colon A \to \Omega_{A/B}$ such that $\mathrm{Hom}_A(\Omega_{A/B}, M) \xrightarrow{\sim} \mathrm{Der}_B(A, M)(f \mapsto f \cdot d)$ for every A-module M. The A-module $\Omega_{A/B}$ is constructed as follows:

The B-algebra $A \otimes_B A$ is regarded as an A-module via $a(x \otimes y) = ax \otimes y$ ($a, x, y \in A$). The multiplication $\mu\colon A \otimes_B A \to A$, $\mu(x \otimes y) = xy$ is then an A-module homomorphism. Set $I = \mathrm{Ker}\,\mu$. We have an exact sequence

$$0 \to I \to A \otimes_B A \xrightarrow{\mu} A \to 0.$$

Since I is an ideal of $A \otimes_B A$, I/I^2 is defined as an A-module.

LEMMA 6.16. (1) *The ideal I is generated as an A-module by $\{a \otimes 1 - 1 \otimes a; a \in A\}$.*

(2) *Set $da = a \otimes 1 - 1 \otimes a \pmod{I^2}$. Then the A-module I/I^2 is generated by $\{da; a \in A\}$. The mapping $d\colon A \to I/I^2$, $a \mapsto da$, is a B-derivation of A.*

(3) *For an A-module M, define $\varphi\colon \mathrm{Hom}_A(I/I^2, M) \to \mathrm{Der}_B(A, M)$ by $f \mapsto f \cdot d$. Then φ is an A-isomorphism.*

PROOF. (1) We have $\sum_i a_i \otimes a_i' \in I$ if and only if $\sum_i a_i a_i' = 0$. Hence, $\sum_i a_i \otimes a_i' = -\sum_i a_i(a_i' \otimes 1 - 1 \otimes a_i')$.

(2) By (1), we know that the A-module I/I^2 is generated by $\{da; a \in A\}$. We have

$$\begin{aligned} d(aa') &= aa' \otimes 1 - 1 \otimes aa' \pmod{I^2} \\ &= a(a' \otimes 1 - 1 \otimes a') \\ &\qquad + a'(a \otimes 1 - 1 \otimes a) - (a \otimes 1 - 1 \otimes a)(a' \otimes 1 - 1 \otimes a') \pmod{I^2} \\ &= a\,da' + a'\,da, \\ d(ba) &= ba \otimes 1 - 1 \otimes ba \pmod{I^2} \\ &= b(a \otimes 1 - 1 \otimes a) \pmod{I^2} \\ &= b\,da \qquad (b \in B). \end{aligned}$$

Hence, d is a B-derivation.

(3) Suppose $f \cdot d = 0$ for $f \in \mathrm{Hom}_A(I/I^2, M)$. Since $\{da; a \in A\}$ generates the A-module I/I^2, we have $f = 0$. Hence, φ is injective. Given $\delta \in \mathrm{Der}_B(A, M)$, define $\tilde{f}\colon A \otimes_B A \to M$ by $\tilde{f}(a \otimes a') = -a\delta(a')$. Since $\tilde{f}(a \otimes 1 - 1 \otimes a) = \delta(a)$ and $\tilde{f}((a \otimes 1 - 1 \otimes a)(a' \otimes 1 - 1 \otimes a')) = a\delta(a') + a'\delta(a) - \delta(aa') = 0$, $\tilde{f}|_I$ induces

an A-module homomorphism $f: I/I^2 \to M$ such that $\delta = f \cdot d$. Therefore, φ is surjective. □

Denote the A-module I/I^2 by $\Omega_{A/B}$ and call it the *module of differential forms* (or simply the *differential module*) of the B-algebra A. $\Omega_{A/B}$ possesses the properties as listed in the following lemma.

LEMMA 6.17. (1) *Let B' be a B-algebra, and let $A' = A \otimes_B B'$. If we regard A' as a B'-algebra in the natural fashion, then we have an A'-module isomorphism $\Omega_{A'/B'} \cong \Omega_{A/B} \otimes_B B'$, where $\Omega_{A/B} \otimes_B B'$ is viewed as an A'-module via $(a \otimes b')(\delta \otimes b'') = a\delta \otimes b'b''$ $(a \in A, \delta \in \Omega_{A/B}, b', b'' \in B')$.*

(2) *Let S be a multiplicatively closed set of A. Then there is an $S^{-1}A$-module isomorphism $\Omega_{S^{-1}A/B} \cong S^{-1}\Omega_{A/B}$.*

(3) *Let C be a ring. Suppose B is a C-algebra. Then there exists the following natural, exact sequence of A-modules*:

$$(*) \qquad \Omega_{B/C} \otimes_B A \to \Omega_{A/C} \to \Omega_{A/B} \to 0.$$

(4) *Let J be an ideal of A, and let $R = A/J$. Then there exists the following natural, exact sequence of R-modules*:

$$(**) \qquad J/J^2 \xrightarrow{\overline{d}} \Omega_{A/B} \otimes_A R \to \Omega_{R/B} \to 0.$$

(5) *$\Omega_{A/B}$ is a finitely generated A-module provided A is a finitely generated B-algebra.*

PROOF. (1) Note that we have an isomorphism $\mathrm{Hom}_{A'}(\Omega_{A/B} \otimes_B B', M') \cong \mathrm{Hom}_A(\Omega_{A/B}, M')$ for an A'-module M'. Then we obtain an A'-module isomorphism $\Omega_{A'/B'} \cong \Omega_{A/B} \otimes_B B'$ as required if we show that the natural A'-module homomorphism α: $\mathrm{Der}_B(A, M') \to \mathrm{Der}_{B'}(A', M')$ is an isomorphism, where $\alpha(\delta)$ is defined by $\alpha(\delta)(a \otimes b') = (1 \otimes b')\delta(a)$ for $\delta \in \mathrm{Der}_B(A, M')$. It is readily shown that α is injective. Given $\delta' \in \mathrm{Der}_{B'}(A', M')$, define a B-homomorphism $\delta: A \to M'$ by $\delta(a) = \delta'(a \otimes 1)$ $(a \in A)$. Then $\delta \in \mathrm{Der}_B(A, M')$ and $\delta' = \alpha(\delta)$. Hence, α is surjective. So α is an isomorphism.

(2) Let M' be an $S^{-1}A$-module. Define an $S^{-1}A$-homomorphism β: $\mathrm{Der}_B(A, M') \to \mathrm{Der}_B(S^{-1}A, M')$ by $\beta(\delta)(a/s) = (s\delta(a) - a\delta(s))/s^2$ for $\delta \in \mathrm{Der}_B(A, M')$. We have only to prove that β is an isomorphism. The proof is easy, so we omit it.

(3) For an A-module M, we can define a sequence of A-modules in the natural fashion,

$$(*)' \qquad 0 \to \mathrm{Der}_B(A, M) \xrightarrow{\rho} \mathrm{Der}_C(A, M) \xrightarrow{\sigma} \mathrm{Der}_C(B, M).$$

Namely, ρ maps a B-derivation $\delta: A \to M$ to the same derivation viewed naturally as a C-derivation, and σ maps a C-derivation $\delta: A \to M$ to the restriction $\delta|_B$. Then we can readily show that $(*)'$ is an exact sequence. The sequence $(*)'$ gives rise to an exact sequence $(*)$. For example, if we identify $\mathrm{Der}_B(A, \Omega_{A/B})$ with $\mathrm{Hom}_A(\Omega_{A/B}, \Omega_{A/B})$ and $\mathrm{Der}_C(A, \Omega_{A/B})$ $\mathrm{Hom}_A(\Omega_{A/C}, \Omega_{A/B})$, then $\rho(1_{\Omega_{A/B}})$: $\Omega_{A/C} \to \Omega_{A/B}$ is the A-homomorphism considered in the sequence $(*)$. Similarly, the A-homomorphism $\sigma(1_{\Omega_{A/C}})$: $\Omega_{B/C} \otimes_B A \to \Omega_{A/C}$ is the one considered in the sequence $(*)$. The exactness of the sequence $(*)$ follows from the fact that the sequence $(*)'$ is exact for an arbitrary A-module M. The proof is left to the reader as an exercise.

(4) Taking the composite of the A-homomorphism $d: A \to \Omega_{A/B}$ with the natural homomorphisms, we obtain

$$d_J^R : J \to A \xrightarrow{d} \Omega_{A/B} \to \Omega_{A/B} \otimes_A R$$

such that $d_J^R(J^2) = (0)$. So we get an R-homomorphism $\overline{d}: J/J^2 \to \Omega_{A/B} \otimes_A R$. For an R-module M, $\overline{d}^*$: $\mathrm{Hom}_A(\Omega_{A/B}, M) \to \mathrm{Hom}_R(J/J^2, M)$ is given as $\overline{d}^*(\delta)(\overline{a}) = \delta(a)$ ($\delta \in \mathrm{Der}_B(A, M)$, $\overline{a} = a \pmod{J^2}$, $a \in J$), where $\mathrm{Hom}_A(\Omega_{A/B}, M)$ is identified with $\mathrm{Der}_B(A, M)$. In order to prove that the sequence $(**)$ is exact, we have only to show that the following sequence of R-modules

$$(**)' \qquad 0 \to \mathrm{Der}_B(R, M) \xrightarrow{\tau} \mathrm{Der}_B(A, M) \xrightarrow{\overline{d}^*} \mathrm{Hom}_R(J/J^2, M)$$

is exact for every R-module M, where τ is given as $\delta \mapsto \delta \cdot \pi$ with the natural residue homomorphism $\pi: A \to R$. It is easy to show that the sequence $(**)'$ is exact.

(5) By hypothesis, we can express A as the residue ring of a polynomial ring over B, $A = B[x_1, \dots, x_n]/J$. Note that $\Omega_{B[x_1,\dots,x_n]/B}$ is generated by $dx_1, \dots, dx_n$ as a $B[x_1, \dots, x_n]$-module. The exact sequence in the assertion (4) then asserts that $\Omega_{A/B}$ is a finitely generated A-module. □

Let $f: X \to Y$ be a morphism of schemes. Let y be a point of Y, let $V = \mathrm{Spec}(B)$ be an affine open neighborhood of y, and let $\mathfrak{U} = \{U_\lambda\}_{\lambda \in \Lambda}$ ($U_\lambda = \mathrm{Spec}(A_\lambda)$) be an affine open covering of $f^{-1}(V)$. Since A_λ is a B-algebra, we can define the differential module $\Omega_{A_\lambda/B}$. We denote by $\Omega_{U_\lambda/V}$ the quasicoherent Module $(\Omega_{A_\lambda/B})^\sim$ on U_λ. For $\lambda, \mu \in \Lambda$, let $U = \mathrm{Spec}(A) \subset U_\lambda \cap U_\mu$ be an affine open set. Consider quasi-coherent Modules $\Omega_{U/V} = (\Omega_{A/B})^\sim$ and $\Omega_{U_\lambda/V}|_U$ on U. There is a B-algebra homomorphism $A_\lambda \to A$, which induces an A-module homomorphism $\Omega_{A_\lambda/B} \otimes_{A_\lambda} A \to \Omega_{A/B}$, and hence, a homomorphism of $\mathscr{O}_U$-Modules $\theta_\lambda: \Omega_{U_\lambda/V}|_U \to \Omega_{U/V}$. If everything is restricted on an affine open set $D(h)$ of $U(\subset U_\lambda)$, then $\Omega_{U_\lambda/V}|_{D(h)} = \Omega^\sim_{A_\lambda[h^{-1}]/B}$ and $\Omega_{U/V}|_{D(h)} = (\Omega_{A[h^{-1}]/B})^\sim$, where $A_\lambda[h^{-1}] = A[h^{-1}]$. Hence, $\theta_\lambda|_U$ (and θ_λ) is an isomorphism. Thus, there is a natural isomorphism $\Omega_{U_\lambda/V}|_{U_\lambda \cap U_\mu} \cong \Omega_{U_\mu/V}|_{U_\lambda \cap U_\mu}$ (for each $\lambda, \mu \in \Lambda$). This way, the $\{\Omega_{U_\lambda/V}\}_{\lambda \in \Lambda}$ get patched together to form a quasicoherent $\mathscr{O}_X$-Module $\Omega_{X/Y}$. We call this $\mathscr{O}_X$-Module the *sheaf of differential forms* attached to the morphism of schemes f. We obtain the following lemma as a corollary of Lemma 6.17.

LEMMA 6.18. (1) *Let $q: Y' \to Y$ be a Y-scheme, let $X' = X \times_Y Y'$, and let $q' = X \times_Y q$. Then $\Omega_{X'/Y'} = q'^*\Omega_{X/Y}$.*

(2) *For an open set U of X, we have $\Omega_{U/Y} \cong \Omega_{X/Y}|_U$.*

(3) *Let $f: X \to Y$ and $g: Y \to Z$ be morphisms of schemes. Then we have the following natural exact sequence of quasi-coherent $\mathscr{O}_X$-Modules*:

$$f^*\Omega_{X/Y} \to \Omega_{X/Z} \to \Omega_{X/Y} \to 0.$$

(4) *Let F be a closed subscheme of X, and let $\mathscr{I}$ be the defining Ideal of F. Then we have the following exact sequence of quasicoherent $\mathscr{O}_X$-Modules*:

$$\mathscr{I}/\mathscr{I}^2 \to \Omega_{X/Y}|_F \to \Omega_{F/Y} \to 0.$$

(5) *Let $f: X \to Y$ be a finitely generated morphism. Then $\Omega_{X/Y}$ is a finitely generated $\mathscr{O}_X$-Module. In particular, if X is a noetherian scheme, $\Omega_{X/Y}$ is a coherent Module.*

PROOF. (1) Let $U = \mathrm{Spec}(A)$, $V = \mathrm{Spec}(B)$, and $V' = \mathrm{Spec}(B')$ be affine open sets of X, Y, and Y', respectively, such that $U \subseteq f^{-1}(V)$ and $V' \subseteq q^{-1}(V)$, and let $U' = U \times_V V'$. Then $\Omega_{X'/Y'}|_{U'} = (\Omega_{A'/B'})^{\sim}$ and $q'^*\Omega_{X/Y}|_{U'} = (\Omega_{A/B} \otimes_B B')^{\sim}$, where $A' = A \otimes_B B'$. By Lemma 6.17, $\Omega_{A'/B'} \cong \Omega_{A/B} \otimes_B B'$. Since X' is covered by affine open sets U' of this kind, we have an isomorphism $\Omega_{X'/Y'} \cong q'^*\Omega_{X/Y}$.

(2) Let $W = \mathrm{Spec}(A)$ be an affine open set of U such that $f(W)$ is contained in an affine open set $\mathrm{Spec}(B)$ of Y. Then the restrictions of $\Omega_{U/Y}$ and $\Omega_{X/Y}|_U$ onto W coincide with $(\Omega_{A/B})^{\sim}$.

(3) Let $U = \mathrm{Spec}(A)$, $V = \mathrm{Spec}(B)$, and $W = \mathrm{Spec}(C)$ be affine open sets of X, Y, and Z, respectively, such that $U \subseteq f^{-1}(V)$ and $V \subseteq g^{-1}(W)$. By virtue of Lemma 6.17, we have an exact sequence of A-modules

$$\Omega_{B/C} \otimes_B A \to \Omega_{A/C} \to \Omega_{A/B} \to 0.$$

This yields an exact sequence of $\mathscr{O}_U$-Modules

$$(f|_U)^*\Omega_{V/W} \xrightarrow{\varphi} \Omega_{U/W} \xrightarrow{\psi} \Omega_{U/V} \to 0.$$

Vary U on affine open sets of $f^{-1}(V)$ with V and W fixed, and then vary V on affine open sets of $q^{-1}(W)$ with W fixed, in order to patch together $\Omega_{U/V}, \Omega_{U/W}$, and $(f|_U)^*\Omega_{V/W}$. The homomorphisms φ and ψ are also patched up under these patching processes. Thus, we obtain the exact sequence in the assertion (3).

(4) By means of Lemma 6.17 (4), we patch up the exact sequences obtained locally, and thus obtain the exact sequence as required.

(5) $\Omega_{X/Y}$ is a quasicoherent $\mathscr{O}_X$-Module by the construction. If $f: X \to Y$ is a finitely generated morphism, then $\Omega_{X/Y}$ is a finitely generated $\mathscr{O}_X$-Module by Lemma 6.17 (5). □

LEMMA 6.19. *Let X be an irreducible, reduced algebraic scheme of dimension n defined over k. Then the following assertions hold*:

(1) *For a closed point x of X, put $\mathscr{O} = \mathscr{O}_{X,x}$, $\mathfrak{m} = \mathfrak{m}_{X,x}$, and $k(x) = \mathscr{O}/\mathfrak{m}$. If $k(x)$ is separable over k, we have*

$$\dim_{k(x)} \Omega_{X/k,x} \otimes_{\mathscr{O}} k(x) \leq \dim_{k(x)} \mathfrak{m}/\mathfrak{m}^2,$$

where $\Omega_{X/k,x}$ is the stalk of $\Omega_{X/k}$ at x.

(2) *Let $K = k(X)$ be the function field of X over k. If K/k is a separable extension, then we have*

$$n \leq \dim_{k(x)} \Omega_{X/k,x} \otimes_{\mathscr{O}} k(x).$$

PROOF. (1) Let L/k be an algebraic extension of fields. We shall show that L/k is separable if and only if $\Omega_{L/k} = (0)$.

"Only if" part. It suffices to show that $\mathrm{Der}_k(L, L) = (0)$. Let $\delta \in \mathrm{Der}_k(L, L)$. Let ξ be an element of L, and let $f(z)$ be the minimal equation of ξ over k. Since ξ is separable over k, $f'(\xi) \neq 0$. Meanwhile, $f'(\xi)\delta(\xi) = \delta(f(\xi)) = 0$. Hence, $\delta(\xi) = 0$. So $\delta = 0$.

"If" part. Suppose L/k is not separable. Then there are an intermediate field M/k and an $a \in M$ such that $L \neq M$ and $L = M(a^{1/p})$, where p is the characteristic of k. Let $\xi = a^{1/p}$. Then it is easy to show that $\mathrm{Der}_M(L, L) \neq (0)$. For example,

write $L = M[t]/(t^p - a)$. Then the M-derivation $\partial/\partial t$ on $M[t]$ induces a nontrivial M-derivation δ on L. (In fact, $\delta(\xi) = 1$.) The exact sequence

$$0 \to \mathrm{Der}_M(L, L) \to \mathrm{Der}_k(L, L) \to \mathrm{Der}_k(M, L)$$

then implies $\mathrm{Der}_k(L, L) \neq (0)$. Here we apply Lemma 6.17 (2) to $k(x) = \mathscr{O}/\mathfrak{m}$ to obtain an exact sequence of $k(x)$-modules

$$\mathfrak{m}/\mathfrak{m}^2 \to \Omega_{\mathscr{O}/k} \otimes_{\mathscr{O}} k(x) \to \Omega_{k(x)/k} \to 0,$$

where $\Omega_{k(x)/k} = (0)$ by virtue of the hypothesis that $k(x)/k$ is separable and the above remark. Since $\Omega_{X/k,x} \otimes_{\mathscr{O}} k(x) = \Omega_{\mathscr{O}/k} \otimes_{\mathscr{O}} k(x)$ by Lemma 6.17 (2), the exact sequence yields the inequality as required.

(2) Before starting our proof of the assertion, we shall make the following remark. Let A be a B-algebra and let M be an A-module. Define the multiplication law in a direct sum $A \oplus M$ of A-modules by $(a, u)(a', u') = (aa', au' + a'u)$, which makes $A \oplus M$ an A-algebra with the identity element $(1, 0)$. A is regarded as a subalgebra of $A \oplus M$ via the embedding $A \to A \oplus M$, $a \mapsto (a, 0)$. Hence, $A \oplus M$ is identified with $A + M\varepsilon$ by the mapping $(a, m) \mapsto a + m\varepsilon$, where we formally introduce an element ε with $\varepsilon^2 = 0$. Then $A \cong A + M\varepsilon/(\varepsilon)$, where $(\varepsilon) = M\varepsilon$. Consider the natural residue homomorphism $\pi\colon A + M\varepsilon \to A$, $a + m\varepsilon \mapsto a$. We call a B-algebra homomorphism $\Delta\colon A \to A + M\varepsilon$ a *B-lifting* of the identity mapping 1_A of A if Δ satisfies the condition $\pi \cdot \Delta = 1_A$. Then we can easily verify that there is a one-to-one correspondence between $\mathrm{Der}_B(A, M)$ and the set $\{\Delta;\ B\text{-lifting of } 1_A\}$ given by $\delta \mapsto \Delta_\delta$, where $\Delta_\delta(a) = a + \delta(a)\varepsilon$.

Now let $K = k(X)$. Since K/k is a separable extension by the hypothesis, there exists a transcendence basis $\{x_1, \ldots, x_n\}$ of K/k such that K is a separable algebraic extension of $K_0 = k(x_1, \ldots, x_n)$. By the remark given in (1), the exact sequence in Lemma 6.17 (3) gives rise to the following surjective homomorphism

$$\Omega_{K_0/k} \otimes_{K_0} K \to \Omega_{K/k} \to 0.$$

We shall show that this is indeed an isomorphism. For this, it suffices to show that the following injective homomorphism

$$0 \to \mathrm{Der}_k(K, K) \to \mathrm{Der}_k(K_0, K)$$

is surjective. Let $\delta_0 \in \mathrm{Der}_k(K_0, K)$. By the above remark, δ_0 corresponds to a k-lifting $\Delta_0\colon K_0 \to K_0 + K\varepsilon$ of 1_{K_0}. If there exists a k-lifting $\Delta\colon K \to K + K\varepsilon$ of 1_K such that $\Delta_0 = \Delta|_{K_0}$, then the derivation $\delta \in \mathrm{Der}_k(K, K)$ corresponding to Δ induces δ_0, i.e., $\delta|_{K_0} = \delta_0$. We shall show the existence of Δ. Since K/K_0 is a separable algebraic extension, we have $K = K_0(\theta) = K_0[t]/(f(t))$, where $f(t)$ is a separable polynomial, i.e., $f'(\theta) \neq 0$. Let $f^{\delta_0}(t)$ be the polynomial obtained by applying δ_0 to the coefficients of $f(t)$. Let $\Delta(\theta) = \theta - (f^{\delta_0}(\theta)/f'(\theta))\varepsilon$. Then it is readily ascertained by a simple computation that $\Delta(f(\theta)) := f^{\Delta_0}(\Delta(\theta)) = 0$, where f^{Δ_0} is the polynomial with coefficients in $K_0 + K\varepsilon$ obtained by applying Δ_0 to the coefficients of f. Thus, we know that Δ_0 is extended to $\Delta\colon K \to K + K\varepsilon$. Consequently, we have $\Omega_{K_0/k} \otimes_{K_0} K \cong \Omega_{K/k}$. Meanwhile, with the notations in (1), we have $\Omega_{\mathscr{O}/k} \otimes_{\mathscr{O}} K = \Omega_{K/k}$ (Lemma 6.17 (2)). We have, therefore,

$$\dim_{K_0} \Omega_{K_0/k} = \dim_K \Omega_{K/k} = \dim_K \Omega_{\mathscr{O}/k} \otimes_{\mathscr{O}} K \leq \dim_{k(x)} \Omega_{\mathscr{O}/k} \otimes_{\mathscr{O}} k(x).$$

(In order to prove the last inequality, one may use the following remark: Let M be a finitely generated $\mathscr{O}$-module, and let $u_1, \ldots, u_r$ be elements of M such that $\overline{u}_1, \ldots, \overline{u}_r$ ($\overline{u}_i = u_i \pmod{\mathfrak{m}M}$) form a linear independence basis of the $k(x)$-module $M/\mathfrak{m}M$. Then $M = \sum_{i=1}^r \mathscr{O}u_i$ by virtue of Nakayama's lemma.) Here it is easy to show that $\mathrm{Der}_k(K_0, K_0) = \mathrm{Der}_k(k[x_1, \ldots, x_n], K_0) = K_0\partial_1 + \cdots + K_0\partial_n$ ($\partial_i = \frac{\partial}{\partial x_i}$) and $\partial_1, \ldots, \partial_n$ are linearly independent over K_0. For example, $\partial_1, \ldots, \partial_n$ are linearly independent because $a_1\partial_1 + \cdots + a_n\partial_n = 0$ ($a_i \in K_0$) entails $(a_1\partial_1 + \cdots + a_n\partial_n)(x_i) = a_i = 0$. Hence, $n = \dim_{K_0} \Omega_{K_0/k}$. □

LEMMA 6.20. *With the same situation as in Lemma* 6.19, *the following assertions hold*:

(1) *For a k-rational point $x \in X$, $\Omega_{X/k,x} \otimes_{\mathscr{O}} k \cong \mathfrak{m}/\mathfrak{m}^2$.*

(2) *Let X be an algebraic variety defined over k. In the case x is a k-rational point of X, X is nonsingular at the point x if and only if $\Omega_{X/k,x}$ is a free $\mathscr{O}_{X,x}$-module of* rank n $(= \dim X)$.

PROOF. (1) It suffices to show that the following homomorphism of k-modules

$$\overline{d}^*: \mathrm{Der}_k(\mathscr{O}, k) \to \mathrm{Hom}_k(\mathfrak{m}/\mathfrak{m}^2, k)$$

is an isomorphism, where $\overline{d}^*$ assigns to $\delta \in \mathrm{Der}_k(\mathscr{O}, k)$ an element $u := \overline{d}^*(\delta)$ such that $u(\overline{z}) = \delta(z)$ ($z \in \mathfrak{m}, \overline{z} = z \pmod{\mathfrak{m}^2}$). Clearly, $\overline{d}^*$ is injective. Conversely, given $u \in \mathrm{Hom}_k(\mathfrak{m}/\mathfrak{m}^2, k)$, define a homomorphism of k-modules $\delta: \mathscr{O} \to k$ by $\delta(\alpha) = 0$ (for each $\alpha \in k$) and $\delta(a) = u(\overline{a})$ ($a \in \mathfrak{m}$, $\overline{a} = a \pmod{\mathfrak{m}^2}$). Then δ is a k-derivation of $\mathscr{O}$ with values in k. By the construction, $\overline{d}^*(\delta) = u$. Hence, $\overline{d}^*$ is an isomorphism.

(2) *The "only if" part.* Since $\mathscr{O}_{X,x}$ is a regular local ring, we have $\dim_k \mathfrak{m}/\mathfrak{m}^2 = n = \dim X$. Moreover, the equalities hold in the assertions (1), (2) of Lemma 6.19. By Nakayama's lemma, we have $\Omega_{\mathscr{O}/k} = \mathscr{O}\delta_1 + \cdots + \mathscr{O}\delta_n$. Since $\Omega_{K/k} = \Omega_{\mathscr{O}/k} \otimes_{\mathscr{O}} K$, we have $\Omega_{K/k} = K\delta_1 + \cdots + K\delta_n$. Since $\dim_K \Omega_{K/k} = n, \delta_1, \ldots, \delta_n$ are linearly independent over K. So $\{\delta_1, \ldots, \delta_n\}$ is a free basis of $\Omega_{\mathscr{O}/k}$.

The "if" part. By the hypothesis, $\dim_k \mathfrak{m}/\mathfrak{m}^2 = n$. So $\mathfrak{m}$ is generated by n elements by virtue of Nakayama's lemma. Hence, $\mathscr{O}$ is a regular local ring. So x is a nonsingular point of X. □

As a corollary of Lemma 6.20 we obtain the following result.

THEOREM 6.21. *Let k be an algebraically closed field, and let X be an algebraic variety of dimension n defined over k. Then X is nonsingular if and only if $\Omega_{X/k}$ is a locally free $\mathscr{O}_X$-Module of rank n.*

PROOF. The result follows straightforwardly from Lemma 6.20 if we note that the set $X(k)$ of k-rational points is dense in X and that a quasicoherent $\mathscr{O}_X$-Module $\mathscr{F}$ is a locally free $\mathscr{O}_X$-Module of rank n if and only if $\mathscr{F}_x$ is a free $\mathscr{O}_{X,x}$-Module for each $x \in X(k)$. □

Let k be an algebraically closed field, and let X be an algebraic variety defined over k. As shown in Lemmas 6.19 and 6.20, $\Omega_{X/k,x} \otimes_{\mathscr{O}} k \cong \mathfrak{m}/\mathfrak{m}^2$ and $\mathrm{Der}_k(\mathscr{O}, k) \cong (\mathfrak{m}/\mathfrak{m}^2)^* := \mathrm{Hom}_k(\mathfrak{m}/\mathfrak{m}^2, k)$ for a closed point x of X. We call $(\mathfrak{m}/\mathfrak{m}^2)^*$ the *Zariski tangent space* of X at the point x. Let $k[\varepsilon] = k + k\varepsilon$ ($\varepsilon^2 = 0$) and let $\mathrm{Hom}_{k\text{-alg}}(\mathscr{O}, k[\varepsilon])$ be the set of k-algebra homomorphisms $\varphi: \mathscr{O} \to k[\varepsilon]$ such that

$$\varphi(a) \pmod{\varepsilon} = a \pmod{\mathfrak{m}} \quad \text{for each } a \in \mathscr{O}.$$

As shown in the proof of Lemma 6.19 (2), there is then a one-to-one correspondence between $\mathrm{Hom}_{k\text{-alg}}(\mathscr{O}, k[\varepsilon])$ and $\mathrm{Der}_k(\mathscr{O}, k)$. Given $\varphi \in \mathrm{Hom}_{k\text{-alg}}(\mathscr{O}, k[\varepsilon])$, the associated morphism of schemes ${}^a\varphi\colon \operatorname{Spec} k[\varepsilon] \to X$ maps the unique point of $\operatorname{Spec} k[\varepsilon]$ to the point x of X and the "tangent vector" ε^* (= the dual element of ε) of $\operatorname{Spec} k[\varepsilon]$ to a "tangent vector" of X at x. Conversely, any morphism of k-schemes $\mu\colon \operatorname{Spec} k[\varepsilon] \to X$, which maps the unique point of $\operatorname{Spec} k[\varepsilon]$ to x, is written as $\mu = {}^a\varphi$ for $\varphi \in \mathrm{Hom}_{k\text{-alg}}(\mathscr{O}, k[\varepsilon])$.

LEMMA 6.22. *Let k be an algebraically closed field, let X be a nonsingular algebraic variety of dimension n, let Y be an algebraic subvariety of dimension r in X, and let $\mathscr{J}$ be the defining (radical) Ideal of Y. Then the following conditions are equivalent to each other*:

(1) *Y is a nonsingular algebraic variety.*

(2) *The sequence of $\mathscr{O}_Y$-Modules*

$$0 \to \mathscr{J}/\mathscr{J}^2 \xrightarrow{\eta} \Omega_{X/k}|_Y \to \Omega_{Y/k} \to 0$$

is an exact sequence, and $\mathscr{J}/\mathscr{J}^2$ is locally a direct summand of $\Omega_{X/k}|_Y$. Namely, there exists an open covering $\{V_\lambda\}_{\lambda\in\Lambda}$ of Y such that $(\mathscr{J}/\mathscr{J}^2)|_{V_\lambda}$ is isomorphic (via η) to a direct summand of $\Omega_{X/k}|_{V_\lambda}$ for each λ.

(3) *For each $y \in Y(k)$, the sequence of k-modules*

$$0 \to (\mathscr{J}/\mathscr{J}^2)_y \otimes k \xrightarrow{\overline{\eta}} (\Omega_{X/k}|_Y)_y \otimes k \to \Omega_{Y/k,y} \otimes k \to 0$$

is an exact sequence.

PROOF. (2) *implies* (3). Obvious.

(3) *implies* (1). For $y \in Y(k)$, set $A = \mathscr{O}_{X,y}$, $R = \mathscr{O}_{Y,y}$, $J = \mathscr{J}_y$, $\mathfrak{m} = \mathfrak{m}_{X,y}$, and $\mathfrak{n} = \mathfrak{m}/J$. The exact sequence in (3) coincides with the following exact sequence

$$0 \to J/\mathfrak{m}J \xrightarrow{\overline{\eta}} \mathfrak{m}/\mathfrak{m}^2 \to \mathfrak{n}/\mathfrak{n}^2 \to 0.$$

Since $\overline{\eta}$ is injective, we have $J \cap \mathfrak{m}^2 = \mathfrak{m}J$. On the other hand, $\dim_k \mathfrak{m}/\mathfrak{m}^2 = n$ and $\dim_k \mathfrak{n}/\mathfrak{n}^2 \ge r$ by Lemmas 6.19 and 6.20. Let $s = \dim_k J/\mathfrak{m}J$. Then we can choose a system of parameters $\{a_1, \dots, a_n\}$ of $\mathfrak{m}$ satisfying the following two conditions:

(i) $a_i \in J (1 \le i \le s)$ and $a_i \pmod{\mathfrak{m}^2}$ $(1 \le i \le s)$ constitute a basis of $J/\mathfrak{m}J$,

(ii) the images of $a_i \pmod{\mathfrak{m}^2}$ $(s+1 \le i \le n)$ in $\mathfrak{n}/\mathfrak{n}^2$ constitute a basis of $\mathfrak{n}/\mathfrak{n}^2$.

Applying Nakayama's lemma, we know that $J = (a_1, \dots, a_s)$. Similarly, $\mathfrak{n} = (\overline{a}_{s+1}, \dots, \overline{a}_n)$ $(\overline{a}_i = a_i \pmod{J})$. By Krull's altitude theorem (Lemma 6.8), $\operatorname{ht}(J) \le s$. Here note that J is a prime ideal. Thus, $\dim R \ge n - s$. (Here we make use of the following result: If A is a localization of a finitely generated k-algebra domain, any maximal prime ideal chain has the same length, which is equal to $\dim A$. See [5] for this result.) Meanwhile, $n - s \ge r = \dim R$ by Lemma 6.20. Hence, $n - s = r$. Therefore, R is a regular local ring, and $\{\overline{a}_{s+1}, \dots, \overline{a}_n\}$ is a regular system of parameters of R. We can alter the above arguments as follows. Since A is a regular local ring and $\{a_1, \dots, a_n\}$ is a regular system of parameters, the $\mathfrak{m}$-adic completion $\widehat{A}$ of A is equal to a formal power series ring $k[[a_1, \dots, a_n]]$, while the $\mathfrak{n}$-adic completion $\widehat{R}$ of R is given as $\widehat{R} = \widehat{A}/J\widehat{A}$. In fact, since R is a finitely generated A-module, $\widehat{R} \cong R \otimes_A \widehat{A} = \widehat{A}/J\widehat{A}$ (Lemma 6.2). Hence, $\widehat{R} \cong k[[\overline{a}_{s+1}, \dots, \overline{a}_n]]$ is a formal power series ring in $(n - s)$ variables. This implies that $\dim R = n - s$ (Lemma 6.11) and R is a regular local ring (Theorem 6.12).

(1) *implies* (2). We employ the same notation as above. We have to show that the sequence of R-modules

$$0 \to J/J^2 \xrightarrow{\eta} \Omega_{A/k} \otimes_A R \to \Omega_{R/k} \to 0$$

is an exact sequence. For this, it suffices to show that η is injective. Applying $\otimes R/\mathfrak{n}$ to the above sequence, we obtain an exact sequence

$$J/\mathfrak{m}J \xrightarrow{\overline{\eta}} \mathfrak{m}/\mathfrak{m}^2 \to \mathfrak{n}/\mathfrak{n}^2 \to 0.$$

Since $\operatorname{Im}\overline{\eta} = J/J \cap \mathfrak{m}^2$, $\overline{\eta}$ is injective if $J \cap \mathfrak{m}^2 = \mathfrak{m}J$. We shall prove that $J \cap \mathfrak{m}^2 = \mathfrak{m}J$. There exists a regular system of parameters $\{a_1, \ldots, a_n\}$ of A such that $\{\overline{a}_{s+1}, \ldots, \overline{a}_n\}$ ($\overline{a}_i = a_i \pmod J$) is a regular system of parameters of R. We may assume that $a_1, \ldots, a_s \in J$. It is clear that $\mathfrak{m}J \subseteq J \cap \mathfrak{m}^2$. We shall show the opposite inclusion. Let $f \in J$. As an element of $\widehat{A} = k[[a_1, \ldots, a_n]]$, f is expressed as a formal series in $a_1, \ldots, a_n$ with coefficients in k. Since $\widehat{R} = k[[\overline{a}_{s+1}, \ldots, \overline{a}_n]]$ and $f \pmod{J\widehat{A}}) = 0$, we have $f(0, \ldots, 0, a_{s+1}, \ldots, a_n) = 0$. Hence, if $f \in J \cap \mathfrak{m}^2$, then $f \in \mathfrak{m}J + \mathfrak{m}^N (N \gg 0)$. Meanwhile, $J \cap \mathfrak{m}^N \subseteq \mathfrak{m}J (N \gg 0)$ by the lemma of Artin-Rees (I.1.31). Hence, $f \in \mathfrak{m}J$. Namely, $J \cap \mathfrak{m}^2 \subseteq \mathfrak{m}J$. In view of the arguments employed in the step showing that (3) implies (1), we show that $J = (a_1, \ldots, a_s)$. Here $\Omega_{A/k}$ is a free A-module with $\{da_1, \ldots, da_n\}$ as a free basis. Hence, $\Omega_{A/k} \otimes_A R$ is a free R-module with $\{\overline{da_1}, \ldots, \overline{da_n}\}$ as a free basis, where $\overline{da_i} = da_i \pmod{J\Omega_{A/k}}$. Noting that J/J^2 is generated by $a_i \pmod{J^2} (1 \le i \le s)$ and $\eta(a_i \pmod{J^2}) = \overline{da_i}$ $(1 \le i \le s)$, we know that J/J^2 is a direct summand of $\Omega_{A/k} \otimes_A R$. □

For an algebraic scheme X over an algebraically closed field k, we call $\Omega_{X/k}$ the *sheaf of differential forms* (the *differential sheaf*, for short) of X. Suppose X is a nonsingular algebraic variety. The dual sheaf $\mathcal{T}_{X/k} := \mathcal{H}om_{\mathcal{O}_X}(\Omega_{X/k}, \mathcal{O}_X)$ is called the *tangent sheaf* of X. If x is a closed point of X, then $\mathcal{T}_{X/k,x} \otimes_{\mathcal{O}} k \cong (\mathfrak{m}/\mathfrak{m}^2)^*$ because $\Omega_{X/k}$ is a locally free $\mathcal{O}_X$-Module, where $\mathcal{O} = \mathcal{O}_{X,x}$ and $\mathfrak{m} = \mathfrak{m}_{X,x}$. $\mathcal{T}_{X/k,x} \otimes_{\mathcal{O}} k$ is therefore identified with the set of tangent vectors of X at the point x. Under the situation of Lemma 6.22, if the equivalent conditions are satisfied, the coherent $\mathcal{O}_Y$-Modules $\mathcal{J}/\mathcal{J}^2$ and $(\mathcal{J}/\mathcal{J}^2)^\vee := \operatorname{Hom}_{\mathcal{O}_Y}(\mathcal{J}/\mathcal{J}^2, \mathcal{O}_Y)$ are called the *conormal sheaf* and the *normal sheaf* of Y in X, respectively. These are locally free $\mathcal{O}_Y$-Modules. We denote $(\mathcal{J}/\mathcal{J}^2)^\vee$ also by $\mathcal{N}_{Y/X}$. Under the same circumstances, we have the following exact sequence of $\mathcal{O}_Y$-Modules:

$$0 \to \mathcal{T}_{Y/k} \to \mathcal{T}_{X/k}|_Y \to \mathcal{N}_{Y/X} \to 0.$$

The next objective is to define the *canonical sheaf* $\omega_{X/k} := \bigwedge^n \Omega_{X/k}$ for a nonsingular algebraic variety X defined over k. For this, we shall recall the notion of exterior products. Let R be a ring, let F be a free R-module of rank n, and let $\{e_1, \ldots, e_n\}$ be a free basis of F. For an integer $r (1 \le r \le n)$, the r-fold exterior power $\bigwedge^r F$ of F is a free R-module generated by a free basis $\{e_{i_1} \wedge \cdots \wedge e_{i_r}; 1 \le i_1, \ldots, i_r \le n\}$ such that

$$e_{i_1} \wedge \cdots \wedge e_{i_j} \wedge e_{i_{j+1}} \wedge \cdots \wedge e_{i_r} = -e_{i_1} \wedge \cdots \wedge e_{i_{j+1}} \wedge e_{i_j} \wedge \cdots \wedge e_{i_r},$$

$$e_{i_1} \wedge \cdots \wedge e_{i_r} = 0 \quad \text{if } i_j = i_l \text{ for some } j \text{ and } l \ (j \ne l).$$

Therefore, $\bigwedge^r F$ has rank $\binom{n}{r}$. In particular, if $r = n$, $\bigwedge^n F$ is a free R-module of rank 1 generated by $e_1 \wedge \cdots \wedge e_n$. Let $\{f_1, \dots, f_n\}$ be another free basis of F. Write

$$^t(f_1, \dots, f_n) = A^t(e_1, \dots, e_n), \qquad A \in \mathrm{GL}(n, R).$$

Then $f_1 \wedge \cdots \wedge f_n = \det(A) \cdot e_1 \wedge \cdots \wedge e_n$, where $\det(A) \in R^* =$\{invertible elements of R\}.

Now let X be a connected scheme. We shall define the n-fold exterior power $\bigwedge^n \mathscr{F}$ for a quasicoherent, locally free $\mathscr{O}_X$-Module of rank n. By hypothesis, there exists an affine open covering $\{U_\lambda\}_{\lambda\in\Lambda}$ of X such that $\mathscr{F}|_{U_\lambda} \cong \mathscr{O}_{U_\lambda}^{\bigoplus n}$ for each $\lambda \in \Lambda$. Write $U_\lambda = \mathrm{Spec}(A_\lambda)$ and $\mathscr{F}|_{U_\lambda} = \widetilde{M}_\lambda$, where M_λ is a free A_λ-module with a free basis $\{e_1^\lambda, \dots, e_n^\lambda\}$. We then set $\bigwedge^n(\mathscr{F}|_{U_\lambda}) = \mathscr{O}_{U_\lambda} \cdot e_1^\lambda \wedge \cdots \wedge e_n^\lambda$. If we write on $U_\lambda \cap U_\mu$,

$$^t(e_1^\mu, \dots, e_n^\mu) = A_{\mu\lambda}{}^t(e_1^\lambda, \dots, e_n^\lambda), \qquad A_{\mu\lambda} \in \mathrm{GL}(n, \Gamma(U_\lambda \cap U_\mu, \mathscr{O}_X)),$$

then we have

$$e_1^\mu \wedge \cdots \wedge e_n^\mu = \det(A_{\mu\lambda}) e_1^\lambda \wedge \cdots \wedge e_n^\lambda,$$
$$f_{\mu\lambda} := \det(A_{\mu\lambda}) \in \Gamma(U_\lambda \cap U_\mu, \mathscr{O}_X)^*,$$

and $f_{\nu\lambda} = f_{\nu\mu} \cdot f_{\mu\lambda}$ on $U_\lambda \cap U_\mu \cap U_\nu$. Hence, $\{\bigwedge^n(\mathscr{F}|_{U_\lambda}); \lambda \in \Lambda\}$ get patched together to form an invertible sheaf $\bigwedge^n \mathscr{F}$. The ambiguity arising from the choice of an open covering $\{U_\lambda\}_{\lambda\in\Lambda}$ and a free basis $\{e_1^\lambda, \dots, e_n^\lambda\}$ disappears if we consider the isomorphism class of $\bigwedge^n \mathscr{F}$. So $\mathscr{F}$ determines an invertible sheaf $\bigwedge^n \mathscr{F}$ up to isomorphisms. Furthermore, we have an isomorphism of invertible sheaves $\bigwedge^m \mathscr{G} \cong (\bigwedge^n \mathscr{F}) \otimes (\bigwedge^r \mathscr{H})$ if we are given an exact sequence of locally free $\mathscr{O}_X$-Modules

$$0 \to \mathscr{F} \to \mathscr{G} \to \mathscr{H} \to 0,$$

where $\mathscr{F}, \mathscr{G}, \mathscr{H}$ have rank n, m, r $(m = n + r)$, respectively.

Let k be an algebraically closed field, and let X be a nonsingular algebraic variety of dimension n defined over k. Since $\Omega_{X/k}$ is a locally free $\mathscr{O}_X$-Module of rank n, we can define the n-fold exterior power $\omega_{X/k} := \bigwedge^n \Omega_{X/k}$. We call this invertible sheaf the *canonical sheaf* of X. We denote it also by ω_X. Denote by K_X a Cartier divisor which gives rise to $\omega_{X/k}$. The divisor K_X is determined by X uniquely up to linear equivalence. We call K_X "the" *canonical divisor* of X. We have $\omega_{X/k} \cong \mathscr{O}_X(K_X)$.

Let x be a closed point of X and let $\{x_1, \dots, x_n\}$ be a regular system of parameters of the regular local ring $\mathscr{O}_{X,x}$. If we regard each x_i as an element of the function field $k(X)$, then there exists an open neighborhood U of x such that for each $x_i \in \Gamma(U, \mathscr{O}_X)$. If y is a closed point of U and $\{y_1, \dots, y_n\}$ is a regular system of parameters of $\mathscr{O}_{X,y}$, then we can express $dx_i = \sum_{j=1}^n a_{ij}\, dy_j$ in $\Omega_{X/k,y}$, where $a_{ij} \in \mathscr{O}_{X,y}$. Write $a_{ij} = \frac{\partial x_i}{\partial y_j}$, and set

$$J\left(\frac{x_1, \dots, x_n}{y_1, \dots, y_n}\right) := \det\left(\frac{\partial x_i}{\partial y_j}\right)_{1\le i,j\le n}.$$

Then we have

$$dx_1 \wedge \cdots \wedge dx_n = J\left(\frac{x_1, \dots, x_n}{y_1, \dots, y_n}\right) dy_1 \wedge \cdots \wedge dy_n.$$

Write $(dx_1 \wedge \cdots \wedge dx_n)(y) \neq 0$ if the value of $J(\frac{x_1, \dots, x_n}{y_1, \dots, y_n})$ at the point y is nonzero. By replacing U by a smaller one if necessary, we may assume that $(dx_1 \wedge \cdots \wedge dx_n)(y) \neq 0$ for each $y \in U(k)$. We then call $\{x_1, \dots, x_n\}$ a *system of parameters* at the point x

with a *coordinate neighborhood* U (or simply a *system of local coordinates* at x). In sum, if $y \in U(k)$, then $\{x_1 - x_1(y), \ldots, x_n - x_n(y)\}$ is a regular system of parameters of $\mathscr{O}_{X,y}$. If x varies, then X is thus covered by coordinate neighborhoods as defined above.

EXAMPLE 1. $\omega_{\mathbf{P}^n/k} \cong \mathscr{O}(-n-1)$.

In fact, let $(T_0, \ldots, T_n)$ be a system of homogeneous coordinates on $\mathbf{P}^n$. Then $\mathbf{P}^n = \bigcup_{i=0}^n D_+(T_i)$ with $U_i = D_+(T_i)$. We can take $\{T_0/T_i, \ldots, \overset{\vee}{(T_i/T_i)}, \ldots, T_n/T_i\}$ as a system of parameters on U_i. Since $T_j/T_i = T_j/T_0 \cdot (T_i/T_0)^{-1}$, a simple computation gives

$$d\left(\frac{T_0}{T_i}\right) \wedge \cdots \wedge d\left(\overset{\vee}{\frac{T_i}{T_i}}\right) \wedge \cdots \wedge d\left(\frac{T_n}{T_i}\right) = -\left(\frac{T_0}{T_i}\right)^{n+1} d\left(\frac{T_1}{T_0}\right) \wedge \cdots \wedge d\left(\frac{T_n}{T_0}\right).$$

Therefore $\omega_{\mathbf{P}^n/k} \cong \mathscr{O}(-n-1)$.

EXAMPLE 2. Let k be an algebraically closed field, and let V be a nonsingular projective algebraic variety of dimension 2 (called an *algebraic surface*). Let C be a nonsingular complete algebraic curve "on" V, which synonimously means that C lies on V as an algebraic subvariety. The defining ideal $\mathscr{J}$ of C is nothing but the sheaf $\mathscr{O}_V(-C)$, and $\mathscr{J}/\mathscr{J}^2 = \mathscr{O}_V(-C) \otimes_{\mathscr{O}_V} \mathscr{O}_C$. So we obtain $\omega_{C/k} \cong (\omega_{V/k} \otimes \mathscr{O}_V(C)) \otimes_{\mathscr{O}} \mathscr{O}_C$ by virtue of Lemma 6.22.

DEFINITION 6.23. Let k be an algebraically closed field, let X and Y be nonsingular algebraic varieties defined over k, and let $f : X \to Y$ be a morphism of k-schemes. We say that f is a *smooth morphism* if f satisfies the following two conditions:
(i) f is a flat morphism.
(ii) For each closed point $y \in Y$, the fiber X_y of f is a nonsingular algebraic variety of dimension r defined over $k(y)(= k)$, where r is independent of the choice of y.

(The condition (i) implies the assertion in condition (ii) that r is independent of the choice of y (Theorem 4.30 (3)). Conversely, condition (ii) implies condition (i), though we will not give the proof.)

We shall treat many examples of smooth morphisms in the Part III. We shall here state the following result.

LEMMA 6.24. *Let $f : X \to Y$ be a smooth morphism as in Definition 6.23. Then $\Omega_{X/Y}$ is a locally free $\mathscr{O}_X$-Module of rank r, and the following sequence is exact:*

$$0 \to f^*\Omega_{Y/k} \xrightarrow{\varphi} \Omega_{X/k} \to \Omega_{X/Y} \to 0.$$

PROOF. Let x be a closed point of X. Set $y = f(x)$, $A = \mathscr{O}_{X,x}$, $\mathfrak{m} = \mathfrak{m}_{X,x}$, $B = \mathscr{O}_{Y,y}$, and $\mathfrak{n} = \mathfrak{m}_{Y,y}$. Then $\overline{A} = A/\mathfrak{n}A \cong \mathscr{O}_{X_y,x}$ and $\overline{\mathfrak{m}} := \mathfrak{m}/\mathfrak{n}A \cong \mathfrak{m}_{X_y,x}$. Let $n = \dim X$ and $m = \dim Y$. Then $r = n - m$, and X, Y, X_y are nonsingular algebraic varieties of dimension n, m, r, respectively. Hence,

$$(f^*\Omega_{Y/k})_x \otimes k \cong \mathfrak{n}/\mathfrak{n}^2, \qquad \Omega_{X/k,x} \otimes k \cong \mathfrak{m}/\mathfrak{m}^2, \quad \text{and} \quad \Omega_{X/Y,x} \otimes k \cong \overline{\mathfrak{m}}/\overline{\mathfrak{m}}^2.$$

First of all, we shall show that the following sequence

$$0 \to \mathfrak{n}/\mathfrak{n}^2 \xrightarrow{\overline{\varphi}} \mathfrak{m}/\mathfrak{m}^2 \to \overline{\mathfrak{m}}/\overline{\mathfrak{m}}^2 \to 0$$

is exact. Choose a regular system of parameters $(u_1, \ldots, u_m)$ of the regular local ring $(B, \mathfrak{n})$ and a regular system of parameters $(\overline{u}_{m+1}, \ldots, \overline{u}_n)$ of the regular local ring $(\overline{A}, \overline{\mathfrak{m}})$ so that $u_i \in \mathfrak{m}$ and $\overline{u}_i = u_i \pmod{\mathfrak{n}A}$ $(m+1 \le i \le n)$. Since the sequence of k-modules

$$\mathfrak{n}/\mathfrak{n}^2 \xrightarrow{\overline{\varphi}} \mathfrak{m}/\mathfrak{m}^2 \to \overline{\mathfrak{m}}/\overline{\mathfrak{m}}^2 \to 0$$

is exact (cf. Lemma 6.17 (3)), $u_1, \ldots, u_n$ generate the ideal $\mathfrak{m}$. Since $n = \dim A$, $(u_1, \ldots, u_n)$ is a regular system of parameters of the local ring $(A, \mathfrak{m})$. So $\overline{\varphi}$ is injective. Then we can write $\Omega_{B/k} \otimes_B A = \sum_{i=1}^m A\, du_i$, $\Omega_{A/k} = \sum_{i=1}^n A\, du_i$ and $\Omega_{A/B} = \sum_{i=m+1}^n A\, du_i$ (compare the proof of Lemma 6.20). Hence, φ is (locally) injective, and $\Omega_{A/B}$ is a free A-module of rank r. □

COROLLARY 6.25. *With the same hypothesis of Lemma* 6.24, *we have* $\omega_{X/k} \cong f^*(\omega_{Y/k}) \otimes \bigwedge^r \Omega_{X/Y}$.

PROOF. Clear from Lemma 6.24. □

DEFINITION 6.26. Let k be an algebraically closed field, let $f: X \to Y$ be a morphism of algebraic k-schemes, and let x be a closed point of X. We say that f is *unramified* at the point x if $\Omega_{X/Y,x} = (0)$, that f is an *unramified morphism* if $\Omega_{X/Y} = (0)$, and that f is an *étale morphism* if f is a flat and unramified morphism.

LEMMA 6.27. *With the same notations as in Definition* 6.26, *the following two conditions are equivalent to each other*:

(1) *f is unramified at a closed point x of X.*

(2) $\mathfrak{m}_{X,x} = \mathfrak{m}_{Y,y}\mathcal{O}_{X,x}$, *where* $y = f(x)$.

PROOF. (1) *implies* (2). Put $A = \mathcal{O}_{X,x}$, $\mathfrak{m} = \mathfrak{m}_{X,x}$, $B = \mathcal{O}_{Y,y}$, and $\mathfrak{n} = \mathfrak{m}_{Y,y}$. Since $\Omega_{X/Y,x} = \Omega_{A/B} = (0)$, we obtain a surjective homomorphism $\Omega_{B/k} \otimes_B A \to \Omega_{A/k} \to 0$. So applying $\otimes_A A/\mathfrak{m}$ to this homomorphism, we obtain a surjective homomorphism $\mathfrak{n}/\mathfrak{n}^2 \to \mathfrak{m}/\mathfrak{m}^2 \to 0$. Hence, $\mathfrak{m} = \mathfrak{n}A$.

(2) *implies* (1). With the same notations as above, the hypothesis $\mathfrak{m} = \mathfrak{n}A$ implies $\Omega_{A/B} \otimes_A A/\mathfrak{m} = (0)$. Since $\Omega_{A/B}$ is a finitely generated A-module, we have $\Omega_{A/B} = (0)$. □

An unramified morphism, e.g., a closed immersion, is not always an étale morphism. If X and Y are algebraic varieties and if $f: X \to Y$ is a dominant unramified morphism, we have $\dim X = \dim Y$ (Problem II.6.4). Here we shall state the following result.

THEOREM 6.28. *Let k be an algebraically closed field of characteristic* 0, *let X and Y be nonsingular algebraic curves defined over k, and let $f: X \to Y$ be a dominant morphism. Let $k(X)$ and $k(Y)$ be the function fields of X and Y, respectively, and let* $n = [k(X) \colon k(Y)]$.

(1) *For a closed point x of X and for $y = f(x)$, $\mathcal{O}_{X,x}$ and $\mathcal{O}_{Y,y}$ are discrete valuation rings of $k(X)$ and $k(Y)$, respectively, and $\mathcal{O}_{X,x} \ge \mathcal{O}_{Y,y}$. Let t and u be generators of $\mathfrak{m}_{X,x}$ and $\mathfrak{m}_{Y,y}$, respectively. Then $u = ct^e$ with $c \in \mathcal{O}_{X,x}^*$ and $e \ge 1$. The morphism f is unramified at x if and only if $e = 1$. Moreover, we have $\Omega_{X/Y,x} \cong \mathcal{O}_{X,x}/(t^{e-1})$. (We denote e by $e(x)$ and call it the* ramification index *of f at the point x.)*

(2) *For a closed point y of Y, we have $\sum_{i=1}^s e(x_i) = n$, where $f^{-1}(y) = \{x_1, \ldots, x_s\}$.*

(3) *The following sequence is exact*:

$$0 \to f^*\Omega_{Y/k} \xrightarrow{\varphi} \Omega_{X/k} \to \Omega_{X/Y} \to 0,$$

where $\mathrm{Supp}(\Omega_{X/Y})$ *is a finite set and* $\mathrm{length}(\Omega_{X/Y}) = \sum_{x\in X}(e(x)-1)$.

(4) $\deg \Omega_{X/k} = n \cdot \deg \Omega_{Y/k} + \mathrm{length}(\Omega_{X/Y})$.

PROOF. (1) The first assertion is stated in the fourth chapter and Problem II.4.7. It should be clear that the number e is determined independently of the choice of t and u. Since $\Omega_{X/k.x} = \mathscr{O}_{X.x}\,dt$ and $\Omega_{Y/k.y} = \mathscr{O}_{Y.y}\,du$, the exact sequence

$$f^*\Omega_{Y/k} \xrightarrow{\varphi} \Omega_{X/k} \to \Omega_{X/Y} \to 0$$

yields $\Omega_{X/Y.x} = \mathscr{O}_{X.x}\,dt/\mathscr{O}_{X.x}\,du \cong \mathscr{O}_{X.x}/(t^{e-1})$. (Here we use the hypothesis that the characteristic of k is zero.) Hence, $\Omega_{X/Y.x} = (0)$ if and only if $e = 1$.

(2) f is a finite morphism. This is verified as follows. Noting that $k(X)$ is a finite algebraic extension of $k(Y)$, let Z be the normalization of Y in $k(X)$, and let $g\colon Z \to Y$ be the normalization morphism. Then g is a finite morphism. By virtue of Theorem 4.23, there exists a morphism $h\colon X \to Z$ such that $f = g \cdot h$. Since h is a birational mapping between normal complete algebraic curves, h is an isomorphism by Theorem 4.29. Namely, we can identify f with g, from which we know that f is a finite morphism. Set $B = \mathscr{O}_{Y.y}$, $\mathfrak{n} = \mathfrak{m}_{Y.y}$, and $\mathrm{Spec}(A) = X \times_Y \mathrm{Spec}(B)$. Then A is a finitely generated B-module, and $f^{-1}(y)$ corresponds bijectively to $\mathrm{Spec}(A \otimes_B B/\mathfrak{n})$ as the sets. Meanwhile, B is a discrete valuation ring and A is a torsion-free B-module. So A is a free B-module (**Problem I.1.11**), whose rank $n = [k(X)\colon k(Y)]$ is equal to $\dim_k A/\mathfrak{n}A$. Since $A/\mathfrak{n}A$ is an artinian ring, we have $A/\mathfrak{n}A \cong \prod_{i=1}^s A_i$, $A_i \cong \mathscr{O}_{X.x_i}/\mathfrak{n}\mathscr{O}_{X.x_i}$ by virtue of the Chinese remainder theorem. (Let $\mathfrak{n}A = \mathfrak{q}_1 \cap \cdots \cap \mathfrak{q}_s$ be the shortest expression by primary ideals. Then $\mathfrak{m}_i := \sqrt{\mathfrak{q}_i}$ $(1 \le i \le s)$ is a maximal ideal of A. Hence, $\mathfrak{q}_i + \mathfrak{q}_j = A$ if $i \neq j$. Then $A/\mathfrak{n}A \cong \prod_{i=1}^s A/\mathfrak{q}_i$ by the Chinese remainder theorem. Since $A/\mathfrak{q}_i \cong A_{\mathfrak{m}_i}/\mathfrak{q}_i A_{\mathfrak{m}_i}$ and $\mathfrak{q}_i A_{\mathfrak{m}_i} = \mathfrak{n}A_{\mathfrak{m}_i}$, we have $A/\mathfrak{n}A \cong \prod_{i=1}^s A_i$. Here we may consider $A_{\mathfrak{m}_i} = \mathscr{O}_{X.x_i}$.) Since length $(\mathscr{O}_{X.x_i}/\mathfrak{n}\mathscr{O}_{X.x_i}) = e(x_i)$, we obtain $\sum_{i=1}^s e(x_i) = n$.

(3) Let x be a closed point of X, and let $y = f(x)$. With the above notations, $(f^*\Omega_{Y/k})_x \cong \mathscr{O}_{X.x}\,du$ and $\Omega_{X/k.x} \cong \mathscr{O}_{X.x}\,dt$. Hence, the homomorphism $\varphi\colon f^*\Omega_{Y/k} \to \Omega_{X/k}$ is injective if we look at it for the stalks at x. So we obtain the above-stated exact sequence. On the other hand, since $\Omega_{X/Y} \otimes_{\mathscr{O}_x} k(X) = \Omega_{k(X)/k(Y)}$ and $k(X)/k(Y)$ is a separable extension, we have $\Omega_{k(X)/k(Y)} = (0)$. This entails that $\mathrm{Supp}(\Omega_{X/Y})$ is a finite set. It follows from (1) that length $(\Omega_{X/Y}) = \sum_{x\in X}(e(x)-1)$.

(4) Refer to Theorem III.7.5. □

Let $(X, \mathscr{A})$ be a ringed space, and let $\mathscr{F}, \mathscr{G}$ be $\mathscr{A}$-Modules. We define a *cup product* of Čech cohomologies

$$\cup\colon \check{H}^p(X, \mathscr{F}) \times \check{H}^q(X, \mathscr{G}) \to \check{H}^{p+q}(X, \mathscr{F} \otimes \mathscr{G})$$

as follows. Firstly, for an open covering $\mathfrak{U} = \{U_i\}_{i\in I}$, define

$$\cup\colon C^p(\mathfrak{U}, \mathscr{F}) \times C^q(\mathfrak{U}, \mathscr{G}) \to C^{p+q}(\mathfrak{U}, \mathscr{F} \otimes \mathscr{G})$$

by $(\sigma \cup \tau)(i_0, \dots, i_{p+q}) = \sigma(i_0, \dots, i_p) \otimes \tau(i_p, \dots, i_{p+q})$, where $\sigma \in C^p(\mathfrak{U}, \mathscr{F})$ and

$\tau \in C^q(\mathfrak{U}, \mathscr{G})$. Denoting by d the boundary operators of the complexes $C^\bullet(\mathfrak{U}, \mathscr{F})$, $C^\bullet(\mathfrak{U}, \mathscr{G})$, and $C^\bullet(\mathfrak{U}, \mathscr{F} \otimes \mathscr{G})$, we have

$$\begin{aligned} d(\sigma \cup \tau)(i_0, \dots, i_{p+q+1}) &= d\sigma(i_0, \dots, i_{p+1}) \otimes \tau(i_{p+1}, \dots, i_{p+q+1}) \\ &\quad + (-1)^p \sigma(i_0, \dots, i_p) \otimes d\tau(i_p, \dots, i_{p+q+1}). \end{aligned}$$

The cup product of cohomologies is this way induced as

$$\cup\colon H^p(\mathfrak{U}, \mathscr{F}) \times H^q(\mathfrak{U}, \mathscr{G}) \to H^{p+q}(\mathfrak{U}, \mathscr{F} \otimes \mathscr{G}).$$

If an open covering $\mathfrak{O}$ of X is a refinement of $\mathfrak{U}$, the following diagram is commutative:

$$\begin{array}{ccc} H^p(\mathfrak{U}, \mathscr{F}) \times H^q(\mathfrak{U}, \mathscr{G}) & \xrightarrow{\cup} & H^{p+q}(\mathfrak{U}, \mathscr{F} \otimes \mathscr{G}) \\ \downarrow & & \downarrow \\ H^p(\mathfrak{O}, \mathscr{F}) \times H^q(\mathfrak{O}, \mathscr{G}) & \xrightarrow{\cup} & H^{p+q}(\mathfrak{O}, \mathscr{F} \otimes \mathscr{G}) \end{array}$$

where the vertical arrows are the homomorphisms induced naturally by the relation $\mathfrak{U} \le \mathfrak{O}$. So the cup product of Čech cohomologies is defined:

$$\cup\colon \check{H}^p(X, \mathscr{F}) \times \check{H}^q(X, \mathscr{G}) \to \check{H}^{p+q}(X, \mathscr{F} \otimes \mathscr{G}).$$

If X is an algebraic scheme over a field k and $\mathscr{F}$ and $\mathscr{G}$ are coherent $\mathscr{O}_X$-Modules, then the cup product is a bilinear mapping of k-vector spaces

$$\cup\colon H^p(X, \mathscr{F}) \times H^q(X, \mathscr{G}) \to H^{p+q}(X, \mathscr{F} \otimes \mathscr{G}).$$

The following theorem is very useful when we treat cohomologies on algebraic varieties.

THEOREM 6.29 (Serre duality theorem). *Let k be an algebraically closed field, and let X be a nonsingular complete algebraic variety of dimension n defined over k. Then we have the following results*:

(1) $H^n(X, \omega_{X/k}) \cong k$.

(2) *For every invertible sheaf $\mathscr{L}$ on X, the cup product*

$$\cup\colon H^i(X, \mathscr{L}) \times H^{n-i}(X, \mathscr{L}^{-1} \otimes \omega_{X/k}) \to H^n(X, \omega_{X/k}) \cong k$$

gives a perfect pairing for every i $(0 \le i \le n)$. Namely, we have $H^{n-i}(X, \mathscr{L}^{-1} \otimes \omega_{X/k}) \cong H^i(X, \mathscr{F})^\vee$, where $\vee$ signifies the dual vector space.

The proof is not easy. A proof of the simplest kind is found in [4, Chapter III]. The reader is advised to compare $\dim H^i(X, \mathscr{L})$ with $\dim H^{n-i}(X, \mathscr{L}^{-1} \otimes \omega_{X/k})$ in the case where $X = \mathbf{P}^n$ and $\mathscr{L} = \mathscr{O}_X(p)$ (cf. Lemma 5.12). As a final subject of the present chapter, we shall present the following result.

THEOREM 6.30. *Let k be an algebraically closed field, and let X be a complete algebraic variety defined over k. Let D_0 be a Cartier divisor on X, let $L \subseteq |D_0|$ be a linear system, and let $\Phi_L\colon X \cdots \to \mathbf{P}^n$ $(n = \dim L)$ be the rational mapping associated with L. Then Φ_L is a closed immersion if and only if the following two conditions are satisfied*:

(1) *For arbitrary closed points P, Q of X, there exists $D \in L$ such that $P \in D$ and $Q \notin D$.*

(2) *Let M be the k-submodule of $H^0(X, \mathscr{O}(D_0))$ associated with L. For an arbitrary closed point P of X, choose an open neighborhood U of P so that an isomorphism*

$\varphi\colon \mathcal{O}(D_0)|_U \xrightarrow{\sim} \mathcal{O}_U$ exists. Let $M_P = \{\sigma \in M; \varphi(\sigma)(P) = 0\}$. Then the natural homomorphism of k-modules $\overline{\varphi}\colon M_P \to \mathfrak{m}_P/\mathfrak{m}_P^2$ is surjective, where $\mathfrak{m}_P = \mathfrak{m}_{X,P}$.

PROOF. *The "only if" part.* We may identify X with a closed subscheme of $\mathbf{P}^n$. Then any element D of L is regarded as the restriction $D = X \cdot H$ onto X of a hyperplane H of $\mathbf{P}^n$ (cf. the remark after Lemma 5.19). By the hypothesis $n = \dim L$, there are no hyperplanes H on $\mathbf{P}^n$ such that $H \supseteq X$. Hence, $M \cong H^0(\mathbf{P}^n, \mathcal{O}(1))$. For a nonzero element σ of $H^0(\mathbf{P}^n, \mathcal{O}(1))$, the hyperplane $H(\sigma)$ defined by $\sigma = 0$ cuts out $D(\sigma) = X \cdot H(\sigma)$ on X. The condition (1) is then equivalent to the condition that for arbitrary closed points P, Q of X, there exists $\sigma \in H^0(\mathbf{P}^n, \mathcal{O}(1))$ such that $P \in H(\sigma)$ and $Q \notin H(\sigma)$. It should be clear that the condition (1) holds. Let $(T_0, \ldots, T_n)$ be homogeneous coordinates of $\mathbf{P}^n$ such that $P = (1, 0, \ldots, 0)$. We may identify M_P with $\{\sum_{i=1}^n a_i T_i; (a_1, \ldots, a_n) \in k^n\}$. Let $t_i = T_i/T_0$. Then $\{\sum_{i=1}^n a_i t_i; (a_1, \ldots, a_n) \in k^n\}$ generates the maximal ideal $\mathfrak{m}_{\mathbf{P}^n,P}$ of $\mathcal{O}_{\mathbf{P}^n,P}$. Hence, $\varphi\colon M_P \to \mathfrak{m}_P/\mathfrak{m}_P^2$ is surjective.

The "if" part. Let $\{\sigma_0, \ldots, \sigma_n\}$ be a k-basis of the k-module M associated with L. For a closed point P of X, the rational mapping Φ_L is expressed as $P \mapsto (\varphi(\sigma_0)(P), \ldots, \varphi(\sigma_n)(P))$ up to a projective translation of $\mathbf{P}^n$ in terms of the open neighborhood U and the isomorphism $\varphi\colon \mathcal{O}(D_0)|_U \xrightarrow{\sim} \mathcal{O}_U$. For an arbitrary closed point P of X, the conclusion (1) implies that $\varphi(\sigma)(P) \neq 0$ for some $\sigma \in M$. So $\rho := \Phi_L$ is defined everywhere. Namely, ρ is a morphism. By condition (1), ρ is also an injection from $X(k)$ to $\mathbf{P}^n(k)$. We claim that $\rho\colon X \to \mathbf{P}^n$ is a closed immersion. In order to prove this assertion, it suffices to verify that $\rho^*\colon \mathcal{O}_{\mathbf{P}^n,\rho(P)} \to \mathcal{O}_{X,P}$ is surjective for an arbitrary closed point P of X. Put $A = \mathcal{O}_{X,P}, \mathfrak{m} = \mathfrak{m}_{X,P}, B = \mathcal{O}_{\mathbf{P}^n,\rho(P)}$ and $\mathfrak{n} = \mathfrak{m}_{\mathbf{P}^n,\rho(P)}$. Since ρ is a proper morphism (Lemma 4.19 (5)), $\rho_*\mathcal{O}_X$ is a coherent $\mathcal{O}_{\mathbf{P}^n}$-Module (Theorem 4.18). Hence, $(\rho_*\mathcal{O}_X)_{\rho(P)}$ is a finitely generated $\mathcal{O}_{\mathbf{P}^n,\rho(P)}$-module. Noting that $(\rho_*\mathcal{O}_X)_{\rho(P)} \cong \mathcal{O}_{X,P}$, we thus see that A is a finitely generated B-module via $\rho^*\colon B \to A$. Condition (2) then implies that $\mathfrak{m} = \rho^*(\mathfrak{n})A + \mathfrak{m}^2$. Hence, $\mathfrak{m} = \rho^*(\mathfrak{n})A$ by Nakayama's lemma. So $A = \rho^*(B) + \mathfrak{m} = \rho^*(B) + \rho^*(\mathfrak{n})A$. Applying again Nakayama's lemma to a B-module $A/\rho^*(B)$, we obtain $A = \rho^*(B)$. □

II.6. Problems

1. Let $R[x_1, \ldots, x_n]$ be a polynomial ring in n variables over R. Show that $\Omega_{R[x_1,\ldots,x_n]/R}$ is a free $R[x_1, \ldots, x_n]$-module with a free basis $\{dx_1, \ldots, dx_n\}$. (Compare the proof of Lemma 6.19 (2).)
2. Let X be an algebraic scheme defined over a field k. Show that if $\Omega_{X/k} = (0)$, then $\dim X = 0$. (First, show that we have only to give a proof in the case where X is irreducible and reduced. Second, show that $\Omega_{K/k} = (0)$ if $K = k(X)$. Finally, show that $\operatorname{tr.deg}_k K = 0$.)
3. Let k be an algebraically closed field. Let V be a hypersurface in $\mathbf{P}_k^n$ defined by $F(T_0, \ldots, T_n) = 0$. Show that the singular locus $\operatorname{Sing}(V)$ of V is defined by
$$F = \frac{\partial F}{\partial T_0} = \cdots = \frac{\partial F}{\partial T_n} = 0.$$
4. Let k be an algebraically closed field, let X and Y be algebraic varieties defined over k, and let $f\colon X \to Y$ be a dominant unramified morphism. Show that $\dim X = \dim Y$. (Make use of problem 2 above.)

Part III

Algebraic Surfaces

CHAPTER 7

Algebraic Curves

Throughout the present part, k denotes an algebraically closed field of characteristic $p \geq 0$, and all algebraic varieties are assumed to be defined over k unless otherwise mentioned. We call k the *ground field*.

Let X be an algebraic scheme proper over k, and let $\mathscr{F}$ be a coherent $\mathscr{O}_X$-Module. Then $H^i(X, \mathscr{F})$ is a finite-dimensional k-vector space. We set $h^i(X, \mathscr{F}) = \dim H^i(X, \mathscr{F})$. If $n = \dim X$, then $h^i(X, \mathscr{F}) = 0$ for each $i > n$ (problem I.2.8). We denote by $\chi(X, \mathscr{F})$ the alternating sum $\sum_{i=0}^{n}(-1)^i h^i(X, \mathscr{F})$ and call it the *Euler-Poincaré characteristic* of $\mathscr{F}$. All points we treat below are closed points unless otherwise specified.

LEMMA 7.1. (1) *If* $0 \to \mathscr{F}_1 \to \mathscr{F}_2 \to \mathscr{F}_3 \to 0$ *is an exact sequence of coherent* $\mathscr{O}_X$*-Modules, then* $\chi(X, \mathscr{F}_2) = \chi(X, \mathscr{F}_1) + \chi(X, \mathscr{F}_3)$.

(2) *If* $\dim \operatorname{Supp}(\mathscr{F}) \leq 0$ *for a coherent* $\mathscr{O}_X$*-Module* $\mathscr{F}$, *then we have* $\chi(X, \mathscr{F}) = h^0(X, \mathscr{F}) = \operatorname{length}(\mathscr{F})$.

PROOF. (1) It follows readily from the cohomology exact sequence (compare Part I, Chapter 2).

(2) This follows from the remark that $h^i(X, \mathscr{F}) = (0)$ for each $i > 0$ and $h^0(X, \mathscr{F}) = \sum_{x \in \operatorname{Supp}(\mathscr{F})} \dim \mathscr{F}_x$. □

Let C be a nonsingular complete algebraic curve. Since each local ring of C has dimension 1, it is regular if and only if it is normal. The Weil divisor group $\operatorname{Div}(C)$ of C is a free abelian group generated by the set $C(k)$ of closed points. For an element $D = \sum_i n_i P_i$ of $\operatorname{Div}(C)$, we denote $\sum_i n_i$ by $\deg D$ and call it the *degree* of D. By Lemma II.5.7, D defines the corresponding invertible sheaf $\mathscr{O}(D)$. D is linearly equivalent to an effective divisor if and only if $H^0(C, \mathscr{O}(D)) \neq 0$. If D itself is an effective divisor, then there exists an element $\sigma \neq 0$ of $H^0(C, \mathscr{O}(D))$ such that $D = D(\sigma)$. For each point P of C, there exist an open neighborhood U of P and $f_U \in \Gamma(U, \mathscr{O}_C)$ such that D is defined by $f_U = 0$ on U. Then $\mathscr{O}(D)|_U = \mathscr{O}_U(f_U)^{-1}$ and $\sigma|_U = f_U \cdot (f_U)^{-1}$. Since $H^0(C, \mathscr{O}(D)) \cong \operatorname{Hom}_{\mathscr{O}_C}(\mathscr{O}_C, \mathscr{O}(D))$, σ corresponds to an $\mathscr{O}_C$-homomorphism $\tilde{\sigma}\colon \mathscr{O}_C \to \mathscr{O}(D)$, and $\tilde{\sigma}$ is given as $\tilde{\sigma}|_U(1) = f_U \cdot (f_U)^{-1}$. We denote this $\mathscr{O}_C$-homomorphism $\tilde{\sigma}$ by the same symbol σ. It is readily shown that σ is injective, $\mathscr{O}(D)/\sigma(\mathscr{O}_C) \cong \mathscr{O}_C/\mathscr{O}(-D) = \mathscr{O}_D$, and $\deg D = \operatorname{length} \mathscr{O}_C/\mathscr{O}(-D)$. Applying Lemma 7.1 to the exact sequence

$$0 \to \mathscr{O}_C \xrightarrow{\sigma} \mathscr{O}(D) \to \mathscr{O}(D)/\sigma(\mathscr{O}_C) \to 0,$$

we obtain $\chi(C, \mathscr{O}(D)) = \chi(C, \mathscr{O}_C) + \deg D$. If D is not effective, write D as $D = D_1 - D_2$ with $D_1 \geq 0$ and $D_2 \geq 0$. Applying $\otimes_{\mathscr{O}_C} \mathscr{O}(D_1)$ to the exact sequence

$$0 \to \mathscr{O}(-D_2) \to \mathscr{O}_C \to \mathscr{O}_{D_2} \to 0,$$

we obtain the exact sequence

$$0 \to \mathscr{O}(D) \to \mathscr{O}(D_1) \to \mathscr{O}_{D_2} \to 0,$$

where $\mathscr{O}_{D_2} \otimes_{\mathscr{O}_C} \mathscr{O}(D_1) = \mathscr{O}_{D_2}$ because $\mathrm{Supp}(\mathscr{O}_{D_2})$ is a finite set. Hence, Lemma 7.1 yields

$$\begin{aligned}\chi(C, \mathscr{O}(D)) &= \chi(C, \mathscr{O}(D_1)) - \deg D_2 \\ &= \chi(C, \mathscr{O}_C) + \deg D_1 - \deg D_2 \\ &= \chi(C, \mathscr{O}_C) + \deg D.\end{aligned}$$

In the equality

$$\chi(C, \mathscr{O}_C) = h^0(C, \mathscr{O}_C) - h^1(C, \mathscr{O}_C) = 1 - h^1(C, \mathscr{O}_C),$$

we have $h^1(C, \mathscr{O}_C) = h^0(C, \omega_{C/k})$ by virtue of the Serre duality theorem (Theorem II.6.29). We write $g(C) := h^1(C, \mathscr{O}_C)$ and call $g(C)$ the *genus* of C. Summarizing the above observations, we obtain the following theorem.

THEOREM 7.2 (Riemann-Roch Theorem). *Let C be a nonsingular complete curve of genus g, and let D be a Weil divisor on C. Then we have:*

(1) $\chi(C, \mathscr{O}(D)) = \deg D + 1 - g$.

(2) $h^i(C, \mathscr{O}(D)) = h^{1-i}(C, \mathscr{O}(K_C - D))$, $i = 0, 1$.

(3) $h^0(C, \mathscr{O}(D)) = 0$ *provided* $\deg D < 0$.

Consider next a singular complete algebraic curve C. Let $\widetilde{C}$ be the normalization of C and let $\nu: \widetilde{C} \to C$ be the normalization morphism. Then ν is a finite morphism, so it is an affine morphism. Hence, we have $R^i\nu_*\mathscr{G} = (0)$ for each $i > 0$ for a quasi-coherent $\mathscr{O}_{\widetilde{C}}$-Module $\mathscr{G}$ (compare (II.3.23)). Therefore, $H^i(\widetilde{C}, \mathscr{G}) \cong H^i(C, \nu_*\mathscr{G})$ for each $i > 0$ by (I.2.27) and (I.2.28). We can verify this assertion by means of Čech cohomologies and (II.5.11), without using the Leray spectral sequence.

Let $\mathscr{L}$ be an invertible sheaf on C. Then $\nu^*\mathscr{L}$ is an invertible sheaf on $\widetilde{C}$. So there exists a Weil divisor $\widetilde{D}$ on $\widetilde{C}$ such that $\nu^*\mathscr{L} \cong \mathscr{O}(\widetilde{D})$. We define $\deg \mathscr{L} = \deg \widetilde{D}$. We shall generalize the Riemann-Roch theorem on C. We define the *arithmetic genus* (or *virtual genus*) of C by $p(C) := h^1(C, \mathscr{O}_C)$. We denote $h^1(\widetilde{C}, \mathscr{O}_{\widetilde{C}})$ by $g(C)$ and call it the *geometric genus* of C. In order to elucidate the relation between $p(C)$ and $g(C)$, consider an exact sequence of $\mathscr{O}_C$-Modules

$$0 \to \mathscr{O}_C \to \nu_*\mathscr{O}_{\widetilde{C}} \to \mathscr{R} \to 0,$$

where we set $\mathscr{R} := \nu_*\mathscr{O}_{\widetilde{C}}/\mathscr{O}_C$. Noting that $\dim \mathrm{Supp}\, \mathscr{R} \le 0$, we obtain

$$\chi(\widetilde{C}, \mathscr{O}_{\widetilde{C}}) = \chi(C, \mathscr{O}_C) + \mathrm{length}\, \mathscr{R}$$

by taking the Euler-Poincaré characteristics. Since $h^0(\widetilde{C}, \mathscr{O}_{\widetilde{C}}) = h^0(C, \mathscr{O}_C) = 1$, we have $p(C) - g(C) = \mathrm{length}\, \mathscr{R}$. So we have the equivalence: $\mathrm{length}\, \mathscr{R} = 0 \Leftrightarrow \mathscr{R} = (0) \Leftrightarrow C \cong \widetilde{C} \Leftrightarrow C$ is nonsingular.

THEOREM 7.3. *Let C and ν be the same as above. Then the following assertions hold*:

(1) *If $\mathscr{F}$ is a quasicoherent $\mathscr{O}_C$-Module, we have an isomorphism* $\mathscr{F} \otimes \nu_*\mathscr{O}_{\widetilde{C}} \cong \nu_*\nu^*\mathscr{F}$.

(2) *For an invertible sheaf* $\mathscr{L}$ *on* C, *we have*

$$\chi(C, \mathscr{L}) = \deg \mathscr{L} + 1 - p(C).$$

PROOF. (1) Define the natural homomorphism

$$\alpha : \mathscr{F} \otimes \nu_* \mathscr{O}_{\widetilde{C}} \to \nu_* \nu^* \mathscr{F}$$

by

$$\Gamma(U, \mathscr{F}) \otimes \Gamma(U, \nu_* \mathscr{O}_{\widetilde{C}}) \to \Gamma(\nu^{-1}(U), \nu^* \mathscr{F}), \qquad f \otimes a \mapsto af.$$

Let $U = \operatorname{Spec}(A)$ be an affine open set of C, let $\nu^{-1}(U) = \operatorname{Spec}(\widetilde{A})$, and let $M = \Gamma(U, \mathscr{F})$. Then $(\mathscr{F} \otimes \nu_* \mathscr{O}_{\widetilde{C}})|_U = (M \otimes_A \widetilde{A})^\sim$ and $(\nu_* \nu^* \mathscr{F})|_U = (M \otimes_A \widetilde{A})^\sim$. Hence, $\alpha|_U$ is an isomorphism. So α is an isomorphism.

(2) We have an exact sequence

$$0 \to \mathscr{L} \to \mathscr{L} \otimes \nu_* \mathscr{O}_{\widetilde{C}} \to \mathscr{R} \otimes \mathscr{L} \to 0,$$

where $\mathscr{R} \otimes \mathscr{L} \cong \mathscr{R}$ because $\dim \operatorname{Supp} \mathscr{R} \le 0$. It follows that $\chi(C, \mathscr{L} \otimes \nu_* \mathscr{O}_{\widetilde{C}}) = \chi(\widetilde{C}, \nu^* \mathscr{L}) = \chi(C, \mathscr{L}) + \operatorname{length}(\mathscr{R})$. By Theorem 7.2, $\chi(\widetilde{C}, \nu^* \mathscr{L}) = 1 - g(C) + \deg \mathscr{L}$. Since $p(C) - g(C) = \operatorname{length}(\mathscr{R})$ as remarked above, we have the equality as stated above. □

Let C be a nonsingular complete algebraic curve of genus g. For a divisor D on C, $|D|$ denotes the complete linear system determined by D. For points P_i $(1 \le i \le n)$ and positive integers m_i $(1 \le i \le n)$, we denote by $|D - \sum_{i=1}^n m_i P_i| + \sum_{i=1}^n m_i P_i$ (or simply, $|D| - \sum_{i=1}^n m_i P_i$) be the linear system $\{D' \in |D|; D' - \sum_{i=1}^n m_i P_i \ge 0\}$. So, $\sum_{i=1}^n m_i P_i$ is contained in the fixed part of $|D - \sum_{i=1}^n m_i P_i| + \sum_{i=1}^n m_i P_i$.

THEOREM 7.4. (1) $\deg K_C = 2g - 2$.

(2) *We have the equivalence*: $g = 1$ *iff* $K_C \sim 0$ *iff* $\omega_{C/k} \cong \mathscr{O}_C$.

(3) *Let* D *be a divisor of degree* d. *If* $d > 2g - 2$ (*or if* $d = 2g - 2$ *and* $D \not\sim K_C$), *then* $\dim |D| = d - g$.

(4) *If* $d > 2g - 1$, *then* $|D|$ *has no base points.*

(5) *If* $d > 2g$, *then* D *is a very ample divisor. Namely,* $\Phi_{|D|} : C \to \mathbf{P}^N$ $(N = \dim |D|)$ *is a closed immersion.*

(6) *A nonsingular complete algebraic curve is a projective algebraic variety.*

(7) *If* S *is a finite set of closed points of* C, *then* $C - S$ *is an affine algebraic curve.*

PROOF. (1) By the Riemann-Roch theorem, $\chi(C, \omega_{C/k}) = \deg K_C + 1 - g$, and by the Serre duality theorem, $\chi(C, \omega_{C/k}) = -\chi(C, \mathscr{O}_C) = g - 1$. It then follows that $\deg K_C = 2g - 2$.

(2) Since $h^0(C, \omega_{C/k}) = g$, $|K_C| \ne \varnothing$ provided $g \ge 1$. Suppose $g = 1$. Let σ be a nonzero element of $H^0(C, \omega_{C/k})$, let $\sigma : \mathscr{O}_C \to \omega_{C/k}$ be the corresponding injective homomorphism, and let $D = D(\sigma)$ which is an effective divisor. We have an exact sequence

$$0 \to \mathscr{O}_C \xrightarrow{\sigma} \omega_{C/k} \to \mathscr{O}_D \to 0,$$

where $\operatorname{length} \mathscr{O}_D = \deg D = \deg K_C = 0$. So $\mathscr{O}_D = (0)$ and $\omega_{C/k} \cong \mathscr{O}_C$. Conversely, if $\omega_{C/k} \cong \mathscr{O}_C$, we clearly have $2g - 2 = 0$.

(3) By the Riemann-Roch theorem, $h^0(C, \mathscr{O}(D)) = h^0(C, \mathscr{O}_C(K - D)) + 1 - g + d$. Since $\deg(K_C - D) < 0$ by the hypothesis $\deg D > 2g - 2$, we have $h^0(C, \mathscr{O}_C(K - D)) = 0$. Hence, $\dim |D| = h^0(C, \mathscr{O}(D)) - 1 = d - g$. Suppose $d = 2g - 2$ and

$h^0(C, \mathcal{O}(K_C - D)) > 0$. By the same reasoning as in (2) above involving the injection $\sigma: \mathcal{O}_C \to \mathcal{O}(K_C - D)$ and an effective divisor $D(\sigma)$, we have $\mathcal{O}(K_C - D) \cong \mathcal{O}_C$. Hence, we know that $h^0(C, \mathcal{O}(K_C - D)) = 0$ provided $K_C \not\sim D$.

(4) For an arbitrary point P, $\deg(D - P) > 2g - 2$. So $\dim |D| = d - g$ and $\dim |D - P| = d - g - 1$. This implies that P is not a base point of $|D|$. In fact, the linear subsystem $|D - P| + P$ has the same dimension as $|D - P|$.

(5) For arbitrary points P, Q of C, $\dim |D - P - Q| = d - g - 2 < d - g - 1 = \dim |D - P|$. Hence, there exists a divisor $D' \in |D|$ such that $P \in D'$ and $Q \notin D'$. Let $M \subset H^0(C, \mathcal{O}(D))$ be the k-submodule associated with the linear subsystem $|D| - P$, and let U be an open neighborhood of P such that an isomorphism $\varphi: \mathcal{O}(D)|_U \xrightarrow{\sim} \mathcal{O}_U$ exists. Suppose $\varphi(\sigma) \in \mathfrak{m}_P^2$ whenever $\sigma \in H^0(C, \mathcal{O}(D))$ satisfies $\varphi(\sigma) \in \mathfrak{m}_P$. Then $|D - 2P| + 2P = |D - P| + P$ and this is a contradiction. So by (II.6.30), $\Phi_{|D|}$ is a closed immersion.

(6) For an arbitrary point P of C, $(2g + 1)P$ is a very ample divisor. Hence, C is isomorphic to a closed subscheme of $\mathbf{P}^{g+1}$ via $\Phi_{|(2g+1)P|}$. So C is a projective algebraic variety.

(7) Write $S = \{P_1, \ldots, P_r\}$. Choose an integer m so that $mr > 2g$. Then $D := m(P_1 + \cdots + P_r)$ is a very ample divisor. So, $\Phi_{|D|}: C \to \mathbf{P}^N$ $(N = mr - g)$ is a closed immersion, and $D = C \cdot H$ for a hyperplane H of $\mathbf{P}^N$. Hence, $C - S$ is a closed subscheme of $\mathbf{A}^N := \mathbf{P}^N - H$. So $C - S$ is an affine algebraic curve. □

THEOREM 7.5 (Formula of Riemann-Hurwitz). *With the hypotheses of Theorem* II.6.28, *we have the following equality*:

$$2g(X) - 2 = n(2g(Y) - 2) + \sum_{x \in X} (e(x) - 1).$$

PROOF. By (II.6.28 (3)), we have $\chi(X, \omega_{X/k}) = \chi(X, f^*\omega_{Y/k}) + \operatorname{length} \Omega_{X/Y}$. Since $\chi(X, \omega_{X/k}) = g(X) - 1$ and $\chi(X, f^*\omega_{Y/k}) = \deg f^*\omega_{Y/k} + 1 - g(X)$, we have only to show that $\deg f^*\omega_{Y/k} = n(2g(Y) - 2)$. For this, it suffices to show that $\deg f^*\mathcal{O}(D) = n \cdot \deg D$ for an effective divisor D on Y. (For an arbitrary divisor D, write $D = D_1 - D_2$ with $D_1 \geq 0$ and $D_2 \geq 0$. Since $\mathcal{O}(D) = \mathcal{O}(D_1) \otimes \mathcal{O}(D_2)^{-1}$ and $f^*\mathcal{O}(D) = f^*\mathcal{O}(D_1) \otimes (f^*\mathcal{O}(D_2))^{-1}$, it suffices to show that the equation $\deg f^*\mathcal{O}(D) = n \cdot \deg D$ only for an effective divisor D.) For $D \geq 0$, look at an exact sequence

$$(*) \qquad 0 \to \mathcal{O}_Y \xrightarrow{\sigma} \mathcal{O}_Y(D) \to \mathcal{O}_D \to 0.$$

As in the proof of (II.6.28 (2)), since $f: X \to Y$ is a flat morphism, it follows that $\operatorname{length}(f_*\mathcal{O}_X \otimes_{\mathcal{O}_Y} k(y)) = n$ for each $y \in Y(k)$. The exact sequence $(*)$ yields an exact sequence

$$0 \to \mathcal{O}_X \to f^*\mathcal{O}(D) \to f^*\mathcal{O}_D \to 0.$$

If we decompose $\mathcal{O}_D$ into a composition series and make use of the above remark, we know that $\operatorname{length} f^*\mathcal{O}_D = n \cdot (\operatorname{length} \mathcal{O}_D)$. Hence, $\deg f^*\mathcal{O}(D) = n \cdot \deg D$. □

We can elucidate the structures of algebraic curves with small genus.

THEOREM 7.6. *Let C be a nonsingular complete algebraic curve of genus g. Then the following assertions hold*:

(1) *The following conditions are equivalent to each other*:

(i) $g = 0$.

(ii) $C \cong \mathbf{P}^1$.
(iii) $k(C)$ *is a rational function field over* k.

(2) *Suppose the characteristic of* k *is different from* 2 *and* 3. *If* $g = 1$, C *is isomorphic to a curve on the projective plane defined by the following cubic equation* $F = 0$:

$$F = X_0X_2^2 - (X_1^3 + aX_0^2X_1 + bX_0^3), \qquad a, b \in k, 4a^3 + 27b^2 \neq 0.$$

PROOF. (1) (i) *implies* (ii). Let P be a point of C. Then $\Phi_{|P|}: C \to \mathbf{P}^1$ is a closed immersion by virtue of Theorem 7.4 (5). $\Phi_{|P|}$ is an isomorphism.

(ii) *implies* (i). If $C \cong \mathbf{P}^1$, then $\omega_{C/k} \cong \mathcal{O}(-2)$ (Example 1 in the Part II, Chapter 6). Hence, $\deg \omega_{C/k} = -2$. So $g = 0$.

(ii) *implies* (iii). Obvious.

(iii) *implies* (i). By hypothesis, C is birational to $\mathbf{P}^1$. So $C \cong \mathbf{P}^1$.

(2) Let P be an arbitrary point of C. To simplify the notation, we denote $H^0(C, \mathcal{O}(mP))$ by $H^0(mP)$ and its dimension by $h^0(mP)$. If $m > 0$, then $h^0(mP) = m$ by the Riemann-Roch theorem. We may also assume $H^0(mP) \subset k(C)$ (compare Part II, Chapter 5). Let $\{1, \xi\}$ be a k-basis of $H^0(2P)$, where $\xi \in k(C)$. Likewise, let $\{1, \xi, \eta\}$ be a k-basis of $H^0(3P)$. ($2P + (\xi) \geq 0$ implies $3P + (\xi) \geq 0$.) Since $\varphi := \Phi_{|3P|}: C \to \mathbf{P}^2$ is a closed immersion, we may assume that $\xi = \varphi^*(X_1/X_0)$ and $\eta = \varphi^*(X_2/X_0)$, where (X_0, X_1, X_2) are homogeneous coordinates of $\mathbf{P}^2$. So $k(C) = k(\xi, \eta)$. As $1, \xi, \xi^2, \eta \in H^0(4P)$, suppose these are linearly dependent over k, i.e., $a + b\xi + c\xi^2 + d\eta = 0$ $(a, b, c, d \in k)$. Then $d = 0$. (If $d \neq 0$, then $\eta \in k(\xi)$ and $k(C) = k(\xi, \eta) = k(\xi)$. So $g = 0$ which is a contradiction.) So the relation $a + b\xi + c\xi^2 = 0$ holds in $k(C)$. So $\xi = \alpha \in k$ which is also a contradiction. We therefore know that $\{1, \xi, \xi^2, \eta\}$ is a k-basis of $H^0(4P)$. Consider next $H^0(5P)$. We have $1, \xi, \xi^2, \eta, \xi\eta \in H^0(5P)$. By the same reasoning as above, $\{1, \xi, \xi^2, \eta, \xi\eta\}$ is a k-basis of $H^0(5P)$. Consider $H^0(6P)$. We have seven elements $1, \xi, \xi^2, \xi^3, \eta, \xi\eta, \eta^2$ in $H^0(6P)$. Hence, there is a nontrivial relation with coefficients in k,

$$(*) \qquad a\eta^2 + b\xi\eta + c\eta = d\xi^3 + e\xi^2 + f\xi + g.$$

If $a = 0$, then $k(C) = k(\xi)$, a contradiction. So we may assume $a = 1$. By replacing η by $\eta' = \eta + (b\xi + c)/2$, we may assume $b = c = 0$ as well. If $d = 0$, then $(*)$ is a quadratic equation in ξ and η, and $k(C)$ becomes a rational function field (Problem III.7.1). Hence, $d \neq 0$. Replace ξ by $\xi' = (d^{1/3})\xi$ to assume $d = 1$. Finally, a change of variable $\xi \mapsto \xi' = \xi + (e/3)$ allows us to assume $e = 0$. Namely, by a linear transformation in ξ and η (more precisely, an affine transformation), the relation $(*)$ is changed to an equation $\eta^2 = \xi^3 + a\xi + b$. By expressing this equation in homogeneous coordinates, we obtain the equation $F = 0$ as given above. Furthermore, C is nonsingular if and only if $4a^3 + 27b^2 \neq 0$ (compare Problem II.6.3). $\square$

A nonsingular complete algebraic curve C is called a *rational curve* (resp., an *elliptic curve*) if $g = 0$ (resp., $g = 1$).

III.7. Problems

1. Suppose the characteristic of k is different from 2.
(1) Show that a conic C on $\mathbf{P}^2$ (i.e., a curve defined by $F = 0$, where F is a homogeneous polynomial of degree 2) is isomorphic to one of the following:
(i) $X_0X_1 = X_2^2$,

(ii) $X_0X_1 = 0$,
(iii) $X_0^2 = 0$.

2. Show that C is isomorphic to $\mathbf{P}^1$ if it is irreducible and reduced.
3. Find the standard forms of quadratic hypersurfaces of $\mathbf{P}^3$.

CHAPTER 8

Intersection Theory on Algebraic Surfaces

In what follows, algebraic surfaces signify nonsingular projective algebraic varieties of dimension 2 unless otherwise mentioned. Let V be an algebraic surface. For a quasicoherent $\mathscr{O}_V$-Module $\mathscr{F}$, we employ the abbreviations $H^i(\mathscr{F}) = H^i(V, \mathscr{F})$, $h^i(\mathscr{F}) = h^i(V, \mathscr{F})$, and $\chi(\mathscr{F}) = \chi(V, \mathscr{F})$.

DEFINITION 8.1. For invertible sheaves $\mathscr{L}_1$ and $\mathscr{L}_2$ on V, we set

$$(\mathscr{L}_1 \cdot \mathscr{L}_2) = \chi(\mathscr{O}_V) - \chi(\mathscr{L}_1^{-1}) - \chi(\mathscr{L}_2^{-1}) + \chi(\mathscr{L}_1^{-1} \otimes \mathscr{L}_2^{-1})$$

and call it the *intersection number* of $\mathscr{L}_1$ and $\mathscr{L}_2$.

By definition, $(\mathscr{L}_1 \cdot \mathscr{L}_2)$ is an integer. The following result is important.

THEOREM 8.2. (1) $(\ \cdot\ )$ *is an integer-valued binary form on* $\operatorname{Pic}(V)$. *Namely, we have*:

(i) $(\mathscr{L}_1 \cdot \mathscr{L}_2)$ *depends only on the isomorphism classes of* $\mathscr{L}_1$ *and* $\mathscr{L}_2$.
(ii) $(\mathscr{L}_1 \cdot \mathscr{L}_2) = (\mathscr{L}_2 \cdot \mathscr{L}_1)$.
(iii) $(\mathscr{L}_1 \otimes \mathscr{L}_1' \cdot \mathscr{L}_2) = (\mathscr{L}_1 \cdot \mathscr{L}_2) + (\mathscr{L}_1' \cdot \mathscr{L}_2)$.
(iv) $(\mathscr{L}_1^{-1} \cdot \mathscr{L}_2) = -(\mathscr{L}_1 \cdot \mathscr{L}_2)$.
(v) $(\mathscr{O}_V \cdot \mathscr{L}_2) = 0$.

(2) *Suppose* $H^0(\mathscr{L}_i) \neq (0)$ *for* $i = 1, 2$. *Write* $\mathscr{L}_i = \mathscr{O}_V(D_i)$ *with* $D_i \geq 0$. *If* D_1 *and* D_2 *have no irreducible components in common* (*no common components, for short*), *then we have*

$$(\mathscr{L}_1 \cdot \mathscr{L}_2) = \sum_{x \in V} \dim_k \mathscr{O}_{V,x}/(f_x, g_x),$$

where $f_x = 0$ *and* $g_x = 0$ *are local defining equations at* x *of* D_1 *and* D_2, *respectively, and* $\dim_k$ *stands for the dimension of a* k-*vector space.*

PROOF. (1) (i), (ii), (v) are clear from the definition. We shall verify (iii). Let C be an irreducible algebraic curve (lying) on V. Consider the case where $\mathscr{L}_2 = \mathscr{O}_V(C)$. From the exact sequence

$$0 \to \mathscr{O}_V(-C) \to \mathscr{O}_V \to \mathscr{O}_C \to 0,$$

we obtain an exact sequence

$$0 \to \mathscr{L}_1^{-1} \otimes \mathscr{O}_V(-C) \to \mathscr{L}_1^{-1} \to (\mathscr{L}_1 \otimes \mathscr{O}_C)^{-1} \to 0.$$

By Theorem 7.3, we have

$$\begin{aligned}(\mathscr{O}_V(C) \cdot \mathscr{L}_1) =& \{\chi(\mathscr{O}_V) - \chi(\mathscr{O}_V(-C))\} \\ &- \{\chi(\mathscr{L}_1^{-1}) - \chi(\mathscr{L}_1^{-1} \otimes \mathscr{O}_V(-C))\} \\ =& \chi(\mathscr{O}_C) - \chi((\mathscr{L}_1 \otimes \mathscr{O}_C)^{-1}) = \deg(\mathscr{L}_1 \otimes \mathscr{O}_C).\end{aligned}$$

Meanwhile, if $\nu\colon \widetilde{C} \to C$ is the normalization morphism, we have

$$\begin{aligned}\deg((\mathscr{L}_1 \otimes \mathscr{L}_2) \otimes \mathscr{O}_C) &= \deg(\nu^*(\mathscr{L}_1 \otimes \mathscr{O}_C) \otimes_{\mathscr{O}_{\widetilde{C}}} \nu^*(\mathscr{L}_2 \otimes \mathscr{O}_C)) \\ &= \deg \nu^*(\mathscr{L}_1 \otimes \mathscr{O}_C) + \deg \nu^*(\mathscr{L}_2 \otimes \mathscr{O}_C) \\ &= \deg(\mathscr{L}_1 \otimes \mathscr{O}_C) + \deg(\mathscr{L}_2 \otimes \mathscr{O}_C).\end{aligned}$$

These observations imply that $(\mathscr{O}_V(C) \cdot \mathscr{L})$ is linear with respect to $\mathscr{L}$.

Next we claim that given an effective divisor $D = \sum_i a_i C_i$ ($a_i > 0$, C_i is irreducible), $(\mathscr{O}_V(D) \cdot \mathscr{L})$ is linear with respect to $\mathscr{L}$. The proof is by induction on $\sum_i a_i$. By definition, we have that

$$(*)\qquad \begin{aligned}&(\mathscr{L}_1 \cdot \mathscr{L}_2) + (\mathscr{L}_1' \cdot \mathscr{L}_2) - (\mathscr{L}_1 \otimes \mathscr{L}_1' \cdot \mathscr{L}_2) \\ &\quad = \chi(\mathscr{O}_V) - \chi(\mathscr{L}_1^{-1}) - \chi(\mathscr{L}_1'^{-1}) - \chi(\mathscr{L}_2^{-1}) \\ &\qquad + \chi((\mathscr{L}_1 \otimes \mathscr{L}_2)^{-1}) + \chi((\mathscr{L}_1' \otimes \mathscr{L}_2)^{-1}) + \chi((\mathscr{L}_1 \otimes \mathscr{L}_1')^{-1}) \\ &\qquad - \chi((\mathscr{L}_1 \otimes \mathscr{L}_1' \otimes \mathscr{L}_2)^{-1}).\end{aligned}$$

The right side of this equality is symmetric in $\mathscr{L}_1, \mathscr{L}_1'$, and $\mathscr{L}_2$. Since the left side $= 0$ if $\mathscr{L}_2 = \mathscr{O}_V(C)$ (C is an irreducible divisor), the left side $= 0$ also if $\mathscr{L}_1' = \mathscr{O}_V(C)$. Hence, $(\mathscr{L}_1 \otimes \mathscr{O}_V(C) \cdot \mathscr{L}_2) = (\mathscr{L}_1 \cdot \mathscr{L}_2) + (\mathscr{O}_V(C) \cdot \mathscr{L}_2)$. If we write $D = D_1 + C$ with $D_1 \geq 0$ and C an irreducible divisor, $(\mathscr{O}_V(D_1) \cdot \mathscr{L}_2)$ is linear with respect to $\mathscr{L}_2$ by the induction hypothesis. So $(\mathscr{O}_V(D) \cdot \mathscr{L}_2) = (\mathscr{O}_V(D_1) \cdot \mathscr{L}_2) + (\mathscr{O}_V(C) \cdot \mathscr{L}_2)$ is also linear with respect to $\mathscr{L}_2$.

We shall now show that $(\mathscr{L}_1 \cdot \mathscr{L}_2)$ is linear with respect to $\mathscr{L}_2$ for an arbitrary $\mathscr{L}_1$. As V is viewed as a closed subscheme of the projective space $\mathbf{P}^N$, we let $\mathscr{O}_V(1) = \mathscr{O}_{\mathbf{P}^N}(1) \otimes \mathscr{O}_V$ and $\mathscr{L}_1(m) = \mathscr{L}_1 \otimes \mathscr{O}_V(m)$. If $m \gg 0$, then $H^0(V, \mathscr{L}_1(m)) \neq (0)$. (If we write $\mathscr{L}_1 = \mathscr{O}_V(D_1 - D_2)(D_1 \geq 0, D_2 \geq 0)$, then there exists a hypersurface F of degree m_0 such that $F \not\supset V$ and $F \supseteq (D_2)_{\text{red}}$, where $(D_2)_{\text{red}} = \sum_i C_i$ if $D_2 = \sum_i a_i C_i$ and $(D_2)_{\text{red}}$, identified with $\operatorname{Supp}(D_2)_{\text{red}}$, is viewed as a closed subscheme of $\mathbf{P}^N$. If we take $m = am_0 (a \gg 0)$, we have $a(F \cdot V) \geq D_2$, where $F \cdot V$ is the effective divisor on V obtained by restricting the local defining equations of F onto V. Since $\mathscr{O}_V(aF \cdot V) \cong \mathscr{O}_V(m)$, we have $\mathscr{L}_1(m) = \mathscr{O}_V(D_1 + (aF \cdot V - D_2))$.) Since the left side of the equality $(*)$ is zero if $\mathscr{L}_2 = \mathscr{O}_V(m)$, by making use of the symmetry in $\mathscr{L}_1, \mathscr{L}_1'$, and $\mathscr{L}_2$, we know that the left side of the equality $(*) = 0$ even if $\mathscr{L}_1' = \mathscr{O}_V(m)$. So we have

$$(\mathscr{L}_1 \cdot \mathscr{L}_2) = (\mathscr{L}_1(m) \cdot \mathscr{L}_2) - (\mathscr{O}_V(m) \cdot \mathscr{L}_2),$$

where the right two terms are shown to be linear with respect to $\mathscr{L}_2$. Hence, $(\mathscr{L}_1 \cdot \mathscr{L}_2)$ is linear with respect to $\mathscr{L}_2$. By virtue of (ii), $(\mathscr{L}_1 \cdot \mathscr{L}_2)$ is linear with respect to $\mathscr{L}_1$ as well. (iv) follows from (iii) and (v).

(2) Look at the following natural sequence of $\mathscr{O}_V$-Modules

$$\begin{aligned}0 \to \mathscr{O}_V(-D_1 - D_2) \to \mathscr{O}_V(-D_1) \oplus \mathscr{O}_V(-D_2) \to \mathscr{O}_V& \\ \to \mathscr{O}_{D_1} \otimes \mathscr{O}_{D_2} \to 0.&\end{aligned}$$

For a point x of V, set $A = \mathscr{O}_{V,x}$, $f = f_x$, and $g = g_x$, where f_x and g_x are the same as in the statement. Restricting the above sequence to the stalks over x, we obtain the following sequence of A-modules:

$$0 \to fgA \xrightarrow{\alpha} fA \oplus gA \xrightarrow{\beta} A \xrightarrow{\gamma} A/(f, g) \to 0,$$

where α and β are defined by $\alpha(fgu) = fgu \oplus (-fgu)$ and $\beta(fv \oplus gw) = fv + gw$, and γ is the residue homomorphism. We shall show that this sequence of A-modules is an exact sequence. If at least one of f and g is an invertible element, the exactness is easily verified. Suppose $f, g \in \mathfrak{m} := \mathfrak{m}_{V,x}$. Then $\operatorname{ht}((f,g)) > 1$. (In fact, suppose there exists a minimal prime divisor $\mathfrak{p}$ of (f,g) with $\operatorname{ht}\mathfrak{p} = 1$. Since A is a UFD (cf. (II.5.16)), we can express $\mathfrak{p} = (h)$. Then $h|f$ and $h|g$, and the irreducible component, which is defined by $h = 0$ near x, is a common component of D_1 and D_2. This contradicts the hypothesis. Hence, $\operatorname{ht}(f,g)) > 1$.) Since $\dim A = 2$, we have $(f,g) \supseteq \mathfrak{m}^N$ for some $N \gg 0$. Noting that f and g have no common divisors in A, we shall verify the following two assertions:

(i) For $u, v \in A$, if $fu + gv = 0$, then for some $w \in A$, $u = gw$, $v = -fw$.

(ii) For $w \in A$, if $fgw \oplus (-fgw) = 0$, then $w = 0$.

Since A is an integral domain, the assertion (ii) is clear. We shall verify assertion (i). Since $fu = -gv$ and f, g are mutually prime, we have $f|v$. Write $v = -fw$ ($w \in A$). Then $u = gw$.

By virtue of the above two assertions, the above sequences of A-modules and $\mathcal{O}_V$-Modules are exact sequences. By taking the Euler-Poincaré characteristics of terms of the sequence of $\mathcal{O}_V$-Modules, we have

$$\begin{aligned}\chi(\mathcal{O}_{D_1} \otimes \mathcal{O}_{D_2}) &= \chi(\mathcal{O}_V) - \chi(\mathcal{O}_V(-D_1)) - \chi(\mathcal{O}_V(-D_2)) \\ &\quad + \chi(\mathcal{O}_V(-D_1 - D_2)) \\ &= (\mathcal{O}_V(D_1) \cdot \mathcal{O}_V(D_2)).\end{aligned}$$

Since $\dim \operatorname{Supp}(\mathcal{O}_{D_1} \otimes \mathcal{O}_{D_2}) \le 0$, we obtain

$$\chi(\mathcal{O}_{D_1} \otimes \mathcal{O}_{D_2}) = \operatorname{length}(\mathcal{O}_{D_1} \otimes \mathcal{O}_{D_2}) = \sum_{x \in V} \dim_k \mathcal{O}_{V,x}/(f_x, g_x). \qquad \square$$

For $\mathcal{L}_1 = \mathcal{O}_V(D_1)$ and $\mathcal{L}_2 = \mathcal{O}_V(D_2)$, we define $(D_1 \cdot D_2) := (\mathcal{L}_1 \cdot \mathcal{L}_2)$ and call it the *intersection number* of D_1 and D_2. We also employ the abbreviations $(\mathcal{L}^2) := (\mathcal{L} \cdot \mathcal{L})$ and $(D^2) = (D)^2 := (D \cdot D)$. By Theorem 8.2 (1), we have $(D_1 \cdot D_2) = (D_1' \cdot D_2)$ if $D_1 \sim D_1'$. With the notation of Theorem 8.2 (2), if D_1 and D_2 are effective divisors without common components, then we define $i(D_1, D_2; x) = \dim_k \mathcal{O}_{V,x}/(f_x, g_x)$ and call it the *local intersection multiplicity* of D_1, D_2 at a point x. Below, we shall apply intersection theory to concrete examples.

THEOREM 8.3 (Theorem of Bézout). *Let C and D be (not necessarily irreducible) algebraic curves on $\mathbf{P}^2$ which have no common irreducible components. Then the following equality holds*:

$$(\deg C) \cdot (\deg D) = (C \cdot D) = \sum_{x \in \mathbf{P}^2} i(C, D; x).$$

PROOF. We shall first show that $(\mathcal{O}(1) \cdot \mathcal{O}(1)) = 1$. Let (X_0, X_1, X_2) be the homogeneous coordinates. Let l_0, l_1 be lines defined by $X_0 = 0$, $X_1 = 0$, respectively. Since $\mathcal{O}(1) \cong \mathcal{O}(l_0) \cong \mathcal{O}(l_1)$, we have

$$(\mathcal{O}(1) \cdot \mathcal{O}(1)) = (l_0 \cdot l_1) = \dim_k \mathcal{O}_P/(u, v) = 1,$$

where $P = (0, 0, 1) = l_0 \cap l_1$, $u = X_0/X_2$, and $v = X_1/X_2$. We choose a line l on $\mathbf{P}^2$. If an algebraic curve C is defined by a homogeneous equation of degree d, then

$C \sim dl$ (Example (II.5.17.1)). Hence, $\deg C := d = (C \cdot l)$. So if $e = \deg D$, we have

$$(C \cdot D) = (dl \cdot el) = de = (\deg C) \cdot (\deg D).$$

The stated equality follows from Theorem 8.2. □

DEFINITION 8.4. Let C and D be disjoint irreducible (and reduced) algebraic curves (lying) on an algebraic surface V. Suppose C and D meet at a point x. Let $f_x = 0$ and $g_x = 0$ be local defining equations of C and D at x, respectively. If $(f_x, g_x) = \mathfrak{m}_x$ (which is equivalent to $i(C, D; x) = 1$), then we say that C and D *cross normally* at x. Then the point x is a nonsingular point of both algebraic curves C and D. If C and D cross normally at every point of intersection, we say that C and D *cross normally*.

COROLLARY 8.5. *Suppose two distinct irreducible algebraic curves C and D cross normally on $\mathbf{P}^2$. Then $\#(C \cap D) = (\deg C) \cdot (\deg D)$, where $\#(C \cap D)$ is the number of intersection points of C and D.*

PROOF. Apply the equality in Theorem 8.3. □

LEMMA 8.6. (1) *Let V be a projective algebraic variety, and let $\mathscr{L}$ be an invertible sheaf on V. For an irreducible algebraic curve C on V, denote by $\mathscr{L}|_C$ the restriction of $\mathscr{L}$ onto C. If $\mathscr{L}$ is an ample invertible sheaf, then we have $\deg(\mathscr{L}|_C) > 0$.*

(2) *Let V be an algebraic surface, and let $\mathscr{L}$ be an ample invertible sheaf. Then $(\mathscr{L}^2) > 0$.*

PROOF. (1) $\mathscr{L}^{\otimes n}|_C = (\mathscr{L}|_C)^{\otimes n}$, and if $n > 0$, $\deg(\mathscr{L}|_C)^{\otimes n} > 0$ is equivalent to $\deg(\mathscr{L}|_C) > 0$. So we may assume that $\mathscr{L}$ is very ample. Then the natural mapping $\Phi_{\mathscr{L}}\colon V \to \mathbf{P}^N$ $(N + 1 = h^0(V, \mathscr{L}))$ associated with $\mathscr{L}$ is a closed immersion. If we choose a k-basis $\{\sigma_0, \dots, \sigma_N\}$ of $H^0(V, \mathscr{L})$, then $\Phi_{\mathscr{L}}$ is given by $P \mapsto (\sigma_0(P), \dots, \sigma_N(P))$. The restriction $\Phi_{\mathscr{L}}|_C$ of $\Phi_{\mathscr{L}}$ onto C is the rational mapping associated with the submodule $\operatorname{Im}(H^0(V, \mathscr{L}) \to H^0(C, \mathscr{L}|_C))$ of $H^0(C, \mathscr{L}|_C)$. (In fact, $\Phi_{\mathscr{L}}(C)$ is contained in a linear subspace $\cap H(\tau)$ of $\mathbf{P}^N$, where τ ranges over nonzero elements of $H^0(V, \mathscr{I}_C \otimes \mathscr{L})$, $\mathscr{I}_C$ being the defining ideal sheaf of C in V, and $H(\tau)$ is a hyperplane of $\mathbf{P}^N$ defined by $\tau = 0$.) In particular, $\Phi_{\mathscr{L}}|_C$ is obtained as a composite of $\Phi_{(\mathscr{L}|_C)}$ and the projection from a projective space to a linear subspace. Clearly, the complete linear system associated with $\mathscr{L}|_C$ has no base points. So $\Phi_{(\mathscr{L}|_C)}$ is a morphism. Since $\Phi_{\mathscr{L}}|_C$ is a closed immersion, so is $\Phi_{(\mathscr{L}|_C)}$ (Problem II.5.6). Hence, $\mathscr{L}|_C$ is a very ample invertible sheaf on C. It suffices, therefore, to show that $\deg \mathscr{L} > 0$ when $V = C$. Now let $\nu\colon \widetilde{C} \to C$ be the normalization morphism. Then there exists exact sequences

$$0 \to \mathscr{O}_C \to \nu_*\mathscr{O}_{\widetilde{C}} \to \mathscr{R} \to 0,$$

and

$$0 \to \mathscr{L} \to \nu_*\nu^*\mathscr{L} \to \mathscr{R} \to 0$$

(compare the proofs of Theorems 7.2 and 7.3). We then obtain an injection $H^0(C, \mathscr{L}) \hookrightarrow H^0(\widetilde{C}, \nu^*\mathscr{L})$. A nonzero element σ of $H^0(\widetilde{C}, \nu^*\mathscr{L})$ defines an effective divisor $D(\neq 0)$ such that $\nu^*\mathscr{L} \cong \mathscr{O}_{\widetilde{C}}(D)$. Hence, $\deg \mathscr{L} = \deg D > 0$.

(2) Take a positive integer n so that $\mathscr{L}^{\otimes n}$ is very ample. Then $(\mathscr{L}^2) = ((\mathscr{L}^{\otimes n})^2)/n^2$. Hence, we may assume that $\mathscr{L}$ is very ample. Then there exists an

effective divisor $D = \sum_{i=1}^{r} a_i C_i$ ($a_i > 0, C_i$: irreducible component) such that $\mathscr{L} = \mathscr{O}_V(D)$. Then we have

$$\begin{aligned}(\mathscr{L}^2) &= (\mathscr{L} \cdot \mathscr{O}_V(D)) \\ &= \sum_{i=1}^{r} a_i(\mathscr{L} \cdot \mathscr{O}_V(C_i)) = \sum_{i=1}^{r} a_i \deg(\mathscr{L}|_{C_i}),\end{aligned}$$

and $\deg(\mathscr{L}|_{C_i}) > 0$ by virtue of (1) above. □

The converse of Lemma 8.6 holds when V is an algebraic surface. We shall state only the following result without giving a proof.

THEOREM 8.7 (Nakai's criterion of ampleness). *Let $\mathscr{L}$ be an invertible sheaf on an algebraic surface V. For $\mathscr{L}$ to be ample it is necessary and sufficient that the following two conditions are satisfied*:

(1) *For every irreducible algebraic curve C on V*, $\deg(\mathscr{L}|_C) > 0$.

(2) $(\mathscr{L}^2) > 0$.

Let V be an algebraic surface, and let P be a closed point. We define a *monoidal transformation* (called also a *blowing-up*) $\sigma: V' \to V$ *with center at* P as follows. Let (u, v) be a system of local parameters at P, and let U be its coordinate neighborhood (compare Part II, Chapter 6). Furthermore, changing U by a smaller one, we assume that $\{P\} = \{x \in U; u(x) = v(x) = 0\}$. Define a closed subset Γ_U of $U \times \mathbf{P}^1$ by

$$\Gamma_U = \{(Q, (\alpha_0, \alpha_1)); Q \in U, (\alpha_0, \alpha_1) \in \mathbf{P}^1, v(Q)\alpha_0 = u(Q)\alpha_1\}$$

and the natural projection $\sigma: \Gamma_U \to U$ by $(Q, (\alpha_0, \alpha_1)) \mapsto Q$. Then $\sigma^{-1}(U - \{P\}) \xrightarrow{\sim} U - \{P\}$ and $\sigma^{-1}(P) \cong \mathbf{P}^1$. So we patch $V - \{P\}$ and Γ_U together along the open sets $U - \{P\}$ and $\Gamma_U - \sigma^{-1}(P) = \sigma^{-1}(U - \{P\})$ to obtain a nonsingular algebraic surface V' and a birational morphism $\sigma: V' \to V$. Shrinking U further to a smaller open neighborhood of P, we may assume that U is an affine open set. Write $U = \operatorname{Spec}(A)$, and let I be the defining ideal of the point P. Then $I = (u, v)$. We shall show that $\sigma^{-1}(U) = \operatorname{Proj}(\bigoplus_{i \geq 0} I^i)$, where $\bigoplus_{i \geq 0} I^i$ is a graded A-algebra such that $I^0 = A$ and $I^i \cdot I^j \subseteq I^{i+j}$. In fact, $\operatorname{Proj}(\bigoplus_{i>0} I^i) = D_+(u) \cup D_+(v)$, $D_+(u) = \operatorname{Spec}(A[v/u])$ and $D_+(v) = \operatorname{Spec}(A[u/v])$. Let T_0, T_1 be indeterminates. Then there exists a surjective homomorphism $\varphi: A[T_0, T_1] \to \bigoplus_{i \geq 0} I^i$ such that $\varphi(T_0) = u$ and $\varphi(T_1) = v$, and we can identify $\operatorname{Proj}(\bigoplus_{i \geq 0} I^i)$ with a closed subscheme $V_+(uT_1 - vT_0)$ of $\operatorname{Proj}(A[T_0, T_1]) = U \times \mathbf{P}^1$. Hence, $\sigma^{-1}(U) = \operatorname{Proj}(\bigoplus_{i \geq 0} I^i)$. Here V' is a projective algebraic variety over k, though we omit the proof. We write $E = \sigma^{-1}(P)$ and call E the *exceptional curve* (*of the first kind*).

Let C be an irreducible algebraic curve through P, and let $f = 0$ be a local defining equation of C at P. Let $\widehat{\mathscr{O}}_{V,P}$ be the $\mathfrak{m}$-adic completion of $\mathscr{O}_{V,P}$. Then $\widehat{\mathscr{O}}_{V,P} = k[[u, v]]$. As an element of $\widehat{\mathscr{O}}_{V,P}$, f is written as a formal power series in u, v

$$f = f_\mu + f_{\mu+1} + \cdots,$$

where f_i is the ith homogeneous part and $f_\mu \neq 0$. We denote μ by $\mu(C; P)$ and call it the *multiplicity* of C at P (compare Lemma 8.8). P is a nonsingular point of C if and only if $\mu(C; P) = 1$. (Prove this assertion by making use of (II.6.20).) Now choose an open covering $\mathfrak{U} = \{U_\lambda\}_{\lambda \in \Lambda}$ of V so that C is defined by $f_\lambda = 0$ on U_λ, where $f_\lambda \in \Gamma(U_\lambda, \mathscr{O}_V)$. Then $\sigma^{-1}(\mathfrak{U}) = \{\sigma^{-1}(U_\lambda\}_{\lambda \in \Lambda}$ is an open covering of V'. The effective divisor on $\sigma^{-1}(U_\lambda)$ defined by $\sigma^*(f_\lambda) = 0$ with λ ranging over Λ are patched together to form an effective divisor $\sigma^*(C)$ on V'. We call $\sigma^*(C)$ the *total transform* of C. As $\sigma^{-1}(C - \{P\}) \cong C - \{P\}$, the closure of $\sigma^{-1}(C - \{P\})$ on V' is an irreducible algebraic curve, which we denote by $\sigma'(C)$ and call the *proper transform* of C. Even if an irreducible algebraic curve C does not pass through P, we can define $\sigma^*(C)$ and $\sigma'(C)$, though $\sigma^*(C) \cong \sigma'(C) \cong C$. If $D = \sum_i a_i C_i$ is a divisor on V, define $\sigma^* D, \sigma' D$ by $\sigma^* D = \sum_i a_i \sigma^* C_i$, $\sigma' D = \sum_i a_i \sigma' C_i$ and call them the *total transform*, the *proper transform* of D, respectively. Clearly, $\sigma^* \mathscr{O}_V(D) \cong \mathscr{O}_{V'}(\sigma^* D)$. We shall prove the following result.

LEMMA 8.8. (1) $(E^2) = -1$.

(2) *Let C be an irreducible algebraic curve through P, and let μ be the multiplicity of C at P. Then we have*

$$\sigma^* C = \mu E + \sigma' C, \quad (\sigma' C \cdot E) = \mu, \quad (\sigma^* C \cdot E) = 0.$$

PROOF. (1) Let $\mathscr{N}_{C/V}$ be the normal sheaf of C on V. We shall show that $\mathscr{N}_{C/V}$ is then an invertible sheaf on C and $(C^2) = \deg \mathscr{N}_{C/V}$. For this, consider an exact sequence

$$0 \to \mathscr{O}_V(-C) \to \mathscr{O}_V \to \mathscr{O}_C \to 0,$$

where $\mathscr{O}_V(-C)$ is equal to the defining ideal sheaf $\mathscr{I}_C$ of C. Taking the tensor product of each term of the exact sequence with $\mathscr{O}_V(-C)$, we have an exact sequence

$$0 \to \mathscr{O}_V(-2C) \to \mathscr{O}_V(-C) \to \mathscr{O}_V(-C)|_C \to 0$$

from which $\mathscr{O}_V(-C)|_C \cong \mathscr{I}_C/\mathscr{I}_C^2$. So $\mathscr{N}_{C/V}$ is an invertible sheaf on C and $\mathscr{N}_{C/V} \cong \mathscr{O}_V(C)|_C$. Hence, $(C^2) = \deg \mathscr{O}_V(C)|_C = \deg \mathscr{N}_{C/V}$.

We shall determine $\mathscr{N}_{E/V'}$. Let (t_0, t_1) be a system of homogeneous coordinates on $E (\cong \mathbf{P}^1)$. For a point Q of E, if $t_0 \neq 0$ at Q, set $w = t_1/t_0$. Then $v = uw$ by the definition of Γ_U, and $u, w - w(Q)$ form a system of parameters at Q. The curve E is then defined by $u = 0$. Similarly, if $t_1 \neq 0$ at Q, set $w' = t_0/t_1$. Then $u = vw'$ and $v, w' - w'(Q)$ form a system of parameters at Q. The curve E is then defined by $v = 0$. Hence, $\mathscr{N}_{E/V'}|_{E_0} = \mathscr{O}_{E_0}(\overline{u})^{-1}$ and $\mathscr{N}_{E/V'}|_{E_1} = \mathscr{O}_{E_1}(\overline{v})^{-1}$, where $E_0 = \{Q \in E; t_0 \neq 0\}$, $E_1 = \{Q \in E; t_1 \neq 0\}$, $\overline{u} = u \pmod{\mathscr{I}_E^2}$ and $\overline{v} = v \pmod{\mathscr{I}_E^2}$. So the transition function of $\mathscr{N}_{E/V'}$ on $E_0 \cap E_1$ is $f_{10} = \overline{u}/\overline{v}$. In view of the relation $vt_0 = ut_1$, we have $\overline{u}/\overline{v} = t_0/t_1$. Thence, we know that $\mathscr{N}_{E/V'} \cong \mathscr{O}_{\mathbf{P}^1}(-1)$. In particular, $(E^2) = -1$.

(2) With the same notation as above, $\sigma^* C$ is defined by $\sigma^*(f) = 0$ near the point Q of E. Suppose $Q \in E_0$. Set $z = w - w(Q)$. Then (u, z) is a system of parameters of V' at Q. We can express $\sigma^* f = u^\mu g$ with $g \in \mathscr{O}_{V',Q}$, and $g \in (\mathscr{O}_{V',Q})^*$ if and only if $f_\mu(1, w(Q)) \neq 0$. In fact, the correspondence $(u, v) \mapsto (u, (z + \alpha)u) (\alpha = w(Q))$ gives rise to a ring homomorphism $\sigma^* : \widehat{\mathscr{O}}_{V,P} \to \widehat{\mathscr{O}}_{V',Q}$ which is continuous with respect to the $\mathfrak{m}$-adic topology, and we can write g as

$$g = f_\mu(1, z + \alpha) + u f_{\mu+1}(1, z + \alpha) + \cdots \in k[[u, z]].$$

In the quotient field of $\widehat{\mathscr{O}}_{V',Q}$, we have $k(V') \cap \widehat{\mathscr{O}}_{V',Q} = \mathscr{O}_{V',Q}$. (Verify this assertion.) This implies $g \in \mathscr{O}_{V',Q}$. Clearly, we have the equivalence

$$g \in (\mathscr{O}_{V',Q})^* \quad \text{iff} \quad f_\mu(1, z + \alpha) \in (\widehat{\mathscr{O}}_{V',Q})^* \quad \text{iff} \quad f_\mu(1, \alpha) \neq 0.$$

Note that if $u \nmid f_\mu(u, v)$, then $f_\mu(1, t) = 0$, as an equation of degree μ, has μ roots, each root being counted with due multiplicity. By replacing the system of parameters (u, v) to $(u + cv, v)$ if necessary, we may assume that $u \nmid f_\mu(u, v)$. By the above argument, we know that the curve $\sigma' C$ is defined by $g = 0$ near the point Q. Hence, $\sigma^* C = \mu E + \sigma' C$. Noting here that the hypothesis $u \nmid f_\mu(u, v)$ implies $Q_\infty := (0, 1) \notin E \cap \sigma' C$, we have

$$\begin{aligned}(\sigma' C \cdot E) &= \sum_{Q \in E_0} \dim_k \mathscr{O}_{V', Q}/(u, g) \\ &= \sum_{Q \in E_0} \dim_k \mathscr{O}_{V', Q}/(u, f_\mu(1, z + \alpha)) \\ &= \mu.\end{aligned}$$

This entails, together with the result in (1) above, that $(\sigma^* C \cdot E) = 0$. □

COROLLARY 8.9. *Let C, D be irreducible algebraic curves on V, let $\mu = \mu(C; P)$, and let $\nu = \mu(D; P)$. Then we have*

$$(\sigma' C \cdot \sigma' D) = (C \cdot D) - \mu\nu \quad \textit{and} \quad (\sigma^* C \cdot \sigma^* D) = (C \cdot D).$$

PROOF. It suffices to show that $(\sigma^* C \cdot \sigma^* D) = (C \cdot D)$. Let $f = 0$ be a local defining equation of C at P. With f taken as an element of $k(V)$, set $A = C - (f)$. Though A is not necessarily an effective divisor, $P \notin \operatorname{Supp}(A) := \bigcup_i A_i$ if $A = \sum_i a_i A_i$ is the irreducible decomposition. Noting here that $\mathscr{O}_V(A) \cong \mathscr{O}_V(C)$, we have

$$\begin{aligned}(\sigma^* C \cdot \sigma^* D) &= (\sigma^* \mathscr{O}_V(A) \cdot \sigma^* \mathscr{O}_V(D)) = (\sigma^* A \cdot \sigma^* D) \\ &= \sum_i a_i (\sigma^* A_i \cdot \sigma^* D).\end{aligned}$$

Since $\sigma^{-1} A_i \cap E = \varnothing$, we have $(\sigma^* A_i \cdot \sigma^* D) = (A_i \cdot D)$. Hence,

$$(\sigma^* C \cdot \sigma^* D) = \sum_i a_i (A_i \cdot D) = (A \cdot D) = (C \cdot D). \quad \square$$

Let $L (\subseteq |D_0|)$ be a linear system on an algebraic surface V with $n := \dim L > 0$. We assume that L has no fixed components and $\operatorname{Bs} L \neq \varnothing$. Let $P \in \operatorname{Bs} L$, and let $\sigma \colon V' \to V$ be the monoidal transformation with center P. Then $\sigma^* L := \{\sigma^* D; D \in L\}$ is a linear system on V', and the module $M(\sigma^* L)$ associated with $\sigma^* L$ is isomorphic to $M(L)$. We call $\sigma^* L$ the *total transform* of L. Let $E = \sigma^{-1}(P)$ be the exceptional curve. For each $D \in L$, we can write $\sigma^* D = \sigma' D + \mu_D E$. Let $\mu = \min_{D \in L} \mu_D$. Then μE is the fixed part of $\sigma^* L$. So we call $\sigma' L := \{\sigma^* D - \mu E; D \in L\}$ the *proper transform* of L by σ. Though $\sigma' L$ has no fixed components, it may still have base points. Take distinct two members D_1, D_2 of L without common components. So $(D_1 \cdot D_2) \geq 0$. In particular, if $\operatorname{Bs} L \neq \varnothing$, $(D_1 \cdot D_2) > 0$. The intersection number $(D_1 \cdot D_2)$ depends only on L, not on the choice of two members D_1, D_2 of L. We define $(L^2) = (D_1 \cdot D_2)$. Then by Corollary 8.9, $(\sigma' L)^2 = (L^2) - \mu^2$.

Let $f \colon W \to V$ be a birational morphism between algebraic surfaces. Suppose f is a composite of monoidal transformations $\sigma_i \colon V_i \to V_{i-1}$ $(1 \leq i \leq N)$ such that $V_N = W$, $V_0 = V$, and $f = \sigma_1 \cdots \sigma_N$. For a divisor D and a linear system L on V, we define the proper transforms $f' D$ and $f' L$ inductively as $f' D = \sigma'_N (\sigma_1 \cdots \sigma_{N-1})' D$

and $f'L = \sigma_N'(\sigma_1 \cdots \sigma_{N-1})'L$. Similarly, we define the total transforms of D and L by $f^*D = \sigma_N^*(\sigma_1 \cdots \sigma_{N-1})^*D$ and $f^*L = \sigma_N^*(\sigma_1 \cdots \sigma_{N-1})^*L$.

LEMMA 8.10. *Let L be a linear system on an algebraic surface V such that* $\dim L > 0$ *and* $\dim \mathrm{Bs}\, L \leq 0$. *Then there exists a birational morphism $\rho: W \to V$ satisfying the following conditions*:

(1) *ρ is a composite of monoidal transformations with centers at points.*

(2) $\rho: W - \rho^{-1}(\mathrm{Bs}\, L) \overset{\sim}{\to} V - \mathrm{Bs}\, L$.

(3) $\rho' L = \rho^* L -$(the fixed part of $\rho^* L$) *and* $\mathrm{Bs}(\rho' L) = \varnothing$.

PROOF. We continue the arguments before stating Lemma 8.10. If $\mathrm{Bs}(\sigma' L) \neq \varnothing$, take $P_1 \in \mathrm{Bs}(\sigma' L)$ and let $\sigma_2: V_2 \to V_1 := V'$ be the monoidal transformation with center P_1. If we set $\sigma_1 = \sigma$, we have $\sigma_2'(\sigma_1' L) = (\sigma_1\sigma_2)' L$, $M(\sigma_2'\sigma_1' L) \cong M(L)$, and $(\sigma_2'\sigma_1' L)^2 < (\sigma_1' L)^2 < (L^2)$. Meanwhile, since the intersection numbers (L^2), $(\sigma_1' L)^2, \ldots$ are nonnegative integers, this process terminates after finitely many times. Then we have only to take as ρ the composite of the monoidal transformations considered in these steps. □

COROLLARY 8.11. *Let V be an algebraic surface, and let $\rho: V \to Y$ be a rational mapping to a projective algebraic variety Y. Then there exists a birational morphism $\tau: W \to V$ satisfying the following conditions*:

(1) *τ is a composite of monoidal transformations with centers at points.*

(2) *$\rho \cdot \tau$ is a morphism.*

PROOF. We may assume that ρ is a dominant rational mapping. (Let U be an open set of V such that U is contained in the domain of definition of ρ. Replace Y by $\overline{\rho(U)}$.) By (II.5.19), there exists a linear system L on V such that $\rho = \Phi_L$. We may assume that L has no fixed components. Then the domain of definition is $V - \mathrm{Bs}\, L$ (II.5.20). Suppose $\mathrm{Bs}\, L \neq \varnothing$. Take $P \in \mathrm{Bs}\, L$, and let $\sigma: V_1 \to V$ be the monoidal transformation with center P. The composite morphism $\rho \cdot \sigma: V_1 \to Y$ is then identified with $\Phi_{\sigma' L}$. So in view of Lemma 8.10, there exists a birational morphism $\tau: W \to V$ such that τ is a composite of monoidal transformatioms and $\mathrm{Bs}(\tau' L) = \varnothing$. Then $\rho \cdot \tau: W \to Y$ is a morphism. □

III.8. Problems

1. Let V be an algebraic surface, and let $P \in V$. For an irreducible algebraic curve C on V with $P \in C$, prove that $\mu(C; P) = \inf_{P \in B} i(C, B; P)$, where B ranges over all irreducible algebraic curves on V such that $B \neq C$ and $P \in B$.
(Hint. Show first that there are sufficiently many curves B as above which are nonsingular at P, and utilize it.)
2. Prove that if C is a nonsingular algebraic curve on $\mathbf{P}^2$ of degree n, then we have
$$g(C) = \frac{1}{2}(n-1)(n-2).$$
(Hint. In view of (II.6.22), $\omega_{C/k} \cong (\omega_{\mathbf{P}^2/k}|_C) \otimes \mathcal{N}_{C/\mathbf{P}^2} \cong \mathcal{O}_{\mathbf{P}^2}(n-3)|_C$.]
3. Let V be an algebraic surface, let L be a linear system, let $\mu > 0$ be a positive integer, and let $P \in V$ be such that $P \notin \mathrm{Bs}\, L$. For a linear subsystem
$$L - \mu P := \{D \in L; D = \sum_i a_i C_i, \mu(D; P) := \sum_i a_i \mu(C_i; P) \geq \mu\},$$

prove that

$$\dim(L - \mu P) \geq \dim L - \frac{1}{2}\mu(\mu + 1).$$

(Hint. Choose $D_0 \in L$ so that $P \notin \operatorname{Supp} D_0$. Then the module M associated with $L - \mu P$ is given as

$$M = \{f \in k(V); D = (f) + D_0 \in L - \mu P, f \in (\mathfrak{m}_{V,P})^\mu\}.$$

If (u, v) is a system of local parameters at P, $f \in (\mathfrak{m}_{V,P})^\mu$ if and only if all coefficients of the terms of degree 0 up to $\mu - 1$ in the Taylor expansion of $f \in \widehat{\mathscr{O}}_{V,P}$ vanish.)

CHAPTER 9

Pencils of Curves

Let V be an algebraic surface. A dominant rational mapping $\rho: V \to B$ from V to a projective algebraic curve B is called a *pencil of curves* (a *pencil*, for short). We assume that B is nonsingular unless otherwise specified. We call ρ an *irrational pencil of curves* or a *rational pencil of curves* according as the genus of B is positive or zero. By (II.5.19), V has a linear system L such that $\rho = \Phi_L$ and $\dim \mathrm{Bs}\, L \leq 0$. Furthermore, by Corollary 8.11, there exists a birational morphism $\tau: W \to V$ such that $\rho \cdot \tau$ is a morphism. Here $\rho \cdot \tau: W \to B$ is a pencil of curves on W. If there exists an open set $U(\neq \emptyset)$ of B such that W_b is irreducible and reduced for each $b \in U$ (we simply say that W_b is irreducible and reduced for "a general point b of B"), then we call the pencil $\rho: V \to B$ an *irreducible pencil*.

LEMMA 9.1. *Given an algebraic surface V, the following are equivalent:*

(1) *giving a pencil of curves $\rho: V \to B$,*

(2) *giving a subfield $k(B)$ of $k(V)$ with* $\mathrm{tr.deg}_k\, k(B) = 1$.

Moreover, under the above equivalent set-up, the pencil ρ is an irreducible pencil if and only if $k(V)/k(B)$ is a regular extension.

PROOF. (1) Given a pencil $\rho: V \to B$, $\rho^*: k(B) \to k(V)$ is an injection because ρ is dominant. Hence, $k(B)$ is a subfield of $k(V)$ with $\mathrm{tr.deg}_k\, k(B) = 1$. Conversely, given a subfield K of $k(V)$ with $\mathrm{tr.deg}_k\, K = 1$, there exists a nonsingular projective algebraic curve B such that $K = k(B)$, because K is a finitely generated field over k. (If we choose an element x of K which is transcendental over k, then we can consider $k(x) = k(\mathbf{P}^1)$. Since $K/k(x)$ is a finite algebraic extension, we have only to take the normalization B of $\mathbf{P}^1$ in K (II.4.23).) The natural inclusion $k(B) \hookrightarrow k(V)$ induces a dominant rational mapping $\rho: V \to B$ such that $K = \rho^*(k(B))$.

(2) By Corollary 8.11, there exists a birational morphism $\tau: W \to V$ such that $\rho \cdot \tau: W \to B$ is a morphism. Replacing V, ρ by $W, \rho \cdot \tau$, we may assume from the beginning that ρ is a morphism.

Suppose ρ is an irreducible pencil. We shall show that $k(V)/k(B)$ is a regular extension. For this, choose a point b of B so that the fiber V_b is irreducible and reduced, and let $\mathscr{O} = \mathscr{O}_{B,b}$. Since $\mathscr{O}$ is a discrete valuation ring, we denote the maximal ideal by $t\mathscr{O}$. Choose an arbitrary closed point P of V_b, and let $(A, \mathfrak{m}) = (\mathscr{O}_{V,P}, \mathfrak{m}_{V,P})$. Then $\mathscr{O} \subset A$ and both A and A/tA are integral domains. We also note that $Q(A) = k(V)$ and $Q(\mathscr{O}) = k(B)$. We have only to show that $Q(A) \otimes_{Q(\mathscr{O})} K'$ is a field if K' is a finite algebraic extension of $Q(\mathscr{O})$. For this, it suffices to show that $A \otimes_{\mathscr{O}} \mathscr{O}'$ is an integral domain if $(\mathscr{O}', u\mathscr{O}')$ is a discrete valuation ring of K' such that $\mathscr{O}' \geq \mathscr{O}$. In fact, we then have $Q(A \otimes_{\mathscr{O}} \mathscr{O}') = Q(A) \otimes_{Q(\mathscr{O})} K'$. We may take as $\mathscr{O}'$ a localization of the integral closure of $\mathscr{O}$ in K'. We shall show that $A' := A \otimes_{\mathscr{O}} \mathscr{O}'$ is an integral domain. First of all, note that A is a flat $\mathscr{O}$-module. (It suffices to show that A has no torsion as an $\mathscr{O}$-module, equivalently in this case that $tb = 0$ implies $b = 0$. But this is clear since A is an integral domain.) Hence, the injection of $\mathscr{O}$-modules $u\colon \mathscr{O}' \to \mathscr{O}'$, $z \mapsto zu$ induces an injective A-homomorphism $u\colon A \otimes_{\mathscr{O}} \mathscr{O}' \to A \otimes_{\mathscr{O}} \mathscr{O}'$, $a \otimes z \mapsto a \otimes zu$. Namely, u is a nonzero divisor of $A' := A \otimes_{\mathscr{O}} \mathscr{O}'$. Suppose $b_1' \cdot c_1' = 0$ for nonzero elements b_1', c_1' of A'. Note that $A'/uA' = (A/tA) \otimes_{\mathscr{O}/t\mathscr{O}} (\mathscr{O}'/u\mathscr{O}') = A/tA$. (In fact, $\mathscr{O}'/u\mathscr{O}' = \mathscr{O}/t\mathscr{O} = k$.) Since A/tA is an integral domain by hypothesis, $b_1' \in uA'$ or $c_1' \in uA'$. In case $b_1' \in uA'$, write $b_1' = ub_2'$. Then $b_2' \cdot c_1' = 0$ because u is a nonzero divisor of A'. Repeating this argument, we have $b_1' \in I := \bigcap_{n \geq 0} u^n A'$ or $c_1' \in I$. On the other hand, A' is a local ring with $\mathfrak{m}' := \mathfrak{m} \otimes \mathscr{O}' + A \otimes u\mathscr{O}'$ as the maximal ideal. (Let $\widetilde{\mathscr{O}}$ be the integral closure of $\mathscr{O}$ in K'. Then $\mathscr{O}'$ is a localization of $\widetilde{\mathscr{O}}$. Since $\widetilde{\mathscr{O}}$ is a finitely generated $\mathscr{O}$-module (I.1.34), $A \otimes_{\mathscr{O}} \widetilde{\mathscr{O}}$ is a finitely generated A-module. Hence, $A \otimes_{\mathscr{O}} \widetilde{\mathscr{O}}$ is a semilocal ring, i.e., a ring with only finitely many maximal ideals, and the maximal ideals of $A \otimes_{\mathscr{O}} \widetilde{\mathscr{O}}$ correspond bijectively to the maximal ideals of $\widetilde{\mathscr{O}}$ because $A/\mathfrak{m} \otimes_A (A \otimes_{\mathscr{O}} \widetilde{\mathscr{O}}) = \widetilde{\mathscr{O}}/t\widetilde{\mathscr{O}}$. A' is a localization of $A \otimes_{\mathscr{O}} \widetilde{\mathscr{O}}$ with respect to one of maximal ideals.) By the lemma of Artin-Rees (I.1.31), we have $uI = I$. Since I is a finitely generated A'-module, if we take a system of generators $\{x_1, \ldots, x_n\}$ of I, we have $x_i = \sum_j ua_{ij}x_j$ with $a_{ij} \in A'$. Let $f = \det(\delta_{ij} - ua_{ij})$. Then $fx_i = 0$ for each i and $f - 1 \in uA' \subset \mathfrak{m}$. Hence, f is invertible, and hence, $I = (0)$. So A' is an integral domain.

(3) Conversely, we shall show that $\rho\colon V \to B$ is an irreducible pencil if $k(V)/k(B)$ is a regular extension. As in (2), we may assume that ρ is a morphism. Furthermore, in order to simplify the subsequent argument we assume that the characteristic of k is zero. Choose an affine open set U of B and affine open sets $\{V_i\}_{i=1}^r$ of V so that $\rho^{-1}(U) = \bigcup_{i=1}^r V_i$. Consider $\rho_i := \rho|_{V_i}\colon V_i \to B$. If we can choose an open set U_i of B so that $(V_i)_b$ is irreducible and reduced for each $b \in U_i$, V_b is irreducible and reduced for each $b \in U \cap (\bigcap_{i=1}^r U_i)$. Hence, replacing V, B by V_i, U, respectively, we may assume that $V = \operatorname{Spec}(R)$ and $U = \operatorname{Spec}(S)$. Set $K = Q(S)$. Since $R_K := R \otimes_S K$ is a finitely generated domain over K, Noether's normalization theorem (I.1.15) implies that there exists an element $t_1 \in R$ such that R_K is an integral extension of $K[t_1]$. Since the characteristic of k is zero, $Q(R)$ is a separable algebraic extension of $K(t_1)$. So we may write $Q(R) = K(t_1, t_2)$. Let $F(t_1, X)$ be the minimal polynomial of t_2 over $K(t_1)$. Replacing t_2 by an element of the form $g(t_1)t_2$ with $g(t_1) \in S[t_1]$, we may assume that t_2 is integral over $S[t_1]$. Then $t_2 \in Q(R)$ is integral over R, and since R is a normal ring, $t_2 \in R$. Replacing U by its open set if necessary, we may assume that $R \supset S[t_1, t_2]$, R is an integral extension of $S[t_1, t_2]$, $Q(R) = Q(S[t_1, t_2])$, and $S[t_1, t_2] = S[T_1, T_2]/(F(T_1, T_2))$. We shall prove the following result. □

ASSERTION 9.1.1. *There exists an open set U of $B = \operatorname{Spec}(S)$ such that $F_{k(b)}(T_1, T_2)$ is an irreducible polynomial over $k(= k(b))$, where $F_{k(b)}(T_1, T_2)$ is obtained from $F(T_1, T_2)$ by replacing the coefficients by their images in $k(b) = \mathscr{O}_{B,b}/\mathfrak{m}_{B,b}$.*

PROOF. Write $F(T_1, T_2) = \sum_\alpha c_\alpha T^\alpha$, $\alpha = (\alpha_1, \alpha_2)$, $T^\alpha = T_1^{\alpha_1} T_2^{\alpha_2}$, $c_\alpha \in S$, $|\alpha| \leq d$ $(d = \deg F)$. Replacing S by a quotient ring of the form $S[1/a]$, we may assume that $c_\alpha \neq 0$ implies $(c_\alpha)^{-1} \in S$. Hence, $\deg F_{k(b)}(T_1, T_2) = d$ for each $b \in B$. Fix a pair of positive integers (p, q) with $d = p + q$. Consider a set of indeterminates $\{T_\beta', T_\gamma''; \beta = (\beta_1, \beta_2), \gamma = (\gamma_1, \gamma_2), |\beta| \leq p, |\gamma| \leq q\}$ and a polynomial ring $C = S[T_\beta', T_\gamma''; |\beta| \leq p, |\gamma| \leq q]$ over S generated by these indeterminates. Let $\mathfrak{a}$ be the ideal of C generated by a collection of elements of C, $\{P_\alpha(T_\beta', T_\gamma'') :=$

$\sum_{\beta+\gamma=\alpha} T'_\beta T''_\gamma - c_\alpha; |\alpha| \le d\}$, and let Ω be an algebraic closure of $K = Q(S)$. Then we have the equivalence of the following two conditions:

For some $F_1, F_2 \in \Omega[T_1, T_2]$, $\deg F_1 = p$, $\deg F_2 = q$, $F = F_1 \cdot F_2$ if and only if the closed set $V(\mathfrak{a} \otimes_S K)$ of $\operatorname{Spec}(C \otimes_S K)$ is not empty.

Similarly, we have the following equivalence

> $G_1, G_2 \in k(b)[T_1, T_2]$, $\deg G_1 = p$, $\deg G_2 = q$, $F_{k(b)} = G_1 \cdot G_2$ if and only if the closed set $V(\mathfrak{a} \otimes_S k(b))$ of $\operatorname{Spec}(C \otimes_S k(b))$ is not empty.

Since $F(T_1, T_2)$ is an irreducible polynomial in $\Omega[T_1, T_2]$, we have $V(\mathfrak{a} \otimes_S K) = \emptyset$. (In fact, since $k(V)/k(B)$ is a regular extension, $k(V) \otimes_{k(B)} \Omega$ is an integral domain and $Q(k(V) \otimes_{k(B)} \Omega) = Q(\Omega[T_1, T_2]/(F(T_1, T_2)))$. Hence, $F(T_1, T_2)$ is an irreducible element of $\Omega[T_1, T_2]$. Hence, $\mathfrak{a} \otimes_S K = C \otimes_S K$. So $1 = \sum_{|\alpha| \le d} h_\alpha P_\alpha$ with $h_\alpha \in C \otimes_S K$. Let a be a nonzero element of S such that $ah_\alpha \in C$ for each α, and let $U_{(p,q)} = \operatorname{Spec} S[a^{-1}]$. Then $V(\mathfrak{a} \otimes_S k(b)) = \emptyset$ whenever $b \in U_{(p,q)}$. If we set $U = \bigcap_{p+q=d} U_{(p,q)}$, the assertion holds true with this U. □

ASSERTION 9.1.2. *There exists an open set U of B such that V_b is irreducible for each $b \in U$.*

PROOF. Note that R is a normal ring, $R \supset S[t_1, t_2]$ is an integral extension, and $Q(R) = Q(S[t_1, t_2])$. Choose an open set $D(h)$ of $\operatorname{Spec} S[t_1, t_2]$ ($h \in S[t_1, t_2]$) so that $D(h) \cap \operatorname{Sing}(\operatorname{Spec} S[t_1, t_2]) = \emptyset$. Then $S[t_1, t_2, h^{-1}] = R[h^{-1}]$. ($S[t_1, t_2, h^{-1}]$ is a normal ring, and $R[h^{-1}] \supset S[t_1, t_2, h^{-1}]$ is an integral extension.) By virtue of Assertion 9.1.1, we can take an open set U of B satisfying the condition:

> $k(b)[t_1, t_2] = k(b)[T_1, T_2]/(F_{k(b)}(T_1, T_2))$ is an integral domain for each $b \in U$.

Here we may assume that the following condition holds:

> $h_{k(b)}$ (= the image of h in $k(b)[t_1, t_2]$) $\neq 0$ for each $b \in U$.

Then it follows that $k(b)[t_1, t_2, (h_{k(b)})^{-1}] = R_{k(b)}[(h_{k(b)})^{-1}]$ for each $b \in U$, where $R_{k(b)} = R \otimes_S k(b)$. For the closed set $V(h)$ of $\operatorname{Spec}(R)$, we have $\dim V_K(h_K) \le 0$, where $V_K(h_K) = V(h) \otimes_S K$. Hence, replacing U by a smaller open set, we may assume that $\dim V(h) \otimes_S k(b) \le 0$ for each $b \in U$. (In fact, for an S-algebra $\overline{R} = R/(h)$, $\overline{R} \otimes_S K$ is an artinian ring by hypothesis. Hence, $\overline{R} \otimes_S K$ is a finitely generated K-module. Then we can find $a \in S$ so that $\overline{R} \otimes_S S[a^{-1}]$ is a finitely generated $S[a^{-1}]$-module. We have only to take $\operatorname{Spec} S[a^{-1}]$ instead of U.) Namely, for each $b \in U$, $\operatorname{Spec} k(b)[t_1, t_2, (h_{k(b)})^{-1}]$ is a dense open set of $\operatorname{Spec} R_{k(b)}$ and it is also irreducible and reduced. This implies that $V_b = \operatorname{Spec} R_{k(b)}$ is irreducible for each $b \in U$. (In fact, $R_{k(b)} = R \otimes_S \mathscr{O}/t(R \otimes_S \mathscr{O})$, where $\mathscr{O} = \mathscr{O}_{B,b}$ and $t\mathscr{O} = \mathfrak{m}_{B,b}$. Here $R \otimes_S \mathscr{O}$ is a normal ring as a quotient ring of R. By (I.1.33), each prime divisor of $t(R \otimes_S \mathscr{O})$ has height 1 and corresponds to an irreducible component of V_b. So each irreducible component of V_b has dimension 1.) □

ASSERTION 9.1.3. *There exists an open set U of B such that V_b is reduced for each $b \in U$.*

PROOF. Look at a sequence of ring extensions $S[t_1] \subset S[t_1, t_2] \subset R$, where we may assume that R is an integral extension of $S[t_1]$. Hence, R is a finitely generated $S[t_1]$-module, and R_K is a finitely generated $K[t_1]$-module. Since R_K is a torsion-free $K[t_1]$-module and $K[t_1]$ is a principal ideal domain, R_K is a free $K[t_1]$-module. Replacing S by a quotient ring of the form $S[a^{-1}]$ if necessary, we may assume that R is a free $S[t_1]$-module. This entails that $R_{k(b)}$ is a free $k(b)[t_1]$-module for each $b \in B$. Then $R_{k(b)}$ is a subring of $R'_{k(b)} := R_{k(b)} \otimes_{k(b)[t_1]} k(b)(t_1)$. Hence, if $R'_{k(b)}$ is reduced, so is $R_{k(b)}$. By Assertion 9.1.2, we may assume that V_b is irreducible for each $b \in B$. Then $R'_{k(b)}$ is a $k(b)(t_1)$-algebra which is an artinian local ring. Since the characteristic of k is zero, we have the equivalence:

$$R'_{k(b)} \text{ is reduced if and only if } \Omega_{R'_{k(b)}/k(b)(t_1)} = \Omega_{R/S[t_1]} \otimes k(b)(t_1) = (0)$$

(compare Problem III.9.1). Here $\Omega_{R/S[t_1]}$ is a finitely generated $S[t_1]$-module, and $\Omega_{R/S[t_1]} \otimes K(t_1) = (0)$. (In fact, $R \otimes_{S[t_1]} K(t_1) = Q(R)$, and $Q(R)/K(t_1)$ is a separable algebraic extension.) Hence, there exists a nonzero element $g(t_1) \in S[t_1]$ such that $g(t_1)\Omega_{R/S[t_1]} = (0)$. If we choose an open set U of B so that $g_{k(b)}(t_1) \neq 0$ for each $b \in U$, it follows that V_b is reduced for each $b \in U$.

This completes the proof of Lemma 9.1. □

Let $\rho\colon V \to B$ be a pencil of curves such that ρ is a morphism. With $K := k(B)$ identified with a subfield of $k(V)$, let $\widetilde{K}$ be the algebraic closure of K in $k(V)$. $\widetilde{K}$ is a finitely generated extension of k with $\operatorname{tr.deg}_k \widetilde{K} = 1$ (I.1.5). Hence, there exist a nonsingular projective algebraic curve $\widetilde{B}$ and a finite morphism $\nu\colon \widetilde{B} \to B$ such that $\rho\colon V \to B$ is a composite of rational mappings

$$\rho\colon V \cdots \xrightarrow{\tilde{\rho}} \widetilde{B} \xrightarrow{\nu} B$$

and $\tilde{\rho}^* k(\widetilde{B})$ coincides with the subfield $\widetilde{K}$ of $k(V)$. We call this decomposition of ρ the *Stein factorization* of ρ. Here $\tilde{\rho}$ is a morphism. (In fact, take affine open sets $\operatorname{Spec} R$ and $\operatorname{Spec} S$ of V and B, respectively, so that $\rho^{-1}(\operatorname{Spec} S) \supset \operatorname{Spec} R$. Let $\widetilde{S}$ be the integral closure of S in $\widetilde{K}$. Then $\operatorname{Spec} \widetilde{S} = \nu^{-1}(\operatorname{Spec} S)$. Furthermore, $\widetilde{S} \subset R$ because R is a normal ring. Thence, $\tilde{\rho}|_{\operatorname{Spec} R}\colon \operatorname{Spec} R \to \operatorname{Spec} \widetilde{S}$ is a morphism.)

COROLLARY 9.2. *Suppose the characteristic of k is zero. $\tilde{\rho}$ is then an irreducible pencil of curves. If $\widetilde{B} \neq B$, a sufficiently general fiber of ρ has* $\deg \nu$ $(:= [k(\widetilde{B})\colon k(B)])$ *connected components. (Even if the characteristic of k is not zero, each fiber of $\tilde{\rho}$ is connected.)*

PROOF. If the characteristic of k is zero, $k(V)/k(\widetilde{B})$ is a regular extension (I.1.8). We can than apply Lemma 9.1 to prove the assertion. We shall not give a proof for the parenthesized assertion. □

LEMMA 9.3 (Stein factorization). *Let $\rho\colon V \to B$ be a pencil of curves such that ρ is a morphism. Then the following assertions hold*:

(1) *If $\rho_*\mathscr{O}_V = \mathscr{O}_B$, then every fiber of ρ is connected.*

(2) *If $k(B)$ is algebraically closed in $k(V)$, then we have $\rho_*\mathscr{O}_V = \mathscr{O}_B$.*

PROOF. (1) Let b be a closed point of B. $\mathscr{O} = \mathscr{O}_{B,b}$ is a discrete valuation ring. We let t be a generator of $\mathfrak{m}_{B,b}$. Replacing V, B by $V \times_B \operatorname{Spec}\mathscr{O}$, $\operatorname{Spec}\mathscr{O}$, respectively, we have only to show that the fiber of ρ over the closed point of $\operatorname{Spec}\mathscr{O}$ is connected when $B = \operatorname{Spec}\mathscr{O}$. For an integer $r \geq 0$, let $V_r = V \otimes_{\mathscr{O}} \mathscr{O}/(t^{r+1})$, where V_0 is the closed fiber. Suppose V_0 is a sum of n connected components. Then $\Gamma(V_0, \mathscr{O}_{V_0})$ has idempotent decomposition of the unity

$$1 = e_1^{(0)} + e_2^{(0)} + \cdots + e_n^{(0)}.$$

Namely, $e_i^{(0)} \in \Gamma(V_0, \mathscr{O}_{V_0})$, $(e_i^{(0)})^2 = e_i^{(0)} (1 \leq i \leq n)$ and $e_i^{(0)} \cdot e_j^{(0)} = 0$ whenever $i \neq j$. In simple terms, if $V_0 = V_{01} \coprod \cdots \coprod V_{0n}$ is the decomposition into connected components, $e_i^{(0)}$ is regular function on V_0 which is 1 if restricted on V_{0i} and 0 if restricted on $V_{0j} (j \neq i)$. Since V_r is homeomorphic to V_0, V_r has n connected components as well. Hence, the unity element 1 of $\Gamma(V_r, \mathscr{O}_{V_r})$ is decomposed into a sum of idempotents

$$1 = e_1^{(r)} + e_2^{(r)} + \cdots + e_n^{(r)}$$

such that $e_i^{(s)} = e_i^{(r)} \pmod{t^{s+1}\mathscr{O}_{V_r}} (1 \leq i \leq n)$ if $s < r$. We shall show that the assumption $n > 1$ leads to a contradiction. For $0 \leq s \leq r$, we have the following commutative diagram:

$$\begin{array}{ccccccccc}
0 & \longrightarrow & t\mathscr{O}_V & \longrightarrow & \mathscr{O}_V & \xrightarrow{p_0} & \mathscr{O}_{V_0} & \longrightarrow & 0 \\
 & & \uparrow{\scriptstyle \eta_{0s}} & & \| & & \uparrow{\scriptstyle \xi_{0s}} & & \\
0 & \longrightarrow & t^{s+1}\mathscr{O}_V & \longrightarrow & \mathscr{O}_V & \xrightarrow{p_s} & \mathscr{O}_{V_s} & \longrightarrow & 0 \\
 & & \uparrow{\scriptstyle \eta_{sr}} & & \| & & \uparrow{\scriptstyle \xi_{sr}} & & \\
0 & \longrightarrow & t^{r+1}\mathscr{O}_V & \longrightarrow & \mathscr{O}_V & \xrightarrow{p_r} & \mathscr{O}_{V_r} & \longrightarrow & 0
\end{array}$$

where η_{sr} is the natural injection $t^{r+1}\mathscr{O}_V \hookrightarrow t^{s+1}\mathscr{O}_V$ and the other homomorphisms are the natural residue homomorphisms. From this diagram, we obtain the following commutative diagram of cohomology sequence,

$$(*) \quad \begin{array}{cccccccc}
0 & \longrightarrow & \Gamma(V, t\mathscr{O}_V) & \longrightarrow & \Gamma(V, \mathscr{O}_V) & \xrightarrow{\pi_0} & \Gamma(V_0, \mathscr{O}_{V_0}) & \longrightarrow & H^1(V, t\mathscr{O}_V) \\
 & & \uparrow{\scriptstyle \mu_{0s}} & & \| & & \uparrow{\scriptstyle \nu_{0s}} & & \uparrow \\
0 & \longrightarrow & \Gamma(V, t^{s+1}\mathscr{O}_V) & \longrightarrow & \Gamma(V, \mathscr{O}_V) & \xrightarrow{\pi_s} & \Gamma(V_s, \mathscr{O}_{V_s}) & \longrightarrow & H^1(V, t^{s+1}\mathscr{O}_V) \\
 & & \uparrow{\scriptstyle \mu_{sr}} & & \| & & \uparrow{\scriptstyle \nu_{sr}} & & \uparrow \\
0 & \longrightarrow & \Gamma(V, t^{r+1}\mathscr{O}_V) & \longrightarrow & \Gamma(V, \mathscr{O}_V) & \xrightarrow{\pi_r} & \Gamma(V_r, \mathscr{O}_{V_r}) & \longrightarrow & H^1(V, t^{r+1}\mathscr{O}_V)
\end{array}$$

where $\pi_s, \mu_{sr}, \nu_{sr}$ are the homomorphisms induced naturally by p_s, η_{sr}, ξ_{sr}. Here note that $\Gamma(V, t^{s+1}\mathscr{O}_V) = t^{s+1}\Gamma(V, \mathscr{O}_V)$ and $H^1(V, t^{s+1}\mathscr{O}_V) = t^{s+1}H^1(V, \mathscr{O}_V)$ for each $s \geq 0$. Furthermore, the hypothesis implies that $\Gamma(V, \mathscr{O}_V) = \mathscr{O}$, and $H^1(V, \mathscr{O}_V)$ is a finitely generated $\mathscr{O}$-module (II.4.18). Since $\mathscr{O}$ is a principal ideal domain, we can write

$$H^1(V, \mathscr{O}_V) = F \oplus T, \qquad F \cong \mathscr{O}^{\oplus m}$$

$$T \cong \mathscr{O}/(t^{\alpha_1}) \oplus \cdots \oplus \mathscr{O}/(t^{\alpha_d}), \qquad \alpha_1 \geq \alpha_2 \geq \cdots \geq \alpha_d.$$

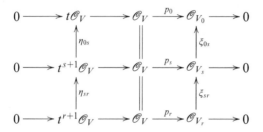

The commutative diagram $(*)$ can be rewritten as follows:

$$\begin{array}{ccccccc}
0 \longrightarrow & \mathscr{O}/t\mathscr{O} & \xrightarrow{\pi_0} & \Gamma(V_0, \mathscr{O}_{V_0}) & \longrightarrow & tH^1(V, \mathscr{O}_V) \\
& \uparrow & & \uparrow \nu_{0s} & & \uparrow \\
0 \longrightarrow & \mathscr{O}/t^{s+1}\mathscr{O} & \xrightarrow{\pi_s} & \Gamma(V_s, \mathscr{O}_{V_s}) & \longrightarrow & t^{s+1}H^1(V, \mathscr{O}_V) \\
& \uparrow & & \uparrow \nu_{sr} & & \uparrow \\
0 \longrightarrow & \mathscr{O}/t^{r+1}\mathscr{O} & \xrightarrow{\pi_r} & \Gamma(V_r, \mathscr{O}_{V_r}) & \longrightarrow & t^{r+1}H^1(V, \mathscr{O}_V).
\end{array}$$

Here $\operatorname{Coker} \pi_r \subseteq t^{r+1}T$ since $t^{r+1}\Gamma(V_r, \mathscr{O}_{V_r}) = (0)$. Hence, $\operatorname{Coker} \pi_r = (0)$ if $r > \alpha_1$. So $\operatorname{Im}(\pi_s) = \operatorname{Im}(\nu_{sr})$ for $r \gg 0$. Here since $\operatorname{Im}(\pi_s) \cong \mathscr{O}/t^{s+1}\mathscr{O}$, we have $e_i^{(s)} \operatorname{Im}(\pi_s) \neq (0)$ for some i and $e_j^{(s)} \operatorname{Im}(\pi_s) = (0)$ for all $j \neq i$ for the idempotent decomposition of the unity $1 = e_1^{(s)} + e_2^{(s)} + \cdots + e_n^{(s)}$ in $\Gamma(V_s, \mathscr{O}_{V_s})$. Meanwhile, $e_j^{(s)}|_{\operatorname{Im}(\nu_{sr})} = e_j^{(r)} \pmod{t^{s+1}\mathscr{O}_{V_r}} \neq (0)$ for each j. This is a contradiction if $n > 1$. So V_0 is connected.

(2) We shall show that $\rho_*\mathscr{O}_V = \mathscr{O}_B$ if $k(B)$ is algebraically closed in $k(V)$. Since $\rho_*\mathscr{O}_V$ is a coherent $\mathscr{O}_B$-Module, $\Gamma(\rho^{-1}(U), \mathscr{O}_V)$ is a finitely generated S-module if $U = \operatorname{Spec}(S)$ is an affine open set of B. We have $\Gamma(\rho^{-1}(U), \mathscr{O}_V) \subseteq \Gamma(\rho^{-1}(U), k(V)) = k(V)$. Each element ξ of $\Gamma(\rho^{-1}(U), \mathscr{O}_V)$ is integral over S, and ξ, as an element of $k(V)$, is therefore algebraic over $Q(S) = k(B)$. Hence, $\xi \in Q(S)$. Since ξ is integral over S and S is a normal ring, we have $\xi \in S$. Hence, $\Gamma(\rho^{-1}(U), \mathscr{O}_V) = S$. So $\rho_*\mathscr{O}_V = \mathscr{O}_S$. □

REMARK 9.4. Suppose, for a pencil of curves $\rho: V \to B$, ρ is a morphism and $k(B)$ is algebraically closed in $k(V)$. Let b be a sufficiently general, closed point of B, and let t be a local parameter at b. t being regarded as an element of $k(V)$, we view the fiber $V_b = V \otimes_{\mathscr{O}} k(b)$ the divisor $(t)_0$ (= the zero part of (t)) on V. If the characteristic of k is zero, then $(t)_0$ is an irreducible divisor by Lemma 9.1. If the characteristic p of k is positive, then we can write $(t)_0 = p^a C$ ($a \geq 0$, C: irreducible component), though we omit a proof.

We suppose a linear system L is given on an algebraic surface V and $n := \dim L > 0$, $\dim \operatorname{Bs} L \leq 0$. Let Φ be the rational mapping $\Phi_L: V \to \mathbf{P}^n$ associated with L. For the domain of definition U of Φ, we denote by $\Phi(V)$ or $\operatorname{Im}\Phi$ the closure of $\Phi(U)$ in $\mathbf{P}^n$ and call it the image of V by Φ. Since $n = \dim L$, there is no hyperplane containing $\Phi(V)$. Hence, putting $\varphi = \Phi|_U$, the natural homomorphism $\mu: H^0(\mathbf{P}^n, \mathscr{O}_{\mathbf{P}^n}(1)) \to H^0(U, \varphi^*\mathscr{O}_{\mathbf{P}^n}(1))$ is injective. Let $\mathscr{L} = \mathscr{O}_V(D)$ with $D \in L$. Then $\varphi^*\mathscr{O}_{\mathbf{P}^n}(1) \cong \mathscr{L}|_U$. By hypothesis, $V - U$ is at most a finite set, and accordingly, $H^0(U, \mathscr{L}|_U) = H^0(V, \mathscr{L})$ (compare the proof of (II.5.19 (2))). Hence, μ gives rise to a homomorphism $H^0(\mathbf{P}^n, \mathscr{O}_{\mathbf{P}^n}(1)) \to H^0(V, \mathscr{L})$. For $\sigma \in H^0(\mathbf{P}^n, \mathscr{O}_{\mathbf{P}^n}(1))(\sigma \neq 0)$, we denote by $H(\sigma)$ the hyperplane of $\mathbf{P}^n$ defined by σ and by $D(\sigma)$ $(\mu(\sigma))_0$ or $V \cdot H(\sigma))$ the effective divisor on V defined by $\mu(\sigma)$.

If $n > 0$, then we have $\dim \Phi(V) \geq 1$. If $\dim \Phi(V) = 1$, then Φ factors as

$$\Phi: V \overset{\rho}{\cdots\to} B \overset{i}{\hookrightarrow} \mathbf{P}^n, \qquad B := \Phi(V).$$

Though B is not necessarily nonsingular, the rational mapping $\rho: V \cdots \to B$ is a pencil of curves. We then say that the linear system L is composed of the pencil ρ.

$k(B)$ is identified with a subfield of $k(V)$. Take a nonsingular projective algebraic curve $\widetilde{B}$ so that $k(\widetilde{B})$ is the algebraic closure of $k(B)$ in $k(V)$ and factor ρ as

$$\rho\colon V \cdots\xrightarrow{\tilde{\rho}} \widetilde{B} \xrightarrow{\nu} B,$$

where $\nu\colon \widetilde{B} \to B$ is the normalization morphism. The homomorphism μ therefore decomposes as follows:

$$\mu\colon H^0(\mathbf{P}^n, \mathscr{O}_{\mathbf{P}^n}(1)) \xrightarrow{i^*} H^0(B, \mathscr{O}_B(1)) \xrightarrow{\nu^*} H^0(\widetilde{B}, \mathscr{O}_{\widetilde{B}}(1)) \xrightarrow{\tilde{\rho}^*} H^0(V, \mathscr{L}),$$

where $\mathscr{O}_B(1) = \mathscr{O}_{\mathbf{P}^n}(1) \otimes \mathscr{O}_B$ and $\mathscr{O}_{\widetilde{B}}(1) = \nu^*\mathscr{O}_B(1)$. Let $d = \deg \mathscr{O}_B(1)$ and $N = \deg \nu := [k(\widetilde{B})\colon k(B)]$. Then for $\sigma \in H^0(\mathbf{P}^n, \mathscr{O}_{\mathbf{P}^n}(1))$, we can write $(\nu^* i^*(\sigma))_0 = \sum_{i=1}^{Nd} \tilde{b}_i$. For $\tilde{b} \in \widetilde{B}$, we define a divisor $V_{\tilde{b}}$ of V as follows:

Let U be the domain of definition of ρ as before, and let t be a local parameter of $\widetilde{B}$ at $\tilde{b}$. We define $V_{\tilde{b}}$ as the closure $\sum_j a_j \overline{C_j}$ of the divisor $(t)_0 = \sum_j a_j C_j$ on U.

If $\tilde{\rho}$ is a morphism, $V_{\tilde{b}}$ is identified with the fiber of $\tilde{\rho}$ at the point $\tilde{b}$. For the above σ, $D(\sigma) = \sum_{i=1}^{Nd} V_{\tilde{b}_i}$. For a pencil of curves $\rho\colon V \to B$ in general and a point $b \in B$, we can define the divisor V_b of V in the same fashion as above.

LEMMA 9.5. *For a pencil of curves $\rho\colon V \to B$, the following assertions hold*:
(1) *If ρ is an irrational pencil, then ρ is a morphism.*
(2) *If ρ is a rational pencil, then $\{V_b; b \in B\}$ is a linear system of dimension one.*

PROOF. If ρ is not a morphism, there exists, by Corollary 8.11, a birational morphism $\tau\colon W \to V$ such that $\rho \cdot \tau$ is a morphism.

(1) Suppose ρ is not a morphism. The morphism τ is given as a composite of monoidal transformations with centers at points. So decomposing τ as

$$\tau\colon W \xrightarrow{\tau_1} V' \xrightarrow{\tau_2} V,$$

we may assume that $\rho \cdot \tau_2$ is not a morphism and τ_1 is a monoidal transformation with center at $P \in V'$. Let $E = \tau_1^{-1}(P)$. By (II.5.19), there exists a linear system L on V' such that $\dim \operatorname{Bs} L \le 0$ and $\rho \cdot \tau_2 = \Phi_L$. Then P is a base point of L, and $\tau \cdot \rho = \Phi_{L'}$, where L' is the proper transform of L by τ_1. Let $\mu = \min_{D \in L} \mu(D; P)$. If D is a sufficiently general member of L, $\tau_1' D := \tau_1^*(D) - \mu E$ does not contain E as an irreducible component and $(\tau_1' D \cdot E) = \mu > 0$. Let $D' \in L'$. Then the image of $M(L')$ by the natural homomorphism $H^0(W, \mathscr{O}_W(D')) \to H^0(E, \mathscr{O}_E(D'))$ defines a linear system $\operatorname{Tr}_E(L')$ on E, where $\mathscr{O}_E(D') = \mathscr{O}_W(D') \otimes_{\mathscr{O}_W} \mathscr{O}_E$. Since $\operatorname{Bs} L' = \emptyset$, $\operatorname{Bs}(\operatorname{Tr}_E(L')) = \emptyset$ and the rational mapping defined by $\operatorname{Tr}_E(L')$ coincides with $\Phi_{L'}|_E$ (compare the proof of Lemma 8.6). $(\rho \cdot \tau)|_E\colon E \to B$ is therefore a dominant morphism. Since E is a nonsingular rational curve, B is also a rational curve by Lüroth's theorem (I.1.36). This contradicts the hypothesis. So ρ is a morphism.

(2) Let b_1, b_2 be any two points of B. Identifying B with $\mathbf{P}^1$, we can choose an inhomogeneous coordinate t of $\mathbf{P}^1$ in such a way that b_1 and b_2 are respectively defined by $t = 0$ and $t^{-1} = 0$. Then $b_1 - b_2 = (t)$. Clearly, $(t)_0 = V_{b_1}$ and $(t^{-1}) = V_{b_2}$. Hence, $V_{b_1} \sim V_{b_2}$ (linear equivalence). □

Conversely, let L be a linear system on V such that $\dim L = 1$ and $\dim \operatorname{Bs} L \le 0$. The rational mapping $\Phi_L\colon V \to \mathbf{P}^1$ is then dominant. Namely, Φ_L is a rational pencil. Below, we call a one-dimensional linear system, which may have fixed components, a *linear pencil*. The next purpose is to show that *first theorem of Bertini* (*Irreducibility theorem*).

THEOREM 9.6 (The first theorem of Bertini). *Suppose the characteristic of k is zero. Let V be an algebraic surface, and let L be a linear system on V such that* $\dim L > 0$ *and L has no fixed components. If L is not composed of a pencil of curves, then a general member of L is irreducible and reduced.*

We reduce the proof of the theorem to the subsequent Lemmas 9.7 and 9.8. The hypothesis that the linear system L is not composed of a pencil of curves implies that $N := \dim L \geq 2$ and $\dim \Phi_L(V) = 2$. Let $\{f_0, \cdots, f_N\}$ be a k-basis of $M(L)$. Then $\Phi_L \colon V \to \mathbf{P}^N$ is given by $P \mapsto (f_0(P), \ldots, f_N(P))$. Hence, $k(\Phi_L(V))$ is the subfield of $k(V)$ generated by $f_1/f_0, \ldots, f_N/f_0$ over k. Here we may assume that $f_1/f_0, f_2/f_0$ are transcendental over k. For $c \in k^*$, let $M_c = k(f_1 + cf_2) + kf_0$ be a subspace of $M(L)$, and let Λ_c be the linear subsystem of L whose k-module is M_c. Λ_c is a linear pencil, and $k(\Phi_{\Lambda_c}(V))$ coincides with $k((f_1 + cf_2)/f_0)$. Replacing f_1 by an element of the form $f_1 + \alpha_2 f_2 + \cdots + \alpha_N f_N$ ($\alpha_i \in k$) if necessary, we may assume that Λ_c has no fixed components if c is a general element of k^*. We shall assume this condition. If we can show that $k((f_1 + cf_2)/f_0)$ is algebraically closed in $k(V)$ for a general element c of k^*, a general member of Λ_c is an irreducible and reduced divisor by Lemma 9.1. Hence, a general member of L is irreducible and reduced as well. To complete a proof of Theorem 9.6, we have only to prove the following result.

LEMMA 9.7. *Let k be a field of characteristic zero, and let K be a finitely generated field extension of k such that $r :=$ tr . $\deg_k K > 0$ and k is algebraically closed in K. Let $x_1, \ldots, x_p$ $(1 \leq p \leq r)$ be a set of elements of K which are algebraically independent over k, and let $\overline{x}_i = c_{i1}x_1 + \cdots + c_{ip}x_p$ $(1 \leq i < p; c_{ij} \in k)$. Then there exists a $(p-1) \times p$-matrix (c_{ij}) with entries in k such that* tr . $\deg_k k(\overline{x}_1, \ldots, \overline{x}_{p-1}) = p - 1$ *and $k(\overline{x}_1, \ldots, \overline{x}_{p-1})$ is algebraically closed in K.*

For a proof of Theorem 9.6, we put $K = k(V)$, $p = 2$, and $x_i = f_i/f_0$ $(i = 1, 2)$ and apply Lemma 9.7. For a proof of Lemma 9.7, we need the following lemma.

LEMMA 9.8. *Let k be a field, let K be a field extension of k, and let x be an element which is transcendental over K. If k is algebraically closed in K, then $k(x)$ is algebraically closed in $K(x)$.*

PROOF. Let $f(x), g(x)$ be mutually prime elements of $K[x]$. We shall show that if $t := f(x)/g(x)$ is algebraic over $k(x)$, then $t \in k(x)$. If $t \in K$, then t is algebraic over k. (In fact, otherwise, the minimal polynomial of t over $k(x)$ has a coefficient not in k. Then x is algebraic over K which contradicts the hypothesis.) Hence, $t \in k$. Suppose $t \notin K$. Then it is clear that t is transcendental over k. Considering an algebraic relation of t over $k(x)$, we see that x is algebraic over $k(t)$. Now write

$$f(x) = a_0x^n + \cdots + a_n, \qquad g(x) = b_0x^n + \cdots + b_n,$$
$$n > 0, \quad a_i, b_j \in K, \quad a_0 \neq 0 \quad \text{or} \quad b_0 \neq 0.$$

Then x is a root of an algebraic equation with coefficients in $K(t)$,

$$(*) \qquad g(X)t - f(X) = (b_0t - a_0)X^n + \cdots + (b_nt - a_n) = 0.$$

This equation is an irreducible equation over $K(t)$. (If it is reducible, there exist elements $F(t,X), G(t,X)$ of $K[t,X]$ and a nonzero element $\varphi(t)$ of $K[t]$ such that $0 < \deg_X F < n$, $F(t,x) = 0$, and

$$\varphi(t) \cdot ((b_0 t - a_0)X^n + \cdots + (b_n t - a_n)) = F(t,X)G(t,X).$$

Meanwhile, since $t - f(X)/g(X)$ is a prime element of $K(X)[t]$ and $f(X)$, $g(X)$ are mutually prime, $g(X)t - f(X)$ is a prime element of $K[t,X]$. (This is an argument used to show that if t is an indeterminate, R: UFD implies $R[t]$: UFD.) Hence, either $\deg_X F = n$ or $\deg_X G = n$. This contradicts the choice of F.) The set of n roots of the equation $(*)$ is a part of the set of conjugate roots of x over $k(t)$. Hence, the coefficients $\zeta_i := (b_i t - a_i)/(b_0 t - a_0)(1 \le i \le n)$ of the minimal equation of x over $K(t)$ are algebraic over $k(t)$. Replacing t by t^{-1} if necessary, we may assume $b_0 \neq 0$. Suppose ζ_i satisfies an irreducible equation over $k(t)$,

$$(\dagger) \qquad \zeta_i^N + \gamma_1(t)\zeta_i^{N-1} + \cdots + \gamma_N(t) = 0, \quad \text{for each } \gamma_j(t) \in k(t),$$

where N depends on i. If we take elements $c_0(t), \ldots, c_N(t)$ of $k[t]$ such that $c_0(t), \ldots, c_N(t)$ have no common factors and $\gamma_j(t) = c_j(t)/c_0(t)$ the equation $(\dagger)$ is rewritten as follows:

$$(\dagger\dagger) \quad c_0(t)(b_i t - a_i)^N + c_1(t)(b_i t - a_i)^{N-1}(b_0 t - a_0) + \cdots + c_N(t)(b_0 t - a_0)^N = 0.$$

Since t is transcendental over K, $(\dagger\dagger)$ is a polynomial identity. Summing up in $(\dagger\dagger)$ the coefficients of terms of highest degree in t and dividing the sum by a power of b_0, we obtain a nontrivial algebraic equation of b_i/b_0 over k. Since $b_i/b_0 \in K$ and k is algebraically closed in K, we have $b_i/b_0 \in k$. Thus, $g(x) = b_0 g_1(x)$ with $g_1(x) \in k[x]$.

If $a_0 b_0 \neq 0$, we can repeat the above argument with t replaced by t^{-1} to conclude that $f(x) = a_0 f_1(x)$ with $f_1(x) \in k[x]$. Then $t = (a_0/b_0)(f_1(x)/g_1(x))$ and $f_1(x)/g_1(x) \in k(x)$. Hence, a_0/b_0 is algebraic over $k(x)$. The observation, made in the case $t \in K$, implies $a_0/b_0 \in k$. Consequently, $t \in k(x)$.

If $a_0 = 0$, then replace t by $t + c$ $(c \in k^*)$. Then $t + c = (cg + f)/g$, and $\deg g(x) = \deg(cg(x) + f(x)) = n$. In view of the case $a_0 b_0 \neq 0$, we have $t + c \in k(x)$. Hence, $t \in k(x)$. □

PROOF OF LEMMA 9.7. We treat only the case $\rho = 2$. Let K' be the algebraic closure of $k(x_1, x_2)$ in K. If $k(c_1 x_1 + c_1 x_2)$ is algebraically closed in K', then it is in K as well. Thus, we may assume that $K = K'$ and $r = 2$. Then K is an algebraic extension of $k(x_1, x_2)$. In the subsequent arguments, we fix an algebraic closure $\overline{K}$ of K. Given a subfield L of K, we take an algebraic closure $\overline{L}$ of L as a subfield of $\overline{K}$. So L is algebraically closed in K if and only if $K \cap \overline{L} = L$. For $c \in k$, set $\overline{x} = x_1 + cx_2$ and $\Omega_c = \overline{k(\overline{x})} \cap K$. We shall show that $\Omega_c = k(\overline{x})$ unless c belongs to a finite subset of k. Set $K_c = \Omega_c(x_2)$. Then $k(x_1, x_2) \subseteq K_c \subseteq K$, and K_c is an intermediate extension of a separable algebraic extension $K/k(x_1, x_2)$. There are only finitely many intermediate extensions of this kind. (In fact, by the abuse of notation, let K/k be a separable algebraic extension, let L/k be a minimal normal extension containing K, and let $G = \mathrm{Gal}(L/k)$. Then an intermediate field M of K/k is given as the invariant subfield of L with respect to a subgroup $G(M)$ of G (Theorem of Galois). Meanwhile, there are only finitely many subgroups of a finite group. Hence, there are only finitely many intermediate fields of K/k.) Hence, there exists a finite subset S (might be an empty set) of k such that, for each $c \in k - S$, there is a $d \in k - S, c \neq d$, such that $K_c = K_d$. Given such c, d, we shall show that $\Omega_c = k(\overline{x})$. Set $K^* = K_c = K_d$. $K^* = \Omega_d(x_2) = \Omega_d(x_1 + cx_2)$, and K^* is a purely transcendental extension of Ω_d. The hypothesis $\overline{k} \cap K = k$ implies $\overline{k} \cap \Omega_d = k$. So by Lemma 9.8, $k(x_1 + cx_2) = \overline{k(x_1 + cx_2)} \cap K^*$. Meanwhile, since Ω_c is algebraic over $k(x_1 + cx_2)$, we see that $\Omega_c = k(x_1 + cx_2) = k(\overline{x})$. $\square$

Let $\rho\colon V \to B$ be a pencil of curves on an algebraic surface V. We say that ρ is a *fibration* if ρ is a morphism and a general fiber of ρ is irreducible and reduced. We call the fiber over a closed point of B a *closed fiber* of ρ (or simply, a fiber), and the fiber over the generic point of B the *generic fiber* of ρ. There might appear fibers of ρ which are reducible or nonreduced.

We shall next prove that in case the characteristic of k is zero, a general fiber of a fibration $\rho\colon V \to B$ on an algebraic surface V is a nonsingular algebraic curve. For a field K, we denote by $\overline{K}$ an algebraic closure of K. A local ring $(R, \mathfrak{m})$ is called a *geometric local ring* over K if it is a localization of a finitely generated K-algebra. Given a geometric local ring R over K, we call R an *absolutely normal ring* (or a *universally normal ring*) if both R and $R \otimes_K \overline{K}$ are normal rings. A ring with only finitely many maximal ideals is called a *semilocal ring*. The intersection of all maximal ideals of a ring is the Jacobson radical. From Lemma 9.9 to Theorem 9.11 below, we restrict ourselves to the case where the ground field has characteristic zero.

LEMMA 9.9. *Let K be a field of characteristic zero, and let $(R, \mathfrak{m})$ be a geometric local domain of dimension one defined over K. Suppose the residue field M of R is an algebraic extension of K. Then the following assertions hold*:

(1) *$R \otimes_K \overline{K}$ has exactly $[M : K]$ maximal ideals.*

(2) *If $Q(R)/K$ is a regular extension, then the next three conditions are equivalent to each other*:

(i) *R is a normal ring.*

(ii) *R is an absolutely normal ring.*

(iii) *$\Omega_{R/K}$ is a free R-module of rank* 1.

PROOF. (1) By hypothesis, we can express $M = K[x]/(f(x))$. Let K' be the decomposition field of the irreducible polynomial $f(x)$ which we take as a subfield of $\overline{K}$. Then $M \otimes_K K' = N_1 \times \cdots \times N_r (r = [M : K])$ and $N_i \cong K'$ for each i. Since by (I.1.18), there is a one-to-one correspondence between maximal ideals of $R \otimes_K K'$ and maximal ideals of $M \otimes_K K'$, $R \otimes_K K'$ is a semilocal ring with exactly r maximal ideals $\{\mathfrak{m}_1, \ldots, \mathfrak{m}_r\}$, and $R \otimes_K K'/\mathfrak{m}_i = N_i$ and $\bigcap_{i=1}^r \mathfrak{m}_i = \mathfrak{m} \otimes_K K'$.

(2) (i) *implies* (ii). Let $K' = \overline{K}$ in (1). Note that $R \otimes_K K'$ is an integral domain by hypothesis. In order to show that $R \otimes_K K'$ is a normal ring, it suffices to show that $(R \otimes_K K')_{\mathfrak{m}_i}$ is a normal ring for every $\mathfrak{m}_i$. Meanwhile, writing $\mathfrak{m} = tR$, we have $\mathfrak{m}_i(R \otimes_K K')_{\mathfrak{m}_i} = \mathfrak{m}(R \otimes_K K')_{\mathfrak{m}_i} = t(R \otimes_K K')_{\mathfrak{m}_i}$. Thus, $(R \otimes_K K')_{\mathfrak{m}_i}$ is a normal ring.

(ii) *implies* (i). Since R is a geometric local ring, we can write $R = A_{\mathfrak{p}}$ for a finitely generated K-algebra domain A and a maximal ideal $\mathfrak{p}$ of A. Let $\widetilde{A}$ be the integral closure of A in $Q(A)$. Then $\widetilde{R} := \widetilde{A} \otimes_A R$ is the integral closure of R in $Q(R)$. By (I.1.34), $\widetilde{A}$ is a finitely generated A-module. Hence, $\widetilde{R}$ is a finitely generated R-module. So $\widetilde{R}/R$ is a finitely generated R-module. Since $\widetilde{R} \otimes_K \overline{K}$ is a finitely generated $R \otimes_K \overline{K}$-module, the hypothesis yields $\widetilde{R} \otimes_K \overline{K} = R \otimes_K \overline{K}$. Hence, $(\widetilde{R}/R) \otimes_K \overline{K} = 0$. This entails $R = \widetilde{R}$.

(i) *implies* (iii). $\mathfrak{m}/\mathfrak{m}^2$ is an M-vector space of rank 1. This implies that in an exact sequence of K-modules

$$\mathfrak{m}/\mathfrak{m}^2 \xrightarrow{d} \Omega_{R/K} \otimes_R M \to \Omega_{M/K} \to 0,$$

d is an injection. Moreover, since M/K is a separable algebraic extension, $\Omega_{M/K} = (0)$. Hence, $\Omega_{R/K} \otimes_R M \cong \mathfrak{m}/\mathfrak{m}^2$. Applying Nakayama's lemma, we know that $\Omega_{R/K}$ is a free R-module of rank 1.

(iii) *implies* (ii). $\Omega_{R\otimes_K \overline{K}/\overline{K}}$ is a free $R \otimes_K \overline{K}$-module of rank 1. Hence, for every maximal ideal $\mathfrak{n}$ of $R \otimes_K \overline{K}$, $\Omega_{(R\otimes_K\overline{K})_\mathfrak{n}/\overline{K}}$ is a free $(R \otimes_K \overline{K})_\mathfrak{n}$-module of rank 1. So it suffices to show that, under the assumption $M = \overline{K}$, condition (iii) implies that R is a normal ring. Then by (II.6.20), R is a regular local ring. Since $\dim R = 1$, R is a discrete valuation ring. R is therefore a normal ring. □

LEMMA 9.10. *Suppose the characteristic of k is zero. Let $\rho\colon V \to B$ be a fibration on an algebraic surface V. Let η be the generic point of B, let $K = k(B)$, and let $V_\eta = V \times_B \operatorname{Spec}(K)$. (We call V_η the* generic fiber *of ρ.) Then the following assertions hold:*

(1) V_η is a normal complete algebraic curve defined over K. Moreover, $V_\eta \otimes_K \overline{K}$ is a nonsingular complete algebraic curve defined over $\overline{K}$.

(2) There exists an open set $U(\neq \emptyset)$ of B such that V_b is a nonsingular complete algebraic curve defined over k for each $b \in U$.

PROOF. (1) It is clear that V_η is a complete algebraic curve defined over K. The function field $K(V_\eta)$ is equal to $k(V)$, and $K(V_\eta)/K$ is a regular extension. (In fact, we can make use of Lemma 9.1 because ρ is a fibration.) Let P be a closed point of V_η, and let Q be a closed point of V such that $Q \in \overline{\{P\}}$. Then the local ring $\mathscr{O}_{V_\eta,P} = \mathscr{O}_{V,P}$ is a quotient ring of the local ring $\mathscr{O}_{V,Q}$. Here $\mathscr{O}_{V,Q}$ is a normal ring as it is a regular local ring. Hence, $\mathscr{O}_{V_\eta,P}$ is a normal ring. V_η is, therefore, normal. By means of Lemma 9.9, $V_\eta \otimes_K \overline{K}$ is normal as well. Then $V_\eta \otimes_K \overline{K}$ is nonsingular as an algebraic curve defined over $\overline{K}$.

(2) By Lemma 9.9 and (1) above, $\Omega_{V_\eta/K}$ is an invertible sheaf on V_η. We shall show that there exists an open set $U(\neq \emptyset)$ of B such that $\Omega_{V/B}|_{\rho^{-1}(U)}$ is an invertible sheaf on $\rho^{-1}(U)$. Let $U = \operatorname{Spec}(A)$ be an arbitrary affine open set of B, and let $\{V_i = \operatorname{Spec}(R_i);\ 1 \leq i \leq n\}$ be a finite affine open covering of $\rho^{-1}(U)$, i.e., $\rho^{-1}(U) = \bigcup_{i=1}^n V_i$. Replacing U and V_i by smaller open sets if necessary, we may assume that $\Omega_{R_i/A} \otimes_A K$ is a free $(R_i \otimes_A K)$-module of rank 1. Take $e \in \Omega_{R_i/A}$ so that $e \otimes 1$ is a free basis of $\Omega_{R_i/A} \otimes_A K$. Then $\Omega_{R_i/A}/R_i e$ is a finitely generated R_i-module and $(\Omega_{R_i/A}/R_i e) \otimes_A K = (0)$. Hence, there exists a nonzero element a_i of A such that $\Omega_{R_i/A} \otimes_A A[a_i^{-1}] \cong R_i \otimes_A A[a_i^{-1}]$. Set $a = a_1 \cdots a_n$, and set $U = \operatorname{Spec} A[a^{-1}]$ anew. Then $\Omega_{V/B}|_{\rho^{-1}(U)}$ is an invertible sheaf on $\rho^{-1}(U)$. Set $W = \rho^{-1}(U)$. We may assume that V_b is irreducible and reduced for each $b \in U$. $\Omega_{W/U}|_{V_b}$ is an invertible sheaf on V_b. For each $P \in V_b$, set $R = \mathscr{O}_{V_b,P}$. Then $\Omega_{V_b/k,P} = \Omega_{R/k}$ is a free R-module of rank 1. R is, therefore, a regular local ring by Lemma 9.9. Namely, V_b is a nonsingular algebraic curve. □

The following result is called the *second theorem of Bertini*.

THEOREM 9.11. *Suppose the ground field k has characteristic zero. Let V be an algebraic surface, and let L be a linear system on V such that* $\dim L > 0$ *and* $\dim \operatorname{Bs} L \leq 0$. *Then a general member of L is nonsingular outside the set* $\operatorname{Bs} L$.

PROOF. By Lemma 8.10, there exists a birational morphism $\tau: W \to V$ such that $\mathrm{Bs}(\tau' L) = \emptyset$ and $\tau: W - \tau^{-1}(\mathrm{Bs}\, L) \xrightarrow{\sim} V - \mathrm{Bs}\, L$. Hence, if D is a general member of L, $\tau' D - \tau^{-1}(\mathrm{Bs}\, L)$ is isomorphic to $D - \mathrm{Bs}\, L$. So replacing V by W, we may assume that $\mathrm{Bs}\, L = \emptyset$. Consider, first of all, the case $\dim \Phi_L(V) = 1$. Then there exists a fibration $\tilde{\varphi}: V \to \widetilde{B}$ such that a general member D of L is written as $D = \sum_{i=1}^{dN} N_{b_i}$ $(b_i \in \widetilde{B})$, where we may assume that b_i's are sufficiently general points of $\widetilde{B}$ and no points of the b_i's appear repeatedly. (In fact, with the notation preceding Lemma 9.5, $\Phi_L: V \to \mathbf{P}^n$ has the Stein factorization

$$\Phi_L: V \xrightarrow{\tilde{\rho}} \widetilde{B} \xrightarrow{\nu} B := \Phi_L(V),$$

and D is written as the pullback $V \cdot H$ of a hyperplane H of $\mathbf{P}^n$. If H is sufficiently general, $B \cap H$ consists of distinct d points $z_1, \ldots, z_d$ of B and $\nu^{-1}(z_i)$ consists of N distinct points for each z_i (compare (II.6.28).) By Lemma 9.10, each V_{b_i} is a nonsingular algebraic curve. (As in this case, even for a reducible algebraic scheme X, we say that X is nonsingular at a point x if the local ring $\mathscr{O}_{X,x}$ is a regular local ring.)

Consider next the case $\dim \Phi_L(V) = 2$. Let $\{f_0, \ldots, f_n\}$ $(f_i \in k(V))$ be a k-basis of $M(L)$. As $L \subseteq |D_0|$, we assume that $f_0 = 1$ by taking D_0 so that $D_0 \in L$. For $\lambda = (\lambda_0, \cdots, \lambda_n) \in k^n$ $(= \{\text{closed points of } \mathbf{A}^n\})$, let Λ_λ be the linear subsystem of L corresponding to a linear subspace $k \cdot 1 + k \cdot (\lambda_1 f_1 + \cdots + \lambda_n f_n)$ of $M(L)$. Setting $D_\lambda = D_0 + (1 + \lambda_1 f_1 + \cdots + \lambda_n f_n)$, we call Λ_λ the *linear pencil* generated by D_0 and D_λ. By hypothesis, $\mathrm{tr.deg}_k\, k(f_1, \ldots, f_n) = 2$. Hence, if λ is general point of k^n, $k(\lambda_1 f_1 + \cdots + \lambda_n f_n)$ is algebraically closed in $k(V)$ (compare the proof of Theorem 9.6). If we replace λ by $c\lambda = (c\lambda_1, \ldots, c\lambda_n)$ $(c \in k^*)$, D_λ is an irreducible and reduced algebraic curve and D_λ is nonsingular outside the points of $\mathrm{Bs}(\Lambda_\lambda) = \mathrm{Supp}\, D_0 \cap \mathrm{Supp}\, D_\lambda$ (Problem III.9.3) by the first case considered above. Since $\mathrm{Bs}\, L = \emptyset$, there exists a member D_1 of L such that $\mathrm{Supp}\, D_0 \cap \mathrm{Supp}\, D_1 \cap \mathrm{Supp}\, D_\lambda = \emptyset$. Writing $D_1 = D_0 + (g)$, we may assume that $k(g, \lambda_1 f_1 + \cdots + \lambda_n f_n)$ has transcendence degree 2 over k. Then we can find $\alpha \in k^*$ so that $k((1 + \alpha\lambda_1 f_1 + \cdots + \alpha\lambda_n f_n)/g)$ is algebraically closed in $k(V)$ (Lemma 9.7). We may view D_λ as a general member of the linear pencil generated by D_1 and $D_0 + (1 + \alpha\lambda_1 f_1 + \cdots + \alpha\lambda_n f_n)$. Hence, D_λ is nonsingular outside $\mathrm{Supp}\, D_0 \cap \mathrm{Supp}\, D_1$. D_λ is, therefore, a nonsingular irreducible algebraic curve. □

Let $\rho: V \to B$ be a fibration on an algebraic surface. For $P \in V$ and $b = \rho(P)$, $\mathscr{O}_{B,b}$ is a principal ideal domain and $\mathscr{O}_{V,P}$ is a torsion-free $\mathscr{O}_{B,b}$-module. So $\mathscr{O}_{V,P}$ is a flat $\mathscr{O}_{B,b}$-module. Under the situation of Lemma 9.10 (2), $\rho: \rho^{-1}(U) \to U$ is a smooth morphism. When the characteristic of k is positive, there exists a fibration for which such an open set does not exist. However, by the proof of Lemma 9.1, we know that there exists an open set U of B such that each fiber of $\rho: \rho^{-1}(U) \to U$ is irreducible and reduced. Since $B - U$ is a finite set, there are, in the fibration, at most finitely many reducible fibers or nonreduced fibers. For a point b of B, if we choose a local parameter t of B at b and regard t as a function on V, V_b is viewed as the zero part $(t)_0$ in an open neighbourhood of V_b. Namely, we have $V_b = (t)_0 = \sum_{i=1}^r a_i C_i$ $(a_i > 0, C_i$: irreducible component) as divisors in an open neighbourhood of V_b. We call V_b a *singular fiber* unless it is a nonsingular irreducible algebraic curve. We set $a = \gcd(a_1, \ldots, a_r)$ and call it the *multiplcity* of V_b. If $a > 1$, we say that V_b is a *multiple fiber*.

DEFINITION 9.12. Let V be an algebraic surface, let C be a nonsingular projective algebraic curve, let $\mathscr{L}$ be an invertible sheaf on $V \times C$, let P, Q be closed points of C, and let $q: V \times C \to C$ be the projection. Then $q^{-1}(P) = V \times (P)$ and $q^{-1}(Q) = V \times (Q)$ are identified with V. Accordingly, $\mathscr{L}_P := \mathscr{L}|_{q^{-1}(P)}$ and $\mathscr{L}_Q := \mathscr{L}|_{q^{-1}(Q)}$ are viewed as invertible sheaves on V. We then say that $\mathscr{L}_P$ and $\mathscr{L}_Q$ are *algebraically equivalent* and write $\mathscr{L}_P \approx \mathscr{L}_Q$. We can define an equivalence relation on the set of invertible sheaves on V which is generated by all the relations $\approx$ as above with $C, \mathscr{L}, P, Q$ ranging over all possible ones. We denote this equivalence relation by the same symbol $\approx$. Note that if $C \cong \mathbf{P}^1$, then $\mathscr{L}_P \sim \mathscr{L}_Q$ (linear equivalence). Hence, the algebraic equivalence is coarser than the linear equivalence (Problem III.9.4).

LEMMA 9.13. *Let V be an algebraic surface, and let D, D', E be divisors on V. If $D \approx D'$ (i.e., $\mathscr{O}_V(D) \approx \mathscr{O}_V(D')$), then $(D \cdot E) = (D' \cdot E)$.*

PROOF. Since the intersection number $(\ \cdot\ )$ is a bilinear form, we may assume that E is an irreducible divisor. The condition $D \approx D'$ means, by definition, the following: There exist nonsingular projective algebraic curves $C_1, \ldots, C_N$, invertible sheaves $\mathscr{L}^{(i)}$ on $V \times C_i$ for each i, and closed points P_i, Q_i on C_i for each i such that

$$\mathscr{O}_V(D) + \sum_{i=1}^{N} \mathscr{L}^{(i)}_{P_i} = \mathscr{O}_V(D') + \sum_{i=1}^{N} \mathscr{L}^{(i)}_{Q_i},$$

where we denote the tensor product $\otimes$ for invertible sheaves by the sum$+$ by confusing invertible sheaves with Weil divisors. Hence, in view of the bilinearity of the intersection form, we have only to prove the lemma in the case where $\mathscr{O}_V(D) = \mathscr{L}_P$ and $\mathscr{O}_V(D') = \mathscr{L}_Q$ for a nonsingular projective algebraic curve C, an invertible sheaf $\mathscr{L}$ on $V \times C$, and closed points P, Q of C.

Let $\alpha: E \times C \to V \times C$ be the natural closed immersion. In the proof of Theorem 8.2 (1), we have shown that $(\mathscr{L}_P \cdot E) = \deg(\mathscr{L}_P|_E)$ and $(\mathscr{L}_Q \cdot E) = \deg(\mathscr{L}_Q|_E)$, where $\deg(\mathscr{L}_P|_E) = \deg(\alpha^*\mathscr{L}|_{E\times(P)})$ and $\deg(\mathscr{L}_Q|_E) = \deg(\alpha^*\mathscr{L}|_{E\times(Q)})$ evidently. On the other hand, if $\nu: \widetilde{E} \to E$ is the normalization morphism of E and $\beta = \alpha \cdot (\nu \times 1_C)$, we have $\deg(\mathscr{L}_P|_E) = \deg(\beta^*\mathscr{L}|_{\widetilde{E}\times(P)})$ and $\deg(\mathscr{L}_Q|_E) = \deg(\beta^*\mathscr{L}|_{\widetilde{E}\times(Q)})$. Thus, we have only to prove the following assertion:

Let E, C be nonsingular projective algebraic curves, let D be an irreducible divisor on $W := E \times C$, and let P, Q be closed points of C. Then the equality $(D \cdot E_P) = (D \cdot E_Q)$ holds on W, where $E_P = E \times (P)$ and $E_Q = E \times (Q)$.

Consider the case where $q(D) = C$ for the natural projection $q: E \times C \to C$. Let $f = q|_D$. Then $(D \cdot E_P) = \dim f_*\mathscr{O}_D \otimes_{\mathscr{O}_C} k(P)$. (In fact, write $D \cap E_P = \{R_1, \ldots, R_m\}$. Let t be a local parameter of C at P. At each point R_i, t is taken as one of local parameters of W. Let x_i be another local parameter of W at R_i, and let $f_i(t, x_i) = 0$ be the local defining equation of D at R_i. Then $(D \cdot E_P) = \sum_{i=1}^m \dim_k \mathscr{O}_{W,R_i}/(f_i, t)$ and the right side of this equality coincides with $\dim f_*\mathscr{O}_D \otimes_{\mathscr{O}_C} k(P)$.) Meanwhile, $f_*\mathscr{O}_D$ is flat as a coherent $\mathscr{O}_C$-Module. Hence, it is a locally free $\mathscr{O}_C$-Module. (In fact, a torsion-free, finitely generated module over a principal ideal domain is a free module.) Hence, its rank is constant at various points of C. Namely, $(D \cdot E_P) = (D \cdot E_Q)$. Consider next the case where $q(D)$ is a closed point P of C. Then $D = E_P$. Since $Q \neq P$, $(D \cdot E_Q) = \deg(\mathscr{O}_W(D)|_{E_Q}) = \deg(\mathscr{O}_W|_{E_Q}) = 0$. We have $(D \cdot E_P) = (E_P)^2 = \deg \mathscr{N}_{E_P/W}$. Since $(\mathscr{N}_{E_P/W})^* = \mathscr{I}_{E_P}/(\mathscr{I}_{E_P})^2 = t\mathscr{O}_W/t^2\mathscr{O}_W \cong \mathscr{O}_{E_P}$, we have $(D \cdot E_P) = 0$. In both cases, we have, therefore, the equality $(D \cdot E_P) = (D \cdot E_Q)$. □

Let $\rho\colon V \to B$ be a fibration. Two fibers V_{b_1}, V_{b_2} of ρ are algebraically equivalent as divisors on V. (Let $\Gamma := \operatorname{Im}(1_V, \rho)(\subset V \times B)$ be the graph of ρ and let $\mathscr{L} := \mathscr{O}(\Gamma)$. Then $\mathscr{L}|_{V\times(b_1)} \cong \mathscr{O}_V(V_{b_1})$ and $\mathscr{L}|_{V\times(b_2)} \cong \mathscr{O}_V(V_{b_2})$.] Let S be an irreducible curve on V, and let F be a general fiber of ρ. Then the intersection number $n := (S \cdot F)$ is independent of the choice of F. If $n > 0$, then we call S an *n-section* of ρ. In particular, if $n = 1$, we call S a *section* (or a *cross-section*) of ρ. If $n = 0$, either S does not meet F, or S coincides with F. Since F is a general fiber, we may assume that S does not coincide with F. Then $\rho(S)$ is a closed point of B, and S is contained in a fiber of ρ. Let F_1 be a fiber of ρ different from F. Then $(F^2) = (F \cdot F_1) = 0$. If we write $F_1 = \sum_{i=1}^r a_i C_i$ ($a_i > 0$, C_i: irreducible component), $(F_1 \cdot C_i) = 0$. By Lemma 9.3, F_1 is connected. Hence, if F_1 is a reducible fiber, $(F_1 - a_i C_i \cdot C_i) > 0$. So $(C_i^2) < 0$. Extending this argument, we obtain the following result.

LEMMA 9.14. *Let $\rho\colon V \to B$ be a fibration, and let V_η be the generic fiber. Then the following assertions hold*:

(1) (i) *Giving a section S of ρ is equivalent to giving a K-rational point of V_η, where $K = k(B)$.*

(ii) *A cross section S of ρ is a nonsingular algebraic curve and is isomorphic to B by ρ.*

(iii) *If ρ has a section, then ρ has no multiple fibers.*

(2) *Let $V_b = \sum_{i=1}^r a_i C_i$ be a reducible fiber of ρ, and let $M = ((C_i \cdot C_j))_{1\le i,j\le r}$ be the* intersection matrix *of the irreducible components of V_b. Then M is negative semidefinite. Namely, for $Z = \sum_{i=1}^r s_i C_i (s_i \in \mathbf{R})$, we have $(Z^2) \le 0$, and $(Z^2) = 0$ if and only if $Z = \alpha V_b$ $(\alpha \in \mathbf{R})$.*

PROOF. (1) (i) and (ii). Let S be a section of ρ. Let P be any closed point of S, and let $b = \rho(P)$. Let t be a local parameter of B at b, and let $y = 0$ be a local defining equation of S at P. Since $1 = (S \cdot V_b) = \dim_k \mathscr{O}_{V,P}/(t, y)$, (t, y) is a system of local parameters of V at P. Hence, $\mathscr{O}_{S,P} = \mathscr{O}_{V,P}/(y)$ and $\mathfrak{m}_{S,P} = (t)$. So S is nonsingular at P. Since P is arbitrary, S is a nonsingular algebraic curve and $\rho_S := \rho|_S$ is an unramified morphism. $\rho_S\colon S \to B$ is a finite morphism and apparently a one-to-one mapping. (In fact, let $\widetilde{B}$ be the normalization of B in $k(S)$. Then ρ_S factors as

$$\rho_S\colon S \xrightarrow{\sigma} \widetilde{B} \xrightarrow{\nu} B,$$

and σ is a birational morphism between nonsingular algebraic curves. Hence, σ is an isomorphism, and ν is a finite morphism as the normalization morphism.) Thus, $\mathscr{O}_{S,P}$ is a finitely generated $\mathscr{O}_{B,b}$-module, and $\mathscr{O}_{S,P} = \mathscr{O}_{B,b} + t\mathscr{O}_{S,P}$. So $\mathscr{O}_{S,P} = \mathscr{O}_{B,b}$ by Nakayama's lemma. Namely, ρ_S is an isomorphism. In particular, S gives rise to a K-rational point. (In fact, the closed immersion $S \hookrightarrow V$ over B gives rise to a K-rational point $S \times_B \operatorname{Spec}(K) \hookrightarrow V_\eta$ by taking fiber products with $\operatorname{Spec} K \to B$.) Conversely, let ξ be a K-rational point of V_η, and let $S = \overline{\{\xi\}}$ be the closure in V. Since $\operatorname{tr.deg}_k k(\xi) = \operatorname{tr.deg}_k K = 1$, S is a complete algebraic curve over k. Since $\rho_S := \rho|_S\colon S \to B$ is a birational morphism, ρ_S is an isomorphism. (In fact, for $P \in S$ and $b = \rho(P)$, $\mathscr{O}_{S,P} \ge \mathscr{O}_{B,b}$ and $\mathscr{O}_{B,b}$ is a discrete valuation ring of K. Hence, $\mathscr{O}_{S,P} = \mathscr{O}_{B,b}$.) Moreover, with the above notation, let $y = 0$ be a local defining equation of S at P. Since $\mathscr{O}_{V,P}/(y) = \mathscr{O}_{B,b}$, we have $\mathfrak{m}_{V,P} = (t, y)$ with a local parameter t of B at b. Hence, $(V_b \cdot S) = 1$. Namely, S is a section of ρ.

(ii) If V_b is a multiple fiber, we can write $V_b = a\Gamma$ with $a > 1$. If S is a section of ρ, we have $(V_b \cdot S) = a(\Gamma \cdot S) \ge a > 1$ which is a contradiction.

(2) For $Z = \sum_{i=1}^{r} s_i C_i$, we make the computation

$$\begin{aligned}
(Z^2) &= \sum_{1\le i,j\le r} s_i s_j (C_i \cdot C_j) \\
&= \sum_{1\le i,j\le r} \frac{s_i}{a_i} \cdot \frac{s_j}{a_j} (a_i C_i \cdot a_j C_j) \\
&= (a_1 C_1 + \cdots + a_r C_r \cdot \left(\frac{s_1}{a_1}\right)^2 a_1 C_1 + \cdots + \left(\frac{s_r}{a_r}\right)^2 a_r (C_r) \\
&\quad - \sum_{i<j} \left(\frac{s_i}{a_i} - \frac{s_j}{a_j}\right)^2 a_i a_j (C_i \cdot C_j) \\
&= -\sum_{i<j} \left(\frac{s_i}{a_i} - \frac{s_j}{a_j}\right)^2 a_i a_j (C_i \cdot C_j) \le 0,
\end{aligned}$$

where $(a_1 C_1 + \cdots + a_r C_r \cdot C_i) = (V_b \cdot C_i) = 0$ for each i. We have

$$(Z^2) = 0 \quad \text{if and only if} \quad \frac{s_i}{a_i} = \frac{s_j}{a_j}$$

whenever $i \neq j$ and $(C_i \cdot C_j) > 0$. Since V_b is connected, s_i/a_i is a real number independent of i. So $(Z^2) = 0$ if and only if $Z = \alpha V_b$ for some $\alpha \in \mathbf{R}$. □

III.9. Problems

1. Let k be a field of characteristic zero, and let A be a k-algebra. We assume moreover that A is an artinian local ring and a finitely generated k-module. Then, following the subsequent steps, verify the assertion that A is reduced if and only if $\Omega_{A/k} = (0)$.
   (i) Show that $\Omega_{A/k} = (0)$ if A is reduced.
   We prove below the converse.
   (ii) For a maximal ideal $\mathfrak{m}$ of A, $\mathfrak{m}^N = (0)$ for some $N > 0$. Let $\overline{A} = A/\mathfrak{m}^2$. Then $\Omega_{\overline{A}/k} = (0)$ if $\Omega_{A/k} = (0)$. Hence, replacing A by $\overline{A}$, we may assume that $\mathfrak{m}^2 = (0)$.
   (iii) The residue field $k' := A/\mathfrak{m}$ is a separable algebraic extension of k. So let $\tilde{k}$ be a normal extension of k containing k', and let $\widetilde{A} = A \otimes_k \tilde{k}$. Then $\widetilde{A}$ decomposes as $\widetilde{A} = A_1 \times \cdots \times A_r$ (a direct product), and A_i is an artinian local ring with residue field $\tilde{k}$. If each A_i is reduced, then A is reduced as well.
   (iv) We may replace A by A_i, and hence, by doing so, assume that $k' = k$. Then $\Omega_{A/k} \otimes_A k \cong \mathfrak{m}$. Hence, $\Omega_{A/k} = (0)$ implies $\mathfrak{m} = (0)$.
2. Let X be a reduced algebraic scheme defined over an algebraically closed field k. If $\mathscr{O}_{X,x}$ is a normal ring at every closed point x of X, show that each connected component of X is irreducible.
3. Let Λ be a linear pencil on an algebraic surface V, and let D_1, D_2 be distinct two members of Λ. Show that $\operatorname{Bs}\Lambda = \operatorname{Supp} D_1 \cap \operatorname{Supp} D_2$.
4. Let V be an algebraic surface, let $C = \mathbf{P}^1$, let $\mathscr{L}$ be an invertible sheaf on $V \times C$ and let $P, Q \in C$. Following the subsequent steps, prove that $\mathscr{L}_P := \mathscr{L}|_{V\times(P)}$ and $\mathscr{L}_Q := \mathscr{L}|_{V\times(Q)}$ are linearly equivalent.
   (i) We can take an inhomogeneous coordinate t on C so that P, Q are defined by $t = 0$, $t = 1$, respectively. So we may assume below that $C = \mathbf{A}^1$.
   (ii) For $x \in V, \mathscr{O}_{V,x}[t]$ is a UFD. So the pullback of $\mathscr{L}$ onto $\operatorname{Spec}\mathscr{O}_{V,x}[t]$ is a

trivial invertible sheaf. Hence, there exists an open neighbourhood U of x such $\mathscr{L}|_{U\times C} \cong \mathscr{O}_{U\times C}$.
(iii) There exists an open covering $\{U_i\}_{i\in I}$ of V such that $\mathscr{L}|_{U_i\times C} \cong \mathscr{O}_{U_i\times C}$. Show that, for the transition functions $\{f_{ij}\}_{i,j\in I}$ of $\mathscr{L}$ with respect to the open covering $\{U_i \times C\}_{i\in I}$ we have $f_{ij} \in \Gamma(U_{ij}, \mathscr{O}_V)^*$, where $U_{ij} = U_i \cap U_j$. Hence, there exists an invertible sheaf $\mathscr{M}$ on V such that $\mathscr{L} = q^*\mathscr{M}$, where $q\colon V\times C \to C$ is the natural projection.
(iv) Show that $\mathscr{L}_P \cong \mathscr{L}_Q$.

5. (v) Let D, D' be divisors on V such that $D' = D + (f)$ for $f \in k(V)$. Let $\varphi\colon V \to \mathbf{P}^1$ be the rational mapping, $x \mapsto (1, f(x))$, defined by f, and let Γ be the graph $\mathrm{Im}(1_V \times \varphi)(\subseteq V \times \mathbf{P}^1)$ of φ. Let $\mathscr{L} = \mathscr{O}(\Gamma)\otimes\mathscr{O}(D\times\mathbf{P}^1)$. Show that $\mathscr{L}_{(\infty)} = \mathscr{O}(D + A)$ and $\mathscr{L}_{(0)} = \mathscr{O}(D' + A)$, where A is some divisor.

CHAPTER 10

The Riemann-Roch Theorem for Algebraic Surfaces

In Chapter 6 of Part II, we defined the canonical Module $\omega_{X/k}$ and the canonical divisor K_X for an n-dimensional, nonsingular algebraic variety X defined over k. For the generic point η of X and $K = k(X)$, we have $\omega_{X/k,\eta} = \bigwedge^n \Omega_{K/k}$. Here if $\{x_1, \ldots, x_n\}$ is a system of local parameters at a closed point x of X, we can write $\bigwedge^n \Omega_{K/k} = K\,dx_1 \wedge \cdots \wedge dx_n$. So if ω is a nonzero element of $\bigwedge^n \Omega_{K/k}$, we can write $\omega = f_P\,dx_1 \wedge \cdots \wedge dx_n$ with $f_P \in K$. We consider the divisor (f_P) on a coordinate neighbourhood U_P of the system of parameters $\{x_1, \ldots, x_n\}$. If P moves on V, then the divisors (f_P) are patched together to give a divisor (ω) which is linearly equivalent to K_X.

In what follows let V be an algebraic surface. All algebraic curves on V are supposed to be closed subschemes unless otherwise mentioned.

LEMMA 10.1. *Let C be an irreducible algebraic curve on V, and let $\mathscr{I}_C$ be the defining ideal sheaf of C. Then the following assertions hold:*

(1) *The following sequence is an exact sequence*

$$0 \to \mathscr{I}_C/\mathscr{I}_C^2 \to \Omega_{V/k}|_C \to \Omega_{C/k} \to 0.$$

(2) *If C is a nonsingular algebraic curve, then we have $\omega_{C/k} \cong (\omega_{V/k} \otimes \mathscr{O}_C) \otimes \mathscr{N}_{C/V}$. If $g(C)$ is the genus of C, we have*

$$g(C) = \frac{1}{2}(C \cdot C + K_V) + 1.$$

Furthermore, we have the following equalities:

$$\chi(\mathscr{O}_V(-C)) = \frac{1}{2}(C \cdot C + K_V) + \chi(\mathscr{O}_V),$$

$$\chi(\mathscr{O}_V(C)) = \frac{1}{2}(C \cdot C - K_V) + \chi(\mathscr{O}_V).$$

PROOF. (1) By (II.6.18), the following sequence is exact.

$$\mathscr{I}_C/\mathscr{I}_C^2 \xrightarrow{\alpha} \Omega_{V/k}|_C \to \Omega_{C/k} \to 0,$$

where $\Omega_{V/k}|_C$ is a locally free $\mathscr{O}_C$-Module of rank 2. For a point $Q \in C$, C is defined by an equation $f = 0$ locally at Q. Then $(\mathscr{I}_C/\mathscr{I}_C^2)_Q = \mathscr{O}_{C,Q}\overline{f}$ with $\overline{f} = f$ $(\mathrm{mod}(\mathscr{I}_{C,Q})^2)$. Hence, $\mathscr{I}_C/\mathscr{I}_C^2$ is an invertible sheaf. Put $\mathscr{O} = \mathscr{O}_{C,Q}$. $\mathscr{O}$ is an integral domain, and $(\Omega_{V/k}|_C)_Q \cong \mathscr{O} \oplus \mathscr{O}$ has no torsion elements. So, $\alpha_Q\colon (\mathscr{I}_C/\mathscr{I}_C^2)_Q \to (\Omega_{V/k}|_C)_Q$ is zero or injective. If α_Q were zero, then $(\Omega_{C/k})_Q \cong \mathscr{O} \oplus \mathscr{O}$ which is a contradiction. Thus, α_Q is injective. Since Q is an arbitrary closed point, α itself is injective.

(2) In the exact sequence of (1), $\Omega_{C/k}$ is also an invertible sheaf. Hence, $\bigwedge^2 \Omega_{V/k}|_C \cong \Omega_{C/k} \otimes (\mathcal{I}_C/\mathcal{I}_C^2)$. This implies that $\omega_{C/k} \cong (\omega_{V/k}|_C) \oplus \mathcal{N}_{C/V}$. On the other hand, $\deg(\omega_{V/k}|_C) = (K_V \cdot C)$ and $\deg \mathcal{N}_{C/V} = -\deg(\mathcal{O}_V(-C) \otimes_{\mathcal{O}_V} \mathcal{O}_C) = (C^2)$. So we have

$$2g - 2 = \deg \omega_{C/k} = (K_V \cdot C) + (C^2).$$

This gives rise to the equality concerning g. In order to obtain the remaining two equalities, we make use of the following exact sequence

$$(*) \qquad 0 \to \mathcal{O}_V(-C) \to \mathcal{O}_V \to \mathcal{O}_C \to 0.$$

Taking the Euler-Poincaré characteristics, we obtain $\chi(\mathcal{O}_V(-C)) = \chi(\mathcal{O}_V) - \chi(\mathcal{O}_C)$. Since $\chi(\mathcal{O}_C) = 1 - h^1(C, \mathcal{O}_C) = 1 - g(C)$, we obtain the equality

$$\chi(\mathcal{O}_V(-C)) = \frac{1}{2}(C \cdot C + K_V) + \chi(\mathcal{O}_V).$$

Next, applying $\otimes \mathcal{O}_V(C)$ to the exact sequence $(*)$, we get an exact sequence

$$0 \to \mathcal{O}_V \to \mathcal{O}_V(C) \to \mathcal{O}_C(C) \to 0,$$

where $\mathcal{O}_C(C) := \mathcal{O}_C \otimes_{\mathcal{O}_V} \mathcal{O}_V(C)$. Making use of the Riemann-Roch theorem on C, we obtain the equality:

$$\begin{aligned}\chi(\mathcal{O}_V(C)) &= \chi(\mathcal{O}_V) + \chi(\mathcal{O}_C(C)) \\ &= \chi(\mathcal{O}_V) + (C^2) - \frac{1}{2}(C \cdot C + K_V) \\ &= \frac{1}{2}(C \cdot C - K_V) + \chi(\mathcal{O}_V). \end{aligned}$$

□

Definition 10.2. For a divisor D on V, we define the *arithmetic genus* $p_a(D)$ by

$$p_a(D) = \frac{1}{2}(D \cdot D + K_V) + 1.$$

We will sometimes refer to this equality by calling it the *arithmetic genus formula*. We shall show in Lemma 10.4 that $p_a(C) \geq 0$ if C is an irreducible divisor.

Lemma 10.3. *Let P be a closed point of V, let $\sigma\colon V' \to V$ be the monoidal transformation with center at P, and let $E = \sigma^{-1}(P)$. Then the following assertions hold*:

(1) *$K_{V'} \sim \sigma^*(K_V) + E$ and $(K_{V'})^2 = (K_V)^2 - 1$.*

(2) *Let $\mathcal{I}_P$ be the defining ideal sheaf of P on V. For every nonnegative integer n, we have*

$$\sigma_* \mathcal{O}_{V'}(-nE) = \mathcal{I}_P^n, \qquad R^1\sigma_* \mathcal{O}_{V'}(-nE) = (0),$$

where $\mathcal{I}_P^0 = \mathcal{O}_V$.

(3) *Let C be an irreducible divisor on V, let μ be the multiplicity of C at P, and let $C' = \sigma'(C)$. Then we have*

$$p_a(C') = p_a(C) - \frac{1}{2}\mu(\mu - 1), \qquad \chi(\mathcal{O}_{C'}) = \chi(\mathcal{O}_C) + \frac{1}{2}\mu(\mu - 1).$$

Proof. (1) Choosing a system of local parameters (u, v) at P, set $\omega = du \wedge dv$, $w = v/u$ is an inhomogeneous coordinate on E, and $\omega = u\, du \wedge dw$ if we consider

(u,w) instead of (u,v). Considering the divisors $(\omega)_V$ and $(\omega)_{V'}$ which a nonzero element ω of $\bigwedge^2 \Omega_{K/k}$ defines on V and V', respectively, we have $\omega_{V'} = \sigma^*(\omega)_V + E$. Hence, $K_{V'} \sim \sigma^* K_V + E$. By virtue of Lemma 8.8 and Corollary 8.9, we get $(K_{V'})^2 = (K_V)^2 - 1$.

(2) Set $\mathscr{O} = \mathscr{O}_{V,P}$, $\mathfrak{m} = \mathfrak{m}_{V,P}$, $W = V' \times_V \operatorname{Spec}\mathscr{O}$ and $\tau = \sigma \times_V \operatorname{Spec}\mathscr{O}$. We have only to show that $\tau_*\mathscr{O}_W(-nE) = \mathfrak{m}^n$ and $R^1\tau_*\mathscr{O}_W(-nE) = (0)$ for each $n \geq 0$. It is easy to see that $\sigma_*\mathscr{O}_{V'} = \mathscr{O}_V$. Hence, $\tau_*\mathscr{O}_W = \mathscr{O}_V$. Noting that $\mathfrak{m}^n\mathscr{O}_W = \mathscr{O}_W(-nE)$, we get $\tau_*\mathscr{O}_W(-nE) = \tau_*(\mathfrak{m}^n\mathscr{O}_W) = \mathfrak{m}^n\tau_*\mathscr{O}_W = \mathfrak{m}^n$. We shall next show that $R^1\tau_*(\mathfrak{m}^n\mathscr{O}_W) = \mathfrak{m}^n R^1\tau_*\mathscr{O}_W$. Since $\mathfrak{m}^n$ is a finitely generated $\mathscr{O}$-module, we write $\mathfrak{m}^n = \sum_{i=1}^N f_i\mathscr{O}$. So we obtain a surjection

$$\bigoplus_{i=1}^N f_i\mathscr{O}_W \xrightarrow{\beta} \mathfrak{m}^n\mathscr{O}_W \longrightarrow 0.$$

Noting that $R^2\tau_*\mathscr{F} = (0)$ for any coherent $\mathscr{O}_W$-Module $\mathscr{F}$, we obtain from the surjective homomorphism β the following surjection:

$$\bigoplus_{i=1}^N R^1\tau_*(f_i\mathscr{O}_W) \to R^1\tau_*(\mathfrak{m}^n\mathscr{O}_W) \to 0,$$

where $R^1\tau_*(f_i\mathscr{O}_W) = f_i R^1\tau_*(\mathscr{O}_W)$. (Check this directly from the definition.) Hence, it follows that $R^1\tau_*(\mathfrak{m}^n\mathscr{O}_W) = \mathfrak{m}^n R^1\tau_*(\mathscr{O}_W)$. In the cohomology exact sequence (concerning $R^i\tau_*(\cdot)$) associated with an exact sequence

$$0 \to \mathfrak{m}\mathscr{O}_W \to \mathscr{O}_W \to \mathscr{O}_E \to 0,$$

we have $R^1\tau_*\mathscr{O}_E = H^1(E, \mathscr{O}_E) = (0)$. Hence, the cohomology sequence yields $\mathfrak{m}R^1\tau_*(\mathscr{O}_W) = R^1\tau_*(\mathscr{O}_W)$. Since τ is a proper morphism, $R^1\tau_*(\mathscr{O}_W)$ is a finitely-generated $\mathscr{O}$-module (compare (II.4.18)). So we get $R^1\tau_*(\mathscr{O}_W) = (0)$ by Nakayama's lemma. Hence, we obtain $R^1\tau_*\mathscr{O}_W(-nE) = \mathfrak{m}^n R^1\tau_*\mathscr{O}_W = (0)$ for each $n \geq 0$.

(3) By Lemma 8.8, $\sigma^*(C) = C' + \mu E$. By means of the arithmetic genus formula, we have

$$\begin{aligned} p_a(C') &= \frac{1}{2}(C' \cdot C' + K_{V'}) + 1 \\ &= \frac{1}{2}(\sigma^*(C) - \mu E \cdot \sigma^*(C + K_V) - (\mu - 1)E) + 1 \\ &= p_a(C) - \frac{1}{2}\mu(\mu - 1). \end{aligned}$$

We shall verify that the second equality holds. We have $\chi(\mathscr{O}_{C'}) = \chi(\mathscr{O}_{V'}) - \chi(\mathscr{O}_{V'}(-C'))$ and $\chi(\mathscr{O}_C) = \chi(\mathscr{O}_V) - \chi(\mathscr{O}_V(-C))$. Furthermore, $\chi(\mathscr{O}_{V'}) = \chi(\mathscr{O}_V)$ and $\chi(\mathscr{O}_{V'}(-C' - \mu E)) = \chi(\mathscr{O}_V(-C))$. (In fact, for a quasicoherent $\mathscr{O}_{V'}$-Module $\mathscr{F}$ and an invertible sheaf $\mathscr{L}$ on V, $R^q\sigma_*(\sigma^*\mathscr{L} \otimes \mathscr{F}) \cong \mathscr{L} \otimes R^q\sigma_*(\mathscr{F})$ for each $q \geq 0$ (problem I.2.9). We have, moreover, a spectral sequence (I.2.28)

$$E_2^{p,q} = H^p(V, R^q\sigma_*(\sigma^*\mathscr{L} \otimes \mathscr{F})) \Rightarrow H^{p+q}(V', \sigma^*\mathscr{L} \otimes \mathscr{F}).$$

Apply these two results to $(\mathscr{L}, \mathscr{F}) = (\mathscr{O}_V, \mathscr{O}_{V'})$ and $(\mathscr{O}_V(-C), \mathscr{O}_{V'})$. In case $(\mathscr{L}, \mathscr{F}) = (\mathscr{O}_V, \mathscr{O}_{V'})$, by Lemma 10.3 (2), $\sigma_*\mathscr{O}_{V'} = \mathscr{O}_V$ and $R^q\sigma_*\mathscr{O}_{V'} = (0)$ for each $q > 0$.

Hence, $H^p(V,\mathscr{O}_V) \cong H^p(V',\mathscr{O}_{V'})$ for each $p \geq 0$. Thus, $\chi(\mathscr{O}_{V'}) = \chi(\mathscr{O}_V)$. In case $(\mathscr{L},\mathscr{F}) = (\mathscr{O}_V(-C),\mathscr{O}_{V'})$, we have

$$R^q\sigma_*(\mathscr{O}_{V'}(-C' - \mu E)) = R^q\sigma_*(\sigma^*\mathscr{O}_V(-C)) = \mathscr{O}_V(-C) \otimes R^q\sigma_*(\mathscr{O}_{V'}).$$

Hence, we obtain $H^p(V,\mathscr{O}_V(-C)) \cong H^p(V',\mathscr{O}_{V'}(-C' - \mu E))$ for each $p \geq 0$. So, $\chi(\mathscr{O}_{V'}(-C' - \mu E)) = \chi(\mathscr{O}_V(-C))$.) Meanwhile, for $1 \leq i \leq \mu$, we have an exact sequence

$$0 \to \mathscr{O}_{V'}(-C' - \mu E) \to \mathscr{O}_{V'}(-C' - (i-1)E) \to \mathscr{O}_E(-\mu + i - 1) \to 0.$$

From this we obtain

$$\begin{aligned}\chi(\mathscr{O}_{V'}(-C' - \mu E)) &= \chi(\mathscr{O}_{V'}(-C' - (i-1)E)) - \chi(\mathscr{O}_E(-\mu + i - 1)) \\ &= \chi(\mathscr{O}_{V'}(-C' - (i-1)E)) + (\mu - i).\end{aligned}$$

So $\chi(\mathscr{O}_{V'}(-C' - \mu E)) = \chi(\mathscr{O}_{V'}(-C')) + \frac{1}{2}\mu(\mu - 1)$. These observations yield the required equality

$$\chi(\mathscr{O}_{C'}) = \chi(\mathscr{O}_C) + \frac{1}{2}\mu(\mu - 1). \qquad \square$$

With the notations of Lemma 10.3, each point on E is called an *infinitely near point of the first order* of P. When C is an irreducible algebraic curve passing through P, the intersection points of E with the proper transform C' of C are called infinitely near points of the first order of P lying on C. If C is nonsingular at P, we have $\mu = 1 = (C' \cdot E)$. So C' meets E in a single point, and C' and E cross normally at this point. However, if C is singular at P, C' might meet E in more than one point and C' might be singular at an intersection point of C' and E. When $P'(\in C' \cap E)$ is a singular point of C', the multiplicity of C' at P' is called the multiplicity of C at P'. Let $\tau\colon V'' \to V'$ be the monoidal transformation with center at P' on E, and let $E' = \tau^{-1}(P')$. A point P'' on E' is an infinitely near point of the first order of P'; we call P'' an infinitely near point of the second order of P. When we speak of P'' lying on the algebraic curve C, we signify that P'' is one of the intersection points of the proper transform $C'' = (\sigma\tau)'C$ with E'. In a similar fashion, we define an infinitely near point of the nth order of P, which we call simply an *infinitely near point* without caring about its order n.

LEMMA 10.4. *Let C be an irreducible algebraic curve on V, and let $\widetilde{C}$ be the normalization of C. Then we have*

(1) $p_a(C) \geq 0$.

(2) $p_a(C) = g(\widetilde{C}) + \sum_P \frac{1}{2}\mu_P(\mu_P - 1)$, *where P ranges over all points of C including infinitely near points and μ_P is the multiplicity of C at P.*

PROOF. Let $\nu\colon \widetilde{C} \to C$ be the normalization morphism. Consider the exact sequence

$$0 \to \mathscr{O}_C \to \nu_*\mathscr{O}_{\widetilde{C}} \to \mathscr{R} \to 0,$$

where $\mathscr{R} = \nu_*\mathscr{O}_{\widetilde{C}}/\mathscr{O}_C$. By virtue of the observation made just before Theorem 7.3, we have $\chi(\mathscr{O}_C) \leq \chi(\mathscr{O}_{\widetilde{C}})$. With C' as in Lemma 10.3, ν factors as

$$\nu\colon \widetilde{C} \xrightarrow{\alpha} C' \xrightarrow{\beta} C,$$

where $\beta = \sigma|_{C'}$ and α is a birational mapping defined by $\alpha := \beta^{-1}\nu$ which becomes a morphism by (II.4.29). Clearly, α and β are finite morphisms. Considering exact sequences for α and β similar to the above one for ν, we obtain $\chi(\mathscr{O}_C) \leq \chi(\mathscr{O}_{C'}) \leq \chi(\mathscr{O}_{\widetilde{C}})$. Note that $\chi(\mathscr{O}_{C'}) - \chi(\mathscr{O}_C) = \frac{1}{2}\mu(\mu - 1)$. This implies that C has only finitely many points P with multiplicity $\mu_P > 1$ including infinitely near points. Hence, repeating the monoidal transformations with centers at points of C finitely many times, we obtain a nonsingular algebraic curve which is birational to C. It is obvious that this nonsingular curve is isomorphic to $\widetilde{C}$. By Lemma 10.3, $p_a(C) = g(\widetilde{C}) + \sum_P \frac{1}{2}\mu_P(\mu_P - 1)$. Since $g(\widetilde{C}) \geq 0$, $p_a(C) \geq 0$ follows. □

LEMMA 10.5. *Let C be an irreducible algebraic curve on V. Then teh following assertions hold*:

(1) $h^1(C, \mathscr{O}_C) = p_a(C)$.

(2) $\chi(\mathscr{O}_V(C)) = \frac{1}{2}(C \cdot C - K_V) + \chi(\mathscr{O}_V)$.

PROOF. (1) With the notations of Lemma 10.3, $\chi(\mathscr{O}_{C'}) + p_a(C') = \chi(\mathscr{O}_C) + p_a(C)$. The proof of Lemma 10.4 implies also that there exists a birational morphism $\tau \colon W \to V$, which is a composite of monoidal transformations, such that the proper transform of C by τ is isomorphic to the normalization $\widetilde{C}$ of C. Therefore, we have

$$\chi(\mathscr{O}_C) + p_a(C) = \chi(\mathscr{O}_{\widetilde{C}}) + p_a(\widetilde{C}) = 1 - h^1(\widetilde{C}, \mathscr{O}_{\widetilde{C}}) + g(\widetilde{C}) = 1.$$

This yields $h^1(C, \mathscr{O}_C) = p_a(C)$.

(2) The equality $\chi(\mathscr{O}_V(C)) = \chi(\mathscr{O}_V) + \chi(\mathscr{O}_C(C))$ follows from the exact sequence

$$0 \to \mathscr{O}_V \to \mathscr{O}_V(C) \to \mathscr{O}_C(C) \to 0.$$

Applying the Riemann Roch theorem (III.7.3) on C, we have

$$\begin{aligned}\chi(\mathscr{O}_C(C)) &= (C^2) + \chi(\mathscr{O}_C) \\ &= (C^2) + 1 - p_a(C) \\ &= (C^2) + 1 - \frac{1}{2}(C \cdot C + K_V) - 1 = \frac{1}{2}(C \cdot C - K_V).\end{aligned}$$

This yields the equality (2). □

We shall next state the Riemann-Roch theorem on an algebraic surface which is the purpose of the present chapter.

THEOREM 10.6 (Riemann-Roch Theorem). *Let V be an algebraic surface, and let D be a divisor on V. Then the following assertions hold*:

(1) $\chi(\mathscr{O}_V(D)) = \frac{1}{2}(D \cdot D - K_V) + \chi(\mathscr{O}_V)$.

(2) $h^i(D) = h^{2-i}(K_V - D)$ $(i = 0, 1, 2)$, *where* $h^i(D) = h^i(V, \mathscr{O}_V(D))$.

PROOF. (1) Case $D \geq 0$. Writing $D = \sum_i a_i C_i$, ($a_i > 0$, C_i: irreducible), we prove the assertion by induction on $\sum_i a_i$. If D is an irreducible divisor, then the assertion is proved in Lemma 10.5. When we decompose $D = A + C$ ($A \geq 0$, C:

irreducible component), we shall prove the assertion, assuming that the equality (1) holds for A. From an exact sequence

$$0 \to \mathcal{O}_V(A) \to \mathcal{O}_V(A+C) \to \mathcal{O}_C(A+C) \to 0,$$

we obtain by virtue of Theorem 7.3 and Lemma 10.5

$$\begin{aligned}\chi(\mathcal{O}_V(A+C)) &= \chi(\mathcal{O}_V(A)) + \chi(\mathcal{O}_C(A+C)) \\ &= \frac{1}{2}(A \cdot A - K_V) + \chi(\mathcal{O}_V) + (C \cdot A + C) - \frac{1}{2}(C \cdot C + K_V) \\ &= \frac{1}{2}(A + C \cdot A + C - K_V) + \chi(\mathcal{O}_V) \\ &= \frac{1}{2}(D \cdot D - K_V) + \chi(\mathcal{O}_V).\end{aligned}$$

In case D is not an effective divisor, write $D = A - B$ with $A \geq 0$ and $B = \sum_j b_j C_j \geq 0$. We shall verify equality (1) by induction on $\sum_j b_j$. When $\sum_j b_j = 0$, the equality (1) has been established as above. So decompose $D = A - (F + C)$ ($F \geq 0$, C: irreducible component) and assume that (1) holds for $A - F$. We shall show that (1) holds for D. Making use of the exact sequence

$$0 \to \mathcal{O}_V(D) \to \mathcal{O}_V(A-F) \to \mathcal{O}_C(A-F) \to 0,$$

we compute as follows:

$$\begin{aligned}\chi(\mathcal{O}_V(D)) &= \chi(\mathcal{O}_V(A-F)) - \chi(\mathcal{O}_C(A-F)) \\ &= \frac{1}{2}(A - F \cdot A - F - K_V) + \chi(\mathcal{O}_V) - (C \cdot A - F) \\ &\quad + \frac{1}{2}(C \cdot C + K_V) \\ &= \frac{1}{2}(A - F - C \cdot A - F - C - K_V) + \chi(\mathcal{O}_V) \\ &= \frac{1}{2}(D \cdot D - K_V) + \chi(\mathcal{O}_V).\end{aligned}$$

(2) It follows from (II.6.29). □

For a positive integer n, we call $P_n := h^0(V, \mathcal{O}_V(nK_V))$ the *n-genus* of V. We denote P_1 by p_g and call it the *geometric genus* of V.

LEMMA 10.7. *Let $\tau\colon W \to V$ be a birational morphism of algebraic surfaces which is a composite of monoidal transformations with centers at points. Then we have*

(1) $h^0(W, \mathcal{O}_W(nK_W)) = h^0(V, \mathcal{O}_V(nK_V))$, *for each* $n \geq 0$.

(2) $h^1(W, \mathcal{O}_W) = h^1(V, \mathcal{O}_V)$.

PROOF. (1) It suffices to prove the assertion in the case where τ is a monoidal transformation with center P. Let $E = \tau^{-1}(P)$. Since $K_W \sim \tau^* K_V + E$, we have

$$\begin{aligned}H^0(W, \mathcal{O}_W(nK_W)) &= H^0(V, \tau_*(\tau^*\mathcal{O}_V(nK_V) \otimes \mathcal{O}_W(nE))) \\ &= H^0(V, \mathcal{O}_V(nK_V) \otimes \tau_*\mathcal{O}_W(nE)).\end{aligned}$$

Here it suffices to show that $\tau_*\mathcal{O}_W(nE) = \mathcal{O}_V$. Let U be an open neighborhood of P in V. Then $H^0(U, \tau_*\mathcal{O}_W(nE)) = H^0(\tau^{-1}(U), \mathcal{O}_W(nE))$. If we regard $\mathcal{O}_W(nE)$ as contained in the function field $k(W) = k(V)$, $f \in H^0(\tau^{-1}(U), \mathcal{O}_W(nE))$ is a rational function on W which, restricted to $\tau^{-1}(U)$, has poles along E of order at most n. Since $\tau^{-1}(U) - E \xrightarrow{\sim} U - \{P\}$, if we consider $f \in k(V)$, f is a rational function on V which is regular on U except for the point P. Since U is nonsingular, $f \in H^0(U, \mathscr{O}_U)$. Hence, $f \in H^0(\tau^{-1}(U), \mathscr{O}_W)$. So $\tau_*\mathscr{O}_W(nE) = \mathscr{O}_V$.

(2) As in (1) above, it suffices to prove the assertion in the case where τ is a monoidal transformation with center at P. The spectral sequence

$$E_2^{p,q} = H^p(V, R^q\tau_*\mathscr{O}_W) \Rightarrow H^{p+q}(W, \mathscr{O}_W)$$

yields an exact sequence (I.2.26),

$$0 \to H^1(V, \tau_*\mathscr{O}_W) \to H^1(W, \mathscr{O}_W) \to H^0(V, R^1\tau_*\mathscr{O}_W).$$

By Lemma 10.3, $\tau_*\mathscr{O}_W = \mathscr{O}_V$ and $R^1\tau_*\mathscr{O}_W = (0)$. So we obtain $H^1(V, \mathscr{O}_V) \cong H^1(W, \mathscr{O}_W)$. □

As proved in the next chapter, a birational morphism $\tau\colon W \to V$ of algebraic surfaces is necessarily a composite of monoidal transformations with centers at points. Hence, P_n, $p_g := h^0(V, \mathscr{O}_V(K_V))$, and $q(V) := h^1(V, \mathscr{O}_V)$ are quantities common to algebraic surfaces V with the same function field. A quantity possessing a property is called a *birational invariant*. We call $q(V)$ the *irregularity* of an algebraic surface V.

As an application of the Riemann-Roch theorem, we shall prove the Hodge index theorem. For this, we need some preparation.

DEFINITION 10.8. Given a divisor D on an algebraic surface V, we say that D is *numerically equivalent to zero* if $(D \cdot C) = 0$ for every irreducible algebraic curve C on V; $D \equiv 0$ by notation. Two divisors are *numerically equivalent*, $D_1 \equiv D_2$ by notation, if $D_1 - D_2 \equiv 0$. Put $\mathrm{Div}^0(V) := \{D \in \mathrm{Div}(V); D \equiv 0\}$. $\mathrm{Div}^0(V)$ is a subgroup of $\mathrm{Div}(V)$. Put $\mathrm{NS}(V) := \mathrm{Div}(V)/\mathrm{Div}^0(V)$, which we call the *Néron-Severi group*. It is known that $\mathrm{NS}(V)$ is a finitely generated abelian group. Hence, $\mathrm{NS}(V)_{\mathbf{R}} := \mathrm{NS}(V) \otimes_{\mathbf{Z}} \mathbf{R}$ is a finitely generated $\mathbf{R}$-module, whose rank we call the *Picard number* and denote by $\rho(V)$. The intersection number $(\cdot)$ for divisors induces a nondegenerate quadratic form on $\mathrm{NS}(V)_{\mathbf{R}}$ which we call the intersection form. Here the intersection form being nondegenerate signifies that $(D \cdot G) = 0$ for each $G \in \mathrm{Div}(V)$ implies that $D \equiv 0$.

By Lemma 9.13 and Problem III.9.4, there are the following implications among the equivalence relations on divisors:

$$\begin{aligned} D_1 \sim D_2 \text{ (linear equivalence)} &\Rightarrow D_1 \approx D_2 \text{ (algebraic equivalence)} \\ &\Rightarrow D_1 \equiv D_2 \text{ (numerical equivalence)}. \end{aligned}$$

The Hodge index theorem, which we state below, asserts that the signature of the intersection form on $\mathrm{NS}(V)_{\mathbf{R}}$ is $(1, \rho(V) - 1)$.

THEOREM 10.9. *Let V be an algebraic surface, and let A be a divisor on V with $(A^2) > 0$. For a divisor D, if $(A \cdot D) = 0$, then either $(D^2) < 0$ or $D \equiv 0$.*

PROOF. Proof consists of three steps.

(1) We shall first prove that the stated assertion is equivalent to the assertion that the signature of the intersection form is $(1, \rho(V) - 1)$. Let $[A]$ be the numerical equivalence class of A. $[A] \not\equiv 0$ by the hypothesis. Let M be the orthogonal subspace to $[A]$ in $\mathrm{NS}(V)_{\mathbf{R}}$. If the signature is $(1, \rho(V) - 1)$, then the intersection form

restricted on M is negative definite. (Here we use Sylvester's law of inertia on real quadratic forms.) The numerical equivalence class $[D]$ of D is an element of M. Hence, if $D \not\equiv 0$, then we have $(D^2) < 0$. Conversely, if the stated assertion holds true, the intersection form restricted on M is negative definite. So the signature is $(1, \rho(V) - 1)$.

Let H be an ample divisor on V. By Sylvester's law of inertia, we have only to prove the theorem when $A = H$. We assume below that $A = H$.

(2) We shall show that the assumption $(D \cdot H) = 0$ and $(D^2) > 0$ leads to a contradiction. For an integer n, we apply the Riemann-Roch theorem to nD to obtain

$$\chi(\mathcal{O}_V(nD)) = \frac{1}{2}(nD \cdot nD - K_V) + \chi(\mathcal{O}_V).$$

Since $h^1(V, \mathcal{O}_V(nD)) \geq 0$, the above equality gives rise to the following inequality:

$$\dim |nD| + \dim |K_V - nD| \geq \frac{1}{2}n^2(D^2) - \frac{1}{2}n(D \cdot K_V) + \chi(\mathcal{O}_V) - 2.$$

Since $(D^2) > 0$ by the hypothesis, the right side of the equality $\to +\infty$ as $|n| \to \infty$. Hence, $\dim |nD| + \dim |K_V - nD| \to +\infty$ as $|n| \to \infty$.

If $\dim |nD| \to \infty$ and $\dim |K_V - nD| \to \infty$, then $\dim |K_V| \geq \dim |K_V - nD| \to \infty$ as $|n| \to \infty$. (In fact, take $D_0 \in |nD|$. Then $F + D_0 \in |K_V|$ for each $F \in |K_V - nD|$. Namely, $D_0 + |K_V - nD| \subseteq |K_V|$, and we may consider $H^0(V, \mathcal{O}_V(K_V - nD)) \subseteq H^0(V, \mathcal{O}_V(K_V))$.) Since $\dim |K_V| \leq p_g - 1$, this is impossible. Suppose $\dim |K_V - nD| \to \infty$ as $n \to +\infty$ and as $n \to -\infty$. Then taking $E_n \in |K_V - nD|$ $(n \gg 0)$, $\dim |2K_V| \geq \dim(E_n + |K_V + nD|) \geq \dim |K_V + nD|$. So $\dim |2K_V| \to \infty$ as $n \to +\infty$. This is a contradiction. Hence, $\dim |nD| \to \infty$ as $n \to +\infty$ or as $n \to -\infty$. If $\dim |nD| \to \infty$ as $n \to +\infty$, then $(D \cdot H) > 0$ (Lemma 8.6). If $\dim |-nD| \to \infty$ as $n \to +\infty$, then $(D \cdot H) < 0$. In either case, we get a contradiction to the hypothesis $(D \cdot H) = 0$. Hence, we must have $(D^2) \leq 0$.

(3) We shall show that $D \equiv 0$ if $(D^2) = 0$. Suppose $D \not\equiv 0$. Then $(D \cdot E) \neq 0$ for some divisor E. Replacing E by $E' := (H^2)E - (E \cdot H)H$, we may assume that $(E \cdot H) = 0$. Set $D' := mD + E$. Then $(D' \cdot H) = 0$ and $(D'^2) = 2m(D \cdot E) + (E^2)$. Hence, we may assume $(D'^2) > 0$ by choosing a suitable integer m. Applying the argument in (2) to D', we have $(D' \cdot H) \neq 0$. This is a contradiction. So $D \equiv 0$ if $(D^2) = 0$. □

III.10. Problems

1. Suppose the characteristic of k is zero. Let C be an algebraic curve of degree n on $\mathbf{P}^2$ defined by the following equation:

$$Y^2 Z^{n-2} = (X - a_1 Z) \cdots (X - a_n Z),$$
$$n \geq 3,\ a_i \in k,\ a_i \neq a_j,\ (i \neq j).$$

Verify the following assertions:
(1) C is irreducible.
(2) If $n = 3$, then C is nonsingular; if $n > 3$, then the singular points of C are $P_\infty := (0, 1, 0)$ and its infinitely near points $P_\infty^{(i)}$ $(1 \leq i \leq [n/2] - 1)$.
(3) $p_a(C) = \frac{1}{2}(n-1)(n-2)$ and $g(\widetilde{C}) = n - [n/2] - 1$, where $\widetilde{C}$ is the normalization of C.

2. Let C be an irreducible algebraic curve on an algebraic surface V. Prove that the following four conditions on C are equivalent to each other:

(1) $(C^2) < 0$ and $(K_V \cdot C) < 0$.
(2) $(C^2) = (K_V \cdot C) = -1$.
(3) $(C^2) = -1$, $p_a(C) = 0$.
(4) $(C^2) = -1$, $C \cong \mathbf{P}^1$.
An algebraic curve C satisfying these conditions is called a (-1) *curve*.

CHAPTER 11

Minimal Algebraic Surfaces

Let V_0 be an algebraic surface, let $\sigma\colon V \to V_0$ be the monoidal transformation with center at P of V_0 and let $E = \sigma^{-1}(P)$ be the exceptional curve. Then $E \cong \mathbf{P}^1$ and $(E^2) = -1$ (Lemma 8.8). Namely, E is a (-1) curve on V (Problem III.10.2). The converse of this result holds.

THEOREM 11.1 (Contractability criterion of Castelnuovo). *Let V be an algebraic surface, and let E be a (-1) curve on V. Then there exist a (nonsingular) algebraic surface, a birational morphism $\sigma\colon V \to V_0$, and a point P of V_0 such that $\sigma\colon V - E \xrightarrow{\sim} V_0 - \{P\}$ and $\sigma(E) = P$. σ is the monoidal transformation with center at P. We call σ the* contraction of the (-1) curve E.

PROOF. Proof consists of four steps.

(1) Let H be a very ample divisor on V such that $H^1(V, \mathscr{O}(H)) = (0)$. To find such H, we take any very ample divisor H on V, and replace H by $nH (n \gg 0)$ if necessary (II.5.13). Set $a := (E \cdot H)$. We may assume $a \geq 2$. Then we have $H^1(V, \mathscr{O}(H + iE)) = (0)$ for each i, $0 \leq i < a$.

We shall prove this result by induction on i. If $i = 0$, the result holds by the choice of H. Assuming that the result holds for $i - 1$, we shall prove the result for i. From the following exact sequence

$$o \to \mathscr{O}(H + (i-1)E) \to \mathscr{O}(H + iE) \to \mathscr{O}_E(a - i) \to 0,$$

we obtain the cohomology exact sequence

$$H^1(V, \mathscr{O}(H + (i-1)E)) \to H^1(V, \mathscr{O}(H + iE)) \to H^1(E, \mathscr{O}_E(a - i)),$$

where the left and right terms are zero. So $H^1(V, \mathscr{O}(H + iE)) = (0)$.

(2) We shall prove that $\mathrm{Bs}|H + aE| = \emptyset$ and $\varphi := \Phi_{|H+aE|}\colon V \to \mathbf{P}^N$ $(N := \dim |H + aE|)$ induces an isomorphism $V - E \xrightarrow{\sim} V_1 - \{P_1\}$, where $V_1 := \varphi(V)$ and $P_1 := \varphi(E)$ is a point of V_1.

Since H is a very ample divisor, $|H + aE|$ has no base points outside E. Hence, if we show that $|H + aE|$ has no base points on E, we will see that $\mathrm{Bs}|H + aE| = \emptyset$. For this, look at an exact sequence

$$0 \to \mathscr{O}(H + (a-1)E) \to \mathscr{O}(H + aE) \to \mathscr{O}_E \to 0$$

and the associated cohomology exact sequence

$$\begin{aligned} 0 \to H^0(V, \mathscr{O}(H + (a-1)E)) \to H^0(V, \mathscr{O}(H + aE)) \xrightarrow{\rho} H^0(E, \mathscr{O}_E) \\ \to H^1(V, \mathscr{O}(H + (a-1)E)). \end{aligned}$$

By (1), $H^1(V, \mathscr{O}(H + (a-1)E)) = (0)$. Hence, the homomorphism ρ is surjective.

Since ρ is induced by the restriction of $\mathscr{O}_V(H+aE)$ onto E, if ρ is surjective there exists $D \in |H+aE|$ such that $E \cap \operatorname{Supp} D = \emptyset$. So $|H+aE|$ has no base points on E. Thus, $\operatorname{Bs}|H+aE| = \emptyset$. In particular, $\varphi := \Phi_{|H+aE|}$ is a morphism. Let $M = \dim |H|$. Since $|H| + aE \subseteq |H+aE|$, we obtain $\Phi_{|H|+aE}\colon V \to \mathbf{P}^M$ as a composite of φ and the projection from $\mathbf{P}^N$ onto $\mathbf{P}^M$. As $\Phi_{|H|+aE}$ gives an isomorphism between $V - E$ and its image, φ also gives rise to an isomorphism between $V - E$ and its image. $\varphi(E)$ is apparently a point P_1 because $E \subseteq \operatorname{Supp} D$ or $E \cap \operatorname{Supp} D = \emptyset$ for each $D \in |H+aE|$.

(3) Let V_0 be the normalization of V_1 in the function field $k(V)$, and let $\nu\colon V_0 \to V_1$ be the normalization morphism. Since V is a normal algebraic variety, the morphism $\varphi\colon V \to V_1$ factors as

$$\varphi\colon V \xrightarrow{\sigma} V_0 \xrightarrow{\nu} V_1,$$

where $\sigma\colon V \to V_0$ is a birational morphism and $\sigma(E)$ is a point P of V_0. Furthermore, $\sigma_*\mathscr{O}_V = \mathscr{O}_{V_0}$. (In fact, since $\sigma_*\mathscr{O}_V$ is a coherent $\mathscr{O}_{V_0}$-Module, V_0 would not be a normal algebraic variety if $\mathscr{O}_{V_0} \subsetneqq \sigma_*\mathscr{O}_V$.) We shall show below that P_0 is a nonsingular point of V_0.

Put $A = \mathscr{O}_{V_0,P}$ and $\mathfrak{m} = \mathfrak{m}_{V_0,P}$. Restricting the morphism $\sigma\colon V \to V_0$ to a neighborhood of P_0, we shall discuss with $\sigma \times_{V_0} \operatorname{Spec} A\colon V \times_{V_0} \operatorname{Spec} A \to \operatorname{Spec} A$. Let $\mathscr{I} = \mathscr{I}_E$ be the defining ideal sheaf of E on V, and let E_n be a closed subscheme defined by $\mathscr{I}^{n+1}$. So $E_0 = E$, and E_n has the same topological space as E though the structure sheaf of E_n is enlarged by the nilpotent elements. Since $\sigma^{-1}(P) = E$ as sets, $\mathscr{I} = \sqrt{\mathfrak{m}\mathscr{O}_V}$. Hence $\mathscr{I}^N \subset \mathfrak{m}\mathscr{O}_V \subseteq \mathscr{I}$ for some $N > 0$. If $r \geq n$, E_n is a closed subscheme of E_r. So there is a ring homomorphism $\theta_{nr}\colon H^0(E_r, \mathscr{O}_{E_r}) \to H^0(E_n, \mathscr{O}_{E_n})$, and we can thus consider the projective limit $\varprojlim_n H^0(E_n, \mathscr{O}_{E_n})$. The results to be proved are summarized in the following lemma. □

LEMMA 11.1.1. (i) *θ_{nr} is surjective if $r \geq n$.*
(ii) $H^0(E_n, \mathscr{O}_{E_n}) = k[[x,y]]/(x,y)^{n+1}$.
(iii) $\widehat{A} \cong \varprojlim_n H^0(E_n, \mathscr{O}_{E_n})$.

PROOF. (1) Since $E \cong \mathbf{P}^1$ and $(E^2) = -1$, we know that

$$(*) \qquad \mathscr{I}^{n+1}/\mathscr{I}^{n+2} = (\mathscr{I}/\mathscr{I})^{\otimes(n+1)} = \mathscr{O}_{\mathbf{P}^1}(n+1) \qquad (n \geq 0).$$

Thus, we obtain an exact sequence

$$0 \to \mathscr{O}_{\mathbf{P}^1}(n+1) \to \mathscr{O}_{E_{n+1}} \to \mathscr{O}_{E_n} \to 0.$$

Since $H^1(\mathbf{P}^1, \mathscr{O}_{\mathbf{P}^1}(n+1)) = (0)$ $(n+1 \geq 0)$, we obtain the next exact sequence

$$(**) \qquad 0 \to H^0(\mathbf{P}^1, \mathscr{O}_{\mathbf{P}^1}(n+1)) \to H^0(E_{n+1}, \mathscr{O}_{E_{n+1}}) \xrightarrow{\theta_{n,n+1}} H^0(E_n, \mathscr{O}_{E_n}) \to 0.$$

In particular, $\theta_{n,n+1}$ is surjective. Since $\theta_{nr} = \theta_{n,n+1} \cdot \theta_{n+1,n+2} \cdots \theta_{r-1,r}$ if $r > n$, θ_{nr} is surjective.

(ii) In the case $n = 0$, $H^0(E_0, \mathscr{O}_{E_0}) = k$ and $h^0(\mathbf{P}^1, \mathscr{O}_{\mathbf{P}^1}(1)) = 2$ in $(**)$. If we choose a k-basis $\{x, y\}$ of $H^0(\mathbf{P}^1, \mathscr{O}_{\mathbf{P}^1}(1))$, $H^0(E_1, \mathscr{O}_{E_1}) = k[[x,y]]/(x,y)^2$ because $H^0(E_1, \mathscr{O}_{E_1}) \supseteq k$. By induction, we assume that $H^0(E_n, \mathscr{O}_{E_n}) = k[[x,y]]/(x,y)^{n+1}$ and prove the result in the case $n+1$. Pull back elements x, y of $H^0(E_n, \mathscr{O}_{E_n})$ to elements x', y' of $H^0(E_{n+1}, \mathscr{O}_{E_{n+1}})$ by $\theta_{n,n+1}$. Then by $(*)$, we see that $H^0(\mathbf{P}^1, \mathscr{O}_{\mathbf{P}^1}(n+1))$ has a k-basis $\{x'^{n+1}, x'^n y', \ldots, y'^{n+1}\}$. So $H^0(E_{n+1}, \mathscr{O}_{E_{n+1}}) = k[[x',y']]/(x',y')^{n+2}$. Then we have only to denote anew x', y' by x, y.

(iii) We have $\mathscr{I}^{nN} \subseteq \mathfrak{m}^n\mathscr{O}_V \subseteq \mathscr{I}^n$ for each $n > 0$. So we have a decomposition

$$\theta_{n-1,nN-1}\colon H^0(\mathscr{O}_V/\mathscr{I}^{nN}) \to H^0(\mathscr{O}_V/\mathfrak{m}^n\mathscr{O}_V) \xrightarrow{\rho_n} H^0(\mathscr{O}_V/\mathscr{I}^n),$$

where ρ_n is a surjection. We shall show that $H^0(\mathscr{O}_V/\mathfrak{m}^n\mathscr{O}_V) = A/\mathfrak{m}^n$ if $n \gg 0$. First, look at the following natural exact sequence:

$$\begin{aligned} 0 &\to H^0(V, \mathfrak{m}^n\mathscr{O}_V) \to H^0(V, \mathscr{O}_V) \to H^0(\mathscr{O}_V/\mathfrak{m}^n\mathscr{O}_V) \\ &\to H^1(V, \mathfrak{m}^n\mathscr{O}_V). \end{aligned}$$

The spectral sequence

$$E_2^{p,q} = H^p(\operatorname{Spec} A, R^q\sigma_*(\mathfrak{m}^n\mathscr{O}_V)) \Rightarrow H^{p+q}(V, \mathfrak{m}^n\mathscr{O}_V)$$

entails $H^1(V, \mathfrak{m}^n\mathscr{O}_V) = H^0(\operatorname{Spec} A, R^1\sigma_*(\mathfrak{m}^n\mathscr{O}_V))$. (By (II.3.4), $H^i(\operatorname{Spec} A, \sigma_*(\mathfrak{m}^n\mathscr{O}_V)) = (0)$ $(i = 1, 2)$. Next apply (I.2.26).) Meanwhile, $R^1\sigma_*(\mathfrak{m}^n\mathscr{O}_V) = \mathfrak{m}^n R^1\sigma_*\mathscr{O}_V$ as in the proof of Lemma 10.3. Since $\operatorname{Supp} R^1\sigma_*\mathscr{O}_V \subseteq \{P\}$, $\mathfrak{m}^n R^1\sigma_*\mathscr{O}_V = (0)$ if $n \gg 0$. Hence, $H^1(V, \mathfrak{m}^n\mathscr{O}_V) = (0)$ $(n \gg 0)$. Noting that $H^0(V, \mathscr{O}_V) = A$ and $H^0(V, \mathfrak{m}^n\mathscr{O}_V) = \mathfrak{m}^n$, we see that $H^0(\mathscr{O}_V/\mathfrak{m}^n\mathscr{O}_V) = A/\mathfrak{m}^n$ $(n \gg 0)$. By the above observations, we obtain a surjection $\rho\colon \widehat{A} \to \varprojlim_n H^0(E_n, \mathscr{O}_{E_n})$, where $\rho = \varprojlim_n \rho_n$. Suppose $\rho_{nN}(a \pmod{\mathfrak{m}^{nN}}) = 0$ for $a \in A$. Then $a \pmod{\mathfrak{m}^{nN}} \in H^0(V, \mathscr{I}^{nN}) \subseteq H^0(V, \mathfrak{m}^n\mathscr{O}_V) = \mathfrak{m}^n$. So $a = 0$ in $\widehat{A}$. Thus, ρ is injective. □

By virtue of the above lemma, $\widehat{A} \cong \varprojlim_n H^0(E_n, \mathscr{O}_{E_n}) = \varprojlim_n k[[x, y]]/(x, y)^{n+1} = k[[x, y]]$, and $\widehat{A}$ is thus a formal power series in two variables. By (II.6.12), A is a regular local ring. We have thus shown that P is a nonsingular point of V_0.

(4) We shall show that $\sigma\colon V \to V_0$ is the monoidal transformation with center at P. Let $\tau\colon V' \to V_0$ be the monoidal transformation with center at P. Then $\gamma := \tau^{-1}\cdot\sigma\colon V \to V'$ is a birational mapping, and $V - E$ and $V' - E'$ $(E' := \tau^{-1}(P))$ are isomorphic to each other by γ. $\mathscr{O} := \mathscr{O}_{V,E}$ is a discrete valuation ring of $k(V)$ and $\mathscr{O} > \mathscr{O}_{V_0,P}$. Denote by v the valuation associated with $\mathscr{O}$. As shown in the step (3) in the proof of $\widehat{A} = k[[x, y]]$, we can choose a regular system of parameters (x, y) of $\mathscr{O}_{V_0,P}$ such that $\{x, y\}$ gives rise to a k-basis of $H^0(E, \mathscr{I}/\mathscr{I}^2)$. Then $x/y \in \mathscr{O}^*$, whence $v(x) = v(y)$. Since $\mathscr{O}_{V',E'} = (\mathscr{O}_{V_0,P}[y/x])_{(x)}$, $\mathscr{O} \geq \mathscr{O}_{V',E'}$. Since $\mathscr{O}_{V',E'}$ is a discrete valuation ring of $k(V)$ as well, we have $\mathscr{O}_{V,E} = \mathscr{O}_{V',E'}$. This shows that the generic points of E and E' correspond to each other under γ. Next let $\Gamma \subset V \times V'$ be the graph of γ (compare (II, Chapter 4)), let W be its normalization, and let $q\colon W \to V$ be the natural projection. Then q is a birational morphism. We shall show that q is an isomorphism. Since the birational mapping γ (and γ^{-1}) between V and V' is isomorphic at the generic points of irreducible curves, q induces also an isomorphism at the generic points of irreducible curves. Let Q be a k-rational point of W. Then $\mathscr{O}_{W,Q} = \bigcap_{Q\in C} \mathscr{O}_{W,C}$ since W is a normal algebraic surface, where C ranges over all irreducible curves on W passing through Q (compare (I.1.33)). Set $P' = q(Q)$. Then $q(C)$ ranges over all irreducible curves on V passing through P'. Namely, $\mathscr{O}_{V,P'} = \bigcap_{Q\in C} \mathscr{O}_{V,q(C)}$. Here since $\mathscr{O}_{W,C} = \mathscr{O}_{V,q(C)}$, we have $\mathscr{O}_{W,Q} = \mathscr{O}_{V,P'}$. Suppose $q(Q) = q(Q') = P'$ for a k-rational point Q'. The above observation shows that $\mathscr{O}_{W,Q} = \mathscr{O}_{W,Q'}$. So $Q = Q'$. Thus, $q\colon W \to V$ is an isomorphism. Similarly, the natural projection $q'\colon W \to V'$ is also an isomorphism. Hence, $\gamma\colon V \to V'$ is an isomorphism. □

COROLLARY 11.2 (Contractibility criterion of Castelnuovo). *With the notations of Theorem* 11.1, $\mathscr{O}_{V,P} = \bigcap_{Q\in E}\mathscr{O}_{V,Q}$.

PROOF. Since $\sigma(Q) = P$ for each $Q \in E$, we have $\mathscr{O}_{V,Q} > \mathscr{O}_{V_0,P}$. So $\bigcap_{Q\in E}\mathscr{O}_{V,Q} \supseteq \mathscr{O}_{V_0,P}$. On the other hand, let C be an irreducible curve through P, and let C' be its proper transform by σ. Since $C' \cap E \neq \emptyset$, $\mathscr{O}_{V,C'} \supset \bigcap_{Q\in E}\mathscr{O}_{V,Q}$. Since $\mathscr{O}_{V,C'} = \mathscr{O}_{V_0,C}$, if C ranges over all irreducible algebraic curves through P, we have

$$\mathscr{O}_{V_0,P} = \bigcap_{P\in C}\mathscr{O}_{V_0,C} = \bigcap_{P\in C}\mathscr{O}_{V,C'} \supseteq \bigcap_{Q\in E}\mathscr{O}_{V,Q}.$$

Thus, $\bigcap_{Q\in E}\mathscr{O}_{V,Q} = \mathscr{O}_{V_0,P}$. □

The following result is called the *factorization theorem of birational morphisms.*

THEOREM 11.3. *Let $f: V \to W$ be a birational morphism of algebraic surfaces. Then f is a composite of monoidal transformations with centers at points.*

PROOF. If $\dim f^{-1}(P) \leq 0$ for each $P \in W$, then f is an isomorphism by the same reasoning as in the step (4) of the proof of Theorem 11.1. Suppose f is not an isomorphism. Namely, suppose $\dim f^{-1}(P) = 1$ for some point P of W. Let $E_1, \dots, E_n$ exhaust all irreducible components of $f^{-1}(P)$. Then the following result holds.

LEMMA 11.3.1. (1) $(E_i^2) < 0$ *for each* i, $1 \leq i \leq n$.

(2) *The intersection matrix* $((E_i \cdot E_j))_{1\leq i,j\leq n}$ *of* $E_1, \dots, E_n$ *is negative semidefinite.* (*After the theorem is proved, we shall see that it is negative-definite.*)

(3) $K_V \sim f^*K_W + \sum_j a_jF_j$ *for each* $a_j > 0$, *where* $\{F_j\}$ *moves over all irreducible algebraic curves on* V *whose images by* f *are points of* W.

PROOF. (1) and (2). There are only finitely many points of $P \in W$ such that $\dim f^{-1}(P) > 0$. Let $\{P_1, \dots, P_s\}$ exhaust these points. Then $f: V - \bigcup_{i=1}^s f^{-1}(P_i) \to W - \{P_1, \dots, P_s\}$ is an isomorphism (compare the argument in the step (4) of the proof of Theorem 11.1). Now let H be a very ample divisor on W. Then there exists an effective divisor H_1 such that H_1 is linearly equivalent to H and $\operatorname{Supp} H_1 \cap \{P_1, \dots, P_s\} = \emptyset$. Then H_1 is identified with f^*H_1. We may assume that $H = H_1$. Then $(H^2) = (f^*H)^2 > 0$ and $(E_i \cdot f^*H) = 0$. Since $E_i \not\equiv 0$ clearly, $(E_i^2) < 0$ by Theorem 10.9. Similarly, since $(\sum_{i=1}^n \alpha_iE_i \cdot f^*H) = 0$, $(\sum_{i=1}^n \alpha_iE_i)^2 \leq 0$. Hence, the intersection matrix $((E_i \cdot E_j))_{1\leq i,j\leq n}$ is negative semidefinite. If we know that $E_1, \dots, E_n$ are numerically independent, i.e., $\alpha_1E_1 + \dots + \alpha_nE_n \equiv 0$ implies $\alpha_1 = \dots = \alpha_n = 0$, $((E_i \cdot E_j))_{1\leq i,j\leq n}$ is negative definite. We shall prove this later.

(3) Let $\{x, y\}$ be a regular system of parameters of W at the point P. Set $E = E_i$, and let u be a generator of the maximal ideal of $\mathscr{O}_{V,E}$. Since $\mathscr{O}_{V,E} > \mathscr{O}_{W,P}$, we can write $x = u^r\xi$, $y = u^s\eta$, $r, s > 0$, $\xi, \eta \in (\mathscr{O}_{V,E})^*$. Here we can choose a nonsingular point Q on E so that the following conditions are satisfied:

(i) E is defined by an equation $u = 0$ near Q.

(ii) $\xi, \eta \in (\mathscr{O}_{V,Q})^*$.

Let $\overline{v}$ be a local parameter of E at Q, and choose an element v of $\mathscr{O}_{V,Q}$ so that $\overline{v}$ is the image of v in $\mathscr{O}_{E,Q}$. Then (u, v) is a system of parameters of V at Q, and the following relation holds:

$$dx \wedge dy = u^{r+s-1}((r\xi + u\xi_u)\eta_v - (s\eta + u\eta_u)\xi_v)\, du \wedge dv,$$

where $d\xi = \xi_u\, du + \xi_v\, dv$ and $d\eta = \eta_u\, du + \eta_v\, dv$. Therefore, we see that if we write $K_V \sim f^*K_W + \sum_j a_j F_j$, then the coefficient a_i of E_i, which appears among F_j's, satisfies $a_i \geq r + s - 1 > 0$. □

Set $G = \sum_{i=1}^n a_i E_i$. Then $(f^*K_W \cdot G) = 0$. Hence $(K_V - G \cdot G) = 0$, where $G \not\equiv 0$ because $G > 0$. As in the proof of the above lemma, $(G \cdot f^*H) = 0$ which implies $(G^2) < 0$. Thus, $(K_V \cdot G) = (G^2) < 0$. So $(K_V \cdot E_i) < 0$ for some E_i. After a change of indices, we may set $E_i = E_1$. Since $(E_1^2) > 0$ by Lemma 11.3.1, E_1 is a (-1) curve on V (Problem III.10.2). By Theorem 11.1, there exist an algebraic surface V_1 and a birational morphism $\sigma_1 \colon V \to V_1$ such that σ_1 is the monoidal transformation with center at a point $P_1 := \sigma_1(E_1)$. In particular, $\sigma_1 \colon V - E_1 \xrightarrow{\sim} V_1 - \{P_1\}$ is an isomorphism. So a birational mapping $f_1 := f \cdot \sigma_1^{-1} \colon V_1 \to W$ is a morphism on $V_1 - \{P_1\}$. We shall show that f_1 is a morphism at the point P_1 as well. By Corollary 11.2, $\mathscr{O}_{V_1,P_1} = \bigcap_{Q \in E_1} \mathscr{O}_{V,Q}$. Since $\mathscr{O}_{V,Q} > \mathscr{O}_{W,P}$, we have also $\mathscr{O}_{V_1,P_1} = \bigcap_{Q \in E_1} \mathscr{O}_{V,Q} \geq \mathscr{O}_{W,P}$. Namely, f_1 is a morphism at the point P_1 and $f_1(P_1) = P$. Repeating the above argument finitely many times,we are reduced to the case where $\dim f^{-1}(P) \leq 0$ for each $P \in W$. Thus, f can be written as a composite of a finite number of monoidal transformations with centers at points. □

COROLLARY 11.4. *Let $f \colon V \to W$ be a birational morphism of algebraic surfaces. Suppose* $\dim f^{-1}(P) > 0$ *for a point P of W. Then the following assertions hold*:

(1) *$f^{-1}(P)$ is a connected union of a finite number of nonsingular rational curves $E_1, \ldots, E_n$.*

(2) *$E_1, \ldots, E_n$ are linearly independent as elements of* $\mathrm{NS}(V)_{\mathbf{R}}$.

(3) *The intersection matrix $((E_i \cdot E_j))_{1 \leq i,j \leq n}$ is negative definite.*

(4) *Any two of $E_1, \ldots, E_n$ cross normally if they cross at all* (*Definition* 8.4) *and no three of them have common points.* (*We simply say that $E_1 + \cdots + E_n$ is a divisor with* simple normal crossings.) *There is a (-1) curve among $E_1, \ldots, E_n$. If one contracts it, then there appears a (-1) curve among the images of the remaining curves under the contraction. Contracting in this way (-1) curves, one by one, $E_1 + \cdots + E_n$ is contracted to the nonsingular point P on W.*

PROOF. In view of Theorem 11.3, (1) and (4) are clear (compare Lemma 8.8 and Corollary 8.9). As explained in the proof of Lemma 11.3.1, (3) follows from (2). We shall prove (2). Decompose f as a composite of monoidal transformations $f = \sigma_n \cdots \sigma_1$, where $\sigma_i \colon V_{i-1} \to V_i$, $V = V_0$, and $W = V_n$. Let P_i be the center of σ_i, and let E_i be the proper transform of $\sigma_i^{-1}(P_i)$ on V. Let A_{i-1} $(1 \leq i \leq n)$ be an ample divisor on V_{i-1}, and let $H_{i-1} = (\sigma_{i-1} \cdots \sigma_1)^*(A_{i-1})$. Then $(H_{i-1} \cdot E_i) > 0$ and $(H_{i-1} \cdot E_j) = 0$ for each $j < i$. Suppose $\alpha_1 E_1 + \cdots + \alpha_n E_n = 0$ for each $\alpha_i \in \mathbf{R}$ with $E_1, \ldots, E_n$ viewed as elements of $\mathrm{NS}(V)_{\mathbf{R}}$. Taking the intersection of both sides of this equality with H_{n-1}, we have $\alpha_n = 0$. Considering successively the intersections with $H_{n-2}, \ldots, H_0$, we get $\alpha_{n-1} = \cdots = \alpha_1 = 0$. □

Let $f \colon V \to W$ be a birational morphism. An (irreducible) algebraic curve on V is called an *exceptional curve* of f if it is brought to a point of W by f. The union of all exceptional curves of f is called the *exceptional set*. If a divisor D on W has the irreducible decomposition $D = \sum_i a_i C_i$, we define the *proper transform* of D by $f'(D) = \sum_i a_i f'(C_i)$, where $f'(C_i)$ is the proper transform of C_i by f. Let $f \colon V \to W$ be a dominant morphism of algebraic surfaces. For an irreducible divisor B on V, we define a divisor f_*B on W by setting $f_*B = 0$ if $f(B)$ is a point and $f_*B = [k(B) \colon k(f(B))]f(B)$ if $f(B)$ is an irreducible curve. For a divisor $A = \sum_i b_i B_i$ on V in general, we define $f_*A = \sum_i b_i f_*B_i$. We call f_*A the *direct* *image* of A by f. If f is a birational morphism, then $A \sim A'$ implies $f_*A \sim f_*A'$. (In fact, $f_*((h)_V) = (h)_W$ for $h \in k(V) = k(W)$.)

LEMMA 11.5. *Let $f : V \to W$ be a birational morphism of algebraic surfaces. Then we have*:

(1) *For a divisor D on W, $f^*(D) - f'(D)$ is a divisor generated by exceptional curves of f.*

(2) *For a divisor D on W and a divisor A on V, the projection formula $(f^*D \cdot A) = (D \cdot f_*A)$ holds.*

(3) *For divisors D, D' on W, if $D \sim D'(D \approx D'$ or $D \equiv D')$, then $f^*D \sim f^*D'(f^*D \approx f^*D'$ or $f^*D \equiv f^*D')$.*

(4) *$f^* \colon \mathrm{Pic}(W) \to \mathrm{Pic}(V)$ is injective, and*

$$\mathrm{Pic}(V) = f^*\,\mathrm{Pic}(W) \oplus \left(\sum_{i=1}^{n} \mathbf{Z}[E_i]\right),$$

where $\{E_1, \dots, E_n\}$ exhaust all irreducible curves belonging to the exceptional set of f, and $[E_i]$ stands for the isomorphism class of $\mathscr{O}_V(E_i)$.

(5) *Similarly, we have*

$$\mathrm{NS}(V)_{\mathbf{R}} = f^*\mathrm{NS}(W)_{\mathbf{R}} \oplus \left(\sum_{i=1}^{n} \mathbf{R}[E_i]\right).$$

Hence, $\rho(V) = \rho(W) + n$.

PROOF. (1) is clear.

(2) We may assume that A is an irreducible divisor. If $f(A)$ is a point then $(f^*D \cdot A) = 0$. Hence, we may assume that $B := f(A)$ is an irreducible divisor on W. Then $A = f'(B)$, and by (1), $f^*B - A$ is generated by exceptional curves of f. So $(f^*D \cdot A) = (f^*D \cdot f^*B)$, and we have only to show that $(f^*D \cdot f^*B) = (D \cdot B)$. Here we may apparently assume that D is irreducible. By definition,

$$\begin{aligned}(f^*D \cdot f^*B) =& \chi(\mathscr{O}_V) - \chi(\mathscr{O}_V(-f^*D)) - \chi(\mathscr{O}_V(-f^*B)) \\ &+ \chi(\mathscr{O}_V(-f^*(D + B))),\end{aligned}$$

and

$$\begin{aligned}(D \cdot B) =& \chi(\mathscr{O}_W) - \chi(\mathscr{O}_W(-D)) - \chi(\mathscr{O}_W(-B)) \\ &+ \chi(\mathscr{O}_W(D + B)).\end{aligned}$$

Hence, it suffices to show that $\chi(V, f^*\mathscr{L}) = \chi(W, \mathscr{L})$ for an invertible sheaf $\mathscr{L}$ on W. Meanwhile, for a spectral sequence

$$E_2^{p,q} = H^p(W, R^q f_* f^*\mathscr{L}) \Rightarrow H^{p+q}(V, f^*\mathscr{L}),$$

we have $R^q f_* f^*\mathscr{L} = \mathscr{L} \otimes R^q f_*\mathscr{O}_V$ (Problem I.2.9). Since f is a composite of monoidal transformations with centers at points, $f_*\mathscr{O}_V = \mathscr{O}_W$ and $R^q f_*\mathscr{O}_V = (0)$ for each $q > 0$ by virtue of Lemma 10.3 (2) and the spectral sequence (I.2.29). Hence, $H^p(W, \mathscr{L}) = H^p(V, f^*\mathscr{L})$ for each $p \geq 0$. Thus, $\chi(V, f^*\mathscr{L}) = \chi(W, \mathscr{L})$.

(3) If $D - D' = (g)$ with $g \in k(W) = k(V)$, then $f^*D - f^*D' = (g)$. Hence, $f^*D \sim f^*D'$. Suppose we are given a nonsingular algebraic curve C, and an invertible sheaf $\mathscr{L}$ on $W \times C$ and points P, Q of C so that $\mathscr{L}_P = \mathscr{O}_W(D)$ and

$\mathscr{L}_Q = \mathscr{O}_W(D')$ (compare Definition 9.12). Put $f_C := f \times 1_C : V \times C \to W \times C$ and $\mathscr{L}^{(f)} = f_C^*(\mathscr{L})$. Then $\mathscr{L}^{(f)}$ is an invertible sheaf on $V \times C$ such that $\mathscr{L}_P^{(f)} = \mathscr{O}_V(f^*D)$ and $\mathscr{L}_Q^{(f)} = \mathscr{O}_V(f^*D')$. This observation entails that $f^*D \approx f^*D'$ if $D \approx D'$. If $D \equiv D'$ the projection formula in (2) above implies $f^*D \equiv f^*D'$.

(4) As in the proof of (2), we have $f_*f^*\mathscr{L} \cong \mathscr{L}$ for an invertible sheaf on W. Hence, $f^*: \operatorname{Pic}(W) \to \operatorname{Pic}(V)$ is injective. It is clear that $\operatorname{Pic}(V)$ is generated by $f^*\operatorname{Pic}(W)$ and the isomorphism classes $[E_i]$ of $\mathscr{O}_V(E_i)(1 \le i \le n)$. If $f^*D + \alpha_1 E_1 + \cdots + \alpha_n E_n \sim 0$ (for each $\alpha_i \in \mathbf{Z}$), then $(\sum_{i=1}^n \alpha_i E_i)^2 = 0$. So $\alpha_1 = \cdots = \alpha_n = 0$ by Corollary 11.4 (2).

(5) Suppose $Nf^*D \equiv 0$ for a divisor D and W and an integer $N \neq 0$. Then $(ND \cdot B) = (Nf^*D \cdot f^*B) = 0$ for any irreducible divisor B on W. Namely, $ND \equiv 0$. This implies that $f^*: \operatorname{NS}(W)_{\mathbf{R}} \to \operatorname{NS}(V)_{\mathbf{R}}$ is injective. The rest is proved as in (4). □

DEFINITION 11.6. Let V_0 be an algebraic surface. Put $\mathfrak{S} = \{V; V$ is an algebraic surface birationally equivalent to $V_0\}$. For $V, V' \in \mathfrak{S}$, define $V \geq V'$ if there exists a birational morphism $f: V \to V'$. If $V \geq V'$ and $V' \geq V$, then we have $\rho(V) = \rho(V')$ by Lemma 11.5. Hence, V and V' are isomorphic to each other by Theorem 11.3. Identifying V and V' if they are isomorphic to each other, we can thereby define an order in $\mathfrak{S}$ by the relation $V \geq V'$. In view of Lemma 11.5 and the fact that $\rho(V) < \infty$, we see that $\mathfrak{S}$ satisfies the minimal condition. We call a minimal element of $\mathfrak{S}$ (not necessarily unique) a *minimal model* of V_0. If V_0 is a minimal model of itself we call V_0 a *minimal algebraic surface*.

What are the conditions for a given surface to be a minimal model and how many minimal models exist? The following two results answer these questions.

LEMMA 11.7. *An algebraic surface V is a minimal algebraic surface if and only if V has no (-1) curves.*

PROOF. *Necessity.* If there exists a (-1) curve E on V, then there is a contraction $\sigma: V \to V_0$ by Theorem 11.1. Hence, V is not a minimal algebraic surface.

Sufficiency. Suppose V is not a minimal algebraic surface. Then there exists a birational morphism $f: V \to W$ which is not an isomorphism. By Theorem 11.3, f is a composite $f = \sigma_n \dots \sigma_1$ of monoidal transformations with centers at points. Let E be the exceptional curve arising from $\sigma_1: V \to V_1$. Then E is a (-1) curve on V. □

THEOREM 11.8. *Let V_0 be an algebraic surface. If $|NK_{V_0}| \neq \emptyset$ for some positive integer N, then V_0 has a unique minimal model up to isomorphisms.*

PROOF. The proof consists of three steps.

(1) Suppose there exist mutually nonisomorphic minimal models V' and V'' of V_0. Let $\rho: V' \cdots \to V''$ be a birational mapping. By Corollary 8.11, there exist an algebraic surface V and birational morphisms $f: V \to V'$ and $g: V \to V''$ such that $g = \rho \cdot f$, where both f and g are composites of monoidal transformations with centers at points. Let $\mathfrak{E}'$ be the exceptional set of f and let $E_1, \dots, E_n$ be its irreducible components. Likewise, let $\mathfrak{E}''$ be the exceptional set of g and let $F_1, \dots, F_m$

be its irreducible components. By Lemma 11.3.1, we have

$$K_V \sim f^*K_{V'} + G, \qquad G = \sum_{i=1}^{n} a_i E_i, \quad a_i > 0 \text{ for each } i$$

$$K_V \sim g^*K_{V''} + H, \qquad H = \sum_{i=1}^{m} b_i F_i, \quad b_i > 0 \text{ for each } i.$$

Note here that $|NK_{V'}| \neq \emptyset$ and $|NK_{V''}| \neq \emptyset$ by Lemma 10.7.

(2) We shall show that there exists a (-1) curve E with $E \subset \mathfrak{E}'$, $E \not\subset \mathfrak{E}''$, and $E \cap \mathfrak{E}'' \neq \emptyset$. Suppose $\mathfrak{E}' = \emptyset$. Then V is isomorphic to V', and hence, does not contain any (-1) curve. So $g\colon V \to V''$ is an isomorphism as well. This contradicts the hypothesis. Thus, $\mathfrak{E}' \neq \emptyset$. Similarly, $\mathfrak{E}'' \neq \emptyset$. Let E be a (-1) curve contained in $\mathfrak{E}'$. If $E \subset \mathfrak{E}''$, let $\sigma_1\colon V \to V_1$ be the contraction of E. Then $g_1 := g \cdot \sigma_1^{-1}\colon V_1 \to V''$ is a morphism (compare the proof of Theorem 11.3). Similarly, $f_1 := f \cdot \sigma_1^{-1}\colon V_1 \to V'$ is a morphism. Then replace V by V_1. Thus, we may assume that none of the (-1) curves in $\mathfrak{E}'$ is contained in $\mathfrak{E}''$. Suppose $E \cap \mathfrak{E}'' = \emptyset$ for a (-1) curve E contained in $\mathfrak{E}'$. Then V and V'' are isomorphic to each other in the neighborhoods of E and $g(E)$. Hence, $g(E)$ is a (-1) curve on V'', and this is a contradiction to the hypothesis that V'' is a minimal model. Since $\mathfrak{E}' \neq \emptyset$, $\mathfrak{E}'$ contains a (-1) curve E, which satisfies, by the above observations, $E \not\subset \mathfrak{E}''$, and $E \cap \mathfrak{E}'' \neq \emptyset$.

(3) Take E as in (2). Let $F := g(E)$. Then F is an irreducible algebraic curve on V'' with $(F^2) \geq 0$. In fact, since $E \cap \mathfrak{E}'' \neq \emptyset$, $g\colon V \to V''$ comprises a monoidal transformation with center at a point of F. By Corollary 8.9, we know that $(F^2) > (E^2) = -1$. The relation $K_V \sim g^*K_{V''} + H$ given in (1) yields

$$-1 = (E \cdot K_V) = (E \cdot g^*K_{V''}) + (E \cdot H) = (F \cdot K_{V''}) + (E \cdot H).$$

Here we note that $g_*E = F$ (Lemma 11.5). Since $\operatorname{Supp} H = \mathfrak{E}''$, the condition on E given in (2) above implies $(E \cdot H) > 0$. Meanwhile, since $|NK_{V''}| \neq \emptyset$ by (1), we may write $NK_{V''} \sim \sum_i r_i C_i$ ($r_i \geq 0$, C_i: irreducible component). Noting here that $(F^2) \geq 0$, we conclude that $(NK_{V''} \cdot F) = \sum_i r_i (C_i \cdot F) \geq 0$. (In fact, $(C_i \cdot F) \geq 0$ if $C_i \neq F$; $(C_i \cdot F) = (F^2) \geq 0$ if $C_i = F$.) So we have $(F \cdot K_{V''}) + (E \cdot H) > 0$ which is a contradiction. This contradiction is caused by our assumption that V_0 has two nonisomorphic minimal models. The theorem is therefore proved. □

DEFINITION 11.9. If an algebraic surface V has a unique minimal model V_0 up to isomorphisms, then we call V_0 the *absolutely minimal model* or simply *minimal model* of V. When we call the absolutely minimal model V_0 the minimal model of V, we call a minimal model in Definition 11.6 a *relatively minimal model* to distinguish one from the other.

DEFINITION 11.10. Let V be an algebraic surface. A quantity associated with V is called a *birational invariant* if it does not vary for various birational models of V. As one of such invariants, we define the Kodaira dimension $\kappa(V)$ as follows. For a canonical divisor K_V of V, set $\mathbf{N}(V) = \{n \in \mathbf{N};\ |nK_V| \neq \emptyset\}$. We define $\kappa(V) = -\infty$ if $\mathbf{N}(V) = \emptyset$. If $\mathbf{N}(V) \neq \emptyset$, we define $\kappa(V)$ by

$$\kappa(V) = \max\{\dim \Phi_{|nK_V|}(V);\ n \in \mathbf{N}(V)\}.$$

Accordingly, $\kappa(V)$ takes one of the values $-\infty, 0, 1, 2$.

THEOREM 11.11. *$\kappa(V)$ is a birational invariant.*

PROOF. In view of Corollary 8.11 and Theorem 11.3, we have only to show that $\kappa(V) = \kappa(V_0)$ if $\sigma: V \to V_0$ is the monoidal transformation with center at a point P. Let $E := \sigma^{-1}(P)$. Then $K_V \sim \sigma^* K_{V_0} + E$ (Lemma 10.3). If $|nK_{V_0}| \neq \emptyset$, then $|n\sigma^* K_{V_0}| + nE \subseteq |nK_V|$. So $|nK_V| \neq \emptyset$. Conversely, if $|nK_V| \neq \emptyset$, then $|nK_{V_0}| \neq \emptyset$ because $\sigma_* K_V \sim K_{V_0}$. We therefore have $\mathbf{N}(V) = \mathbf{N}(V_0)$. Furthermore, $H^0(V, \mathcal{O}(nK_V)) = H^0(V_0, \mathcal{O}(nK_{V_0}))$. This entails $\kappa(V) = \kappa(V_0)$. □

Theorem 11.8 is equivalent to saying that V has the absolutely minimal model provided $k(V) \geq 0$.

III.11. Problems

Let $P_1, \ldots, P_r$ $(1 \leq r \leq 8)$ be points of $\mathbf{P}^2$, and let $\sigma: V \to \mathbf{P}^2$ be a composite of monoidal transformations with centers at $P_1, \ldots, P_r$.

1. Let C be an irreducible algebraic curve of degree d on $\mathbf{P}^2$, let $m_i = \mu(C; P_i)$, and let $C' := \sigma'(C)$. Show that the following equalities hold:

$$(C'^2) = d^2 - \sum_{i=1}^{r} m_i^2, \qquad (C' \cdot K_V) = -3d + \sum_{i=1}^{r} m_i.$$

2. With the notations of the problem 1, C' is a (-1) curve if and only if

$$d^2 - \sum_{i=1}^{r} m_i^2 = -3d + \sum_{i=1}^{r} m_i = -1.$$

With the additional conditions that $m_1 \geq m_2 \geq \cdots \geq m_r$ and

$$\binom{d+2}{2} - \frac{1}{2}\sum_{i=1}^{r} m_i(m_i+1) \geq 1,$$

show that $(d; m_1, \ldots, m_r)$ is one of the following 6 collections:

$$(1; 1^2), (2; 1^5), (3; 2, 1^6), (4; 2^3, 1^5), (5, 2^6, 1^2), (6; 3, 2^7),$$

where $(1; 1^2)$ stands for $(1; 1, 1, \underbrace{0, \ldots, 0}_{r-2})$ and the other expressions are similar abbreviations.

(Hint: We have only to consider the case $r = 8$ by putting $m_{r+1} = \cdots = m_8 = 0$. Then derive the relation $18 = \sum_{i=1}^{8}(m_i - 1)^2 + \sum_{i<j}(m_i - m_j)^2$.)

3. Assume that any one of the collections $(d; m_1, \ldots, m_r)$ in problem 2 above is realized uniquely by an irreducible algebraic curve passing through the points $P_1, \ldots, P_r$. We, therefore, assume that for any substitution $(P_{i_1}, \ldots, P_{i_r})$ of $(P_1, \ldots, P_r)$, there is a unique irreducible algebraic curve of degree d with the assigned multiplicity m_j at P_{i_j} (for each j, $1 \leq j \leq r$). Then show that the number of (-1) curves on V is given by the following table.

TABLE

r	1	2	3	4	5	6	7	8
N	1	3	6	10	16	27	56	240

We say that the points $P_1, \ldots, P_r$ are in general position if $P_1, \ldots, P_r$ satisfy the condition required at the beginning of this problem. An algebraic surface V_r obtained by a composite of monoidal transformations with centers at such r points on $\mathbf{P}^2$ is called a *del Pezzo surface* together with $\mathbf{P}^2$ and $\mathbf{P}^1 \times \mathbf{P}^1$.

CHAPTER 12

Ruled Surfaces and Rational Surfaces

Let B be a nonsingular algebraic curve and let $\mathscr{F}$ be a locally free $\mathscr{O}_B$-Module of rank r. Choose an open covering $\mathfrak{U} = \{U_\lambda\}_{\lambda\in\Lambda}$ of B such that $\mathscr{F}|_{U_\lambda}$ is a free $\mathscr{O}_{U_\lambda}$-Module for every $\lambda \in \Lambda$, that is, $\mathscr{F}|_{U_\lambda} = \mathscr{O}_{U_\lambda}e_1^{(\lambda)} + \cdots + \mathscr{O}_{U_\lambda}e_r^{(\lambda)}$ for a free basis $\{e_1^{(\lambda)}, \dots, e_r^{(\lambda)}\}$. For $\lambda, \mu \in \Lambda$, on $U_{\lambda\mu} := U_\lambda \cap U_\mu$, we can write

(a) $$e_i^{(\mu)} = \sum_{j=1}^{r} a_{ij}e_j^{(\lambda)}, \qquad a_{ij} \in \Gamma(U_{\lambda\mu}, \mathscr{O}_B),$$

where $A_{\mu\lambda} := (a_{ij})$ is an $(r \times r)$ matrix with entries in $\Gamma(U_{\lambda\mu}, \mathscr{O}_B)$ and there is a relation $A_{\nu\lambda} = A_{\nu\mu} \cdot A_{\mu\lambda}$ on $U_{\lambda\mu\nu} := U_\lambda \cap U_\mu \cap U_\nu$ for $\lambda, \mu, \nu \in \Lambda$. Moreover, $A_{\lambda\lambda}$ is the identity matrix of size r. We call $\{A_{\mu\lambda}\}$ the *transition matrices* of $\mathscr{F}$ with respect to $\mathfrak{U}$.

We define a *symmetric $\mathscr{O}_B$-Algebra* $\mathcal{S}^\bullet(\mathscr{F})$ generated by $\mathscr{F}$ as $\mathcal{S}^\bullet(\mathscr{F}) = \bigoplus_{i\geq 0}\mathcal{S}^i(\mathscr{F})$, where $\mathcal{S}^i(\mathscr{F})$ is the ith symmetric tensor product of $\mathscr{F}$. With the above notation, we have $\Gamma(U_\lambda, \mathcal{S}^\bullet(\mathscr{F})) = \Gamma(U_\lambda, \mathscr{O}_B)[e_1^{(\lambda)}, \dots, e_r^{(\lambda)}]$(= a polynomial ring in r variables over $\Gamma(U_\lambda, \mathscr{O}_B)$). If we assume U_λ to be an affine open set, $\mathrm{Proj}(\Gamma(U_\lambda, \mathcal{S}^\bullet(\mathscr{F})))$ is identified with $U_\lambda \times \mathbf{P}^{r-1}$ and $\{e_1^{(\lambda)}, \dots, e_r^{(\lambda)}\}$ is its system of homogeneous coordinates. For each $\lambda, \mu \in \Lambda$, $U_\lambda \times \mathbf{P}^{r-1}$ and $U_\mu \times \mathbf{P}^{r-1}$ are glued up by the relation (a) above and a B-scheme $\mathrm{Proj}(\mathcal{S}^\bullet(\mathscr{F}))$ is, thus, obtained. We denote it simply by $\mathbf{P}(\mathscr{F})$ and call it the *projective bundle* associated with $\mathscr{F}$.

Since $\{e_1^{(\lambda)}, \dots, e_r^{(\lambda)}\}$ is a system of homogeneous coordinates of $U_\lambda \times \mathbf{P}^{r-1}$, we define an open set $U_{\lambda.i}$ of $U_\lambda \times p^{r-1}$ consisting of points for which $e_i^{(\lambda)} \neq 0$. We then have $U_\lambda \times \mathbf{P}^{r-1} = \bigcup_{i=1}^{r} U_{\lambda.i}$. Furthermore, $\{e_i^{(\lambda)}\mathscr{O}_{U_{\lambda.i}}\}_{1\leq i\leq r}$ are patched together to form an invertible sheaf $\mathscr{O}_\lambda(1)$ on $U_\lambda \times \mathbf{P}^{r-1}$, and the $\{\mathscr{O}_\lambda(1)\}_{\lambda\in\Lambda}$ are patched together to form an invertible sheaf $\mathscr{O}_{\mathbf{P}(\mathscr{F})}(1)$ on $\mathbf{P}(\mathscr{F})$. We call $\mathscr{O}_{\mathbf{P}(\mathscr{F})}(1)$ the *tautological invertible sheaf* on $\mathbf{P}(\mathscr{F})$. The transition function of $\mathscr{O}_{\mathbf{P}(\mathscr{F})}(1)$ on $U_{\lambda.i} \cap U_{\mu.j}$ is given by the relation (a) as $\sum_{l=1}^{r} a_{jl}e_l^{(\lambda)}/e_i^{(\lambda)}$. Let $f : \mathbf{P}(\mathscr{F}) \to B$ be the structure morphism as a B-scheme. Then there is an isomorphism $\varphi\colon \mathscr{F} \to f_*\mathscr{O}_{\mathbf{P}(\mathscr{F})}(1)$ which is given by $(\varphi|_{U_\lambda})(e_i^{(\lambda)}) = e_i^{(\lambda)}$ $(1 \leq i \leq r, \lambda \in \Lambda)$.

LEMMA 12.1. *Let B be a nonsingular algebraic curve, and let $\mathscr{F}$ be a locally free $\mathscr{O}_B$-Module of rank r. Then the following assertions hold*:

(1) *There is a sequence of locally free $\mathscr{O}_B$-Modules*

$$(0) = \mathscr{F}_0 \subset \mathscr{F}_1 \subset \cdots \subset \mathscr{F}_r = \mathscr{F}$$

such that $\mathscr{F}_i/\mathscr{F}_{i-1}$ is an invertible sheaf on B for $1 \leq i \leq r$. If we set $\det\mathscr{F} =$

$\bigotimes_{i=1}^{r} \mathscr{F}_i/\mathscr{F}_{i-1}$, $\det \mathscr{F}$ *is determined independently of the choice of the above sequence of locally free* $\mathscr{O}_B$*-Modules.*

(2) *If B is a projective algebraic curve, then we have*

$$\chi(B, \mathscr{F}) = \deg(\det \mathscr{F}) + r\chi(\mathscr{O}_B).$$

PROOF. (1) Let $K = k(B)$. The generic fiber $\mathbf{P}(\mathscr{F})_\eta := \mathbf{P}(\mathscr{F}) \times_B \operatorname{Spec} K$ of the structure morphism $f\colon \mathbf{P}(\mathscr{F}) \to B$ is isomorphic to $\mathbf{P}_K^{r-1}$, so $\mathbf{P}(\mathscr{F})_\eta$ has a K-rational point. Let ξ be a K-rational point, and let $S = \overline{\{\xi\}}$ be the closure of ξ in $\mathbf{P}(\mathscr{F})$. Then $f|_S\colon S \to B$ is a birational proper morphism. Since B is a nonsingular algebraic curve, $f|_S$ is an isomorphism. The inverse $(f|_S)^{-1}$ gives rise to a closed immersion $\sigma\colon B \xrightarrow{\sim} S \hookrightarrow \mathbf{P}(\mathscr{F})$ such that $f \cdot \sigma = \mathrm{id}_B$. A morphism $\sigma\colon B \to \mathbf{P}(\mathscr{F})$ with $f \cdot \sigma = \mathrm{id}_B$ or its image $S = \sigma(B)$ is called a *section* (or a *cross section*) of f. If we identify S with B, $\mathscr{O}_{\mathbf{P}(\mathscr{F})}(1)|_S$ is an invertible sheaf on B. With the defining ideal sheaf $\mathscr{I}$ of the closed subscheme S of $\mathbf{P}(\mathscr{F})$, we have the following exact sequence

$$o \to \mathscr{I} \otimes \mathscr{O}_{\mathbf{P}(\mathscr{F})}(1) \to \mathscr{O}_{\mathbf{P}(\mathscr{F})}(1) \xrightarrow{\pi} \mathscr{O}_{\mathbf{P}(\mathscr{F})}(1)|_S \to 0.$$

Thence, we obtain an exact sequence

$$0 \to f_*(\mathscr{I} \otimes \mathscr{O}_{P(\mathscr{F})}(1)) \to \mathscr{F} \xrightarrow{\psi} \mathscr{O}_{\mathbf{P}(\mathscr{F})}(1)|_S,$$

where $\psi = f_*(\pi)$. We shall show that ψ is a surjection. Replacing, if necessary, the open covering $\mathfrak{U}$ by a finer covering using the notation prior to Lemma 12.1, we may assume that for every $\lambda \in \Lambda$, $\sigma(U_\lambda) \subset U_{\lambda,i}$ (for some i). Suppose $\sigma(U_\lambda) \subset U_{\lambda,1}$ for some λ. Then $(\mathscr{O}_{\mathbf{P}(\mathscr{F})}(1)|_S)_{U_\lambda} = \mathscr{O}_{U_\lambda}(e_1^{(\lambda)}|_S)$, $e_i^{(\lambda)}|_S = \alpha_i(e_1^{(\lambda)}|_S)$ with $\alpha_i \in \Gamma(U_\lambda, \mathscr{O}_B)$ $(1 \le i \le r)$, and $\psi|_{U_\lambda}$ maps $e_1^{(\lambda)}, e_i^{(\lambda)}$ to $e_1^{(\lambda)}|_S, \alpha_i \cdot (e_1^{(\lambda)}|_S)$, respectively. Hence, $\psi|_{U_\lambda}$ is surjective. Since λ is arbitrary, ψ is surjective.

Set $\mathscr{F}_r := \mathscr{F}$, $\mathscr{F}_{r-1} := f_*(\mathscr{I} \otimes \mathscr{O}_{\mathbf{P}(\mathscr{F})}(1))$, and $\mathscr{L}_r := \mathscr{O}_{\mathbf{P}(\mathscr{F})}(1)|_S$. We then have an exact sequence

$$0 \to \mathscr{F}_{r-1} \to \mathscr{F}_r \xrightarrow{\psi} \mathscr{L}_r \to 0.$$

Since $\mathscr{F}_r$ and $\mathscr{L}_r$ are locally free $\mathscr{O}_B$-Modules of rank r and 1, respectively, $\mathscr{F}_{r-1}$ is a locally free $\mathscr{O}_B$-Module of rank $r-1$. Repeating the above argument, we obtain exact sequences of locally free $\mathscr{O}_B$-Modules,

$$\text{(b)} \qquad 0 \to \mathscr{F}_{i-1} \to \mathscr{F}_i \to \mathscr{L}_i \to 0 \qquad (1 \le i \le r),$$

where $\mathscr{F}_0 = (0)$ and every $\mathscr{L}_i$ is an invertible sheaf.

If we replace the open covering $\mathfrak{U}$ by a finer covering if necessary, then we may choose a free basis $\{e_1^{(\lambda)}, \dots, e_r^{(\lambda)}\}$ of $\mathscr{F}$ on U_λ in such a way that $\{e_1^{(\lambda)}, \dots, e_i^{(\lambda)}\}$ is a free basis of $\mathscr{F}_i|_{U_\lambda}$. Then the transition function $A_{\mu\lambda}$ of $\mathscr{F}$ on $U_{\lambda\mu}$ given by the relation (a) is a lower triangular matrix, and its diagonal components are the transition functions of $\mathscr{L}_1, \dots, \mathscr{L}_r$. Hence, $\det(A_{\mu\lambda})$ is the transition function of the invertible sheaf $\mathscr{L}_1 \otimes \cdots \otimes \mathscr{L}_r$. So $\det \mathscr{F} := \mathscr{L}_1 \otimes \cdots \otimes \mathscr{L}_r$ is independent of the choice of the sequence of Modules $(0) = \mathscr{F}_0 \subset \mathscr{F}_1 \subset \cdots \subset \mathscr{F}_r$.

(2) The exact sequence (b) yields $\chi(\mathscr{F}_i) = \chi(\mathscr{F}_{i-1}) + \chi(\mathscr{L}_i)$. So we have

$$\chi(\mathscr{F}) = \sum_{i=1}^{r} \chi(\mathscr{L}_i) = \sum_{i=1}^{r} \{\deg \mathscr{L}_i + \chi(\mathscr{O}_B)\} = \deg(\det \mathscr{F}) + r\chi(\mathscr{O}_B). \qquad \square$$

LEMMA 12.2. *Let $\mathscr{F}$ be a locally free Module of rank r over $B = \mathbf{P}^1$. Then there exist integers $d_1, \dots, d_r$ such that $\mathscr{F} \cong \mathscr{O}(d_1) \oplus \cdots \oplus \mathscr{O}(d_r)$.*

PROOF. We note that $\mathrm{Pic}(\mathbf{P}^1) = \mathbf{Z}[\mathscr{O}(1)]$ by virtue of Example II.5.17.1. Though we give a proof below only in the case $r = 2$, it is not difficult to extend the proof to the general case. The proof consists of three steps.

(1) By Lemma 12.1, there exists an exact sequence

$$\text{(c)} \qquad 0 \to \mathscr{L}_1 \to \mathscr{F} \xrightarrow{\psi} \mathscr{L}_2 \to 0, \qquad \mathscr{L}_i = \mathscr{O}(d_i),\ i = 1, 2.$$

If $\mathscr{F}$ contains an invertible sheaf $\mathscr{L}$ as an $\mathscr{O}_B$-sub-Module, then $\deg \mathscr{L} \leq \max(d_1, d_2)$. In fact, if $\psi(\mathscr{L}) \neq (0)$, $\psi|_{\mathscr{L}} \colon \mathscr{L} \to \mathscr{L}_2$ corresponds to a nonzero element of $H^0(B, \mathscr{L}_2 \otimes \mathscr{L}^{-1})$. So $\deg(\mathscr{L}_2 \otimes \mathscr{L}^{-1}) \geq 0$. Namely, $d_2 \geq \deg \mathscr{L}$. If $\psi(\mathscr{L}) = (0)$, then $\mathscr{L} \subseteq \mathscr{L}_1$. Hence, $H^0(B, \mathscr{L}_1 \otimes \mathscr{L}^{-1}) \neq (0)$. So $d_1 \geq \deg \mathscr{L}$. Thus, $\deg \mathscr{L} \leq \max(d_1, d_2)$.

(2) Choose an exact sequence (c) so that $d_1 = \deg \mathscr{L}_1$ is the largest among all exact sequences of the same kind. The largest value exists because of step (1). We shall prove by *reductio ad absurdum* that $d_2 \leq d_1$. Suppose $d_2 > d_1$ on the contrary. Replacing $\mathscr{F}$ by $\mathscr{F} \otimes \mathscr{O}(-d_1 - 1)$, we may assume that $d_1 = -1$ and $d_2 \geq 0$. The exact sequence (c) then gives rise to a cohomology exact sequence

$$0 \to H^0(B, \mathscr{F}) \xrightarrow{H^0(\psi)} H^0(B, \mathscr{L}_2) \to H^1(B, \mathscr{O}(-1)),$$

where $H^0(\psi)$ is an isomorphism because $H^1(B, \mathscr{O}(-1)) = (0)$. Since $d_2 \geq 0$, $H^0(B, \mathscr{L}_2) \neq (0)$. So $H^0(B, \mathscr{F}) \neq (0)$. Let σ be a nonzero element of $H^0(B, \mathscr{F})$. With the notation before Lemma 12.1, write $\sigma|_{U_\lambda} = s_1 e_1^{(\lambda)} + s_2 e_2^{(\lambda)}$ with $s_1, s_2 \in \Gamma(U_\lambda, \mathscr{O}_B)$. We may assume $s_1 \neq 0$. Since $\mathbf{P}(\mathscr{F})|_{U_\lambda} = U_\lambda \times \mathbf{P}^1$, define a rational mapping $\tau \colon B \to \mathbf{P}(\mathscr{F})$ as the graph of a mapping $Q \in U_\lambda \mapsto (s_2(Q), -s_1(Q)) \in \mathbf{P}^1$. If η is the generic point of B, the closure $\overline{\{\tau(\eta)\}}$ gives rise to a section of $f : \mathbf{P}(\mathscr{F}) \to B$. Namely, τ is extended to a morphism $\tau \colon B \xrightarrow{\sim} \overline{\{\tau(\eta)\}} \hookrightarrow \mathbf{P}(\mathscr{F})$. This morphism τ entails the decomposition $\mathscr{F}$ in the form of an exact sequence

$$0 \to \mathscr{G}_1 \to \mathscr{F} \to \mathscr{G}_2 \to 0,$$

where $\mathscr{G}_1$ and $\mathscr{G}_2$ are invertible sheaves, and where $\mathscr{G}_1 = f_*(\mathscr{I} \otimes \mathscr{O}_{\mathbf{P}(\mathscr{F})}(1))$ with the defining ideal sheaf $\mathscr{I}$ of the section $S := \tau(B)$. In particular, $\sigma|_{U_\lambda} \in \Gamma(U_\lambda, \mathscr{G}_1)$. Since $\lambda \in \Lambda$ is arbitrary, we have $\sigma \in H^0(B, \mathscr{G}_1)$. So $\deg \mathscr{G}_1 \geq 0$. This contradicts the choice of the sequence (c) for which $d_1 = -1$ is the largest.

(3) The exact sequence (c) entails an exact sequence

$$0 \to \mathscr{L}_1 \otimes \mathscr{L}_2^{-1} \to \mathscr{F} \otimes \mathscr{L}_2^{-1} \xrightarrow{\psi'} \mathscr{L}_2 \otimes \mathscr{L}_2^{-1} \to 0,$$

where $\psi' := \psi \otimes \mathscr{L}_2^{-1}$. Consider the cohomology exact sequence

$$0 \to H^0(B, \mathscr{L}_1 \otimes \mathscr{L}_2^{-1}) \to H^0(B, \mathscr{F} \otimes \mathscr{L}_2^{-1}) \xrightarrow{H^0(\psi')} H^0(B, \mathscr{L}_2 \otimes \mathscr{L}_2^{-1})$$
$$\to H^1(B, \mathscr{L}_1 \otimes \mathscr{L}_2^{-1}),$$

where $H^1(B, \mathscr{L}_1 \otimes \mathscr{L}_2^{-1}) = H^1(B, \mathscr{O}(d_1 - d_2)) \cong H^0(B, \mathscr{O}(-2 - d_1 + d_2)) = (0)$. (In fact, since $d_1 \geq d_2$, $-2 - d_1 + d_2 < 0$.) $H^0(\psi')$ is, therefore, surjective. Since $H^0(B, \mathscr{L}_2 \otimes \mathscr{L}_2^{-1}) = \mathrm{Hom}(\mathscr{L}_2, \mathscr{L}_2)$ there is an element $\overline{\alpha} \in H^0(B, \mathscr{L}_2 \otimes \mathscr{L}_2^{-1})$ corresponding to the identity mapping $\mathrm{id} \colon \mathscr{L}_2 \to \mathscr{L}_2$. Take $\alpha \in H^0(B, \mathscr{F} \otimes \mathscr{L}_2^{-1})$

so that $\overline{\alpha} = H^0(\psi')(\alpha)$. Let $\beta\colon \mathscr{L}_2 \to \mathscr{F}$ be an $\mathscr{O}_B$-homomorphism corresponding to α. Then $\psi \cdot \beta = \mathrm{id}$. So $\mathscr{F}$ decomposes as $\mathscr{F} \cong \mathscr{L}_1 \oplus \beta(\mathscr{L}_2)$. □

The following result is due to M. Noether.

THEOREM 12.3 (M. Noether). *Let $\rho\colon V \to B$ be a fibration on an algebraic surface V. Suppose general fibers of ρ are nonsingular rational curves. Then V is birational to $B \times \mathbf{P}^1$.*

PROOF. The proof consists of three steps.

(1) Let V_η (resp., V_b) be the generic fiber (resp., a general fiber) of ρ. V_η is an algebraic curve defined over $K = k(B)$, and V_b is isomorphic to $\mathbf{P}^1$ by hypothesis. We shall show that $\chi(\mathscr{O}_{V_\eta}) := \sum_{i=0}^{1}(-1)^i h^i(V_\eta, \mathscr{O}_{V_\eta}) = \chi(\mathscr{O}_{V_b})$. In the subsequent argument, we use the condition that V_b is an irreducible algebraic curve, not the condition that $V_b \cong \mathbf{P}^1$. Let $g\colon W \to T$ be the morphism obtained from ρ as the base change by a flat morphism $T := \operatorname{Spec} \mathscr{O}_{B,b} \to B$. We have $R^1 g_* \mathscr{O}_W = (R^1 \rho_* \mathscr{O}_V)_b$. Writing $\mathfrak{m}_{B,b} = t\mathscr{O}_{B,b}$, we have an exact sequence of $\mathscr{O}_W$-Modules

$$0 \to t\mathscr{O}_W \to \mathscr{O}_W \to \mathscr{O}_{V_b} \to 0.$$

Hence, we obtain an exact sequence of $\mathscr{O} := \mathscr{O}_{B,b}$-Modules:

$$\begin{aligned} 0 \to g_* t\mathscr{O}_W &\to g_*\mathscr{O}_W \to H^0(V_b, \mathscr{O}_{V_b}) \to R^1 g_* t\mathscr{O}_W \\ &\to R^1 g_* \mathscr{O}_W \to H^1(V_b, \mathscr{O}_{V_b}) \to R^2 g_* t\mathscr{O}_W \to R^2 g_* \mathscr{O}_W \to 0. \end{aligned}$$

Since g is a proper morphism, $R^i g_* \mathscr{O}_W$ is a finitely generated $\mathscr{O}$-module (II.4.18) and $R^i g_*(t\mathscr{O}_W) = tR^i g_* \mathscr{O}_W$. Hence, $R^2 g_* \mathscr{O}_W = (0)$ by Nakayama's lemma. Since $g_* \mathscr{O}_W = \mathscr{O} := \mathscr{O}_{B,b}$, the above cohomology exact sequence yields the following exact sequence:

$$0 \to tR^1 g_* \mathscr{O}_W \to R^1 g_* \mathscr{O}_W \to H^1(V_b, \mathscr{O}_{V_b}) \to 0.$$

Hence, $H^1(V_b, \mathscr{O}_{V_b}) \cong R^1 g_* \mathscr{O}_W \otimes_{\mathscr{O}} k \cong R^1 \rho_* \mathscr{O}_V \otimes_{\mathscr{O}_B} k(b)$, where the second isomorphism follows from (II.4.7.1) because g is the base change of ρ by a flat morphism $T \to B$. Similarly, noting that $\operatorname{Spec} K \to B$ is a flat morphism, we obtain an isomorphism

$$(R^1 \rho_* \mathscr{O}_V)_\eta = R^1(\rho_K)_* \mathscr{O}_{V_\eta} = H^1(V_\eta, \mathscr{O}_{V_\eta}),$$

where $\rho_K = \rho \otimes_{\mathscr{O}_B} K$. Let $\mathscr{T}$ be the torsion sub-Module of $R^1 \rho_* \mathscr{O}_V$. (For an affine open set U, let $\mathscr{T}_U$ be the $\mathscr{O}_U$-Module obtained from the torsion submodule of $\Gamma(U, R^1 \rho_* \mathscr{O}_V)$. Then the $\{\mathscr{T}_U\}$ are glued together to form a coherent $\mathscr{O}_B$-Module $\mathscr{T}$.) Note that $\operatorname{Supp} \mathscr{T}$ is a finite set. Choose a point b so that $b \notin \operatorname{Supp} \mathscr{T}$. Then $\operatorname{rank}(R^1 \rho_* \mathscr{O}_V)_b = \operatorname{rank}(R^1 \rho_* \mathscr{O}_V)_\eta$. Hence, $h^1(V_b, \mathscr{O}_{V_b}) = h^1(V_\eta, \mathscr{O}_{V_\eta})$. This implies $\chi(\mathscr{O}_{V_b}) = \chi(\mathscr{O}_{V_\eta})$.

(2) Let $\overline{K}$ be an algebraic closure of K, and let $\overline{V}_\eta = V_\eta \otimes_K \overline{K}$. Since $K(V_\eta) = k(V)$ is a regular extension of K (Lemma 9.1), $\overline{V}_\eta$ is an irreducible reduced algebraic curve defined over $\overline{K}$. Noting that $H^1(\overline{V}_\eta, \mathscr{O}_{\overline{V}_\eta}) = H^1(V_\eta, \mathscr{O}_{V_\eta}) \otimes_K \overline{K} = (0)$, we have $p_a(\overline{V}_\eta) = 0$ (Lemma 10.5). By Lemma 10.4, $\overline{V}_\eta$ is a nonsingular algebraic curve of genus 0. Hence, $\overline{V}_\eta \cong \mathbf{P}^1_{\overline{K}}$ (Theorem 7.6). If we set $\Omega = \Omega_{V_\eta/K}$, we have $\Omega \otimes_K \overline{K} = \Omega_{\overline{V}_\eta/\overline{K}}$. These observations give

$$h^0(V_\eta, \Omega^{-1}) = h^0(\overline{V}_\eta, (\Omega_{\overline{V}_\eta/\overline{K}})^{-1}) = h^0(\mathbf{P}^1, (\Omega_{\mathbf{P}^1})^{-1}) = h^0(\mathbf{P}^1, \mathscr{O}(2)) = 3.$$

Let $\{f_0, f_1, f_2\}$ be a K-basis of $H^0(V_\eta, \Omega^{-1})$, and let $\varphi\colon V_\eta \cdots \to \mathbf{P}^2_K$ be the rational mapping associated with $\{f_0, f_1, f_2\}$. Then φ is defined over K and $\varphi \otimes_K \overline{K} = \Phi_{|-K_{\mathbf{P}^1}|}$, where $K_{\mathbf{P}^1}$ is the canonical divisor of $\overline{V}_\eta = \mathbf{P}^1_{\overline{K}}$. Since $\varphi \otimes_K \overline{K}$ is a closed immersion, φ is a closed immersion as well. (Prove this as an exercise.) Since $\varphi^*\mathscr{O}_{\mathbf{P}^2}(1) = \Omega^{-1}$ and $\deg(\Omega_{\overline{V}_\eta/\overline{K}})^{-1} = 2$, $\varphi(V_\eta)$ is a conic (= a curve of degree 2) in $\mathbf{P}^2_K$. Namely, with homogeneous coordinates (X_0, X_1, X_2) of $\mathbf{P}^2_K$, $\varphi(V_\eta)$ is defined by a homogeneous equation $Q(X_0, X_1, X_2) = 0$ of degree 2 with coefficients in K.

(3) Here we refer to a theorem of Tsen. But we need some preparation before stating the result.

Let K be a field. Take an arbitrary homogeneous polynomial $f(X_1, \ldots, X_n)$ of degree d with coefficients in K. If the equation $f(X_1, \ldots, X_n) = 0$ has necessarily a root $(\alpha_1, \ldots, \alpha_n)$ (for all $\alpha_i \in K$) other than $(0, \ldots, 0)$ whenever $n > d$, we call K a *C_1-field.* □

LEMMA 12.3.1 (Theorem of Tsen). *Let $k(B)$ be the function field of an algebraic curve B defined over an algebraically closed field k. Then $k(B)$ is a C_1-field.*

With the previous notations $K = k(B)$, K is a C_1-field. Since $3 > 2$, the quadratic homogeneous equation $Q(X_0, X_1, X_2) = 0$ has a root $(\alpha_0, \alpha_1, \alpha_2)$ other than $(0, 0, 0)$ with all $\alpha_i \in K$. Namely, $\varphi(V_\eta)$ has a K-rational point. Let $C = \varphi(V_\eta)$, and let P be a K-rational point of C. Then $h^0(C, \mathscr{O}_C(P)) = h^0(\overline{C}, \mathscr{O}_{\overline{C}}(P)) = 2$, where $\overline{C} \otimes_K \overline{K} \cong \mathbf{P}^1_{\overline{K}}$. The morphism $\Phi_{|P|}\colon \overline{C} \to \mathbf{P}^1_{\overline{K}}$ is an isomorphism and is defined by means of a K-basis of $H^0(C, \mathscr{O}_C(P))$. So $\Phi_{|P|}$ is considered as the base change $\varphi \otimes_K \overline{K}$ of an isomorphism of K-schemes $\varphi\colon C \to \mathbf{P}^1_K$. Namely, V_η is isomorphic to $\mathbf{P}^1_K$ over K. Thus, V is birational to $\mathbf{P}^1 \times B$. □

DEFINITION 12.4. An algebraic surface V is called a *ruled surface* if V is birational to $B \times \mathbf{P}^1$, where B is a nonsingular complete algebraic curve. A fibration $\rho\colon V \to B$ is called a *$\mathbf{P}^1$-fibration* if general fibers are isomorphic to $\mathbf{P}^1$. The reducible fibers and nonreduced fibers of ρ are inclusively called *singular fibers.* We call ρ a *$\mathbf{P}^1$-bundle* or *$\mathbf{P}^1$-fiber bundle* if every closed fiber of ρ is isomorphic to $\mathbf{P}^1$. Note that the generic fiber V_η of a $\mathbf{P}^1$-fibration $\rho\colon V \to B$ is isomorphic to $\mathbf{P}^1$ over $k(B)$.

LEMMA 12.5. *Let $\rho\colon V \to B$ be a $\mathbf{P}^1$-fibration. Then ρ has a section. Hence, there are no multiple fibers in ρ. Let $F = \sum_{i=1}^n a_i C_i$ ($a_i > 0$, C_i: irreducible component) be a singular fiber of ρ. Then the following assertions hold*:

(1) *There exists a (-1) curve appearing as an irreducible component of F. Suppose C_1 is such a (-1) curve. If $a_1 = 1$, then there exists another (-1) curve among the irreducible components of F.*

(2) *Let $\sigma_1\colon V \to V_1$ be the contraction of C_1. Then the rational mapping $\rho_1 = \rho \cdot \sigma_1^{-1}\colon V \cdots \to B$ is a morphism and is a $\mathbf{P}^1$-fibration for which $F_1 := (\sigma_1)_* F$ is a fiber. If F_1 is a singular fiber of ρ_1, we obtain also a $\mathbf{P}^1$-fibration by contracting a (-1) curve which is an irreducible component of F_1. Repeating the contractions of this kind, the direct image of F becomes finally a fiber of a $\mathbf{P}^1$-fibration which is isomorphic to $\mathbf{P}^1$.*

(3) *Every C_i $(1 \le i \le n)$ is isomorphic to $\mathbf{P}^1$. Furthermore, no three components of F have a common point, and there appear no loops among the irreducible components of F. (Suppose, for example, irreducible components $C_1, \ldots, C_r$ satisfy the condition $(C_i \cdot C_j) = 1$ for $(i, j) = (1, 2), (2, 3), \ldots, (r-1, r), (r, 1)$ and $(C_i \cdot C_j) = 0$, otherwise. We then say that $C_1, \ldots, C_r$ form a* loop.)

PROOF. (1) The generic fiber V_η of ρ is isomorphic to $\mathbf{P}^1$ over $k(B)$. Hence, V_η has a $k(B)$-rational point. It follows from Lemma 12.14 that ρ has a section and ρ has no multiple fibers. Let F be a closed fiber of ρ. Suppose F is irreducible and reduced. Since F is algebraically equivalent to a fiber, say G, which is isomorphic to $\mathbf{P}^1$, we have $(F \cdot K_V) = (G \cdot K_V) = -2 - (G^2) = -2$. Since $(F^2) = 0$, we have $p_a(F) = 0$. By Lemma 10.4, F is then isomorphic to $\mathbf{P}^1$. Suppose F is a singular fiber. Write $F = \sum_{i=1}^n a_i F_i$. Then $r \geq 2$. By Lemma 9.14, $(C_i^2) < 0$ for each i. Since $(F \cdot K_V) = -2$, $(C_i \cdot K_V) < 0$ for some i, say $i = 1$. Then $(C_1^2) < 0$ and $(C_1 \cdot K_V) < 0$. So C_1 is a (-1) curve (Problem III.10.2). Suppose $a_1 = 1$. Then we have

$$-2 = (F \cdot K_V) = -1 + \sum_{i \neq 1} a_i (C_i \cdot K_V).$$

So there exists $j > 1$ such that $(C_j \cdot K_V) < 0$. This C_j is then a (-1) curve. Thus, the assertion (1) holds.

(2) Let $P_1 := \sigma_1(C_1)$. By Corollary 11.2, $\mathscr{O}_{V_1, P_1} = \bigcap_{Q \in C_1} \mathscr{O}_{V,Q}$. Since $\mathscr{O}_{V,Q} > \mathscr{O}_{B,b}$ with $b = \rho(F)$, we have $\mathscr{O}_{V_1, P_1} > \mathscr{O}_{B,b}$. This implies that ρ_1 is regular at the point P_1. If F_1 is reducible, we can repeat the contractions of this kind. Finally, we obtain an irreducible reduced fiber in a $\mathbf{P}^1$-fibration. This fiber must be isomorphic to $\mathbf{P}^1$ as we have shown above.

(3) Conversely, a singular fiber F of ρ is obtained by repeating the monoidal transformations with centers at points (and infinitely near points as well) on a fiber of a $\mathbf{P}^1$-fibration which is isomorphic to $\mathbf{P}^1$. Then every irreducible component of F is isomorphic to $\mathbf{P}^1$, and no three of the irreducible components have a common point. It is clear by this construction that there appear no loops among irreducible components of F. □

Let V be an algebraic surface. We call V a *rational algebraic surface* (or a *rational surface*, for short) if the function field $k(V)$ is a purely transcendental extension of k. Suppose V is a ruled surface birational to $B \times \mathbf{P}^1$. Then $k(V)$ is a purely transcendental extension of $k(B)$. By virtue of Lüroth's theorem (I.1.36), V is a rational surface if and only if B is a rational curve. If B is irrational, we call V an *irrational ruled surface*. We note that a rational surface is a ruled surface.

LEMMA 12.6. *Let V be an irrational ruled surface. Then V has a $\mathbf{P}^1$-fibration. A minimal model of V has a $\mathbf{P}^1$-bundle structure.*

PROOF. There exists a birational mapping $\theta\colon V \cdots \to B \times \mathbf{P}^1$, where B is an irrational algebraic curve. By Corollary 8.11, there exists a birational morphism $\sigma\colon W \to V$ such that $\tau := \theta \cdot \sigma\colon W \to B \times \mathbf{P}^1$ is also a birational morphism. Let $p\colon B \times \mathbf{P}^1 \to B$ be the natural projection. Then $q := p \cdot \tau\colon W \to B$ is a $\mathbf{P}^1$-fibration. In fact, since τ is a composite of monoidal transformations with centers at points (Theorem 11.3), almost all fibers of p remains intact under τ. As the birational morphism $\sigma\colon W \to V$ is also a composite of monoidal transformations with centers at points, let E be a (-1) curve on W which is contracted to a point by σ. By Lüroth's theorem, the morphism $q|_E\colon E \to B$ is not dominant. Namely, E is an irreducible component of a closed fiber of the $\mathbf{P}^1$-fibration $q\colon W \to B$. Let $\sigma_1\colon W \to W_1$ be the contraction of E. Then $q_1 := q \cdot \sigma_1^{-1}\colon W_1 \to B$ is a $\mathbf{P}^1$-fibration by Lemma 12.5. The mapping $\sigma \cdot \sigma_1^{-1}\colon W_1 \to V$ is a birational morphism. If it is not an isomorphism, we repeat the foregoing arguments. Hence, V has a $\mathbf{P}^1$-fibration $\rho\colon V \to B$. If ρ has reducible fibers, we contract successively (-1) curves contained in the closed fibers as irreducible components to obtain an algebraic surface with a $\mathbf{P}^1$-fibration $\rho_0\colon V_0 \to B$ such that all closed fibers are irreducible fibers. Then ρ_0 is a $\mathbf{P}^1$-bundle. Furthermore, there are no (-1) curves on V_0. So by Lemma 11.7, V_0 is a (relatively) minimal model of V. □

LEMMA 12.7. *Let $\rho\colon V \to B$ be a $\mathbf{P}^1$-bundle. Then there exists a locally free Module $\mathscr{F}$ of rank 2 defined over B such that V is isomorphic to $\mathbf{P}(\mathscr{F})$ as B-schemes.*

PROOF. Let ξ be a $k(B)$-rational point of V_η, and let $S = \overline{\{\xi\}}$. Then S is a section of ρ. We shall show that $\mathscr{F} := \rho_*\mathscr{O}_V(S)$ is a locally free $\mathscr{O}_B$-Module of rank 2. For this purpose, let b be an arbitrary closed point of B, and let t be a local parameter of B at b. Since $V_b \cong \mathbf{P}^1$, we have $\mathscr{O}_V(S) \otimes \mathscr{O}_{V_b} \cong \mathscr{O}_{\mathbf{P}^1}(1)$ which we denote by $\mathscr{O}_{V_b}(1)$. Let $g\colon W \to T$ be the base change of ρ by a flat morphism $T := \operatorname{Spec} \mathscr{O}_{B,b} \to B$. We have an exact sequence

$$0 \to t\mathscr{O}_W(S) \to \mathscr{O}_W(S) \to \mathscr{O}_{V_b}(1) \to 0,$$

where $\mathscr{O}_W(S) = \mathscr{O}_V(S) \otimes_{\mathscr{O}_V} \mathscr{O}_W$. Set $\mathscr{O} := \mathscr{O}_{B,b}$. Then this exact sequence entails an exact sequence of finitely generated $\mathscr{O}$-modules

$$0 \to tg_*\mathscr{O}_W(S) \to g_*\mathscr{O}_W(S) \to H^0(V_b, \mathscr{O}_{V_b}(1)) \to tR^1g_*\mathscr{O}_W(S)$$
$$\to R^1g_*\mathscr{O}_W(S) \to H^1(V_b, \mathscr{O}_{V_b}(1)).$$

Since $H^1(V_b, \mathscr{O}_{V_b}(1)) = (0)$, we have $R^1g_*\mathscr{O}_W(S) = (0)$ by Nakayama's lemma. Thus, we obtain an exact sequence

$$0 \to tg_*\mathscr{O}_W(S) \to g_*\mathscr{O}_W(S) \to H^0(V_b, \mathscr{O}_{V_b}(1)) \to 0.$$

Since $g_*\mathscr{O}_W(S) = \rho_*\mathscr{O}_V(S) \otimes_{\mathscr{O}_B} \mathscr{O}_T$, we have after all $\rho_*\mathscr{O}_V(S) \otimes_{\mathscr{O}_B} k(b) \cong H^0(V_b, \mathscr{O}_{V_b}(1))$. Since b is an arbitrary closed point of B, we know that $\rho_*\mathscr{O}_V(S)$ is a locally free $\mathscr{O}_B$-Module of rank 2. On the other hand, $\rho_*\mathscr{O}_V(S)_\eta \cong H^0(V_\eta, \mathscr{O}_{V_\eta}(1))$. Let $\{e_1, e_2\}$ be a $k(B)$-basis of $\mathscr{F}_\eta$, and let $\theta_\eta\colon V_\eta \to \mathbf{P}(\mathscr{F})_\eta = \operatorname{Proj} k(B)[e_1, e_2]$ be the associated $k(B)$-rational mapping which is in fact an isomorphism. Regard θ_η as a birational mapping $\theta\colon V \cdots \to \mathbf{P}(\mathscr{F})$ of B-schemes. Namely, if $f\colon \mathbf{P}(\mathscr{F}) \to B$ is the structure morphism of the B-scheme $\mathbf{P}(\mathscr{F})$, then $\rho = f \cdot \theta$. Let b be a closed point of B. With the above notation, we see that we can choose a free basis $\{\tilde{\sigma}_1, \tilde{\sigma}_2\}$ of a free $\mathscr{O}$-module $g_*\mathscr{O}_W(S)$ of rank 2 so that $\{\sigma_1, \sigma_2\}$ is a k-basis of $H^0(V_b, \mathscr{O}_{V_b}(1))$, where $\sigma_i = \tilde{\sigma}_i \pmod{tg_*\mathscr{O}_W(S)}$, $i = 1, 2$. The restriction of $\{\tilde{\sigma}_1, \tilde{\sigma}_2\}$ onto V_η gives rise to a $k(B)$-basis of $H^0(V_\eta, \mathscr{O}_{V_\eta}(1))$. Let $\tilde{\theta}\colon W \to \mathbf{P}(\mathscr{F}_b) := \operatorname{Proj} \mathscr{O}[\tilde{\sigma}_1, \tilde{\sigma}_2]$ be the morphism associated with $\{\tilde{\sigma}_1, \tilde{\sigma}_2\}$. Then $\tilde{\theta}_\eta$ coincides with θ_η up to a projective transformation of $\mathbf{P}^1_{k(B)}$. Moreover, $\tilde{\theta}_b$ is the morphism $V_b \to \mathbf{P}(\mathscr{F} \otimes k(b))$ associated with a k-basis $\{\sigma_1, \sigma_2\}$. Hence, we know that $\theta \times_B T = \tilde{\theta}$. Since b is arbitrary, θ is an isomorphism.

We can define θ as follows. Let $\mathfrak{U} = \{U_\lambda\}_{\lambda \in \Lambda}$ be an open covering of B such that $\mathscr{F}|_{U_\lambda}$ is a free $\mathscr{O}_{U_\lambda}$-Module for each $\lambda \in \Lambda$. Let $\{e_1^{(\lambda)}, e_2^{(\lambda)}\}$ be an $\mathscr{O}_{U_\lambda}$-free basis of $\mathscr{F}|_{U_\lambda}$. Then we can define a rational mapping $\theta_\lambda\colon \rho^{-1}(U_\lambda) \to \mathbf{P}(\mathscr{F}|_{U_\lambda}) = \operatorname{Proj} \mathscr{O}_{U_\lambda}[e_1^{(\lambda)}, e_2^{(\lambda)}]$ over U_λ naturally by $Q \mapsto (e_1^{(\lambda)}(Q), e_2^{(\lambda)}(Q))$. The rational mappings θ_λ and θ_μ are transformed to each other by the projective transformation induced by the transition matrix between $\{e_1^{(\lambda)}, e_2^{(\lambda)}\}$ and $\{e_1^{(\mu)}, e_2^{(\mu)}\}$. Thence we know that the $\{\theta_\lambda\}_{\lambda \in \Lambda}$ are glued together to form a rational mapping $\theta\colon V \cdots \to \mathbf{P}(\mathscr{F})$ over B. The previous argument entails, apparently, that θ_λ is an isomorphism for each $\lambda \in \Lambda$. □

LEMMA 12.8. *Let $\mathscr{F}$ be a locally free $\mathscr{O}_B$-Module of rank 2, let $\rho: \mathbf{P}(\mathscr{F}) \to B$ be the $\mathbf{P}^1$-bundle over B associated with $\mathscr{F}$, and let $\mathscr{O}_{\mathbf{P}(\mathscr{F})}(1)$ be the tautological invertible sheaf. Then we have* $\operatorname{Pic}(\mathbf{P}(\mathscr{F})) = \rho^* \operatorname{Pic}(B) \oplus \mathbf{Z}[\mathscr{O}_{\mathbf{P}(\mathscr{F})}(1)]$.

PROOF. Let η be the generic point of B, and let $K = k(B)$. Write $\mathscr{F}_\eta = Ke_1 + Ke_2$. Let ξ be a K-rational point of $\mathbf{P}(\mathscr{F})_\eta = \mathbf{P}^1_K$ which is given as $(0, 1)$ in terms of homogeneous coordinates (e_1, e_2), and let $S = \overline{\{\xi\}}$. Then S is a section of ρ. Now let D be an irreducible divisor on $\mathbf{P}(\mathscr{F})$. If $\rho(D) = B$, then $D_\eta := D \times_B \operatorname{Spec} K$ is an effective divisor on $\mathbf{P}^1_K$ which is defined by a homogeneous equation $G(e_1, e_2) = 0$ with coefficients in K. Let $d = (D \cdot F)$ for a general fiber F of ρ. Then $d = \deg G$. Let $g := G(e_1, e_2)/e_1^d$. Then g is viewed as a rational function on $\mathbf{P}(\mathscr{F})$ defined over k. Moreover, the divisor $D - dS - (g)$ has no irreducible components which meet $\mathbf{P}(\mathscr{F})_\eta$. Namely, we can write

$$D - dS - (g) = \sum_{i=1}^{r} a_i \rho^{-1}(b_i), \qquad a_i \in \mathbf{Z},\ b_i \in B.$$

This implies that $\operatorname{Pic}(\mathbf{P}(\mathscr{F})) = \rho^* \operatorname{Pic}(B) \oplus \mathbf{Z}[\mathscr{O}_{\mathbf{P}(\mathscr{F})}(S)]$. Meanwhile, $\mathscr{O}_{\mathbf{P}(\mathscr{F})}(1)$ and $\mathscr{O}_{\mathbf{P}(\mathscr{F})}(S)$ as restricted to $\mathbf{P}(\mathscr{F})_\eta$ are isomorphic. Hence, $\mathscr{O}_{\mathbf{P}(\mathscr{F})}(1) \cong \mathscr{O}_{\mathbf{P}(\mathscr{F})}(S) \otimes \rho^* \mathscr{L}$ with $\mathscr{L} \in \operatorname{Pic}(B)$. The assertion follows from this description. □

COROLLARY 12.9. *Let $\mathscr{F}, \mathscr{G}$ be a locally free $\mathscr{O}_B$-Modules of rank 2. Then $\mathbf{P}(\mathscr{F})$ is isomorphic to $\mathbf{P}(\mathscr{G})$ as B-schemes if and only if $\mathscr{G} \cong \mathscr{F} \otimes \mathscr{L}$ with $\mathscr{L} \in \operatorname{Pic}(B)$.*

PROOF. *Necessity* Let $f: \mathbf{P}(\mathscr{F}) \to B$ and $g: \mathbf{P}(\mathscr{G}) \to B$ be respective structure morphisms and let $\varphi: \mathbf{P}(\mathscr{F}) \to \mathbf{P}(\mathscr{G})$ be a B-isomorphism. By Lemma 12.8, $\varphi^* \mathscr{O}_{\mathbf{P}(\mathscr{G})}(1) \cong \mathscr{O}_{\mathbf{P}(\mathscr{F})}(1) \otimes f^* \mathscr{L}$ for $\mathscr{L} \in \operatorname{Pic}(B)$. Hence, $f_* \varphi^* \mathscr{O}_{\mathbf{P}(\mathscr{G})}(1) \cong f_*(\mathscr{O}_{\mathbf{P}(\mathscr{F})}(1) \otimes f^* \mathscr{L}) = \mathscr{F} \otimes \mathscr{L}$. Meanwhile, if we set $\psi = \varphi^{-1}$, the pullback homomorphism $\varphi^*: \operatorname{Pic}(\mathbf{P}(\mathscr{G})) \to \operatorname{Pic}(\mathbf{P}(\mathscr{F}))$ coincides with the direct image homomorphism $\psi_*: \operatorname{Pic}(\mathbf{P}(\mathscr{G})) \to \operatorname{Pic}(\mathbf{P}(\mathscr{F}))$. Hence, $f_* \varphi^* = f_* \psi_* = g_*$. So $f_* \varphi^* \mathscr{O}_{\mathbf{P}(\mathscr{G})}(1) = g_* \mathscr{O}_{\mathbf{P}(\mathscr{G})}(1) = \mathscr{G}$. Thus, $\mathscr{G} \cong \mathscr{F} \otimes \mathscr{L}$.

Sufficiency. This is clear from the construction of $\mathbf{P}(\mathscr{F})$ and $\mathbf{P}(\mathscr{G})$. □

Define a $\mathbf{P}^1$-bundle F_n over $\mathbf{P}^1$ as $F_n = \mathbf{P}(\mathscr{O} \oplus \mathscr{O}(n))$, where n is a nonnegative integer, $\mathscr{O} = \mathscr{O}_{\mathbf{P}^1}$ and $\mathscr{O}(n) = \mathscr{O}_{\mathbf{P}^1}(n)$. We call F_n the *Hirzebruch surface* of degree n. Put $\mathscr{F} = \mathscr{O} \oplus \mathscr{O}(n)$ and choose an open covering $\mathfrak{U} = \{U_\lambda\}_{\lambda \in \Lambda}$ of $\mathbf{P}^1$ such that $\mathscr{O}(n)|_{U_\lambda} \cong \mathscr{O}_{U_\lambda} e_1^{(\lambda)}$, a free $\mathscr{O}_{U_\lambda}$-Module for each $\lambda \in \Lambda$. Then $\mathscr{F}|_{U_\lambda} = \mathscr{O}_{U_\lambda} e_0 + \mathscr{O}_{U_\lambda} e_1^{(\lambda)}$ and $(e_0, e_1^{(\lambda)})$ are homogeneous coordinates of $\mathbf{P}(\mathscr{F})|_{U_\lambda} = \operatorname{Proj} \mathscr{O}_{U_\lambda}[e_0, e_1^{(\lambda)}]$, where e_0 is taken independently of $\lambda \in \Lambda$. Let M_λ (resp., M'_λ) be the section on U_λ defined by $e_1^{(\lambda)} = 0$ (resp., $e_0 = 0$) relative to homogeneous coordinates $(e_0, e_1^{(\lambda)})$. Then $\{M_\lambda\}_{\lambda \in \Lambda}$ (resp., $\{M'_\lambda\}_{\lambda \in \Lambda}$) are patched together to give a section M (resp., M'). (We say that M (resp., M') is the section defined by the natural projection $\mathscr{F} := \mathscr{O} \oplus \mathscr{O}(n)$ to $\mathscr{O}$ (resp., $\mathscr{O}(n)$.) If $\pi: F_n \to \mathbf{P}^1$ is the structure morphism of F_n, M (resp., M') is defined on $\pi^{-1}(U_\lambda) := U_\lambda \times \mathbf{P}^1$ by the equation $e_1^{(\lambda)}/e_0 = 0$ (resp., $e_0, e_1^{(\lambda)} = 0$). Let $\mathscr{I}$ be the defining ideal sheaf of M in F_n. Then $(\mathscr{I}/\mathscr{I}^2)|_{U_\lambda} = \mathscr{O}_{U_\lambda} \cdot (e_1^{(\lambda)}/e_0)$. Hence, if we identify M with $\mathbf{P}^1$ via π, $\mathscr{I}/\mathscr{I}^2 \cong \mathscr{O}_{\mathbf{P}^1}(n)$. Since $(M^2) = \deg(\mathscr{I}/\mathscr{I}^2)^\vee$, we have $(M^2) = -n$. Similarly, if $\mathscr{J}$ is the defining ideal sheaf of M', we have $\mathscr{J}/\mathscr{J}^2 \cong \mathscr{O}_{\mathbf{P}^1}(-n)$ and $(M'^2) = n$. Furthermore, $(M \cdot M') = 0$ by the definition of M and M'. Extending the above observation, we obtain the following result.

THEOREM 12.10. *(1) F_n $(n = 0, 1, 2, \dots)$ exhaust all $\mathbf{P}^1$-bundles over $\mathbf{P}^1$ up to isomorphism.*

(2) Let $\pi \colon F_n \to \mathbf{P}^1$ be the Hirzebruch surface of degree n, let M, M' be the above-defined sections of π, and let l be a general fiber of π. Then we have:

$$M' \sim M + nl, \quad (M \cdot M') = 0, \quad (M^2) = -n, \quad (M \cdot l) = 1,$$
$$\operatorname{Pic}(F_n) = \mathbf{Z}[l] \oplus \mathbf{Z}[M], \qquad K_{F_n} \sim -2M - (n+2)l.$$

In the case $n \neq 0$, an irreducible divisor C on F_n with $(C^2) < 0$ is identical with the section M. (We call M the minimal section *of F_n.) In the case $n = 0$, $F_0 \cong \mathbf{P}^1 \times \mathbf{P}^1$.*

PROOF. (1) Let V be a $\mathbf{P}^1$-bundle over $\mathbf{P}^1$. Then $V = \mathbf{P}(\mathscr{F})$ for a locally free $\mathscr{O}_{\mathbf{P}^1}$-Module $\mathscr{F}$ of rank 2 (Lemma 12.7). By Lemma 12.2, $\mathscr{F} \cong \mathscr{O}(d_1) \oplus \mathscr{O}(d_2)$ for integers d_1, d_2. By Corollary 12.9, $V \cong \mathbf{P}(\mathscr{O} \oplus \mathscr{O}(n))$, where $n = d_2 - d_1$ if $d_2 \geq d_1$ $(n = d_1 - d_2$ if $d_1 \geq d_2)$. Namely, every $\mathbf{P}^1$-bundle over $\mathbf{P}^1$ is isomorphic to a Hirzebruch surface over $\mathbf{P}^1$.

(2) By Lemma 12.8, $M' \sim M + rl$. Since $(M^2) = -n$, $(M \cdot l) = 1$ and $(M'^2) = n$, we have $n = -n + 2r$. So $r = n$. Let C be an irreducible divisor on F_n. Write $C \sim aM + bl$. Here $a = (C \cdot l)$, and l moves in a linear pencil $|l|$. Since C is irreducible, we have $a \geq 0$. If $a = 0$, then $C \in |l|$. Suppose $(C^2) < 0$. Then $a > 0$. Since $(C^2) = a(2b - an) < 0$, we have $2b < an$. Then $(C \cdot M) = b - an < 0$. So $C = M$. The other assertions are readily ascertained. □

We shall state the next result without proof.

THEOREM 12.11. *Let V be an algebraic surface.*

(1) V has Kodaira dimension $\kappa(V) = -\infty$ if and only if V is a ruled surface.

(2) Relatively minimal models of an irrational ruled surface are $\mathbf{P}^1$-bundles.

(3) Relatively minimal models of a rational surface are exhausted by $\mathbf{P}^2$ and F_n $(n = 0, 2, 3, \dots)$. Hence, they are $\mathbf{P}^1$-bundles except for $\mathbf{P}^2$.

We proved the assertion (2) in Lemma 12.6. Let $\rho \colon V \to B$ be a $\mathbf{P}^1$-bundle, let l be a closed fiber, and let P be a point on l. Let $\sigma \colon V' \to V$ be the monoidal transformation with center at P, let $E = \sigma^{-1}(P)$, and let $l' = \sigma'(l)$. Then l' is a (-1) curve on V' which is therefore contractible. Let $\tau \colon V' \to \widetilde{V}$ be the contraction of l'. Then $\tilde{\rho} := \rho \cdot \sigma \cdot \tau^{-1} \colon \widetilde{V} \to B$ is again a $\mathbf{P}^1$-bundle. We denote by elm_P the birational mapping $\tau \cdot \sigma^{-1} \colon V \cdots \to \widetilde{V}$ and call it the *elementary transformation* with center at P. A $\mathbf{P}^1$-bundle $\rho_0 \colon V_0 \to B$ is called a *trivial* $\mathbf{P}^1$-bundle if it is isomorphic to $p_1 \colon B \times \mathbf{P}^1 \to B$ (p_1 being the natural projection) as B-schemes.

The following theorem will explain the significance of elementary transformations.

THEOREM 12.12. *Let B be a nonsingular complete algebraic curve. Then every $\mathbf{P}^1$-bundle over B is obtained, up to isomorphisms, from the trivial $\mathbf{P}^1$-bundle $V_0 = B \times \mathbf{P}^1$ by applying a finite number of elementary transformations.*

PROOF. We consider only the case $B = \mathbf{P}^1$. Regard $F_0 = \mathbf{P}^1 \times \mathbf{P}^1$ as the trivial $\mathbf{P}^1$-bundle over $\mathbf{P}^1$ be the first projection $(x, y) \mapsto x$. Let l be a closed fiber, let P be a point on l, and let M be the fiber of the second projection $F_0 = \mathbf{P}^1 \times \mathbf{P}^1 \to \mathbf{P}^1$, $(x, y) \mapsto y$ which passes through the point P. With the above notations σ and τ, $\widetilde{M} := \tau(\sigma'(M))$ is a (-1) curve on the $\mathbf{P}^1$-bundle $\widetilde{F_0}$ and a cross section as well. By Theorem 12.10, $\widetilde{F_0} \cong F_1$ because $\widetilde{M}$ is the minimal section of $\widetilde{F_0}$. Next take a point

P on the minimal section of F_1. Then $\mathrm{elm}_P F_1 = F_2$. Similarly, if $n > 0$ and M_n is the minimal section of F_n, we have $\mathrm{elm}_P F_n \cong F_{n+1}$ (if $P \in M_n$) and $\mathrm{elm}_P F_n \cong F_{n-1}$ (if $P \notin M_n$).

The minimal section M_1 of F_1 is a (-1) curve, and the contraction of M_1 produces $\mathbf{P}^2$ out of F_1. □

III.12. Problems

1. Let B be a nonsingular complete algebraic curve, let $\mathscr{F}$ be a locally free $\mathscr{O}_B$-Module of rank 2, and let $V = \mathbf{P}(\mathscr{F})$. Suppose we have an exact sequence

$$0 \to \mathscr{L}_1 \xrightarrow{\alpha} \mathscr{F} \xrightarrow{\beta} \mathscr{L}_2 \to 0,$$

where $\mathscr{L}_1$ and $\mathscr{L}_2$ are invertible sheaves on B. Let M_2 be the section of V associated with the surjective homomorphism β. Show that

$$\omega_{V/k} \cong \mathscr{O}_V(-2M_2) \otimes p^*(\Omega_{B/k} \otimes \mathscr{L}_2 \otimes \mathscr{L}_1^{-1}).$$

(Hint: Let $\mathscr{I}$ be the defining ideal sheaf of M_2. Then we have an exact sequence

$$0 \to \mathscr{I}/\mathscr{I}^2 \to \Omega_{V/k} \otimes \mathscr{O}_{M_2} \to \Omega_{M_2/k} \to 0.$$

From this we obtain $\omega_{V/k} \otimes \mathscr{O}_{M_2} \cong \Omega_{B/k} \otimes \mathscr{I}/\mathscr{I}^2$ if we identify M_2 with B. Here $\mathscr{I}/\mathscr{I}^2 \cong \mathscr{L}_1 \otimes \mathscr{L}_2^{-1}$ and $\omega_{V/k} \cong \mathscr{O}_V(-2M_2) \otimes p^*\mathscr{L}$ with some $\mathscr{L} \in \mathrm{Pic}(B)$. Determine $\mathscr{L}$ by making use of the above relation.)

2. Let M and l be the minimal section and a general fiber of the Hirzebruch surface F_n, respectively. For a divisor $aM + bl$ on F_n $(a, b \geq 0)$, show that the following equalities hold:

$$\dim H^0(F_n, \mathscr{O}(aM + bl)) = \begin{cases} (a+1)(b+1) - \frac{1}{2}a(a+1)n & (b \geq an), \\ (\alpha+1)(b+1) - \frac{1}{2}\alpha(\alpha+1)n & (b < an); \end{cases}$$

$$\dim H^1(F_n, \mathscr{O}(aM + bl)) = \begin{cases} 0 & (b \geq an), \\ (a-\alpha)\{\frac{n}{2}(a+\alpha+1) - (b+1)\} & (b < an), \end{cases}$$

where $\alpha = [\frac{a}{n}]$.

(Hint. Use an exact sequence

$$0 \to \mathscr{O}((a-1)M + bl) \to \mathscr{O}(aM + bl) \to \mathscr{O}_M(b - an) \to 0.)$$

Solutions to Problems

Part I

Problems I.1.

1. $S = k[x_1, \ldots, x_n] - (0)$ is a multiplicatively closed set, and $S' = \{1 \otimes f; f \in S\}$ is a multiplicatively closed set of $k' \otimes_k k[x_1, \ldots, x_n]$. Show that $(k' \otimes_k k[x_1, \ldots, x_n])_{S'} \cong (k'[x_1, \ldots, x_n])_S = k'(x_1, \ldots, x_n)$.

2. A necessary and sufficient condition for $f(x)$ to be a separable polynomial in $k'[x]$ is that $k'[x]/(f(x))$ is a separable algebraic extension of k'. Verify that this condition holds by taking it into account that $k'[x](f(x)) \cong k' \otimes_k k[x]/(f(x)), k[x]/(f(x))$ is a separable algebraic extension and k'/k is a purely inseparable extension.

3. Suppose R is a UFD. Any element ξ of the quotient field $Q(R)$ is written as $\xi = a/b$, where $a, b \in R$ and a, b are coprime. If ξ is integral over R, ξ satisfies a relation:

$$\xi^n + c_1\xi^{n-1} + \cdots + c_n = 0, \qquad c_i \in R.$$

From this derive a relation

$$a^n + c_1 b a^{n-1} + \cdots + c_n b^n = 0$$

and show that $b | a$.

4. Necessity is easy to show. To show sufficiency, use the ideal I given in the hint. We have $I \not\subset \mathfrak{m}$ by the hypothesis that $R_\mathfrak{m}$ is a normal ring. We then have $I = R$ because $\mathfrak{m}$ is an arbitrary maximal ideal of R.

5. Let $\mathfrak{p}$ be a prime ideal as in the problem. Since $\mathfrak{p} \neq (0)$, we may take a nonzero element f of $\mathfrak{p}$. If $f = f_1 f_2$, we have $f_1 \in \mathfrak{p}$ or $f_2 \in \mathfrak{p}$. Hence, we may assume that f is an irreducible element. Since $k[x_1, \ldots, x_n]$ is a UFD, f is a prime element. Namely, (f) is a prime ideal contained in $\mathfrak{p}$. Hence, $\mathfrak{p} = (f)$.

6. (1) Clearly, $I \subseteq (x) \cap (x^2, y)$. Suppose conversely, $f \in (x) \cap (x^2, y)$. We may write $f = x^2 g + yh = xl$. This expression implies $x | h$. So $f \in (x^2, xy)$. Here (x) is a prime ideal, and (x^2, y) is a primary ideal because $\sqrt{(x^2, y)} = (x, y)$.

(2) Clearly $(x) \subseteq (I : x + y)$. If $f \in (I : x + y)$, we may write $(x + y)f = x^2 g + xyh$. Since $yf \in (x)$, we may write $f = xf_1$; hence, $f \in (x)$. It is easy to show that $(x, y) = (I : x)$.

7. $A/\mathfrak{m}$ is a finitely generated k-algebra domain. By Noether's normalization theorem, $A/\mathfrak{m}$ contains a polynomial ring $R = k[x_1, \ldots, x_d]$ over k as a subring and $A/\mathfrak{m}$ is integral over R. Meanwhile, since $A/\mathfrak{m}$ is a field, so is R (Lemma 1.10). Hence, $R = k$, and $A/\mathfrak{m}$ is a finite algebraic extension of k.

8. Write $f(x) = (x - \alpha_1) \cdots (x - \alpha_n)$ with all $\alpha_i \in k$. Then $A = k[x, (x - \alpha_1)^{-1}, \ldots, (x - \alpha_n)^{-1}]$, and $(x - \alpha_1), \ldots, (x - \alpha_n)$ are invertible elements of A. Let

ξ_i be the residue class of $(x - \alpha_i)$ in A^*/k^*. We shall show that A^*/k^* is a free abelian group with a free basis $\{\xi_1, \dots, \xi_n\}$. If $f \in A^*$, then we can write $f = g/\prod_{i=1}^n (x - \alpha_i)^{\lambda_i}$ ($g \in k[x]$, $\lambda_i \geq 0$). Noting that $f^{-1} \in A^*$, we may write $f^{-1} = h/\prod_{i=1}^n (x - \alpha_i)^{\mu_i}$ in a similar way. Then $gh = \prod_{i=1}^n (x - \alpha_i)^{\lambda_i + \mu_i}$. So $g = c\prod_{i=1}^n (x - \alpha_i)^{m_i}$ ($c \in k^*$, $m_i \geq 0$). Thus, we know that A^*/k^* is generated by $\xi_1, \dots, \xi_n$. If $\xi_1, \dots, \xi_n$ are linearly dependent, we may assume that there is a relation

$$\gamma_1\xi_1 + \cdots + \gamma_s\xi_s = \gamma_{s+1}\xi_{s+1} + \cdots + \gamma_n\xi_n \qquad \left(\gamma_i \geq 0, \sum_{i=1}^n \gamma_i > 0\right).$$

This corresponds to a relation $\prod_{i=1}^s (x - \alpha_i)^{\gamma_i} = c\prod_{s+1}^n (x - \alpha_i)^{\gamma_i}$ for some $c \in k^*$. This contradicts the hypothesis that $k[x]$ is a UFD.

9. (1) The same as (II.4.9).

(2) Set $n = \operatorname{tr.deg}_k Q(S)$. By Noether's normalization theorem, S contains a polynomial ring $R := k[x_1, \dots, x_n]$ as a subring and S is an integral extension of R. Let $\mathfrak{n} := R \cap \mathfrak{m}$. Then $\mathfrak{n}$ is a maximal ideal of R, and $\text{K-dim}\, S_\mathfrak{m} = \text{K-dim}\, R_\mathfrak{n}$. By the proof of (I.1.19), we know that $\text{K-dim}\, R_\mathfrak{n} = n$. Hence, $\text{K-dim}\, A = \operatorname{tr.deg}_k Q(S)$.

(3) Set $r = \text{K-dim}\, A$ and $s = \text{K-dim}(B/\mathfrak{m}B)$. Let $\{u_1, \dots, u_r\}$ be a system of parameters of $(A, \mathfrak{m})$. Then $I = \sum_{i=1}^r u_i A$ is a primary ideal belonging to $\mathfrak{m}$. So $\sqrt{I} = \mathfrak{m}$, and hence, $\sqrt{\mathfrak{m}B} = \sqrt{IB}$. Hence, $\operatorname{Spec}(B/IB)$ is the same as $\operatorname{Spec}(B/\mathfrak{m}B)$ as topological spaces. Thus, $\text{K-dim}(B/\mathfrak{m}B) = \text{K-dim}(B/IB)$. Choose elements $u_{r+1}, \dots, u_{r+s}$ ($u_i \in \mathfrak{n}$ for each i) of the local ring $(B, \mathfrak{n})$ such that $\{\overline{u}_{r+1}, \dots, \overline{u}_{r+s}\}$ ($\overline{u}_i := u_i \pmod{IB}$) is a system of parameters of the local ring $(B/IB, \mathfrak{n}/IB)$. Then $\mathfrak{n}$ is the radical of $\sum_{i=1}^{r+s} u_i B$. By the altitude theorem of Krull, we have $\operatorname{ht}\mathfrak{n} \leq r + s$. This entails

$$\text{K-dim}(B) \leq r + s = \text{K-dim}(A) + \text{K-dim}(B/\mathfrak{m}B).$$

10. Let $\mathfrak{N}$ be the nilradical of A, let $\overline{A} = A/\mathfrak{N}$, and let $\overline{B} = B/\mathfrak{N}B$. Then $\overline{B}$ is a flat $\overline{A}$-module via $\overline{\varphi} := \varphi \otimes_A \overline{A} \colon \overline{A} \to \overline{B}$. (For an $\overline{A}$-module P, we have $P \otimes_{\overline{A}} \overline{B} = P \otimes_A B$). Furthermore, $\text{K-dim}\, A = \text{K-dim}\, \overline{A}$, $\text{K-dim}\, B = \text{K-dim}\, \overline{B}$, and $B/\mathfrak{m}B = \overline{B}/\overline{\mathfrak{m}}\overline{B}$, where $\overline{\mathfrak{m}} = \mathfrak{m}/\mathfrak{N}$. Thus, we may assume from the beginning that $\mathfrak{N} = (0)$. Let $\mathfrak{p}_1, \dots, \mathfrak{p}_t$ exhaust all minimal prime ideals of A. Then $\mathfrak{p}_1 \cup \cdots \cup \mathfrak{p}_t = \{a \in A;\ a \text{ is a zero divisor}\}$. ($\mathfrak{p}_1 \cup \cdots \cup \mathfrak{p}_t \subseteq \{a \in A; a \text{ is a zero divisor}\}$ by (I.1.23). Conversely, let $a (\neq 0)$ be a zero divisor of A. Since A is a noetherian ring, there is a maximal element in the set {an ideal of the form $((0) : b)$ containing the ideal $((0) : a)$}. Let it be $((0) : c)$. Then it is readily shown that $((0) : c)$ is a prime ideal. Hence, by (I.1.23), $((0) : c)$ coincides with one of $\mathfrak{p}_1, \dots, \mathfrak{p}_t$. Thus, $a \in \mathfrak{p}_1 \cup \cdots \cup \mathfrak{p}_t$. Note here that since $\sqrt{(0)} = (0)$, A has no embedded prime divisors of (0). (The proof is easy.)) We prove by induction on $r := \text{K-dim}\, A$ that the equality holds in Problem 9 (3). If $r = 0$, then A is a field and $B = B/\mathfrak{m}B$. So the equality holds. Suppose $r > 0$. With the above notations, $\mathfrak{m} \supsetneq \mathfrak{p}_1 \cup \cdots \cup \mathfrak{p}_t$. Hence, there exists an element u of $\mathfrak{m}$ which is not a zero divisor. Then u is not a zero divisor of B. (The injection $u \colon A \to A$, $x \mapsto ux$, induces an injection $u \otimes B \colon B \to B$, $y \mapsto uy$, because B is a flat A-module.) Hence, A and B have systems of parameters including u. (Compare (II.6.9) for a proof.) This implies that $\text{K-dim}\, A/uA = \text{K-dim}\, A - 1$ and $\text{K-dim}\, B/uB = \text{K-dim}\, B - 1$. Set $B_1 := B/uB$ and $A_1 := A/uA$. By the induction hypothesis, we have

$$\text{K-dim}\, B_1 = \text{K-dim}\, A_1 + \text{K-dim}\, B_1/\mathfrak{m}B_1.$$

Now since $B_1/\mathfrak{m}B_1 = B/\mathfrak{m}B$, we know that the equality holds in Problem 9 (3).

11. If M is a finitely generated R-module, it decomposes as $M \cong F \oplus T$, where F is a free R-module and T is a torsion R-module. If $T \neq (0)$, there exist nonzero elements $a \in R$ and $t \in T$ such that $at = 0$. An exact sequence

$$0 \to R \overset{\times a}{\to} R \to R/aR \to 0,$$

if one applies the functor $\oplus_R T$, induces an exact sequence

$$T \overset{\times a}{\to} T \to T/aT \to 0,$$

where $\times a\colon T \to T$ is not injective. (In fact, $t \mapsto at = 0$.) Thus, M is not a flat R-module if $T \neq (0)$. Namely, if M is R-flat, then $T = (0)$. Conversely, if $T = (0)$, M is a free R-module, and therefore, a flat R-module.

If M is not a finitely generated R-module, then M is written as a sum $M = \varinjlim_{\lambda} M_\lambda$ of finitely generated R-submodules M_λ. If M has no torsion elements, then each M_λ is a free R-module. Hence, M, as an inductive limit of flat R-modules, is a flat R-module. (Note that $N \otimes_R (\varinjlim_{\lambda} M_\lambda) \cong \varinjlim_{\lambda} (N \otimes_R M_\lambda)$.) Conversely, if M has torsion elements, then M is not a flat R-module. This is proved in the same fashion as for the case of a finitely generated R-module.

Problems I.2.

1. (1) For each $x \in X$, there exist an open neighbourhood U of x and the following commutative exact diagram:

$$\begin{array}{ccccccccc} & & 0 & & 0 & & & & \\ & & \uparrow & & \uparrow & & & & \\ 0 & \longrightarrow & \mathscr{F}|_U & \xrightarrow{\alpha|_U} & \mathscr{G}|_U & \xrightarrow{\beta|_U} & \mathscr{H}|_U & \longrightarrow & 0 \\ & & \uparrow{\scriptstyle \rho} & & \uparrow{\scriptstyle \gamma} & & & & \\ 0 & \longrightarrow & (\mathscr{A}|_U)^n & \xrightarrow{\eta} & (\mathscr{A}|_U)^{(I)} & & & & \\ & & & & \uparrow{\scriptstyle \delta} & & & & \\ & & & & (\mathscr{A}|_U)^{(J)} & & & & \end{array}$$

where the middle column, which is an exact sequence, exists by the hypothesis that $\mathscr{G}$ is quasicoherent, and where ρ exists because $\mathscr{F}$ is finitely generated. Let $\{e_1, \dots, e_n\}$ be a free basis of $(\mathscr{A}|_U)^n$. Replacing U by a smaller open neighbourhood if necessary, we may assume that $\alpha \cdot \rho(e_i) (\in \Gamma(U, \mathscr{G}))$ is equal to the image $\gamma(\xi_i)$ of an element $\xi_i \in \Gamma(U, (\mathscr{A}|_U)^{(I)})$. Then define η by $e_i \mapsto \xi_i$. For η to be injective, we have only to replace, if necessary, $(\mathscr{A}|_U)^{(I)}$ and η by $(\mathscr{A}|_U)^{(I)} \oplus (\mathscr{A}|_U)^n$ and $(\eta, 1)$, respectively, where 1 signifies the identity morphism of $(\mathscr{A}|_U)^n$. We then have to replace $(\mathscr{A}|_U)^{(J)}$ and δ by $(\mathscr{A}|_U)^{(J)} \oplus (\mathscr{A}|_U)^n$ and $(\delta, 1)$, respectively. Under this set-up, the following sequence is exact

$$(\mathscr{A}|_U)^n \oplus (\mathscr{A}|_U)^{(J)} \overset{\eta \times \delta}{\to} (\mathscr{A}|_U)^{(I)} \overset{(\beta|_U) \cdot \gamma}{\to} \mathscr{H}|_U \to 0.$$

This implies that $\mathscr{H}$ is quasicoherent.

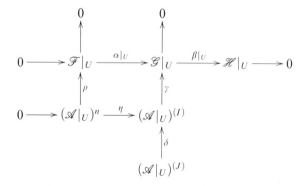

(2) For each $x \in X$, there exist an open neighbourhood and the following commutative exact diagram

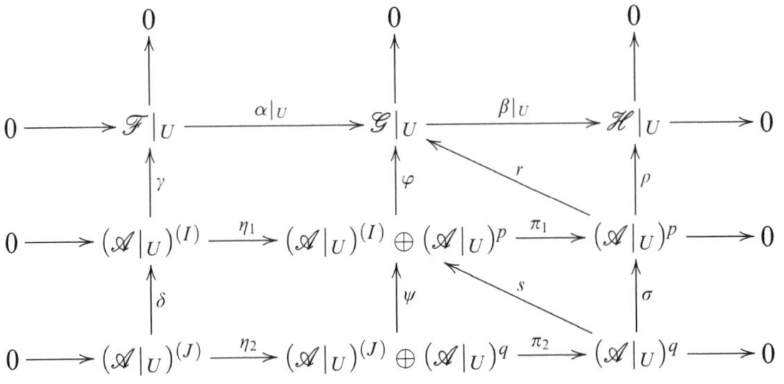

where the second and third rows are the natural exact sequences given by the direct sum decompositions $(\mathscr{A}|_U)^{(I)} \oplus (\mathscr{A}|_U)^p$ and $(\mathscr{A}|_U)^{(J)} \oplus (\mathscr{A}|_U)^q$. With U replaced by a smaller open neighbourhood of x, there exists a homomorphism $r\colon (\mathscr{A}|_U)^p \to \mathscr{G}|_U$ such that $\rho = (\beta|_U) \cdot r$. Define a homomorphism $\varphi\colon (\mathscr{A}|_U)^{(I)} \oplus (\mathscr{A}|_U)^p \to \mathscr{G}|_U$ by $\eta_1 \cdot (\varphi|_{(\mathscr{A}|_U)^{(I)}}) = (\alpha|_U) \cdot \gamma$ and $\varphi|_{(\mathscr{A}|_U)^p} = r \cdot \pi_1$. Then φ is surjective. Replacing U by a smaller one if necessary, we may assume that $\operatorname{Ker} \rho = \pi_1(\operatorname{Ker} \varphi)$. Furthermore, we may assume that there exists a homomorphism $s\colon (\mathscr{A}|_U)^q \to (\mathscr{A}|_U)^{(I)} \oplus (\mathscr{A}|_U)^p$ such that $\operatorname{Im}(s) \subseteq \operatorname{Ker} \varphi$ and $\pi_1 \cdot s = \sigma$. Define a homomorphism $\psi\colon (\mathscr{A}|_U)^{(J)} \oplus (\mathscr{A}|_U)^q \to (\mathscr{A}|_U)^{(I)} \oplus (\mathscr{A}|_U)^p$ so that $\eta_2 \cdot (\psi|_{(\mathscr{A}|_U)^{(J)}}) = \eta_1 \cdot \delta$ and $\psi|_{(\mathscr{A}|_U)^q} = s \cdot \pi_2$. In the above construction, we employ the exactness of the first and third columns. It is now easy to show that the middle column is an exact sequence.

2. Answer is given in the problem.

3. Answer is given in the problem.

4. Let V be an open set of X. It suffices to show that a $\Gamma(V, \mathscr{A})$-homomorphism between the modules of Čech n-cochains

$$\rho\colon C^n(\mathfrak{U}, F) \to C^n(V \cap \mathfrak{U}, \mathscr{F})$$

is surjective. Write $\mathfrak{U} = \{U_i\}_{i \in I}$. For $s = (i_0, \dots, i_n) \in I^{n+1}$,

$$\Gamma(U_{i_0} \cap \cdots \cap U_{i_n}, \mathscr{F}) \to \Gamma(V \cap U_{i_0} \cap \cdots \cap U_{i_n}, \mathscr{F})$$

is surjective. (The restriction $\mathscr{F}|_U$ of a scattered sheaf $\mathscr{F}$ onto an open set U is a scattered sheaf.) For $\alpha = (\alpha(s))_{s \in I^{n+1}}$ of $C^n(V \cap \mathfrak{U}, \mathscr{F})$, we have only to define $\tilde{\alpha} = (\tilde{\alpha}(s))_{s \in I^{n+1}}$ as follows. If $i_j = i_k$ for some $j \neq k$, $\tilde{\alpha}(s) = 0$. If $i_0 < i_1 < \cdots < i_n$, take $\tilde{\alpha}(s)$ in $\Gamma(U_{i_0} \cap \cdots \cap U_{i_n}, \mathscr{F})$ so that $\tilde{\alpha}(s)$ is mapped to $\alpha(s)$ by the restriction morphism. If σ is a permutation of $\{0, 1, \dots, n\}$, define $\tilde{\alpha}(\sigma(s)) = \operatorname{sgn}(\sigma)\tilde{\alpha}(s)$, where $\sigma(s) = (i_{\sigma(0)}, \dots, i_{\sigma(n)})$. Then $(\tilde{\alpha}(s))_{s \in I^{n+1}} \in C^n(\mathfrak{U}, \mathscr{F})$.

5. It is not hard to follow the given steps, one by one. We omit further details.

6. With the notation of Problem 5, $H^n_{\mathrm{ab}}(X, \mathscr{F}) \cong \widetilde{H}^n(X, \mathscr{F}) \cong \widetilde{H}^n(Y, \mathscr{F}|_Y) \cong H^n_{\mathrm{ab}}(Y, \mathscr{F}|_Y)$.

7. Let Y be a subset of a noetherian space X, endowed with the induced topology. Let $F_0 \supset F_1 \supset F_2 \supset \cdots$ be a descending chain of closed sets of Y. Let $\overline{F}_i$ be the closure of F_i in X. Then $\overline{F}_0 \supset \overline{F}_1 \supset \overline{F}_2 \supset \cdots$ is a descending chain of closed sets of X, and $F_i = \overline{F}_i \cap Y$. By hypothesis, $\overline{F}_N = \overline{F}_{N+1} = \cdots$ for some $N > 0$ which entails $F_N = F_{N+1} = \cdots$. Hence, Y is also a noetherian space.

Let U be an open set of X, and let $\mathfrak{U} = \{U_\alpha\}_{\alpha \in A}$ be an open covering of U. If $|A| = \infty$, choose a subset I of A which can be identified with $\{1, 2, 3, \dots\}$. Let $F_n = U - \bigcup_{i=1}^n U_i$ $(n \in I)$. Then we obtain a descending chain $F_1 \supset F_2 \supset F_3 \supset \cdots$ of closed sets of U. Hence, $F_N = F_{N+1} = \cdots$ for some N. If $F_N \neq \varnothing$, $U \supsetneqq \bigcup_{i=1}^N U_i = \bigcup_{i=1}^{N+1} U_i = \cdots$. So $U_{N+1}, U_{N+2}, \dots$ are unnecessary as members of the open covering $\mathfrak{U}$. So we may get rid of $U_{N+1}, U_{N+2}, \dots$ from $\mathfrak{U}$. Then we can take anew $U_{N+1} \in \mathfrak{U}$ so that $\bigcup_{i=1}^N U_i \subsetneqq \bigcup_{i=1}^{N+1} U_i$. Since U is a noetherian space, this process ends after repeated finitely many times. Namely, a finite number of open sets belonging to $\mathfrak{U}$ constitute a finite open covering of U.

Let $\mathfrak{U} = \{U_\alpha\}_{\alpha \in A}$ be a finite open covering of an open set of U, and let $\{F_i; i \in I\}$ be an inductive system of $\mathscr{A}$-Modules. Then we know that

$$\prod_{\alpha \in A} \left(\varinjlim_I \mathscr{F}_i \right)(U_\alpha) = \prod_{\alpha \in A} \varinjlim_I (\mathscr{F}_i(U_\alpha)) = \varinjlim_I \prod_{\alpha \in A} \mathscr{F}_i(U_\alpha).$$

Similarly, we have

$$\prod_{\alpha, \beta \in A} \left(\varinjlim_I \mathscr{F}_i \right)(U_\alpha \cap U_\beta) = \varinjlim_I \prod_{\alpha, \beta \in A} \mathscr{F}_i(U_\alpha \cap U_\beta).$$

Since $\mathscr{F}_i$ is a sheaf, the exactness of the functor $\varinjlim_I$ entails the exactness of the following sequence, which corresponds to the axiom of a sheaf:

$$\left(\varinjlim_I \mathscr{F}_i \right)(U) \to \prod_{\alpha \in A} \left(\varinjlim_I \mathscr{F}_i \right)(U_\alpha) \rightrightarrows \prod_{\alpha, \beta \in A} \left(\varinjlim_I \mathscr{F}_i \right)(U_\alpha \cap U_\beta).$$

if $\mathscr{F}_i$ is a scattered sheaf, then the restriction morphism $\rho^i_{UX} \colon \mathscr{F}_i(X) \to \mathscr{F}_i(U)$ is surjective. Then

$$\varinjlim_I \rho^i_{UX} \colon \left(\varinjlim_I \mathscr{F}_i \right)(X) \to \left(\varinjlim_I \mathscr{F}_i \right)(U)$$

is surjective. Thus, $\varinjlim_I \mathscr{F}_i$ is a scattered sheaf.

Consider the standard scattered resolution of $\mathscr{F}_i$,

$$\mathscr{S}^\bullet(\mathscr{F}_i) \colon 0 \to \mathscr{F}_i \xrightarrow{\eta} \mathscr{S}^0(\mathscr{F}_i) \xrightarrow{d^0} \mathscr{S}^1(\mathscr{F}_i) \to \cdots \to \mathscr{S}^n(\mathscr{F}_i) \xrightarrow{d^n} \cdots.$$

Then $\{\mathscr{S}^\bullet(\mathscr{F}_i); i \in I\}$ is naturally an inductive system of complexes. Noting that $(\varinjlim_I \mathscr{F}_i)_x = \varinjlim_I \mathscr{F}_{i,x}$ for each $x \in X$, we can prove by induction that $\varinjlim_I \mathscr{S}^n(\mathscr{F}_i) = \mathscr{S}^n(\varinjlim_I \mathscr{F}_i)$. Hence, $\varinjlim_I \mathscr{S}^\bullet(\mathscr{F}_i)$ is the standard scattered resolution of $\varinjlim_I \mathscr{F}_i$. This entails, by virtue of the result on the coincidence of various cohomologies, that $H^n(X, \varinjlim_I \mathscr{F}_i) \cong \varinjlim_I H^n(X, \mathscr{F}_i)$.

8. Prove the assertion in each step. It is not so hard.

9. (1) Note that the direct image functor Φ_* (resp., the inverse image functor Φ^*) with respect to $\Phi = (f, \varphi) \colon (X, \mathscr{A}) \to (Y, \mathscr{B})$ is abbreviated as f_* (resp. f^*). For an $\mathscr{A}$-Module $\mathscr{F}$, there is a natural homomorphism of $\mathscr{A}$-Modules $\gamma \colon f^* f_* \mathscr{F} \to \mathscr{F}$. (If U is an open set of X, $\gamma(U) : \varinjlim_{f(U) \subset V} \mathscr{F}(f^{-1}(V)) \to \mathscr{F}(U)$ is the inductive limit of the restriction morphisms $\rho_{U, f^{-1}(V)}$.) There is a $\mathscr{B}$-homomorphism $\alpha \colon \mathscr{G} \otimes_{\mathscr{B}} f_*\mathscr{F} \to f_*(f^*\mathscr{G} \otimes_{\mathscr{A}} \mathscr{F})$ which corresponds to $f^*\mathscr{G} \otimes_{\mathscr{A}} \gamma : f^*\mathscr{G} \otimes_{\mathscr{A}} f^* f_*(\mathscr{F}) \cong f^*(\mathscr{G} \otimes_{\mathscr{B}} f_*\mathscr{F}) \to f^*\mathscr{G} \otimes_{\mathscr{A}} \mathscr{F}$ (compare (I.2.9)). In order to show that α is an

isomorphism, it suffices to show that α_x is an isomorphism for each $x \in X$. Suppose $\mathscr{G}$ is a locally free $\mathscr{B}$-Module. Then α being an isomorphism follows from α being an isomorphism for an open neighbourhood of each point $y \in Y$. So we may assume that $\mathscr{G}$ is a free $\mathscr{B}$-Module. We may assume additionally that $\mathscr{G} = \mathscr{B}$. Then α is reduced to the identity morphism $1_{f_*\mathscr{F}}: f_*\mathscr{F} \to f_*\mathscr{F}$.

(2) It suffices to show that $f^*\mathscr{E} \otimes \mathscr{I}$ is an injective $\mathscr{A}$-Module if $\mathscr{I}$ is an injective $\mathscr{A}$-Module. Namely, it suffices to show that if $\varphi: \mathscr{F} \to \mathscr{G}$ is an injective homomorphism of $\mathscr{A}$-Modules, $\varphi^*: \operatorname{Hom}_{\mathscr{A}}(\mathscr{G}, f^*\mathscr{E} \otimes \mathscr{I}) \to \operatorname{Hom}_{\mathscr{A}}(\mathscr{F}, f^*\mathscr{E} \otimes \mathscr{I})$ is surjective. Set $\mathscr{E}^\vee := \operatorname{Hom}_{\mathscr{B}}(\mathscr{E}, \mathscr{B})$. Then we have

$$\operatorname{Hom}_{\mathscr{A}}(\mathscr{G}, f^*\mathscr{E} \otimes \mathscr{I}) \cong \operatorname{Hom}_{\mathscr{A}}(\mathscr{G} \otimes f^*\mathscr{E}^\vee, \mathscr{I})$$
$$\operatorname{Hom}_{\mathscr{A}}(\mathscr{F}, f^*\mathscr{E} \otimes \mathscr{I}) \cong \operatorname{Hom}_{\mathscr{A}}(\mathscr{F} \otimes f^*\mathscr{E}^\vee, \mathscr{I}).$$

If we note that $\mathscr{E}^\vee$ is a locally free $\mathscr{B}$-Module and $\otimes_{\mathscr{A}} f^*\mathscr{E}^\vee$ is an exact functor, the surjectivity of φ^* follows from the hypothesis that $\mathscr{I}$ is an injective $\mathscr{A}$-Module.

(3) follows from (1) and (2).

Part II

Problems II.3.

1. Let M be an A-module which is not a noetherian module. Then there is an ascending chain of A-submodules of M,

$$N_0 \subsetneqq N_1 \subsetneqq \cdots \subsetneqq N_n \subsetneqq \cdots.$$

The modules N_n are identified with the ideals $(0) \oplus N_n$ of R. Hence, R is not a noetherian ring. Meanwhile, $(0) \oplus M$ is contained in the nilradical of R. So $\operatorname{Spec} R$ is the same as $\operatorname{Spec} A$ as topological spaces. Since A is a noetherian ring, $\operatorname{Spec} A$ is a noetherian space. Thus, $\operatorname{Spec} R$ is a noetherian space, though R is not a noetherian ring.

2. For $\mathfrak{p} \in \operatorname{Spec} A$, we have $I_{\mathfrak{p}} = \bigoplus_{\lambda \in \Lambda} K(\mathfrak{p}_\lambda)_{\mathfrak{p}}$. Since $K(\mathfrak{p}_\lambda)_{\mathfrak{p}} = (A_{\mathfrak{p}_\lambda}/\mathfrak{p}_\lambda A_{\mathfrak{p}_\lambda})_{\mathfrak{p}} = (0)$ if $\mathfrak{p} \not\supset \mathfrak{p}_\lambda$ and $K(\mathfrak{p}_\lambda)_{\mathfrak{p}} = K(\mathfrak{p}_\lambda)$ if $\mathfrak{p} \supset \mathfrak{p}_\lambda$, we have $\operatorname{Supp}(I) = \bigcup_{\lambda \in \Lambda} V(\mathfrak{p}_\lambda)$.

3. We omit the solution.

Problems II.4.

1. Since L/K is a finite separable algebraic extension, there is a monic polynomial $f(x) \in K[x]$ such that $L = K[x]/(f(x))$ with $f'(x) \not\equiv 0$. Since K' is a splitting field of $f(x) = 0$, we may write $f(x) = \prod_{i=1}^n (x - \alpha_i)$ (each $\alpha_i \in K'$, $n = \deg f$). By virtue of the Chinese Remainder Theorem, we then have

$$K' \otimes_K L = K'[x]/\left(\prod_{i=1}^n (x - \alpha_i)\right) \cong \prod_{i=1}^n K'[x]/(x - \alpha_i) \cong \prod_{i=1}^n K'.$$

Clearly, $\operatorname{Spec}(K' \otimes_K L)$ consists of n points.

2. Put $X = V \cup V'$, where $V \cong V' \cong \mathbf{A}_k^1$, $P \in V$, and $P' \in V'$. Then $V \times_k V'$ is an open set of $X \times_k X$ and $(P, P') \in V \times_k V'$. Since $V \times_k V' = \operatorname{Spec} k[t, t']$ and $\overline{(\Delta_{X/k})} \cap (V \times_k V') = \operatorname{Spec} k[t, t']/(t - t')$, we have $(P, P') \in \overline{\Delta_{X/k}}$. Similarly, $(P', P) \in \overline{\Delta_{X/k}}$. In order to show that $\overline{\Delta_{X/k}} = \Delta_{X/k} \cup \{(P', P), (P, P')\}$, we have only to note that $X \times_k X = (V \times_k V) \cup (V \times_k V') \cup (V' \times_k V) \cup (V' \times_k V')$ and look at the closure of $\Delta_{X/k}$ restricted on respective open sets.

3. (1) Let $X' = X \times_Y Y'$. To show that the base change $f': X' \to Y'$ is a closed immersion, we may replace Y' by an affine open neighbourhood U' of a point of $f'(X')$. Furthermore, we may assume that $U' \subseteq g^{-1}(U)$ for an affine open set U of Y. Set $U' = \operatorname{Spec} A'$ and $U = \operatorname{Spec} A$. Since f is a closed immersion, we may write $f^{-1}(U) = \operatorname{Spec} B$, where $B \cong A/I$, I being an ideal of A. Then $f'^{-1}(U') = \operatorname{Spec}(A' \otimes_A B) \cong \operatorname{Spec}(A'/IA')$. Hence, $f': X' \to Y'$ is a closed immersion.

(2) We may assume $Z = \operatorname{Spec} A$. Then $Y = \operatorname{Spec} B$, where $B \cong A/I$ with an ideal I of A. Similarly, $X = \operatorname{Spec} C$, where $C \cong B/J$ with an ideal J of B. Let $\pi: A \to B$ be the natural residue homomorphism, and let $\widetilde{J} = \pi^{-1}(J)$. Then $I \subset \widetilde{J}$ and $J \cong \widetilde{J}/I$. Hence, $C \cong A/\widetilde{J}$. Namely, we see that $g \cdot f: X \to Z$ is a closed immersion.

4. (1) Set $t = y/x$. Let $\overline{k}$ be an algebraic closure of k, let $\alpha = a^{1/n}$, and let ω be a primitive nth root of 1. Then $t^n - a$ splits as $t^n - a = (t-\alpha)(t-\alpha\omega)\cdots(t-\alpha\omega^{n-1})$ in $\overline{k}$. Hence, if $a^{1/m} \notin k$ (for each m, $1 < m \leq n, m|n$), then $t^n - a$ is irreducible over k. Thus, $y^n - ax^n$ is irreducible over k under the same condition as above. Since $y^n - ax^n = \prod_{i=0}^{n-1}(y - \alpha\omega^i x)$ over $\overline{k}$, $C \otimes_k \overline{k}$ is a union of n lines $y = \alpha\omega^i x$ $(0 \leq i < n)$ through the point of origin on $\mathbf{A}^2_{\overline{k}}$.

(2) Argue as in (1) above.

5. (1) This part is clear.

(2) Let $\mathscr{O}$ be a discrete valuation ring of $k(Y)$ containing k. Then $t \in \mathscr{O}$ or $u \in \mathscr{O}$. If $t \in \mathscr{O}$, then $\mathscr{O} = k[t]_{(t-\alpha)}$ for some $\alpha \in k$. If $u \in \mathscr{O}$, then $\mathscr{O} = k[u]_{(u-\beta)}$ for some $\beta \in k$. If $\beta \neq 0$, then $\mathscr{O} = k[t]_{(t-\beta^{-1})}$.

(3) Let $\mathscr{O}$ be a discrete valuation ring such that $k \subset \mathscr{O}$ and $k(Y) \subset Q(\mathscr{O})$. Then $\mathscr{O} \cap k(Y)$ is a discrete valuation ring of $k(Y)$, i.e., the quotient field of $\mathscr{O} \cap k(Y)$ is $k(Y)$. So $\mathscr{O} \cap k(Y) = k[t]_{(t-\alpha)}$ $(\alpha \in k)$ or $\mathscr{O} \cap k(Y) = k[u]_{(u)}$. Namely, the specialization (of the generic point) of Y along $\mathscr{O}$ is either $t = \alpha$ or $t = \infty$, and it is thereby uniquely determined. Hence, by (II.4.15), Y is separated over k.

(4) Let $\mathscr{O}$ be a discrete valuation ring such that $k \subset \mathscr{O}$ and $k(Y) \subset Q(\mathscr{O})$. Then, as in (3), $\mathscr{O}$ dominates a point $t = \alpha$ or $t = \infty$. Hence, Y is complete.

(5) There is no point on X which is dominated by the discrete valuation ring $k[u]_{(n)}$ $(t = u^{-1})$ of $k(X) = k(t)$. Moreover, $k[t]_{(t)}$ dominates two points P and P'.

6. An answer is given in the problem.

7. Let $\mathscr{O}$ be a discrete valuation ring of $k(X)$ containing k. Since X is complete, there exists a closed point x of X such that $\mathscr{O} \geq \mathscr{O}_{X,x}$. Note that $\mathscr{O}_{X,x}$ is a normal local ring of dimension 1, hence, a discrete valuation ring (I.1.29). Then $\mathscr{O} = \mathscr{O}_{X,x}$. Since X is separated over k, such a point x is uniquely determined by $\mathscr{O}$. Thus, we have an injective mapping of sets

$$\varphi: \{\mathscr{O};\ \text{a DVR of } k(X), k \subset \mathscr{O}\} \to \{x;\ \text{a closed point of } X\},$$

$$\varphi(\mathscr{O}) = x \quad \text{if and only if} \quad \mathscr{O} = \mathscr{O}_{X,x}.$$

Clearly, φ is surjective, too.

8. Put $X = \operatorname{Spec} A$ and $S = \operatorname{Spec} R$. The morphism $f: X \to S$ is a quasicompact morphism. (We have to show that $f^{-1}(V)$ is quasicompact for every quasicompact open set V of S. V has a finite affine open covering $V = \bigcup_{i=1}^n D(f_i)$, where $f_i \in R$ and $f^{-1}(D(f_i)) = D(\varphi(f_i))$, $\varphi: R \to A$ being the ring homomorphism associated with f. Since $D(\varphi(f_i))$ is a compact open set of X and $f^{-1}(V) = \bigcup_{i=1}^n D(\varphi(f_i))$, $f^{-1}(V)$ is also a compact open set.) Thus, f being a finitely generated morphism

is the same as f being a locally, finitely generated morphism. Namely, for each $x \in X$, there exist affine open neighbourhoods U of x and V of $s = f(x)$ such that $U \subseteq f^{-1}(V)$ and $\Gamma(U, \mathscr{O}_U)$ is a finitely generated $\Gamma(V, \mathscr{O}_V)$-algebra. If $D(b)$ is an affine open neighbourhood of s in V, we may replace V, U by $D(b), f^{-1}(D(b)) \cap U$, respectively. Thus, we may assume from the beginning that $V = D(b)$. Then $\Gamma(U, \mathscr{O}_U)$ is a finitely generated $R[b^{-1}]$-algebra. So $\Gamma(U, \mathscr{O}_U)$ is a finitely generated R-algebra. After all, there exists a finite affine open covering $X = \bigcup_{i=1}^n U_i$ of X such that $A_i := \Gamma(U_i, \mathscr{O}_X)$ is a finitely generated R-algebra for each $i, 1 \le i \le n$. If $D(g)$ is an affine open set contained in U_i, then $A[g^{-1}]$ is a finitely generated A-algebra. Hence, $A[g^{-1}]$ is a finitely generated A_i-algebra. This entails that $A[g^{-1}]$ is a finitely generated R-algebra. This remark allows us to assume that $U_i = D(g_i)$ $(g_i \in A)$. Let $\{u_{ij}/g_i^M; 1 \le j \le N\}$ $(u_{ij} \in A, M > 0)$ be a system of generators of the R-algebra $A[g_i^{-1}]$. Taking u_{ij} repeatedly if necessary, we may assume that N is independent of i. On the other hand, since $X = \bigcup_{i=1}^n D(g_i)$, there is a relation $\sum_{i=1}^n g_i h_i = 1$ $(h_i \in A)$. Then we claim that $A = R[u_{ij}, g_i, h_i; 1 \le i \le n, 1 \le j \le N]$. In fact, for each $\xi \in A$, there are $F_i \in R[g_i, u_{ij}; 1 \le j \le N]$ and an $r > 0$ such that $g_i^r \xi = F_i$ for each i, $1 \le i \le n$. We have also

$$1 = \left(\sum_{i=1}^n g_i h_i \right)^{rn} = \sum_{i=1}^n g_i^r H_i, \qquad H_i \in R[g_i, h_i; 1 \le i \le n].$$

Hence, $\xi = \sum_{i=1}^n g_i^r H_i \xi = \sum_{i=1}^n F_i H_i \in R[u_{ij}, g_i, h_i; 1 \le i \le n, 1 \le j \le n]$.

9. It is not hard to follow the given steps, one by one.

Problems II.5.

1. (1) This is clear by the definition.

(2) Let $x \in \sqrt{I}$. Write $x = x_0 + x_1 + \cdots$ as a sum of homogeneous elements. Suppose $x_i \in \sqrt{I}$ $(i < r)$ and $x_r \notin \sqrt{I}$. Since $x^N \in I$ for some $N > 0$, $(x^N)_{rN} = x_r^N + y$ with $y \in (x_0, \ldots, x_{r-1})_{rN} \subseteq \sqrt{I}$. Since $(x^N)_{rN} \in I$, it follows that $x_r^N \in \sqrt{I}$. So $x_r \in \sqrt{I}$. This is absurd.

2. Repeat the arguments in (Part I, Chapter 1), replacing all ideals and elements there by homogeneous ideals and homogeneous elements. We omit the details of the proof.

3. A sketch of solution is given in the problem.

4. Let $\mathfrak{V} = \{V_\lambda\}_{\lambda \in \Lambda}$ be an affine open covering of Y such that $\{f^{-1}(V_\Lambda); \lambda \in \Lambda\}$ is an affine open covering of X. Set $U_\lambda = f^{-1}(V_\lambda)$. Clearly, two Čech complexes $C^\bullet(\mathfrak{V}, f_*\mathscr{F})$ and $C^\bullet(\mathfrak{U}, \mathscr{F})$ are isomorphic, where $\mathfrak{U} = \{U_\lambda\}_{\lambda \in \Lambda}$. Hence, $H^p(\mathfrak{V}, f_*\mathscr{F}) \cong H^p(\mathfrak{V}, \mathscr{F})$ for each $p \ge 0$. Note that for each $m \ge 0$, $V_{\lambda_1} \cap \cdots \cap V_{\lambda_m}$ is an affine open set of Y and $U_{\lambda_1} \cap \cdots \cap U_{\lambda_m}$ is an affine open set of X. By (II.3.14), $H^n(V_{\lambda_1} \cap \cdots \cap V_{\lambda_m}, f_*\mathscr{F}) = H^n(U_{\lambda_1} \cap \cdots \cap U_{\lambda_m}, \mathscr{F}) = (0)$ for each $n > 0$. Then by virtue of (I.2.22), $H^p(\mathfrak{V}, f_*\mathscr{F}) \cong H^p(Y, f_*\mathscr{F})$ and $H^p(\mathfrak{U}, \mathscr{F}) \cong H^p(X, \mathscr{F})$ for each $p \ge 0$. Thus, $H^p(X, \mathscr{F}) \cong H^p(Y, f_*\mathscr{F})$ for each $p \ge 0$.

5. $\mathrm{Cl}(R)$ is the quotient group of the free abelian group $\bigoplus_{\mathrm{ht}\,\mathfrak{p}=1} \mathbf{Z}[\mathfrak{p}]$ generated by all height 1 prime ideals of R modulo linear equivalence. If R is a UFD, then every height 1 prime ideal of R is a principal ideal (compare Problem I.1.4). Hence, $\mathrm{Cl}(R) = (0)$. Conversely, suppose $\mathrm{Cl}(R) = (0)$. Let $\mathfrak{p}$ be a height 1 prime ideal of R. Then $\mathfrak{p} = (f)$ $(f \in Q(R))$ by hypothesis. We claim that $f \in R$. In fact, $f \in R_\mathfrak{q}$ for every height 1 prime ideal $\mathfrak{q}$ of R. [$f \in \mathfrak{p}R_\mathfrak{p}$ if $\mathfrak{q} = \mathfrak{p}$, and $f \in (R_\mathfrak{q})^*$ if $\mathfrak{q} \ne \mathfrak{p}$.] Hence, $f \in \bigcap_\mathfrak{q} R_\mathfrak{q} = R$ (I.1.33).

We shall show that any irreducible element a of R is a prime element. In fact, any prime divisor $\mathfrak{p}$ of a principal ideal aR has height 1 (I.1.33). Since $\mathfrak{p} = (f)$ with $f \in R$, we have $f|a$. Since a is an irreducible element, we have $aR = fR$. Namely, a is a prime element. This implies that R is a UFD.

6. We may assume that the projection $\pi\colon \mathbf{P}^N \to \mathbf{P}^n$ is given by $(x_0, x_1, \ldots, x_N) \mapsto (x_0, x_1, \ldots, x_n)$, where $(x_0, x_1, \ldots, x_N)$ are homogeneous coordinates of $\mathbf{P}^N$. Define a linear subspace L by $x_0 = \cdots = x_n = 0$. Then $\mathbf{P}^N - L$ is the domain of definition of π. Put $Y = \mathbf{P}^N - L$, $Z = \mathbf{P}^n$ and $p = \pi|_Y$. p is an affine morphism. Since $\varphi = \pi \cdot \psi$ is a morphism, $\psi(X) \cap L = \varnothing$. For each $x \in X$, set $y = \psi(x)$ and $z = \varphi(x)$. By hypothesis, there exists an affine open neighbourhood $W = \operatorname{Spec} R$ of z such that $\varphi^{-1}(W) \cong \operatorname{Spec}(R/I)$, where I is an ideal of R. Putting $p^{-1}(W) = \operatorname{Spec} B$ and $\varphi^{-1}(W) = \operatorname{Spec} A$, we obtain the following commutative diagram

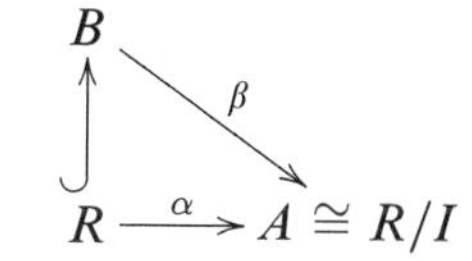

where R is identified with a subring of B. We have ${}^a\beta = \psi|_{\varphi^{-1}(W)}$ and ${}^a\alpha = \varphi|_{\varphi^{-1}(W)}$. Apparently, β is a surjective ring homomorphism. Hence, $A \cong B/I$ for an ideal J of B. Thus, ψ is a closed immersion.

7. It is not hard to verify the assertions given in the steps.

Problems II.6.

1. Put $A = R[x_1, \ldots, x_n]$ and $\Omega = \Omega_{A/R}$. For an arbitrary A-module M, the A-homomorphism $\varphi\colon \operatorname{Hom}_A(\Omega, M) \to \operatorname{Der}_R(A, M)$ is an isomorphism, where $\varphi(\alpha)(a) = \alpha(da)$ $(a \in A)$ for $\alpha \in \operatorname{Hom}_A(\Omega, M)$. Besides, Ω is an A-module generated by $dx_1, \ldots, dx_n$. Any element $\delta \in \operatorname{Der}_R(A, M)$ is given by assigning elements $\delta(x_i)$ of M for each i, $1 \le i \le n$ which can be arbitrary elements of M. If $a_1 dx_1 + \cdots + a_n dx_n = 0$ $(a_i \in A)$ is a nontrivial relation, then we have $a_1\delta(x_1) + \cdots + a_n\delta(x_n) = 0$. This is a contradiction because we can take $\delta(x_1), \ldots, \delta(x_n)$ arbitrarily. Hence, Ω is a free A-module with a free basis $\{dx_1, \ldots, dx_n\}$.

2. Let $\mathscr{N}$ be the sheaf of nilradicals of X. Since X is an algebraic k-scheme, $\mathscr{N}^r = (0)$ for a positive integer r. We may assume that $\mathscr{N}^{r-1} \neq (0)$. Put $\mathscr{I} = \mathscr{N}^{r-1}$ and $Y = (X, \mathscr{O}_X/\mathscr{I})$. We have an exact sequence (II.6.18):

$$\mathscr{I}/\mathscr{I}^2 \to \Omega_{X/k} \otimes_{\mathscr{O}_X} \mathscr{O}_Y \to \Omega_{Y/k} \to 0.$$

If $\Omega_{X/k} = (0)$, then $\Omega_{Y/k} = (0)$. Next we repeat the above argument for the sheaf of nilradicals of Y. We thus know that $\Omega_{X_{\mathrm{red}}/k} = (0)$. In order to verify the requirement, we may assume that $X = X_{\mathrm{red}}$. Next let X_1 be an irreducible component of X. Applying (II.6.18 (3)) to the natural closed immersion $f\colon X_1 \to X$, we obtain an exact sequence

$$f^*\Omega_{X/k} \to \Omega_{X_1/k} \to \Omega_{X_1/X} \to 0.$$

Here it is readily shown that $\Omega_{X_1/X} = (0)$. (To show this, we may assume that $X_1 = \operatorname{Spec} B$, $X = \operatorname{Spec} A$, and $B = A/I$. By means of an isomorphism $\operatorname{Hom}_B(\Omega_{B/A}, M) \cong \operatorname{Der}_A(B, M)$, we have only to show that any element of $\operatorname{Der}_A(B, M)$ is zero.) Then $\Omega_{X_1/k} = (0)$. Noting that $\dim X = \sup_i \dim X_i$ when X_i ranges over all irreducible components of X, we have only to prove that $\dim X = 0$ in the case where X is irreducible. We assume that X is reduced and irreducible. Set

$K = k(X)$ and apply (II.6.18(3)) to the natural morphism η: $\operatorname{Spec} K \to X$. We know as above that $\Omega_{\operatorname{Spec}(K)/k} = (0)$. Hence, $\Omega_{K/k} = (0)$. Let $n = \operatorname{tr.deg}_k K$, and let $\{x_1, \ldots, x_n\}$ be a transcendence basis of K over k. Setting $K_0 = k(x_1, \ldots, x_n)$, we have an exact sequence

$$\Omega_{K_0/k} \otimes_{K_0} K \to \Omega_{K/k} \to \Omega_{K/K_0} \to 0.$$

Hence, $\Omega_{K/K_0} = (0)$. This implies, as shown in (II.6.19), that K is a separable algebraic extension of K_0. Namely, $\{x_1, \ldots, x_n\}$ is a separating transcendence basis of K over k. Let M be a K-module. Then $\operatorname{Der}_k(K, M) = \operatorname{Der}_k(K_0, M)$. (Write $K = K_0(\theta)$, and let $f(t)$ be a minimal polynomial of θ. Let $\delta \in \operatorname{Der}_k(K_0, M)$. Then δ is uniquely extended to an element of $\operatorname{Der}_k(K, M)$ by putting $\delta(\theta) = -f'(\theta)^{-1} f^{\delta}(\theta)$, where $f^{\delta}(t)$ is the polynomial obtained by applying δ to the coefficients of $f(t)$.) Since $\operatorname{Der}_k(K_0, M) \cong \operatorname{Hom}_{K_0}(\Omega_{K_0/k}, M) \cong \operatorname{Hom}_{K_0}(\bigoplus_{i=1}^n K_0\, dx_i, M) \cong M^{\oplus n}$ (= a direct sum of n copies of M) and $\operatorname{Der}_k(K, M) \cong \operatorname{Hom}_K(\Omega_{K/k}, M) = (0)$, we have $n = 0$.

3. Let $P \in \operatorname{Sing} V$. Suppose $X_0 \neq 0$ at P. Let $x_i = X_i/X_0$ $(1 \le i \le n)$ and $f(x_1, \ldots, x_n) = (X_0)^{-d} F(X_0, \ldots, X_n)$, where $d = \deg F$. By (II.6.15), $P \in \operatorname{Sing} V$ if and only if $f(P) = (\partial f/\partial x_i)(P) = 0$ for each i, $1 \le i \le n$. (Note that $\dim V = n - 1$.) Noting that $\partial f/\partial x_i = (X_0)^{-(d-1)}(\partial F/\partial X_i)$, we know that $P \in \operatorname{Sing} V$ if and only if $F = (\partial F/\partial X_1) = \cdots = (\partial F/\partial X_n) = 0$ at P.

Make the same argument in the case $X_i \neq 0$ at P.

4. By hypothesis $\Omega_{X/Y} = (0)$. This entails $\Omega_{X_K/K} = (0)$, where $K = k(Y)$ and $X_K = X \times_Y \operatorname{Spec} K$; X_K is a reduced and irreducible algebraic K-scheme. Let $L = k(X)$. Then $L = K(X_K)$. Since $\Omega_{X_K/K} = (0)$, we have $\Omega_{L/K} = (0)$. So, $\operatorname{tr.deg}_K L = 0$ by Problem II.6.2. It then follows that $\dim X - \dim Y = \operatorname{tr.deg}_K L = 0$.

Part III

Problems III.7.

1. (1) There exists a 3×3 symmetric matrix A with entries in k such that $F(X_0, X_1, X_2) = (X_0, X_1, X_2)A^t(X_0, X_1, X_2)$. Since the characteristic of k is not 2, there exists an invertible matrix P such that PA^tP is a diagonal matrix. Hence, we may assume from the beginning that A is a diagonal matrix, i.e., $F = a_0X_0^2 + a_1X_1^2 + a_2X_2^2$. According to rank A, further changes of variables reduce F to one of the standard forms (i), (ii), and (iii).

(2) C is irreducible and reduced only in the case (i). Then C is the image of $\Phi_{|2P|}: \mathbf{P}^1 \to \mathbf{P}^2$, where P is a closed point of $\mathbf{P}^1$. (If we choose homogeneous coordinates (ξ_0, ξ_1) of $\mathbf{P}^1$ so that P is given as $(1, 0)$, then we have $H^0(\mathbf{P}^1, \mathcal{O}(2P)) = k\xi_0^2 + k\xi_0\xi_1 + k\xi_1^2$. Set $X_0 = \xi_0^2$, $X_1 = \xi_1^2$ and $X_2 = \xi_0\xi_1$. Then C is given by $X_0X_1 = X_2^2$ and $\Phi_{|2P|}$ gives rise to an isomorphism between $\mathbf{P}^1$ and C.)

(3) As in (1), we can express $F = a_0X_0^2 + a_1X_1^2 + a_2X_2^2 + a_3X_3^2$, where $a_i = 0$ or 1 and $a_0 \ge a_1 \ge a_2 \ge a_3$. Hence, after a suitable change of variables, it is classified into the following standard forms: (i) $X_0X_1 = X_2X_3$, (ii) $X_0X_2 = X_1^2$, (iii) $X_0X_1 = 0$, and (iv) $X_0^2 = 0$. In the cases (ii), (iii), and (iv), the quadratic hypersurface is a projective cone consisting of lines which pass through points of a conic on $\mathbf{P}^2$ and the point $(0, 0, 0, 1)$. In case (i), it is isomorphic to $\mathbf{P}^1 \times \mathbf{P}^1$. (An isomorphism is given by $(t_0, t_1) \times (u_0, u_1) \mapsto (t_0u_0, t_1u_1, t_0u_1, t_1u_0)$.)

Problems III.8.

1. Set $\mathscr{O} = \mathscr{O}_{V,P}$ and $\mathfrak{m} = \mathfrak{m}_{V,P}$. Since P is a nonsingular point of V, $\mathfrak{m}/\mathfrak{m}^2 = k\overline{u} + k\overline{v}$ for a local system of parameters (u, v) at P, where $\overline{u} = u \pmod{\mathfrak{m}^2}$ and $\overline{v} = v \pmod{\mathfrak{m}^2}$. If we take an affine open neighborhood $\operatorname{Spec} A$ of P, we have $(\mathscr{O}, \mathfrak{m}) = (A_{\mathfrak{M}}, \mathfrak{M}A_{\mathfrak{M}})$, where $\mathfrak{M}$ is a maximal ideal of A. Now for $(\alpha, \beta) \in k^2 - (0, 0)$, choose $g \in \mathfrak{m}$ such that $\alpha\overline{u} + \beta\overline{v} = g \pmod{\mathfrak{m}^2}$. Since $g \in A_{\mathfrak{M}}$, write $g = a/b$ with $a, b \in A$ and $b \notin \mathfrak{M}$. Let D be a closed subset of $\operatorname{Spec} A$ defined by $a = 0$. Then each irreducible component of D has dimension 1. (Each prime divisor of aA in a normal ring A has height 1.) Furthermore, there is a unique irreducible component of D passing through P, and P is a nonsingular point on the irreducible component. Let B be the closure of the irreducible component passing through P, which is an irreducible algebraic curve. B is nonsingular at the point P. Suppose the irreducible algebraic curve C is defined by $f = 0$ in an open neighbourhood of P, where $f \in \mathfrak{m}_{V,P}$. Then we have

$$i(C, B; P) = \operatorname{length} \mathscr{O}/(f, g) = \operatorname{length} k[[u, v]]/(f_\mu + \cdots, (\alpha u + \beta v) + \cdots).$$

Consider the case $\beta \neq 0$. Then $k[[u, v]]/(g) = k[[u]]$ and $v = \lambda u +$ (terms in u of degree ≥ 2), where $\lambda = -\alpha/\beta$. Choose (α, β) so that $f_\mu(1, \lambda) \neq 0$. Then we have

$$\begin{aligned} i(C, B; P) &= \operatorname{length} k[[u]] \Big/ \left(f_\mu(1, \lambda)u^\mu + \begin{pmatrix} \text{terms in } u \text{ of degree} \\ \geq (\mu + 1) \end{pmatrix} \right) \\ &= \operatorname{length} k[[u]]/(u^\mu) = \mu. \end{aligned}$$

Namely, we have $\mu(C, P) = \inf_{P \in B} i(C, B; P)$.

2. As given in the Hint, $\omega_{C/k} \cong \mathscr{O}_{\mathbf{P}^2}(n-3)|_C$. Since $C \sim nH$ on $\mathbf{P}^2$ with a hyperplane H on $\mathbf{P}^2$, there is an exact sequence

$$0 \to \mathscr{O}_{\mathbf{P}^2}(-n) \to \mathscr{O}_{\mathbf{P}^2} \to \mathscr{O}_C \to 0.$$

Taking tensor products with the invertible sheaf $\mathscr{O}_{\mathbf{P}^2}(n-3)$, we have an exact sequence

$$0 \to \mathscr{O}_{\mathbf{P}^2}(-3) \to \mathscr{O}_{\mathbf{P}^2}(n-3) \to \mathscr{O}_{\mathbf{P}^2}(n-3) \otimes \mathscr{O}_C \to 0.$$

Since $h^i(\mathbf{P}^2, \mathscr{O}_{\mathbf{P}^2}(-3)) = 0$ for $i = 0, 1$ (II.5.12), the cohomology sequence entails $h^0(C, \mathscr{O}_{\mathbf{P}^2}(n-3) \otimes \mathscr{O}_C) = h^0(\mathbf{P}^2, \mathscr{O}_{\mathbf{P}^2}(n-3)) = \binom{n-1}{2} = (n-1)(n-2)/2$. Namely, we have $g = (n-1)(n-2)/2$.

3. As explained in the Hint, we have for $f \in k(V)$:

$f \in M$ iff $f \in M(L)$ ($=$ the module associated with L) and all the coefficients of f, viewed as an element of $k[[u, v]]$, vanish for the terms of degree between 0 and $\mu - 1$.

Let $n = \dim_k M(L)$, and let $\{f_1, \ldots, f_n\}$ be a k-basis of $M(L)$. Then we have

$$(*) \qquad f = \alpha_1 f_1 + \cdots + \alpha_n f_n \quad \text{all } \alpha_i \in k.$$

Since we can choose $f_1, \ldots, f_n$ from $\mathscr{O}_{V,P}$, the comparison of the coefficients of terms of degree between 0 and $\mu - 1$ in the relation $(*)$ yields altogether $\mu(\mu+1)/2$ linear equations in $\alpha_1, \ldots, \alpha_n$. Hence, we have

$$\dim_k M \geq n - \frac{\mu(\mu+1)}{2}.$$

Problems III.9.

1. (i) A is a field if it is reduced. Since the characteristic of k is zero and $\dim_k A < \infty$, A/k is a finite separable algebraic extension. By the result verified in the proof of (II.6.19), we have $\Omega_{A/k} = (0)$.

(ii) Conversely, suppose $\Omega_{A/k} = (0)$. Suppose A is not reduced. Let $\mathfrak{m}$ be the nilradical, and let $\overline{A} = A/\mathfrak{m}^2$. Then by an exact sequence

$$J/J^2 \to \Omega_{A/k} \otimes_A \overline{A} \to \Omega_{\overline{A}/k} \to 0 \qquad (J = \mathfrak{m}^2),$$

$\Omega_{A/k} \neq (0)$ provided $\Omega_{\overline{A}/k} \neq (0)$. So we may assume from the beginning that $\mathfrak{m}^2 = (0)$.

(iii) Define a ring homomorphism $\varphi\colon A \to \widetilde{A}$ by $\varphi(a) = a \otimes 1$. Since A is k-flat, φ is an injection. So A is viewed as a subring of $\widetilde{A}$. If each A_i is reduced, then $\widetilde{A}$ is apparently reduced which implies that A is reduced.

(iv) Since $\Omega_{\widetilde{A}/\tilde{k}} \cong \Omega_{A/k} \otimes_k \tilde{k} \cong \prod_{i=1}^r \Omega_{A_i/\tilde{k}}$, we have the equivalences: $\Omega_{A/k} = (0)$ iff $\Omega_{\widetilde{A}/\tilde{k}} = (0)$ iff $\Omega_{A_i/\tilde{k}} = (0)$ for each i. Hence, we may assume $k' = k$, and we have only to show that "$\Omega_{A/k} = (0)$ implies $\mathfrak{m} = (0)$". Then A decomposes as $A = k \oplus \mathfrak{m}$ and the product is given by $(\alpha, x) \cdot (\beta, y) = (\alpha\beta, \beta x + \alpha y)$. If (α, x) corresponds to $a \in A$, then $\alpha = a \pmod{\mathfrak{m}}$ and $x = a - \alpha$. Set $x = \delta(a)$. If (β, y) corresponds to $b \in A$, then $\delta(ab) = \beta x + \alpha y = \beta\delta(a) + \alpha\delta(b) = b\delta(a) + a\delta(b)$. Thus, δ is a k-derivation of A with values in $\mathfrak{m}$. Suppose $\mathfrak{m} \neq (0)$. Then $\delta \neq 0$. So $\mathrm{Der}_k(A, \mathfrak{m}) \cong \mathrm{Hom}_A(\Omega_{A/k}, \mathfrak{m}) \neq (0)$. This contradicts the hypothesis $\Omega_{A/k} = (0)$.

2. We may assume that X is connected. Let $X = X_1 \cup \cdots \cup X_r$ be the irreducible decomposition of X. If X is reducible, there are two distinct irreducible components X_i, X_j of X with $X_i \cap X_j \neq \varnothing$. Suppose $X_1 \cap X_2 \neq \varnothing$. Let P be a closed point of $X_1 \cap X_2$, and let $\mathscr{O} = \mathscr{O}_{X,P}$. Then X_1 and X_2 correspond to minimal prime divisors $\mathfrak{p}_1, \mathfrak{p}_2$ of $\mathscr{O}$. By (I.1.23), $\mathfrak{p}_1 = ((0) : a_1)$ and $\mathfrak{p}_2 = ((0) : a_2)$ for some $a_1, a_2 \in \mathscr{O}$. Since $\mathscr{O}$ is an integral domain, $\mathfrak{p}_1 = \mathfrak{p}_2 = (0)$ which is a contradiction. What is necessary in this proof is that every local ring of X is an integral domain.

3. Let M be the k-module associated with Λ, which we take as a submodule of $H^0(V, \mathscr{O}_V(D_1))$. Let σ_1, σ_2 be elements of M such that $D_i = (\sigma_i)_0$ $(i = 1, 2)$. Then any element σ of M is uniquely written as $\sigma = \alpha_1\sigma_1 + \alpha_2\sigma_2$ with $\alpha_1, \alpha_2 \in k$. If $P \in \operatorname{Supp} D_1 \cap \operatorname{Supp} D_2$, then $\sigma_1(P) = \sigma_2(P) = 0$. So $\sigma(P) = 0$ and $P \in \operatorname{Supp}(\sigma)_0$. Namely, $P \in \operatorname{Bs}\Lambda$. The inclusion $\operatorname{Bs}\Lambda \subseteq \operatorname{Supp} D_1 \cap \operatorname{Supp} D_2$ is clear.

4. It is not hard to solve problems following the instructions in the steps. We omit the details.

Problems III.10.

1. (1) Set $x = X/Z$ and $y = Y/Z$. Then $y^2 = (x - a_1) \cdots (x - a_n)$ is the defining equation of $C_0 := C \cap \mathbf{A}^2$, where $\mathbf{A}^2$ is the complement of the hyperplane $H : Z = 0$ in $\mathbf{P}^2$. Since $C \cap H = \{(0, 1, 0)\}$, we have only to show that C_0 is irreducible. Set $f = y^2 - \prod_{i=1}^n (x - a_i)$ and $R = k[x, y]/(f)$. If we view f as a polynomial in y over the polynomial ring $k[x]$, then f is irreducible by Eisenstein criterion of irreducibility. Since $k[x, y]$ is a UFD, f is a prime element. Hence, R is an integral domain. Thus, C is an irreducible algebraic curve.

(2) Applying the Jacobian criterion in the Problem II.6.3, we know that C is nonsingular if $n = 3$ and that $P_\infty := (0, 1, 0)$ is the unique singular point of C if

$n > 3$. Set $u = X/Y$ and $v = Z/Y$. In an open neighbourhood $U_0 = \operatorname{Spec} k[u, v]$ of P_∞ in $\mathbf{P}^2$, C is then defined by an equation $v^{n-2} = (u - a_1 v) \cdots (u - a_n v)$. Thus, $\mu(C, P_\infty) = n - 2$. Let $\sigma_1 : U_1 \to U_0$ be the monoidal transformation with center at the point P_∞, let $E_1 = \sigma_1^{-1}(P_\infty)$ and let $C_1 = \sigma_1'(C)$. Then $U_1 = U_{10} \cup U_{11}$ with $U_{10} = \operatorname{Spec} k[u, v_1]$ and $U_{11} = \operatorname{Spec} k[u_1, v]$, where $v_1 = v/u$ and $u_1 = u/v$. The curve C_1 does not meet the line $v = 0$ on U_{11}. (The defining equation of $C_1 \cap U_{11}$ is $1 = v^2(u_1 - a_1) \cdots (u_1 - a_n)$.) Hence, $C_1 \subset U_{10}$, and C is defined by an equation $v_1^{n-2} = u^2(1 - a_1 v_1) \cdots (1 - a_n v_1)$. Its singular point is $P_\infty^{(1)} : (u, v_1) = (0, 0)$ and $\mu(C_1, P_\infty^{(1)}) = 2$. Let $\sigma_2 : U_2 \to U_1$ be the monoidal transformation with center at the point $P_\infty^{(1)}$, and let $C_2 := \sigma_2'(C_1)$. If we set $u = v_1 u_2$, C_2 has a unique singular point $P_\infty^{(2)} : (u_2, v_1) = (0, 0)$ on $U_{21} = \operatorname{Spec} k[u_2, v_1]$, and C_2 is defined locally at $P_\infty^{(2)}$ by $u_2^2 = v_1^{n-4} \cdot$ (an invertible element). So $\mu(C_2, P_\infty^{(2)}) = 2$. In this way, we can show that C has infinitely near points $P_\infty^{(1)}, \ldots, P_\infty^{(r)}$ $(r = [\frac{n}{2}] - 1)$ and has multiplicity 2 at these points.

(3) We compute

$$p_a(C) = \frac{1}{2}(C + K_{\mathbf{P}^2} \cdot C) + 1 = \frac{1}{2} n(n-3) + 1 = \frac{1}{2}(n-1)(n-2),$$

and

$$\begin{aligned} g(\widetilde{C}) &= p_a(C) - \frac{1}{2}(n-2)(n-3) - r = (n-2) - \left(\left[\frac{n}{2}\right] - 1\right) \\ &= n - \left[\frac{n}{2}\right] - 1 \quad \text{(cf. (III.10.4))}. \end{aligned}$$

2. (1) *implies* 2. Use the arithmetic genus formula and the result $p_a(C) \geq 0$. Since $-2 \leq p_a(C) - 2 = (C^2) + (C \cdot K_V) \leq -2$, it follows that $(C^2) = (C \cdot K_V) = -1$.

(2) *implies* 3. Use the arithmetic genus formula.

(3) *implies* (4). By Lemma 10.4, C has no singular points, and $g(C) = 0$. So $C \cong \mathbf{P}^1$ by Theorem 7.6.

(4) *implies* (1). Use the arithmetic genus formula.

Problems III.11.

1. Put $E_i = \sigma^{-1}(P_i)$. By (III.8.8) and (III.10.3), $\sigma^* C = C' + \sum_{i=1}^r m_i E_i$ and $K_V \sim \sigma^*(K_{\mathbf{P}^2}) + \sum_{i=1}^r E_i$. Hence, we have

$$d^2 = (\sigma^* C)^2 = (C'^2) + \sum_{i=1}^r m_i^2,$$

$$(C' \cdot K_V) = (\sigma^* C \cdot \sigma^*(K_{\mathbf{P}^2})) + \sum_{i=1}^r m_i = -3d + \sum_{i=1}^r m_i.$$

2. The condition for C' to be a (-1) curve is $(C'^2) = (C' \cdot K_V) = -1$. This is the same as

$$d^2 - \sum_{i=1}^r m_i^2 = -3d + \sum_{i=1}^r m_i = -1.$$

Suppose $m_1 \geq \cdots \geq m_r$. Setting $m_{r+1} = \cdots = m_8 = 0$ if necessary, we may assume that σ is the monoidal transformation with centers as 8 points. (The condition $m_{r+1} = \cdots = m_8 = 0$ is equivalent to the condition that C does not pass through $P_{r+1}, \ldots, P_8$.

The proper transform of C by the monoidal transformation with centers at 8 points has the same self-intersection number as the proper transform of C by the monoidal transformation with centers at r points.) Eliminating d from the above two equations in d and m, we obtain an equation

$$18 = \sum_{i=1}^{8}(m_i - 1)^2 + \sum_{i<j}(m_i - m_j)^2.$$

3. Consider the case $r = 8$. The other cases are treated in the same way. First of all, there are 8 exceptional curves of the monoidal transformation σ with centers at 8 points, which are (-1) curves. We next look for (-1) curves which are the proper transforms by σ of certain irreducible curves C on $\mathbf{P}^2$. We follow the classification of all possible cases in the Problem 2. In the case of $(1; 1^2)$, C is a line passing through two points among $P_1, \ldots, P_8$. Hence there are $\binom{8}{2}$ of such C's. In the case of $(2; 1^5)$, C is a conic passing through 5 points among $P_1, \ldots, P_8$. Hence, there are $\binom{8}{5}$ of such C's. In the case of $(3; 2, 1^6)$, C is a cubic curve passing through 7 points of $P_1, \ldots, P_8$, one of which is a double point of C. So there are $\binom{8}{7} \cdot \binom{7}{1}$ of such C's. Similar observations entail that there are altogether as many (-1) curves as

$$8 + \binom{8}{2} + \binom{8}{5} + \binom{8}{7} \cdot \binom{7}{1} + \binom{8}{3} + \binom{8}{2} + \binom{8}{1} = 240.$$

Problems III.12.

4. Let $V = \mathbf{P}(\mathscr{F})$, let $\rho\colon V \to B$ be the structure morphism, and let V_η be the generic fiber of ρ. Then $V_\eta \cong \mathbf{P}^1_{k(\eta)}$ and $\Omega_{V_\eta/k(\eta)} \cong \omega_{V/k} \otimes k(\eta)$. So we can write $\omega_{V/k} \cong \mathscr{O}(-2M_2) \otimes \rho^*\mathscr{L}$ with $\mathscr{L} \in \operatorname{Pic}(B)$ (III.12.8). Meanwhile, $\Omega_{B/k} \otimes \mathscr{I}/\mathscr{I}^2 \cong \omega_{V/k} \otimes \mathscr{O}_{M_2}$ (Hint) and $\mathscr{I}/\mathscr{I}^2 \cong \mathscr{L}_1 \otimes \mathscr{L}_2^{-1}$. (Write down local defining equations.) Hence $\omega_{V/k} \otimes \mathscr{O}_{M_2} \cong (\mathscr{O}_V(-2M_2) \otimes \mathscr{O}_{M_2}) \otimes \mathscr{L} \cong \mathscr{L}_1^2 \otimes \mathscr{L}_2^{-2} \otimes \mathscr{L}$ and $\omega_{V/k} \otimes \mathscr{O}_{M_2} \cong \Omega_{B/k} \otimes \mathscr{L}_1 \otimes \mathscr{L}_2^{-1}$. So we obtain $\mathscr{L} \cong \Omega_{B/k} \otimes \mathscr{L}_2 \otimes \mathscr{L}_1^{-1}$.

2. Taking tensor products of $\mathscr{O}(aM + bl)$ with each term of an exact sequence

$$0 \to \mathscr{O}(-M) \to \mathscr{O} \to \mathscr{O}_M \to 0,$$

we obtain the following exact sequence

$$(*) \qquad 0 \to \mathscr{O}((a-1)M + bl) \to \mathscr{O}(aM + bl) \to \mathscr{O}_{\mathbf{P}^1}(b - an) \to 0.$$

Suppose $b \geq an$ and $a \geq 1$. We proceed by induction on a. Since $b \geq (a-1)n$, we assume that

$$h^0(F_n, \mathscr{O}((a-1)M + bl)) = a(b+1) - \frac{1}{2}(a-1)an$$
$$h^1(F_n, \mathscr{O}((a-1)M + bl)) = 0.$$

The cohomology sequence attached to the exact sequence $(*)$ entails

$$\begin{aligned} h^0(F, \mathscr{O}(aM + bl)) &= a(b+1) - \frac{1}{2}(a-1)an + (b - an + 1) \\ &= (a+1)(b+1) - \frac{1}{2}a(a+1)n, \end{aligned}$$
$$h^1(F_n, \mathscr{O}(aM + bl)) = 0.$$

In order to show that $h^0(F_n, \mathcal{O}(M + bl)) = 2(b + 1) - n$, proceed by induction on b by making use of an exact sequence

$$0 \to \mathcal{O}(M + (b - 1)l) \to \mathcal{O}(M + bl) \to \mathcal{O}_l \to 0.$$

The other cases can be treated in a similar fashion.

List of Notation

$A := B$	give the set B the name A; define A by the condition B.
$A - B$	$A \backslash (A \cap B)$ if A and B are subsets of a set S; difference of A and B if they are elements of an abelian group.
$(I : a)$	ideal quotient; $(I : a) = \{x \in R; ax \in I\}$ if I is an ideal of a ring R.
$\sqrt{I}$	radical of an ideal I.
$R_S, R_{\mathfrak{p}}$	quotient ring, localization.
$\text{K-}\dim R, \dim R$	Krull dimension of R.
$\mathscr{O} \geq \mathscr{O}'$	a local ring $(\mathscr{O}, \mathfrak{m})$ dominates a local ring $(\mathscr{O}', \mathfrak{m}')$, i.e., $\mathscr{O} \supseteq \mathscr{O}', \mathfrak{m} \cap \mathscr{O}' = \mathfrak{m}'$.
$\mathrm{ht}(\mathfrak{p})$	height of a prime ideal $\mathfrak{p}$.
$\mathrm{tr.deg}_k K$	transcendence degree of an extension field K/k.
$\mathrm{Gal}(K/k)$	Galois group of a normal algebraic extension.
$\prod A_i, \prod_{i \in I} A_i$	direct product of sets, etc.
$\coprod A_i, \coprod_{i \in I} A_i$	direct sum of sets, etc.
$\varinjlim_i A_i, \varprojlim_i A_i$	inductive limit, projective limit.
$\mathscr{F} \oplus \mathscr{G}$	direct sum of sheaves of modules.
$\mathscr{A}^{(I)}, \mathscr{A}^n$	direct sum of $\|I\|$ copies (or n copies) of a sheaf of commutative rings.
$\mathscr{F} \otimes_A \mathscr{G}$	tensor product of $\mathscr{A}$-Modules.
$\mathrm{Hom}_{\mathscr{A}}(\mathscr{F}, \mathscr{G})$	group of homomorphisms of $\mathscr{A}$-Modules.
$\mathscr{H}om_{\mathscr{A}}(\mathscr{F}, \mathscr{G})$	$\mathscr{A}$-Module of homomorphisms of $\mathscr{A}$-Modules.
$\mathscr{F}^{\vee}$	dual $\mathscr{A}$-Module, $\mathscr{H}om_{\mathscr{A}}(\mathscr{F}, \mathscr{A})$.
$\mathrm{Ker}\, \varphi, \mathrm{Coker}\, \varphi, \mathrm{Im}\, \varphi$	kernel, cokernel, and image of an $\mathscr{A}$-homomorphism $\varphi : \mathscr{F} \to \mathscr{G}$ of $\mathscr{A}$-Modules.
$f_* \mathscr{F}, f^* \mathscr{G}$	direct image, inverse image of a module of sheaves.
$\Gamma(U, \mathscr{F})$	module of sections of a sheaf of modules $\mathscr{F}$ over an open set U.
$H^n(X, \mathscr{F})$	cohomology group defined by an injective resolution of a sheaf of modules $\mathscr{F}$.
$H^n(\mathfrak{U}, \mathscr{F})$	Čech cohomology group of $\mathscr{F}$ defined by an open covering $\mathfrak{U}$.
$\check{H}^n(X, \mathscr{F})$	Čech cohomology group of $\mathscr{F}$; by the definition, it is $\varprojlim_{\mathfrak{U}} H^n(\mathfrak{U}, \mathscr{F})$.
$R^n f_* \mathscr{F}$	higher direct image of $\mathscr{F}$.
$\mathrm{Spec}(R)$	spectrum of a commutative ring R.

$V(I), D(I), D(a)$	closed set, open sets in the Zariski topology.
$\widetilde{R}, \widetilde{M}$	quasicoherent sheaves associated with R and an R-module M.
$\mathfrak{p}_x$	prime ideal of R corresponding to a point x of Spec(R).
$k(x)$	residue field of a point x.
$\mathbb{A}_k^n$	n-dimensional affine space over k.
$\dim X$	Krull dimension of a scheme X.
$\operatorname{codim}_X Z$	dodimension of a closed set Z in X.
X_{red}	reduced form of X.
$X(k)$	set of k-rational points of a k-scheme X.
$k(X)$	rational function field of a k-scheme X.
$\coprod X_i$	direct sum of schemes.
$X \times_S Y$	fiber product.
$f : X \to Y$	a morphism of schemes.
$\operatorname{Hom}_S(X, Y)$	set of S-morphisms from an S-scheme X to an S-scheme Y.
X_y	fiber of $f : X \to Y$ over a point y of Y.
$f : X \cdots \to Y$	a rational mapping of schemes.
Γ_f	graph of a morphism (or a rational mapping) f.
$x \to x'$	specialization of points x to x' on a scheme.
A_+	irrelevant ideal of a graded ring $A = \sum_{n\geq 0} A_n$.
Proj$A$	homogeneous spectrum of A.
$V_+(E), S_+(E), D_+(a)$	colsed set, open sets of Proj$A$.
$\mathscr{O}_X(\ell)$	$A(\ell)^\sim$.
$\mathscr{F}(\ell)$	$\mathscr{F} \otimes_{\mathscr{O}_X} \mathscr{O}_X(\ell)$.
$\mathbb{P}_k^n$	n-dimensional projective space over k.
$\mathcal{S}^\cdot(\mathscr{F})$	symmetric algebra of a locally free Module.
$\mathbb{P}(\mathscr{F})$	projective bundle associated with $\mathscr{F}$.
Pic(X)	Picard group of X.
$D_1 \sim D_2$	linear equivalence of divisors.
$D_1 \approx D_2$	algebraic equivalence of divisors.
$D_1 \equiv D_2$	numerical equivalence of divisors.
Cl(X)	divisor class group of X.
$D \geq 0$	an effective divisor.
Supp$D$	support of a divisor.
(f)	divisor of a rational function f.
$(f)_0, (f)_\infty$	zero part, polar part of f.
$\lvert D\rvert$	a complete linear system.
$M(L)$	k-module associated with a linear system L.
Φ_L	rational mapping attached to a linear system L.
$\Phi_{\mathscr{L}}$	rational mapping defined by $H^0(X, \mathscr{L})$ for an invertible sheaf $\mathscr{L}$ on X.
BsL	set of base points of a linear system of L.
$\lvert D\rvert - \sum_{i=1}^n m_i P_i$	linear subsystem of $\lvert D\rvert$ consisting of divisors on an algebraic surface V which pass through the points P_i $(1 \leq i \leq n)$ with multiplicity m_i.
$X \cdot H(\sigma)$	pullback of a hyperplane $H(\sigma)$ by Φ_L.

$\widehat{R}$	completion of R with respect to a linear topology.
$R[[x_1, \ldots, x_n]]$	formal power series ring in n variables over R.
$\Omega_{A/B}, \Omega_{X/Y}$	module of differential forms, sheaf of differential forms.
$\mathrm{Der}_B(A, M)$	A-module of B-derivations of A.
$\mathrm{Sing}X$	set of singular points of an algebraic variety X.
$\mathscr{T}_{X/k}$	tangent sheaf of X.
$\mathscr{N}_{Y/X}$	normal sheaf of a closed subvariety Y of X.
$\omega_{X/k}$	canonical sheaf of X.
K_X	canonical divisor of X.
$h^i(X, \mathscr{F})$	$\dim_k H^i(X, \mathscr{F})$.
$\chi(X, \mathscr{F})$	Euler-Poincaré characteristic of $\mathscr{F}$.
$g(C)$	(geometric)genus of an algebraic curve C.
$p(C)$	arithmetic (virtual) genus of C.
$(\mathscr{L}_1 \cdot \mathscr{L}_2), (D_1 \cdot D_2)$	intersection number of invertible sheaves (or divisors) on an algebraic surface V.
$(\mathscr{L}^2), (D^2)$	self-intersection number.
$i(D_1, D_2; P)$	local intersection multiplicity at a point P.
$\mu(C; P)$	multiplicity of an algebraic curve C on V at a point P.
$p_a(D)$	arithmetic genus of a divisor D.
$P_n, P_n(V)$	n-genus of an algebraic surface V.
$p_g, p_g(V)$	geometric genus of V.
$q(V)$	irregularity of V.
$\rho(V)$	Picard number of V.
$\mathrm{NS}(V)$	Néron-Severi group.
F_n	Hirzebruch surface of degree n.
elm_P	elementary transformation with center at a point P.

Bibliography

1. R. Godement, *Théorie de faisceaux*, Hermann, Paris.
2. A. Grothendieck, *Sur quelques points d'algèbre homologiques*, Tôhoku Math. J. **9** (1957), 119–221.
3. A. Grothendieck et J. Dieudonné, *Élements de géométrie algébrique* (*EGA*), Publication de l'Inst. Hautes Études Sci. Publ. Math., **4, 8, 11, 17, 20, 24, 28, 32**.
4. R. Hartshorne, *Algebraic geometry*, Springer-Verlag, Berlin-Heidelberg-New York.
5. H. Matsumura, *Commutative algebra*, Benjamin, New York, 1970.
6. ———, *Commutative ring theory*, Cambridge Univ. Press, London.
7. M. Nagata, *Theory of commutative fields*, Translations of Mathematical Monographs, vol. 125, Amer. Math. Soc., Providence, R.I., 1993.
8. ———, *Local rings*, Interscience Tracts in Pure and Applied Mathematics, John Wiley & Sons, New York, 1962.

Index

Recent Titles in This Series

(Continued from the front of this publication)

(See the AMS catalog for earlier titles)